MILD SILVER PROTEIN
THE MICRO SILVER BULLET
Dr. M. Paul Farber
B.A., B.S., M.A., M.S., N.D., Ph.D., D.C.

An Autobiography of a Holistic Physician, Scientist, Researcher,
Author, Philosopher, Musician and Poet.

from
Dana
10-20-98

With Contributing Authors
JOHN PARKS TROWBRIDGE, M.D.
ALEX DUARTE, O.D., PH.D.
LEE LORENZEN, PH.D.
DR. GARRY SMITH, N.D. H.M.D.

D1595387

The medical information and procedures contained in this book are not intended as a substitute for consulting your physician. Any attempt to diagnose and treat an illness should come under the direction of a physician who is familiar with nutritional therapy.

The publisher believes that the information presented in this book should be available to the public.

Because there is always some risk involved, the publisher and authors are not responsible for any adverse effects or consequences resulting from the use of any of the suggestions, preparations, or procedures in this book. All matters regarding your physical health should be, supervised by a medical professional.

For further information call or write:

Distributed by MYCA, Inc.
9639 Hillcroft # 117
Houston, TX 77096
TEL: (713) 772-3277 FAX: 774-0482
www.silverbulletgold.com

ISBN 1-887742-01-8

Printed in the United States Of America

How Silver Relates To The Immune System Of The Earth And The Human Body

The Farber Theory of Relative Planetary Immunity

I believe that today's modern world has been deprived of a natural immune system that in the past was provided by inorganic silver and other elements that were put into place from Day One. There is no question in my mind that the incremental rise of new and virulent infectious diseases through the years can be directly correlated to the depletion of the vast silver reserves (and other minerals) on the planet.

The industrial revolution and the synthetic technologies of the last hundred years have gone a long way towards destroying the balance and harmony of nature, virtually disrupting the "checks and balances" system which kept the infectious microorganisms from proliferating, mutating, and assuming increasingly alarming control.

It is my hypothesis that for today's modern world, the **immune system** provided through the action of natural inorganic silver...is sitting in boxes and crates in the middle of Fort Knox, Geneva, Switzerland and other such places of mineral wealth storage throughout the world. It's also sitting in factories which manufacture and distribute silver components and in the millions of jewelry stores around the world who capitalize on silver's commercial value.

The bottom line? Vast inventories of the planet's silver supply is not sitting where the Creator planted it with a distinct and beneficial purpose in mind...but has been unearthed and redistributed primarily for the satisfaction of greed and the acquisition of wealth. The *real wealth* intrinsic to inorganic silver is just now beginning to be understood.

I will explain.

Between the years of 1982-1989, my wife Marie and I lived and worked on the top of a stretch of the Rocky Mountains in Ouray. This was the western slope of Colorado at an elevation of 8,000-10,000 feet. It was beautiful country and often we would go hiking with our two dogs through the mountain slopes and passes. Or we would take the 4-wheel jeep. During this time we were able to observe many of the abandoned silver mines spanning over a century of mining activity. It was a sad thing to witness firsthand the abuse and the rape of the countryside, but we also noticed the countless mountain lakes, rivers and streams (whose courses had often times been altered) moving downhill from the higher elevations and spreading out and far into the horizon, as though on a mission to provide *life* to the underlying world beyond.

It would be many years later that the *connection* between precious minerals, their *transportation* and dissemination to their true destiny, and the *prolongation of life* would become obvious to me. I have found this very simple concept to be profound in its implications.

Since the beginning of time, the Earth has gone through its cycles of 4 seasons: Winter, Spring, Summer and Fall. For thousands, perhaps millions of years the clouds have taken the finite amount of water (H_2O) from the earth into the atmosphere...while the forces of gravity, solar energy and wind then forced this water back down to the earth in the form of rain, ice or snow. While lightning electrically charged the ions in the atmosphere, the water (in one of its three forms) passed through it and then fell upon the trees, the vegetation, and the earth.

On its journey, this *electrically charged water* passed over and through large deposits of Silver, Gold and thousands of other minerals and trace minerals (absorbing them) before making its way into the waterfalls, mountain streams and eventually into the mighty rivers. The water transportation cycle was in full swing.

The rivers then carried both macroscopic and microscopic particles of these elements into smaller streams and tributaries, until finally deposited onto the rich natural organic soils of the earth. Then man (and nature) planted **seeds** into the soil and as the plants began to develop and grow, they absorbed the nutrients and minerals which the earth had to offer...including SILVER. Then when these plants, seeds and nuts were harvested, they became the beginnings of the food chain for Man and also the animals, from which mankind derived its meat.

Thus Man and The Animal Kingdom, as well as the water and soil of the planet, became rich in deposits of silver, broken down into electrically charged microscopic particles.

During this process of LIFE, the earth also contained the biological microorganisms (both healthy and pathological to man), which were part of the Creation. During this undisturbed period, there existed a magnificent set of checks and balances in Nature. One of these irrefutable laws of Nature involved the *beneficial effect* of electrically charged silver ions (when teamed with a larger proliferation of "friendly bacteria")...keeping the "unfriendly" bacteria, viruses, fungi and yeast *under control* and in check. This went on since the beginning of time.

But then the vast deposits of silver (and other minerals) began to be "harvested" and hoarded by civilizations throughout the centuries...and reached its most efficient "rape" through the technological advances of the last hundred years. As silver became less plentiful, it became less prevalent in the food chain, and there was less of the *natural protection* that had been "built in" to the system. That's the crisis situation the human population finds itself in today: when the *silver hedge of protection* was compromised, many of the infectious microorganisms were unshackled and "let loose" to escape into Pandora's box of destruction and pandemonium. But all is not lost.

We know what the problem is, and I believe we also have the answer: Mild Silver Protein. I believe we can safely and efficiently restore the wealth of silver back into the human population and re-establish the powerful immune system that we were destined to have from the beginning.

Silver is a precious metal, but not <u>precious</u> as a measure of a man's wealth...but precious as a measure of the quality of a man's life.

A friend who was a Medical Doctor once said to me: "Dr. Farber, you are the only non-M.D. I know who is a G.P. (General Practitioner)." I replied, "What do you mean? I'm not a G.P." He then replied, "Obviously, the Good Lord chose you to be a Divine Guinea Pig."

"When I was asked at one time by a fellow professional associate who was a medical doctor what my area of specialty was, my answer was I SPECIALIZE IN FINDING THE NATURAL ANSWER TO SO-CALLED INCURABLE DISEASES."

"It is said that for every ailment on the earth there is a natural remedy. Therefore, there is no such thing as an incurable disease, although there are patients who cannot be healed when they refuse to obey the laws of nature."

Dr. M. Paul Farber

ABOUT DR. M. PAUL FARBER...

With over 30 years' experience in the healthcare field, Dr. Farber is tri-lingual (English, Spanish, Ancient Hebrew) and also has a working knowledge in Latin, especially with respect to medical terminology. The Farber family counts among its members many Doctors, Attorneys and professional businessmen, including an Associate Doctor to Dr. Michael DeBakey (Houston) and also a Federal Court Judge.

EDUCATION: Dr. Farber has over 30 years of formal higher education, including the following degrees:

- *Bachelor of Arts* – University of Texas (Austin) in Experimental Psychology, also having been an Associate to a Professor and Instructor. Graduated in 1969 with a "high A" average and was on the Dean's List. Minors in Philosophy and Sociology.
- *Bachelor of Science* – Clayton University (Birmingham) in Holistic Healthcare and Nutrition. Was on Dean's List.
- *Master of Arts* – University of Missouri (Kansas City) in Clinical Psychology (1971).
- *Master of Science* – Clayton University in Holistic Healthcare and Nutrition. Was on Dean's List with "high A" average.
- *Doctor of Naturopathy (N.D.)* – Clayton University
- *Doctor of Philosophy (Ph.D.)* – Clayton University in Holistic Healthcare and Nutrition.
- *Doctor of Chiropractic (D.C.)* – Cleveland Chiropractic College (Kansas City). Graduated in 1975 in top 10% of his class.
- *Post-graduate degree work* at the Palmer College of Chiropractic, Davenport, Iowa, in 1995.

BOARDS:
Scientific Advisory Board and Board of Directors of the National Mineral Industry Group

Dr. Farber has also completed post-graduate courses in Kinesiology, X-Ray Diagnosis and Interpretation, Sacral Occipital Technique, Activator Non-force Technique, Spinal Biomechanics, Orthopaedics and Neurology, Athletic Injuries, Advanced Computer Technology, high state-of-the-art Imaging Units (including the CAT Scan, Magnetic Resonance Imaging (M.R.I.) and Electro Myelogram Technology (E.M.G.).

Dr. Farber has studied under and lectured with (among many others):

Dr. Paavo Airola, world-famous author and nutritionist who wrote 15 books on nutrition and sold over 15 million copies;

Dr. Robert Mendehlson, noted pioneer and author who was famous for his views on "upleveling" the quality of medical healthcare throughout the world;

Dr. V. D. Ladd, instructor on Medicines and Director of Hospital Affairs in India;

Dr. Gordon Ruesink, scientist and researcher;

Dr. John Sunderlage, noted expert in Acupuncture and also a Chiropractic Physician;

Ruth Bender, one of the last living original students of Dr. Albert Einstein in Austria. Dr. Farber conducted personal studies in the fields of Nuclear Energy and the Theory of Relativity as relating to the Healing Arts and Sciences.

Among Dr. Farber's inventions (now under development) are:

– Computerized Electromagnetic Solanoid Adjusting Tool;
– Computerized Holographic Cranial Diagnostic Unit;
– Computerized Kinesiological Muscle Testing Unit;
– Computerized Electro-Acupuncture Unit;
– Electronic Vital Function Monitoring Board;
– Kinesiological Robotics Unit;
– Electromagnetic Field Korlean Analyser;
– Sacral Occipital Balance Unit

Dr. Farber Founded and Established:

- The first Natural Science University in Texas
- The Healing Arts Chiropractic Clinic in Houston, administering 45,000 treatments and receiving patients from all over the world
- The "Little Switzerland Health Center and Mountain Retreat" in Colorado
- The Farber Nutritional Evaluation Center
- The Chiropractic Nutrition Committee of Colorado (also a former member of the Board of Directors of the Colorado State Chiropratic Society)
- The Colonel Leonard Farber Mild Silver Protein Foundation For Research and Development
- Founder of "Health Stop" – Indoor Spinal Screening Kiosk in Malls, the First of its Kind in the Nation.

PERSONAL INFORMATION...

Dr. Farber writes and composes music and has the ability to play 10 musical instruments, including classical acoustic guitar, electric guitar, piano, banjo, mandolin, flute, harmonica, violin, drums and percussion instruments. He is also a Marksman in the crossbow, compound bow and long bow and has a Brown Belt in Karate (for the purpose of physical discipline).

In addition he is well-versed in building and construction, having been a licensed General Contractor in the state of Colorado.

From 1975 to 1982, Dr. Farber owned and operated the Healing Arts Chiropractic Clinic in Houston, Texas. The practice was successful and during that period of time patients seeking help from long-term disabilities made special arrangements to come to this total health care clinic from France, England, Spain, Germany, the Canary Islands, Guatemala, Mexico, Japan, Canada, and India, as well as from the United States. The clinic treated over 1,500 patients and administered over 45,000 treatments.

In 1982, the clinic was sold and Dr. Farber and J. Marie moved to the western slope of Colorado to the city of Ouray located high up in the mountains and often referred to as "The Little Switzerland of America." They then founded "The Little Switzerland Holistic Health Center and Mountain Health Retreat." The center was successful and was given national recognition in various magazines and journals.

The center attracted several internationally famous authors and lecturers with whom Dr. Farber interacted, including Dr. Robert Mendehlson, author of "Confessions of a Medical Heretic," "Male Practice" and other best selling books. Dr. Farber has patterned his profession after his mentor, Dr. Mendehlson, who was internationally known as "The People's Doctor."

Dr. Farber was also privileged to have studied with and lectured with Dr. Paavo Ariola, another world renowned author and nutritionist who wrote over 15 books in the field of nutrition, selling over 15 million copies. Dr. Farber was the last Doctor of Chiropractic to be certified in the field of nutrition by Dr. Ariola prior to passing away.

During his stay in Colorado, Dr. Farber completed a 120-hour course in Traditional Acupuncture and Electro-Acupuncture and successfully completed the State Board Certification. While in Colorado, he was founder and chairman of the "Chiropractic Acupuncture Committee of Colorado."

In 1991 on a Caribbean cruise, Dr. Farber and wife Marie were privileged to interact with and learn from Dr. Carl Cleveland, Jr. (president of Cleveland Chiropractic College in Los Angeles) and also Dr. Carl Cleveland III, a former classmate and also president of Cleveland Chiropractic College in Kansas City. Shortly thereafter, Dr. Farber founded the Colonel Leonard Farber Memorial Fund in order to provide treatment to the impoverished peoples of the world.

Dr. Farber began writing this book, "The Micro Silver Bullet," in 1992…and is also co-authoring a book with Dr. John Parks Trowbridge (co-author with Dr. Morton Walker, D.P.M., of "The Yeast Syndrome") on the subject of Candida Yeast Infection. The proposed title is "The Yeast Syndrome: The Completed Solution."

ADDITIONAL BOOKS IN PROGRESS
3. "THE MICRO GOLD BULLET, A NATURAL ANSWER TO MENTAL DISEASE AND ARTHRITIS"
4. "SCIENTIFICALLY DOCUMENTED ANSWERS TO CANCER"
5. "THE FOREST FOR THE TREES, AN END TO THE AIDS EPIDEMIC"
6. "BABY BOOMER BREAKTHROUGHS"
As Recommended By The People's Doctor
A Scientifically & Anecdotally Documented Answer To The Five Scourges Of The BABY BOOMER GENERATION

DIABETES
HYPOGLYCEMIA
CONGESTIVE HEART FAILURE
IMPOTENCE
INSOMNIA
(With a Special Section On a Natural Answer to Multiple Sclerosis and Cancer)

BOOKLETS
1. "AS RECOMMENDED BY THE PEOPLE'S DOCTOR, PRODUCT LINE"
2. "UNDERSTANDING AND CONQUERING THE COMMON COLD"
3. "HOW TO PSYCHOLIGICALLY SURVIVE AND CONQUER PAIN"
4. "QUANTUM LEAP, MEDICINES OF THE 21ST CENTURY"
5. "PRELIMINARY SCIENTIFIC STUDIES"
5. "THE DEAD SEA SCROLLS OF MODERN MEDICINE"
7. "MOST EFFECTIVE NATURAL HOLISTIC SUPPORTATIVE METHODS"
8. "DSHEA – DIETARY SUPPLEMENT HEALTH AND EDUCATION ACT BOOKLET

PERSONAL HOLISTIC DIARY

Colloidal Silver Supplements:

Misunderstood and Misrepresented by Doctors from the Food and Drug Administration

By Stacey Smith, D.C.

To the Editor:

"Silver Compounds have been used as medicinals for centuries." This opening quote in a commentary published in the Journal of American Medical Association, October 18, 1995, volume 274 #15, was one of the only concise and factual statements in the article.[1,2] The authors of this writing refer to the toxicity of silver in relation to the development of a condition known as argyria. The condition results from the accumulation of large particles of silver being trapped in internal organs, capillary beds, or the epidermis. The silver creates a bluish gray color through its presence in the skin as well as a silver-induced increase in melanin adding to the dark appearance.[3]

The second bibliographical reference is an article discussing argyria published in 1987 in the "American Family Physician." The cases of argyria were caused by exposure to silver nitrate (topically), inhalation of silver in the form of arsphenamine (Salvarsan® and Neo Silver® and ingestion was in the form of a silver product (Argyrol®)[4] which is known to contain silver nitrate. None of the cases involved the use of a colloidal silver product.

The authors then infer side effects from colloidal silver by quoting another case of argyrosis producing several abnormalities including "neurologic defects." These serious problems occurred when a man was exposed to inorganic silver sulfide ($AgS2$) not colloidal silver. The individual's argyria developed after long-term self-treatment with oral intake.[4]

The third case referenced by this group states that "diffuse silver deposition in visceral organs have been reported with long-term use of oral silver products." Again, when we locate the case documentation we find that in fact the patient was not taking colloidal silver or even a liquid silver product. She had been using "silver nitrate sticks on the oral mucosa for over two and a half years."[5]

These case history presentations represent biased and unprofessional writing. The authors' apparent inability to understand the difference between a silver nitrate, sulfide, or other silver compound demonstrates their lack of understanding basic chemical properties. The matrix, substrate, and particle size are all critical to the varied functions and reactions with use of these products.

A modern day properly prepared colloidal silver product should be .001 microns in diameter with a concentration of 3 to 15 parts per million.[6] Some idea of the minuteness of these particles can be gathered from the fact that a cubic millimeter is estimated to contain 1,000,000,000 of them. These particles are animated by what is known as brownian movement and are enabled to remain in suspension in a liquid medium almost indefinitely.[7] The particle size was further demonstrated by electron microscopy at Scripps Institute, University of California, San Diego.[8] The significance of the particle size, .001 micron, is in relation to understanding capillary perfusion. The diameter of the capillary lumen is 4-9 microns, therefore the body has no problem in excreting the silver particles.[9, 10, 11] That is why there has not been a single case of argyria from a properly manufactured modern day colloidal silver product. The cases of argyria reported in the 1920's and 1930's resulted because the technology of the day was unable to produce a colloidal silver product with a small enough particle size.

Current research has continued to show the colloidal silver solutions to be effective against a myriad of microbes, fungi, and viruses.

A) Temple University, School of Medicine, found "that mild silver protein inhibited HIV-1 replication in sup. T1 cells as measured by a reduction in the appearance of syncytia in cell culture."[12.]

B) A study performed by Temple University, School of Medicine, was performed testing a silver micro-bullet preparation (1500 ppm) against candida albicans and cryptococcus neoformans in vitro. Not only was it effective in the concentration, but the reports indicates "four strains of c. neoformans were tested and killed at 150-300 ppm and growth was inhibited in a concentration as low as 0.3 ppm.[13]

C) Two studies have been conducted with colloidal silver and its effectiveness against borrelia burgdorferi. The first study conducted at Fox Chase Cancer Center, Philadelphia, Pennsylvania, showed growth inhibition in low concentrations (2-10 ppm) and much faster action in higher concentrations (15-75 ppm).[14]

The Department of Health and Human Services, Rocky Mountain Laboratories, tested cultured spirochetes of the borrelia burgdorferi (B31) and the relapsing fever agent b hermsti (HS-1). In both tests using 150 and 15 ppm colloidal silver, none of the treated cultures contained live spirochetes after 24 hours.[15]

D) University of California, Los Angeles, School of Medicine department of obstetrics and gynecology, conducted a test using the silver solution for antimicrobial action as disinfectants. The silver solutions proved to be antibacterial for concentrations of 10^5 organisms per milliliter of streptococcus pyogenes, staphylococcus aureus, neisseria gonorrhea, gardurella vaginalis, salmonella typhi, and other enteric pathogens and fungicidal for candida albicans, candida elobata, and m. furfur.[16]

E) Department of Health, Alleghem, Pennsylvania, after a two-year study reported that "silver is equal to chlorine in maintaining essentially coliform-free pool water and is better than chlorine in destroying pseudomonas and staphylococcus auracus organisms." The department further reported that "during the two seasons with the silver treated pool there have been no eye, ear, nose or throat irritations or infections reported." It should also be noted that there were "no visible growths of algae during the testing period." The health department reported the following conclusions:

"Silver disinfection is easier and safer than other purifying agents,"

"Silver is an effective bactericide for swimming pool water treatment," and

"Silver does not produce changes in pH, thus eliminating the need to add pH adjusting chemicals."[17]

F) Confirmed analysis on product purity and concentration has been essential among reputable manufacturers for quality control. Voluntary production of documents providing proof of testing obtained showing analysis by Acta Lab,[6] Ill-Industrial Laboratories,[18] and Kimbal Laboratories[19] in support and confirmed testing.

G) A toxicity study was performed at the Division of Comparative Medicine at the University of Toronto. The 1995 study was conducted with rats. There were no observed adverse effects seen within the treatment period. The data when extrapolated to the human scale means that a 60 kilogram individual would have to be given 3600 mg (3.6 grams) to receive an amount equivalent to the test animals. This corresponds to the injection of 1 ml. of a solution containing 300,000 ppm of mild silver protein.[20]

In conclusion, standardizations of silver colloids for human use would be welcomed by the reputable health food manufacturers. It seems a sad commentary upon the medical doctors of the Food and Drug Administration that a reliable non-toxic antibiotic would be shunned and misrepresented within the Journal of American Medical

Association. We are in an age of increased resistance to antibiotics by many microorganisms. Complimentary alternative therapies to the standard drug treatment regime must be considered without bias if the patient population of the future is going to benefit.

[1]Journal of American Medicine, October 18, 1995, volume 274 #15, letters Fung, M.D., Weintraus M.D., Bowen, M.D., Food and Drug Administration, Rockorle, M.D.

[2]Goodman, L.S, Gilman, A., "Goodman and Gilman's The Pharmacological Basis of Therapeutics." 5th edition, New York, NY: MacMillan Publishing Co., Inc., 1975, pages 930-35 and 999-1,000.

[3]Greene, R.M., Su WPD, Argyria "American Family Physician," 1987; 36:151-54.

[4]Westhofer, M., Schafer, H., Generalized argyrosis in man, ultrastructural and x-ray microanalytical findings. "Arch. Otorhimolaryngol," 1986; 243, 260-64.

[5]Marshal, J.P., Schneider, R. P., Systemic argyria secondary to topical silver nitrate, "Arch. Dermatol," 1977; 113:1077-70.

[6]Certificate of analysis, Acta Laboratories, Inc., 27101 Aliso Creek Road, Suite 126, Aliso Viejo, CA 92656. Lab #95D-0486-00, lot #0023, production date 4-19-93, product/material, colloidal silver.

[7]"Electrical Colloids," Leonard Keene Hirchberg, A.M., M.D., John Hopkins.

[8]Photographic analysis, July 11, 1995, University of California, San Diego, Scripps Institute of Oceanography, LaJolla, Scanning electron microscope model S-360 Cambridge at 300,000X power magnification.

[9]Morris J. Karnovsky, edited by Crone and Lassen. Alfred Benzon Symposium II, Copenhagen 22-26. June 1969, "Capillary Permeability," Academic Press, New York.

[10]Guyton, Textbook of Medical Physiology, 1986, W.B. Sanders, CO. CHP 30, pages 348-49. "Capillary Dynamics."

[11]Hardaway, Robert M., M.D., Futura Publishing Co., Mount Kisco, New York, 1981, "Capillary Perfusion in Health and Disease."

[12]Henderson, Earl E., Professor Temple University, School of Medicine, department of microbiology and immunology, February 2, 1995, "Result Mild Silver Protein, Inhibition of HIV-1."

[13]Buckley, Helen R., Ph.D., Professor Temple University School of Medicine, department of microbiology and immunology, February 2, 1995.

[14]Bayer, Margret, Ph.D., Fox Chase Cancer Center, Philadelphia, Pennsylvania, January 3, 1995, "Silver Protein Mediated Borrelia Burgdorferi Growth Inhibition."

[15]Department of Health and Human Services, National Institutes of Health, Rocky Mountain Laboratories, Janaury 13, 1995, Schuan, Tom, Ph.D., Burgdorfer, Willy, Ph.D.

[16]Ford, Larry C. M.D., UCLA, department of obstetrics and gynecology, UCLA School of Medicine, November 1, 1988.

[17]Allegheny County Health Department, Pennsylvania, Test results 152,000-gallon pool, seasons 1974, 75.

[18]Industrial Laboratories Company, Denver, CO, Sample: colloidal silver.

[19]Kimbal Laboratories, Draper, UT, Elemental analysis: colloidal silver.

[20]Renlund, R.C. DMV University of Toronto, division of comparative medicine, "Toxicity of Mild Silver Protein."

BIASED AND UNPROFESSIONAL WRITING
WHY DOES IT OCCUR?

WHY IS ANTIQUATED KNOWLEDGE AND
A LACK OF UNDERSTANDING
DANGEROUS?

WHY DOES THIS *SAD COMMENTARY*
PROVOKE BOTH
PITY AND CAUTION?

Quoting Dr. Stacey Smith in his article **COLLOIDAL SILVER SUPPLEMENTS; Misunderstood and Misrepresented by Doctors From the Food and Drug Administration.** "These case histories represent both biased and unprofessional writing. The authors apparent inability to understand the difference between a silver nitrate, sulfide, or other silver compounds demonstrates their lack of understanding of basic chemical properties. The matrix substrate, and particle size are all critical to the varied functions and reactions with use of these products."

A report also recently appeared in the NNFA Today Newsletter-October edition. NNFA is the National Nutritional Food Association. Their article entitled "Silver Anti-microbial Products, Can They Deliver as Promised in my opinion could have very well been written from the knowledge and viewpoints of individuals with outdated 100-YEAR-OLD information with NO KNOWLEDGE of the Current Up To Date Research which Dr. Smith summarized. Since I was personally involved in conducting and supervising much of this Scientific Research done in conjunction with the Top Universities and Research Institutions mentioned, I have had the opportunity to be 100 YEARS AHEAD of the authors of both of these articles discussed. These articles are like "so-called scientists" with blueprints from the Wright Brothers trying to evaluate the Modern Day Space Age Technology of the Space Shuttle. Many of their statements like, "To our knowledge, no silver preparations have been properly demonstrated against internal infection" could have been written in THE DARK AGES and many of their other comments are addressed in Dr. Smith's article. Their discussions of argyria and silver salts is also ARCHAIC. If they think tests have only been done in test tubes then they need to pull their head out of the sand and read all of the IN VIVO STUDIES AND CASE HISTORIES documented my book *THE MICRO SILVER BULLET*.

Dr. Stacey Smith further stated, "In conclusion standardization of silver colloids for human use would be welcomed by reputable Health Food Manufacturers. It seems a SAD COMMENTARY upon the medical directors of the Food and Drug Administration that a reliable non-toxic antibiotic would be shunned and misrepresented within the Journal of the American Medical Association. We are in an age of increased resistance to antibiotics by many micro-organisms. Complimentary Alternative Therapies to the standard drug treatment regime must be considered without bias if the PATIENT POPULATION OF THE FUTURE is going to benefit."

I will now address the three questions which I posed at the beginning of this OPINION WHICH I AM EXER-CISING UNDER MY CONSTITUTIONAL RIGHT OF *FREE SPEECH   UNDER THE FIRST AMENDMENT OF THE BILL OF RIGHTS.*
BIASED AND UNPROFESSIONAL WRITING
WHY DOES IT OCCUR?

In MY OPINION this occurs from TWO OLD DEMONS which have HAUNTED MANKIND for Centuries. These are the SPECIAL INTEREST EXPLOITATION OF POLITICS AND ECONOMICS.   Unfortunately, individuals who become involved in these two areas are NOT INTERESTED IN THE WELFARE OF THE PEOPLE but instead in the WELFARE OF THEIR OWN POCKETS.

I am not making an accusation against any particular special interest group. But in the words of Jesus Christ I say to THE PEOPLE:
"BE AS WISE AS SERPENTS, BUT AS GENTLE AS DOVES"
PROTECT THE HEALTH AND ECONOMIC WELFARE OF YOU, YOUR FAMILY, AND YOUR FRIENDS

WHY IS ANTIQUATED KNOWLEDGE AND A LACK OF UNDERSTANDING DANGEROUS?

In MY OPINION if one accepts information from a Supposedly Respected Professional Source and it turns out that their viewpoint is based upon Antiquated Knowledge and A Lack Of Understanding, they may not proceed with the THERAPEUTIC ANSWER which would have HEALED them and SOLVED their Health Problem. I recently had a Scientific AIDS STUDY which was partially SABOTAGED with LIES, AND DECEIT, AND FALSEHOODS from a SPECIAL INTEREST GROUP that was unfortunately connected with AN UNETHICAL PHARMACEUTICAL COMPANY. I have a Great Deal of Respect for ETHICAL Pharmaceutical Companies. Their Discoveries of Drugs which work and have few if any side effects have done much good for mankind. However, when one acts in an unethical and unprofessional manner, it brings disgrace upon the whole industry. *The BOTTOM LINE as far as the people in the study went is that those who stayed STEADFAST AND COMPLETED THE STUDY GOT COMPLETELY WELL. THOSE WHO ACCEPTED THE LIES AND FALSEHOODS AND DROPPED OUT CONTINUED TO BE SICK AND COULD POSSIBLE DIE.*

As one can see, this is a VERY SERIOUS MATTER. Be very cautious of those who profess wisdom but in Truth are committing Falsehoods and Deceit and operating from a FALSE FOUNDATION of ANTIQUATED KNOWLEDGE AND A LACK OF UNDERSTANDING. IT IS TRULY DANGEROUS AND CAN RESULT IN EXTREME AVOIDABLE ILLNESSES AND EVEN DEATH.

WHY DOES THIS SAD COMMENTARY EVOKE BOTH PITY AND CAUTION?

It is Pitiful that EVIL AND DISHONESTY reside in Our World. I have been a Loyal Viewer of *"60 MINUTES"* for the past 28 years and it never ceases to amaze me how every week this VERY EXCELLENT AND HONEST NEWS SHOW can come up with two or three topics which are Similar Examples in different areas and sometimes the Same Areas of what I have been discussing in this Rebuttal Article.

A SPECIAL NOTE: I AM NOT OPPOSED TO THE F.D.A. AND I FEEL THAT WE NEED AN HONEST, UPRIGHT, AND PEOPLE-ORIENTED REGULATORY AGENCY. HOWEVER, I DO FEEL THAT FUTURE REFORMS SHOULD CREATE A MORE REPRESENTATIVE AGENCY WHICH INCLUDES HOLISTIC PHYSICIANS, NATUROPATHS, NUTRITIONIST, CHIROPRACTORS, AS WELL AS REPRESENTATIVES FROM ALL MAJOR ALTERNATIVE HEALTH CARE FIELDS. THIS MUST BE ACCOMPLISHED THROUGH THE CONSTITUTIONAL PROCESS AND THE BALLOT BOX OF A FREE AND EDUCATED DEMOCRACY.

<u>ON THE FRONT COVER OF LIFE MAGAZINE,</u>
<u>SEPTEMBER 1996</u>
THE HEALING REVOLUTION
Surgery or acupuncture?
Antibiotics or herbs?
BOTH ARE BETTER.
More and More M.D.s
are mixing **ANCIENT MEDICINE**
and **NEW SCIENCE** to treat
everything from the
common cold to heart disease.

WRITTEN UNDER MY CONSTITUTIONAL
FIRST AMENDMENT RIGHTS!!!!!!!!!!!!!!
Dr. M. Paul Farber
B.A., B.S., M.A., M.S., N.D., Ph.D., D.C.
Author
"THE MICRO SILVER BULLET"
A Preliminary Scientifically Documented
Answer To The Three Largest Epidemics
In The World
LYME DISEASE
AIDS VIRUS
YEAST INFECTION
(And The Common Cold)

HOW LONG CAN THE TRUTH ABOUT ANTIBIOTICS BE IGNORED AND DENIED

Because of Special Professional Interest Groups
Economic Special Interest Groups and
Political Special Interest Groups

In NEWSWEEK Magazine one of our most Respected and Long-Running Periodicals on March 28, 1994, the Title of the Front Cover makes the following statement:

"ANTIBIOTICS *THE END OF MIRACLE DRUGS?*
WARNING

NO LONGER
EFFECTIVE
AGAINST
KILLER
BUGS

Subtitles go on to read:
In 1992, 13,300 hospital patients died of infections that resisted every drug doctors tried

THE END OF ANTIBIOTICS
SCIENCE THOUGHT IT HAD VANQUISHED INFECTIOUS DISEASES, BUT NOW THE BUGS ARE FIGHTING BACK

TOO MUCH OF A GOOD THING
FROM OVERPRESCRIBING TO SATISFYING WHO COMPLAIN TOO MUCH DOCTORS ARE NOW PART OF THE ANTIBIOTIC PROBLEM

ANTIBIOTIC SALES HAVE SOARED
in recent years, but the drugs that doctors prescribe are often inappropriate."

Also in TIME Magazine, another one of our most Respected and Long-Running Periodicals on September 12, 1994, the Title of the Front Cover makes the following statement.

"REVENGE OF THE KILLER MICROBES
Are we losing the war against Infectious Diseases?

Subtitles go on to read:

MEDICINE: THE KILLERS ALL AROUND
New Viruses and drug resistant bacteria
are reversing human victories over infectious disease

Some microbes can reproduce in just 20 minutes.
The price of doing nothing will be millions of lives.

Doctors and the public were not alone in feeling cocky about infectious disease a decade ago. The drug companies did too. Scientists are sanguine about regaining the upper hand against infectious disease but now realize that no strategy will work forever. As long as microbes have the ability to neutralize medicine's weapons, the drug companies will have to keep adding to the arsenal."

Special Note: Highlights from these two articles from TIME and NEWSWEEK are reprinted with written permission from TIME and NEWSWEEK from THE BEST SELLING BOOK:

THE MICRO SILVER BULLET™
A Preliminary Scientifically Documented Answer
To The Three Largest Epidemics In The World
LYME DISEASE
AIDS VIRUS
YEAST INFECTION
(And The Common Cold)

by
Dr. M. Paul Farber
B.A., B.S., M.A., M.S., N.D., Ph.D., D.C.

CONTROVERSIAL ISSUES CONCERNING DR. WEIL'S COLUMN ON COLLOIDAL SILVER

In his column "Ask Dr. Weil" in the January/February 1995 issue of *Natural Health,* Andrew Weil, M.D., for whom I a have great deal of respect and admiration, answered a reader's questions concerning possible side effects, toxicity, and accumulation of metals in products labeled colloidal silver. Dr. Weil addressed several controversial issues concerning colloidal silver and silver salts, to which I will now respond.

1. Dr. Weil said that solutions of silver salts, when used as disinfectant are "caustic to tissue."

I do not approve of using silver in salt solutions. Unless the silver is suspended in a mild silver protein solution, it could very well be caustic.

2. Dr. Weil stated: 'As a drug already in use before the establishment of Food and Drug Administration (FDA), colloidal silver is not regulated for safety and efficacy."

I have warned my readers not to purchase colloidal silver products without critical scientific scrutiny, which unfortunately is impossible unless one has access to a licensed, impartial pharmaceutical lab, such as I have with Mild Silver Protein. Colloidal silver can be made improperly by a non-licensed lab. Upon investigation, I have found that colloidal silver products can be and have been improperly labeled with an incorrect ppm (parts per million). If one had a ppm that was too high and the silver was improperly suspended, it could be toxic. I have two independent licensed pharmaceutical labs regulating Mild Silver Protein. Our records are open to anyone who wishes to inquire. Mild Silver Protein is an extremely pure, non-toxic, nutritional mineral supplement free of nitrates and nitrites and perfectly suspended with space-age technology, and it has extremely high antibiotic, antimicrobial, and antiparasitic, as well as antispirochetal, qualities.

3. Dr. Weil said that some professionals and business persons make "extravagant claims" about colloidal silver. I agree. Beware of extravagant claims. Do not accept any statement that cannot be substantiated with impeccable, empirical scientific studies performed by renowned Ph.D. scientists from credible universities and institutions, such as I have made available with Mild Silver Protein.

4. Dr. Weil stated, "I do not recommend it [colloidal silver] as an 'antibiotic and antiparasitic' for internal use, both because I feel that patients with internal significant infections should be evaluated by physicians and because silver definitely accumulates in the body."

I agree that everyone with internal infections needs a holistic, nutritionally educated physician who has taken the time and effort to review all the current studies on Mild Silver Protein, along with the professionals' credentials, that are mentioned in my book. Improperly made colloidal silver products could possible and quite probably accumulate in the body. Mild Silver Protein does not!

5. Finally, Dr. Weil concluded: "The main consequence of this accumulation is a permanent bluish-gray discoloration of the skin and nails, called *argyria,*which is now rare but was common earlier this century when silver preparations were in widespread use. Argyria is benign from the point of view of general health, but the cosmetic effect can be severe, making people look like 'corpses come suddenly to life.'"

I agree that improperly made colloidal silvers could cause argyria, and many of those produced in the past, especially earlier in the century, were replete with that problem. Again, this is why I advise readers not to buy untested colloidal silver products that may be improperly made. Mild Silver Protein has passed all testing and has not been found to cause argyria. I have taken it every day for over one and three-fourth years, and the only thing blue in my body are my eyes, which have been that way since the day I was born. As a result of the daily usage of Mild Silver Protein, I have not contracted any infections – viral, bacterial, or fungal. It has been like having a second immune system. In contrast, many of my patients and friends have been ill for weeks at a time.

I want to thank Dr. Weil for his comments, many of which substantiated my own views about improperly made colloidal silver products. I plan on sending Dr. Weil an autographed, complimentary copy of my book which is advertised in the L.D.U. I will let the scientific evidence speak for itself.

I was able to begin half a dozen pioneering patients on Mild Silver Protein about one month ago. I am pleased to inform you that it is working faster than I anticipated, and many of them are either symptom free or close to it, with no side effects. I feel that this is a preview of the positive other side of the coin of all our past sufferings, which will come to an end to make room for our healing and recovery. However, we are proceeding scientifically and cautiously, and at my request, Dr. Charles Crist has graciously agreed to prepare an evaluation progress report form (published in this issue) that will accompany all orders of Mild Silver Protein. Buyers will also receive directions for usage with each order.

I have endeavored to live up to the image of my mentor Dr. Robert Mendehlson, the original "People's Doctor," and have personally answered in detail questions from all my callers who are sick with Lyme Disease. I care about you as human beings, about your lives and your illnesses, and about your future recovery.

Too Many Cooks Spoil the Cure

A word of caution from whom I consider a very wise medical doctor. I, Dr. Farber, advise all doctors and patients to read this article carefully.

"A 72-year-old man was brought to a hospital emergency room by his daughters — they feared he might have Alzheimer's disease. The patient had been unable to care for himself for the previous two weeks. He had become depressed, irritable and confused.

Whereas he had been a sharp individual who had been tapering down his office activities as an attorney, he now had become forgetful and could not attend to his business affairs. A review of his medications showed he had been on digoxin (heart), Inderal (a beta blocker), Lasix (a diuretic) and Benadryl capsules (allergy).

Examination revealed a confused man whose blood pressure was low at 100/60. His children added that he had been running to the bathroom frequently and several times had been incontinent. He had also been constipated. His lungs and abdomen were satisfactory, his heart showed a slow rate of 56. There was no evidence of paralysis, but he showed an elevated digoxin level, a low potassium level and diminished kidney function.

The man was admitted to the hospital. Digoxin and Lasix were stopped for a while. The Inderal dosage was reduced and Benadryl medication stopped. He soon began to improve. Potassium medication was administered to correct his decreased level, and he became more alert and assumed his usual personality.

The cause for his abnormal behavior was obvious – the mixture of drugs. Digoxin and Inderal can slow the heart considerably; Lasix can cause potassium depletion. In the elderly male, Benadryl, an antihistamine, can cause urinary obstruction and sedative effects. Also in the elderly, the kidney and liver have reduced efficiency in metabolizing and inactivating drugs.

Although adults over 65 represent only 12 percent of the American population, the group accounts for 30 percent of all prescription drug usage. It is estimated that two-thirds take one or more drugs daily; many take at least four prescription medications plus three or four over-the-counter drugs. Much of this is because of problems that require multiple medications. The other important factor relates to a longer life expectancy.

Older individuals see more than one physician and 60 percent of all visits include a prescription. The combination of multiple physicians, automatic refills at pharmacies, over-the-counter medications, the sharing of drugs and the confusion sometimes present culminates in what may be called polypharmacy.

Sometimes the patient pressures for unnecessary medication. There is often no review of current medications, prescribed or over-the-counter. Patients may be given conflicting drugs.

The physician must consider a patient's age, the need to adjust dosage because of altered response and review other medications being taken.

The aging process itself is responsible for pharmacologic changes in the metabolism and elimination of drugs. End organ responsiveness changes so that there are different effects at the site of action. And there is often poor compliance. Food can also influence drug absorption, metabolism and elimination.

Many over-the-counter items can produce serious side effects. Antihistamines such as Benadryl, Chlor-Trimeton and Pyribenzamine can cause increased pressure within the eyes, urinary retention, prostate difficulty, constipation and disorientation. Anti-inflammatory agents such as Motrin, Advil and Naprosyn, used commonly for arthritis, can cause fluid retention, stomach irritation and occasional kidney dysfunction.

If not monitored carefully, diuretics can produce low potassium levels, low blood pressure and fatigue.

Benzodiazepines such as Xanax, Valium, Librium and Klonopin may cause confusion, lethargy, lack of coordination and depression. Demerol and codeine used pre- or post-operatively can cause delirium in some older individuals. Sulfa drugs can cause skin rash, fever, nausea, liver and blood disturbances.

Drugs for high blood pressure can cause lethargy, chronic cough, asthma, disturbances in cardiac rhythm and depression. Antidepressants are often valuable and yet care must be exerted in monitoring, since anticholinergic effects such as cardiac disturbances, gastrointestinal problems and neurologic abnormalities can occur.

Drug interaction accounts for significant toxicity. Every time a physician adds a new drug to the list, there is an increased possibility of a reaction. For example, angiotensin-converting enzyme inhibitors such as captopril, lisinopril, enalapril and Zestril can elevate potassium levels, and if potassium therapy is added serious reactions can occur. The addition of quinidine to patients already on digoxin can elevate digoxin levels to a toxic range.

The combination of an antihypertensive medication (clonidine, methyidopa) with a tricyclic antidepressant can cause memory impairment and confusion and can suggest a dementia problem. Patients in this category have been misdiagnosed with Alzheimer's disease. Only when the medications have been discontinued have the mental changes dramatically returned to normal.

Prescribing for any patient requires great care. In the elderly, one must make certain there is proper dosage and be aware that the fewer drugs, the better. Families as well as physicians must be doubly alert."

AIDS STUDY

**Eight People Recover from the Aids Virus
in a scientifically documented study.
An additional seven Aids patients recover
as verified by anecdotal reports.**

Testimonials
**Aids Virus
Gulf War Syndrome**

Cardiovascular Consultants Inc.
458 26th Street
San Diego, CA 92102

June 18, 1996

Dr. Paul Farber,

Enclosed are the results of the first three months of
clinical trials of HIV infected patients using Collag-40.
Anecdotally, all patients are feeling well with no clinical
symptoms or active opportunistic infections. As the
records indicate, CD-4 Cells are in general on the way up,
all individuals that started with active P-24 antigenicity
have reverted to negative. It is about a 50/50 result on
PCR to date as to the measurement of viral lode in the
blood stream. It is my belief that with the patients that are
having increases in PCR during this initial phase is due to
die off mechanism of possible dead virus still in the blood
stream and still being counted by the methodology used
to measure PCR.

Sincerely,

Myer Rice, M.D., Ph.D.

The *Farber "Heimer"* Reaction

Dr. M. Paul Farber, B.A., B.S., M.A., M.S., N.D., Ph.D., D.C.

June 26, 1996

In the process of conducting Scientific Research, certain PHENOMENA occur which may be totally unexpected but also Surprisingly Relevant to the INITIAL HYPOTHESIS upon which the Scientific Analysis was Originally Based. In the Original Scientific Study on the HIV (AIDS) VIRUS which I, Dr. M. Paul Farber am conducting with Fellow Research Scientists Dr. Earl Rice, M.D., and Dr. Garry Smith, D.H.M., N.D., I Hypothesized that since COLL/AG-40 not only inhibited Replication of HIV and any Latent Formation as well as KILLING the HIV VIRUS in VITRO in Scientific Laboratory Studies conducted by Dr. Earl Henderson, Ph.D., of Temple University in Philadelphia, Pennsylvania, along with Dr. M. Paul Farber of The FARBER FOUNDATION FOR RESEARCH AND DEVELOPMENT that COLL/AG-40 would accomplish the SAME Scientific Reaction IN VIVO in a Population of 10 Live AIDS Patients who were HIV Positive and exhibited a Positive Viral Load as measured by a P24 Laboratory Test which measures for the P24 Number for a Specific Reaction.

The SCIENTIFIC PROTOCOL which I, Dr. Farber, designed was what I term THE (5, 4, 3, PROTOCOL). This consists of having a Participant in the study first receive a PCR (POLYMERS CHAIN REACTION) TEST to measure the VIRAL LOAD, which is the amount of the HIV VIRUS which is present in the blood stream of the body. The Participant then begins with 1 Tablespoon of COLL/AG-40 on a 5 TIMES a day basis. This Dosage is taken Sublingually, which means it is held under the tongue for 1 minute, Swished around the mouth for 10 Seconds, then Gargled and Swallowed. Acidophilus (Preferably a 7 Strain Acidophilus is taken 3 hours before and 3 hours after each dosage to replace the Good Bacteria as Mild Silver Protein will not discriminate between Good and Harmful Bacteria. This process is then repeated for a total of 5 times a day for the first month. Another PCR as well as a P24 are conducted at the end of the First Month to measure the Presence of and the Amount of the VIRAL LOAD. This Process is then repeated the second month using a 4 Times A Day Dosage. The PCR and the P24 are repeated again and a Statistically Comparative Study of the VIRAL LOADS is performed. The third month requires a 3 Times A Day Dosage of the COLL/AG-40, MILD SILVER PROTEIN and another PCR and P24 are conducted at the end of the third month and then become a part of the Statistically Comparative Study. I recommend that each participant stay on 3 Times A Day until there is NO AIDS (HIV) VIRUS left in the body.

THE FARBERHEIMER REACTION

Named in Honor of Dr. Jeriah Herxheimer who identified the HERXHEIMER REACTION which identified the Die Off which occurs when certain micro-organisms such as the spirochete which causes Lyme Disease and the Candida Micro-organism which causes Yeast Infections die and give off toxins which create a limited symptomatology for 1-3 weeks till they pass from the body.

My Initial Hypothesis was that the VIRAL LOAD would consistently decrease during the first 3 months. In some of the Participants this proved to be true. However, in other Participants there was a dramatic increase in the Viral Load even though myself and my Fellow Scientist and Researchers had no doubt that the MILD SILVER PROTEIN was KILLING the Virus. Upon further Analysis of the PCR test it became apparent that the PCR measures both the LIVING as well as the DEAD Virus. This measurement is based upon ATOMIC WEIGHT which does not discriminate between DEAD and LIVING Virus. Therefore since indeed the COLL/AG-40 was LYSING the Living AIDS Virus making it into a DEAD rather than a LIVING Virus, it is therefore possible for the VIRAL LOAD to increase during the first few months of the study. I recommend Cleansing The Body by drinking at least 7 or more full glasses of water a day and receiving Colonic Irrigations on a once a week basis to help to remove the DEAD VIRUS from the body. It is this increase in the Viral Load due to the presence of Substantial Amounts of Dead Virus which I have dubbed the FARBERHEIMER REACTION.

A good analogy could be drawn from the GULF WAR in which the Armed Forces of Saddam Hussein of Iraq invaded Kuwait. Literally Hundreds of Thousands of soldiers were killed in the military battles. If one were to measure the weight of all the Dead Soldiers as well as the Few Remaining Living Soldiers once the battles ended, this Weight would be Extremely High. However, if all of the DEAD Soldiers were removed and buried the weight of the number of LIVING Soldiers would be very LOW. It is my Scientific Contention that this Same Phenomena holds TRUE for the AIDS VIRUS when it is LYSED (KILLED) by the COLL/AG-40 IN VIVO, in the Living Human Body. It is now my SCIENTIFIC HYPOTHESIS that in certain individuals that are severely infected with a large degree of virus that it could take up to 6 months or even more before the VIRAL LOAD ATOMIC WEIGHT MEASUREMENT turns around and eventually bottoms out a 0, meaning there is no more AIDS (HIV) Virus left in the body.

The next question is, will one still test HIV+ after all the HIV Virus in the body has been LYSED (KILLED). The answer is YES because the HIV+ TEST measures for the presence of ANTIBODIES and not the PRESENCE OF THE VIRUS. Once a person has an ANTIBODY in his system it will be there for the rest of their Natural life even though the Virus which caused the Antibody to form in the first place is no longer present. In my opinion this method of using the HIV ANTIBODY TEST to determine if a person has AIDS is not only ILLOGICAL but also DESTRUCTIVE to those individuals who are diagnosed by this method and actually don't have the virus present in their bodies.

Chronology of Events for B. Thomas

Diagnosed HIV+ in 1989 from drug use, had symptoms previous to diagnosis.

Drugs prescribed by doctors: AZT, DDI, DDC, Insulin, Tylenol #2, Tylenol 500, Reston, Prozac, Ceftin, Novolin, Flagyl, Lasix, etc.

Symptoms: Cuts were not healing – opportunistic infections, stomach and intestinal problems, sleeping problems, night sweats, fevers, nausea, swollen glands and lymph nodes, groin swelling, rectal bleeding, nose bleeding, aches in joints.

May 12, 1994 – HIV+ – diagnosis – consistent with AIDS

May 6, 1996 – Informed had to quit work because of condition, told had three weeks to live. Stopped all medications to cleanse body to prepare to take all natural, nontoxic product.

May 13, 1996 – First dosage taken of FDA approved product. Three days later sweats stopped, cuts started healing, sleep improved, gland swelling went down. After continued use, all bleeding stopped – started feeling better and progressing.

June 6, 1996 – Tested blood three weeks and one day into using product. Blood tests suggests testing for HIV. HIV not conclusive anymore, two year earlier test said blood was consistent with AIDS.

June 9, 1996 – Blood test white cell count had increased from 180 in May to 350 without any outside attempt to rebuild white cell count.

July 13, 1996 – Commenced additional natural product to rebuild immune system while continuing to kill virus with original product.

July 30, 1996 – Health continuing to improve, symptoms gone, stamina increasing, gained ten pounds since mid June.

Prognosis – Long and healthy life as long as Mr. Thomas does not continue life habits that brought about condition in the first place.

B Thomas

Cardiovascular Consultants Inc.
458 26th Street
San Diego, CA 92102

September 30, 1996

Dr. Paul Farber,

Filer Smith from Seattle, Washington, is a participant in the Coll/Ag-40, Mild Silver Protein study. His latest test results indicate that his P-24 is negative. PCR has dropped and his T-Cell Subsets continue to have a small rise or seem stable.

Sincerely,

Myer Rice, M.D., Ph.D

Filer Smith
10446-65th Ave.
South Seattle WA 98178
(206) 721-3564

Dr. M. Paul Farber
4582-E Kingwood Dr., Ste. #210
Kingwood, Texas 77345

The following symptoms were occurring over a number of years before I was diagnosed HIV+. Loss of feeling in toes on right side of body, urgency, circular rashes over my body during a given month, loss of muscular control in my hands, glands on both sides of my neck swollen, and a loss of forty pounds overall.

After I had exhausted all possible reasons for these symptoms, a neurologist suggested that I might consider a test for HIV/AIDS. I was diagnosed HIV+ in October of 1995, my counts indicated that I had most likely contracted this virus 5-7 years prior. I have to date never consumed HIV/AIDS specific drugs for this virus.

Having never taken an HIV/AIDS-related drug, allowed me free choice over endless studies. During my research on how to help combat this virus, I came upon the COll/AG-40 study. After meeting all the qualifications for the protocol deemed necessary by Dr. M. Paul Farber and Dr. Myer Rice, I began the patient protocol for The Mild Silver known as Coll/Ag-40.

Before starting the protocol I had a PCR of 169,760 copies/cc dated 1/22/96, on 12/7/95 I tested positive for the following bands related to HIV/AIDS (GP 120m, GP160, GP 41 and P24 Antigen). On 12/22/95 CD 19 (3%) low, CD 4 (21%) low, CD3 (35%) low, CD 16 (41%) high, CD 4/cd 8 (.69) low, CD 4 ABS, count 232 (low).
The first month after taking The Mild Silver Protein known as Coll/Ag-40 blood was drawn to measure the specific HIV-1 P24 core antigen. On 5/23/96 this antigen was not detected and is currently not detected. I am tested once a month. My PCR level has gone from 236,222 copes/cc down to 62,201 copies/cc as of 9/6/96. As of 9/3/96 my CD4/CD8 is measuring 5100/cmm (above normal), CD3 65% (normal), CD4 28% (low normal), CD8 35% (normal) Every count just keeps turning for the better.

Overall, my health is great, I feel and look awesome. I've gained all my weight, and some since I began the study 6 months ago. I was just married a month ago, my wife and I now look forward to the day we may have children instead of planning a funeral. I have feeling back in my toes, my glands aren't large and swollen, my hands are functioning normal, my urgency is still persisting but I have faith this will pass too, moreover, my immune system is so built up that I haven't suffered even a cold. The only side effect I had was 2 days of a minor bloody nose in the very beginning of the study. I hope that if you are reading this you will tell someone about the results I have had with the Coll/Ag 40 , so they too can live their life knowing their HIV+ status will soon be "POSITIVELY NEGATIVE."

I, Filer Smith, give Dr. M. Paul Farber permission to reprint this document and use it in any medium deemed necessary by him so that he may better human existence more than he already has.

Sincerely

Filer Smith

Testimonial regarding
Roxie Faye Prince
A Victim of AIDS

She started taking Mild Silver Protein Tuesday, May 28, 1996.

Roxie is given 1/2 tablespoon by mouth five times a day. She is also given 1-2 Acidophilus capsules daily and also takes 9.5 ml DDI by mouth twice daily.

Roxie's T-cell count as of March, 1996 was 427 @ 31%. She will have a full blood count performed in August, 1996. Roxie was diagnosed HIV+ June 6, 1990, after mother's diagnosis. Roxie has always suffered with several health problems since birth, related to her HIV status. The following is a list of her most common ailments:

1) Chronic infections within lymph glands in throat
2) Occasional ear infections (usually follows glandular infections)
3) Constant cough – worsening at bedtime
4) Minor skin irritations and undiagnosed rashes
5) Several eye infections
6) Poor appetite – low weight

The day (May 28, 1996) Roxie started taking Mild Silver Protein she had a noticeable swelling in her left gland. There was no pain or any other common symptoms, So I suggested we wait to see what the day would bring. Normally, I rush Roxie to the doctor at the first sign of swelling because she commonly is in bed the next day with severe swelling, fever, severe pain and no appetite. So please realize that this was a risk that I was asking of her! But, she agreed to wait and see if the protein would make any difference. The following day the same amount of swelling (no increase) was present, but there were no other symptoms! While still feeling pesimistic, we couldn't help but get excited! By the fourth day, all swelling was gone, while no other symptoms appeared. This was amazing! Roxie has had to be treated with Ceftin every time she's had gland infections! She was thrilled.

Within a week after beginning the Mild Silver Protein, Roxie's chronic coughing disappeared! Her energy level increased noticeably and she seems to have a much better appetite. Her physical appearance shows signs of improvement. Not only is she gaining weight, but her skin color even seems more healthy. She has had no skin irritations, even after a couple of sunburns from swimming too long!

There have been no physical problems for the last eight weeks for Roxie. She is having a great summer due to this incredible improvement. While we are hesitant to become to optimistic, all of the positive signs are hard to ignore! We pray each day that God will continue his healing and we thank him each day for the Yoders, Dr. Farber and Mild Silver Protein. Roxie's little brother, Cody, told me one day that he hopes that the protein cures his sister, but that he'll be sad, too, because it didn't save his mom and dad. So our hope is not only for our little Roxie, but for all of the other victims of this horrible disease.

Patricia Marshall

Dear Dr. Farber.

In the middle of May, McKenzie was exposed to a petroleum seal oil. She became very ill. She was admitted to the hospital for a few days. She was doing much better at this point. After about three weeks McKenzie became ill again. She became totally inactive. Could not jump up and down from furniture. She did not groom herself. Her hair began to fall out in clumps and her nails split and began to peel. She was very stiff; her joints were sore. She would cry out if you touched her.

Back to the vet. Blood tests were run. McKenzie was given a corticosterone shot. The diagnosis was feline aids. We were told there was no cure and it was just a matter of time before McKenzie would die.

I went to my local health food store for something to ease her symptoms. I was given some literature and bought a bottle of colloidal silver. McKenzie was given the smallest dosage – $1/2$ teaspoon daily.

By the second day McKenzie was feeling better. I gave her 2 oz. over about a one-month period. She improved very fast and was back to her old self in about two weeks. Now seven months later she is doing great. None of her symptoms have reoccurred.

Pat Case

Dedicates this story to Dr. Thomas Craig and Texas A&M

I give my permission to reprint this story.

The Farber-Henderson
Mild Silver Protein HIV "AIDS" Antigen
Capture Diagnostic Analysis

Detection of HIV Virus In Blood
Progressive Virucidal Diminution
Total HIV Virus Eradication

The common, accepted diagnostic test utilized by the medical profession to determine whether an individual is infected with HIV, which then classifies that individual as having AIDS...is essentially a "Blood Antibody Test." If a particular blood test shows the presence of antibodies toward the HIV virus, then that person is diagnosed with AIDS. Four major questions must then be answered:

1. Why do some people who are diagnosed in this manner (as having the HIV virus and thus AIDS) never get sick?

2. Why does the presence of HIV Antibodies not necessarily mean that a person has the HIV virus and therefore AIDS?

3. Why should a person continue to have HIV Antibodies in his or her blood for the rest of their natural life if a scientifically proven method were utilized (which we now have)...Mild Silver Protein... to kill the HIV virus, inhibit replication and any latent formation?

4. What is a much more logical and effective method to determine whether a person has the HIV virus, how much of the HIV virus they actually have in their blood, and when is that HIV virus partially and then completely eradicated?

A More Effective Method...And The Answers
To The Previous Questions

The more effective method for determining whether an individual has the HIV virus (and therefore AIDS) is the Farber-Henderson Mild Silver Protein HIV "AIDS" Antigen Capture Diagnostic Analysis. With this scientific diagnostic method, the medical laboratory is actually testing for the *presence and amount* of the HIV virus in the blood stream of the individual tested. If the test is "positive," the individual then begins the Mild Silver Protein treatment and is then re-tested for Antigen Capture on a weekly basis for a three-month period to evaluate a *progressive decrease* in the HIV virus leading to an eventual eradication of the virus and thus an end to AIDS.

Now the answers

1. Why do some people who are diagnosed in this manner (antibody blood test) as having the HIV virus never get sick?

As one can see in the answer to question #3, having the presence of a specific antibody in the blood does not scientifically conclude that microorganisms such as the AIDS virus are actually present in the body. Therefore, to conclude that an individual has AIDS is not always correct, leading to a false diagnosis. There is therefore no reason that a person should come down with AIDS and become ill, since the HIV virus is not present in the blood. But most importantly, because of the false diagnosis, the person could be prescribed in my opinion a highly toxic substance such as AZT, which appears to create an Auto-Immune-Deficiency-Syndrome which destroys the immune system and can therefore lead to a simulated form of AIDS. The eventual invasion of opportunistic microorganisms could lead to disease and eventual death. That individual would have been better off if they had been left alone and never received any so-called AIDS TREATMENT.

2. Why does the presence of HIV antibodies not necessarily mean that a person has the HIV virus and therefore AIDS?

When the immune system of the human body is invaded with an infectious microorganism it immediately creates and produces an antibody that can neutralize and destroy it. It is as if a new genetic pattern has been created by the body which can handle that particular microorganism and others similar to it. Once a pattern for this antibody is created, it and the antibodies which it creates will be a part of the body's bloodstream for possibly the rest of that person's life span. For example, once a person has a smallpox vaccination or a polio vaccination, the pattern for those antibodies as well as the antibodies themselves will be present for the rest of that person's life, even though they do not have smallpox or polio.

It is therefore possible to get a positive blood test for that particular antibody, even though the microorganism which initially caused that antibody is no longer present.

3. Why would a person continue to have HIV antibodies in the blood for the rest of their life if a scientifically proven method (Mild Silver Protein) had been used and the HIV virus were destroyed?

Again, antibody production is the natural response of the body's immune system to microorganism invasion such as viruses, bacteria, spirochetes, yeast, fungi, etc. It is possible to remove all the HIV virus from the blood and still retain the genetic pattern for AIDS antibodies in the blood for the person's life span.

FROM "PENICILLIN"
TO "MILD SILVER PROTEIN"
THE ANTIBIOTIC ANSWER TO LYME DISEASE

Willy Burgdorfer, Ph.D., M.D. (hon)
Scientist Emeritus
Rocky Mountain Laboratories

In 1949, Dr. Sven Hellerström from the Dermatological Clinic of the Karolinska Institute in Stockholm, Sweden presented a paper "Erythema chronicum migrans Afzelius with meningitis" at the 43rd Annual Meeting of the Southern Medical Association in Cincinnati, Ohio. In presenting his case, he provided convincing evidence that both erythema and subsequent meningocerebrospinal symptoms may develop following a tick bite. He also reported on the successful treatment of his patient with penicillin, a drug shown previously by his colleague Dr. Hollström to be effective in the treatment of Erythema chronicum migrans (ECM).

In the United States, ECM was first reported in 1970 on a physician bitten by a tick while grouse hunting in northeastern Wisconsin. The attending physician, Dr. Rudolf Scrimenti, recognized the similarity of the patient's skin reaction to the lesions of European ECM and promptly and successfully treated the patient with penicillin. Similarly, a cluster of four ECM cases occurred in 1975 in southeastern Connecticut. The treatment of three patients with penicillin and of one with erythromycin resulted in complete resolution of symptoms within 48 to 72 hours.

Considered unrelated to ECM were skin lesions in

13 of 51 residents in the eastern Connecticut towns of Lyme, Old Lyme, and East Haddam where, since 1972, clusters of inhabitants had been suffering of an illness characterized by recurrent attacks of asymmetric swelling and pain in large joints, especially the knee. Since such arthritic conditions were not known to be associated with ECM in Europe, the illness was thought to be a new clinical entity and was named Lyme Arthritis, later changed to Lyme Disease once it was realized that arthritis was only one of several clinical manifestations of this disease.

The search for effective antibiotics in the treatment of Lyme Disease began in 1982 with my discovery of a spirochete now known as *Borrelia burgdorferi* as the causative agent of Lyme Disease and of ECM and related disorders (acrodermatitis chronica atrophicans, lymphadenosis benigna cutis) in Europe. The antibiotics found effective include tetracyclines (doxycycline, minocycline), penicillins (penicillin G amoxycillin), cephalosporins (cefotaxim, ceftriaxone), and erythromycin. Application of these drugs depends on the time the disease is being diagnosed. Early Lyme Disease is treated orally whereas late Lyme Disease requires parenteral or a combination of parenteral and oral applications. Treatment failures have been reported for each of these drugs particularly for the tetracyclines that are only temporarily effective unless that are applied over long periods of time, i.e. months even years.

Controversy exists over the length of treatment. Some investigators consider 21 to 30 days sufficient for the elimination of the spirochetes, while others believe that patients must be kept on therapy until they are completely free of symptoms.

The diagnosis of Lyme Disease is a clinical one and is based on the development and recognition of the skin lesion (erythema migrans) a few days, weeks, or even months, after the bite of an infected tick. Unfortunately in up to 40% of patients this skin lesion does not develop, is not recognized or is overlooked. Thus, without treatment, the disease spreads throughout the body and may affect the muscular, skeleton, cardiac and nervous systems.

Indeed Dr. Farber's recent claim having rediscovered from the medical literature the use of "Mild Silver Protein" as an effective bacteriocidal antibiotic, and having used this drug to successfully cure himself from late stage Lyme Disease, comes at a time when thousands of patients suffering of this disease are refused extended antibiotic treatment because their physicians are unable to associate their clinical manifestations with those of Lyme Disease.

According to medical journals around the world, Mild Silver Protein is a powerful, nontoxic wide-spectrum antibiotic that had been used successfully in the treatment of more than 650 diseases. Although never established scientifically, it appears that silver colloids disable the enzyme(s) used by bacteria, fungal and viral agents for their oxygen metabolism causing them to suffocate upon contact. *In vitro* studies with Dr. Farber's Mild Silver Protein and the Lyme Disease spirochete, *B. burgdorferi,* revealed a 100% killing effect within less than five minutes after exposure to the silver preparation.

At the time these lines are being written, more

than 2,500 people with late and persisting Lyme Disease are on Mild Silver Protein. The future will show whether Dr. Farber's "Silver Micro-Bullet" is right on target.

"Promising Preliminary Scientific Data Has Been Gathered..."

Dr. **John Parks Trowbridge, M.D., is**
a Co-Author of *The Yeast Syndrome*
along with **Dr. Morton Walker, D.P.M.**

The problem with any innovative advance in medical science is the suspicion with which it is initially viewed by "the establishment." Clinging to their structured viewpoint and defined treatment programs, many of these physicians and scientists are hesitant to embrace any <u>change</u> that challenges their assumptions and theories.

The only effective promotion that will displace an established treatment philosophy is to *discover and publicize the truth*. Truth in science is considered to be that which can be seen clearly and repeatedly, under the same experimental conditions. While this is laudable, it also places an expensive barrier between a good idea and its definitive scientific proof. That is to say, a great many dollars can be spent on research projects in order to "prove" a new truth–and raising this money could take many, many years (if it is gathered at all). All during this frustrating delay, the established viewpoint and standards of care continue to be <u>what is heard</u> and <u>what is done.</u> A whole generation (or two) of physicians and scientists can grow into their careers with "wrong" information, when the truth might be known to a few courageous people who have not yet found the money to fund the studies to show that they are right.

A great tragedy would be for Dr. Farber's ideas to suffer the fate of being casually dismissed by "the establishment" because "scientific studies" have not been forthcoming. Preliminary data have been gathered from several sources–and the results are *startlingly supportive* of the theories Dr. Farber has advanced. Now, quite simply, is the time for more intensive scientific scrutiny, to determine more precisely the significance and application of this novel approach to treating serious illnesses.

The following pages will document for you these early studies. You are, quite literally, witnessing **scientific discoveries** as they progress. This event could be likened to arriving in the New World a couple of weeks after the landing of Christopher Columbus: you would be a first-person witness to the fascination he had with the marvels he was encountering.

Studies by **Margret Bayer, Ph.D.**, at the Fox Chase Cancer Center in Philadelphia have shown that the growth and replication (spread) of Lyme disease bacteria (Borrelia burgdorferi spirochetes) are measurably slowed or stopped by Mild Silver Protein when viewed in the laboratory test tube.

Willy Burgdorfer, Ph.D., and **Tom Schwan,** Ph.D., work at the Rocky Mountain Laboratories, National Institutes of Health, Public Health Service, United States Department of Health and Human Services. In their studies of two Borelia bacteria-B. burgdorferi causing Lyme disease and B. Hermsii, causing relapsing fever-test tube mixing with Mild Silver Protein was <u>uniformly deadly.</u> Additional studies, in the test tube and in laboratory animals are underway and could be reported soon. The future is about to become a reality.

Turning attention to one of the most serious and challenging health problems in the industrialized nations, we find that a new treatment option might be available for the Yeast Syndrome. **Helen Buckley,** Ph.D., Professor of Microbiology and Immunology at Temple University School of Medicine, Philadelphia, Pennsylvania, has done test tube studies with several *Candida albicans* (yeast strains) and several *Cryptococcus neoformans* strains. "Cryptococcus" is an opportunistic (fungus) infection that is a final deadly problem for many people suffering with AIDS. In both cases, <u>growth was blocked</u> by test tube exposure to very small doses of Mild Silver Protein.

Hold on to your chairs, now! The one disease problem getting most of our attention now is AIDS, Acquired Immune Deficiency Syndrome. Whenever talk turns to AIDS, a shiver goes down the spine of most people. The problem is simple: here's an often deadly disease without any obvious treatment. The key word here is "obvious." This problem is claimed to result from exposure to and infection by a specific virus, such as HIV-1 (Human Immunodeficiency Virus, type 1). Modern medicine has found few approaches to slowing the growth of this virus inside human bodies.

Earl Henderson, Ph.D., another Professor of Microbiology and Immunology at Temple University's School of Medicine, has recently reported very exciting data using a special formulation of Mild Silver Protein. Dr. Henderson's experiments tested the ability of Mild Silver Protein to block production of HIV in human T-cell lymphocytes (white blood cells). At very low doses (as shown on the accompanying letter of February 2, 1995, reporting his findings), the Mild Silver Protein dramatically blocked viral production – with little *if any* toxicity.

Later studies in Dr. Henderson's laboratory involved the human lymphoblastoid B-cell line (a different white blood cell) and HIV-1 survival and reactivation. In varying low dosages, the special formula of Mild Silver Protein eliminates the infectious HIV or significantly reduces HIV infective ability.

These tests are done "in the test tube," and they light the way to future research in human beings. "Current" medications have been woefully ineffective against the HIV virus. More importantly, the side effects of AIDS treatments have sometimes been as deadly as the disease itself. Here, perhaps is where Mild Silver Protein really shines.

Dr. Henderson reported "little if any acute toxicity" to the white blood cells at dosages that were effective against the HIV virus. As he notes: *"These results are very encouraging and suggest additional experiments that could be done."* I agree!

John Barltrop, D.Sc., and R.C. Renlund, D.V.M., have reported more than just *test tube* studies: they have summarized experiments where Mild Silver Protein was given to rats to observe their reactions.

Rats were injected with the solution or it was added to their drinking water. In all cases, clinical and behavior and pathological evaluations showed <u>no evidence of acute or long-term toxic changes.</u> The dosages used were many, many times what has been effective for human beings for a variety of ailments. Truly this might be the "Micro Silver Bullet" that medical science has been seeking ever since the discovery of Penicillin.

So, I invite you to treasure this opportunity to open the back hall doors of medical research laboratories. You are witnessing the first tentative steps at proving what I believe will be found to be a **major scientific truth.** You and I have a serious responsibility now: let's be sure that this approach survives the critics whose voices will soon be heard. We need this to be <u>studied thoroughly</u>, to see what promise it holds to preserve and enhance not only our own lives but also those of our children and grandchildren.

Welcome to a glimpse of a better future.

Mild Silver Protein
Preliminary Scientific Laboratory Results

The studies and laboratory reports reproduced below (in condensed form but with context in tact) represent the particular findings that took place under specific laboratory conditions described in each individual study by the scientist and researcher performing that study. Any inferences or conclusions as to the meaning and effect of these findings to the human population can only be accomplished through scientific hypothesis. Actual documented results of the effects of using Mild Silver Protein can only occur by statistically analyzed data pertaining to human usage. Endorsement of Mild Silver Protein by individuals, universities or laboratories is not intended nor is it implied. **To review complete original studies of the following summaries turn to the back of this book. You can also observe the Curriculae Vitae on the scientists who performed the experimentations.**

(1) **From the Rocky Mountain Laboratories** (January 13, 1995):"...we have received...a sample (12ml) of your Mild Silver Protein (1500 ppm) preparation and have evaluated its effectiveness in a preliminary pilot study against the Lyme Disease spirochete, Borrelia burgdorferi (B31) and against the relapsing fever agent, B. hermsii (HS-1).

"In both tests, BSK cultured spirochetes were treated with 150 and 15 ppm of Mild Silver Protein. When examined 24 hours later, **none of the treated cultures contained live spirochetes.** Few spirochetes, all dead, were observed at 48 hours."

Dr. Willy Burgdorfer, Ph.D.
Scientist Emeritus

(2) **From the Fox Chase Center** (January 24, 1995): ..." Preliminary laboratory studies on Borrelia burgdorferi spirochetes revealed that Mild Silver Protein solutions **reduce the growth rate of these cells** significantly and eventually lead to cell death.

"...More studies are definitely necessary to obtain a clearer picture of the interaction between silver protein and Borrelia burgdorferi. As these preliminary studies suggest, growth and replication of Lyme **spirochetes are measurably inhibited by Mild Silver Protein** in the in vitro setting."

Margret Bayer, Ph.D.

(3) From **Temple University** (February 2, 1995): "Preliminary studies on your Silver Micro-Bullet preparation (1500 ppm) show it to be **effective in inhibiting and killing** strains of *Candida albicans* and *Cryptoccus neoformans* in vitro.

"...Additional studies should be done to evaluate *in vivo* effectivity."

Helen R. Buckley, Ph.D.
Professor

(4) From **Temple University** (February 2, 1995): "...We tested the ability of Mild Silver Protein to inhibit human immunodeficiency virus type 1 (HIV-1) replication in the human T cell line, SupT 1, as measured by syncytia formation. We found that **Mild Silver Protein inhibited HIV-1 replication** in SupT 1 cells as measured by a reduction in the appearance of syncytia in cell culture. There appeared to be **little if any acute toxicity** associated with the dose of Mild Silver Protein which inhibited HIV-1 replication...

"...These results are very encouraging and suggest additional experiments that could be done..."

Earl E. Henderson, Ph.D.
Professor of Microbiology

(5) From **Temple University** (March 20, 1995): "...My laboratory has studied the effects of Special Formulation of Mild Silver Protein on human immunodeficiency virus Type 1 (HIV-1) survival and on latency reactivation of

HIV-1 in the human lymphoblastoid B cell line, M57-3...

"...The results of the ...experiment show that exposure of HIV-1 to 1000 ppm of Special Formulation of Mild Silver Protein for one hour at 37 degrees Centigrade **completely eliminates infectious HIV-1** as measured by syncytia formation on SupT 1 cells..."

Earl E. Henderson, Ph.D.
Professor of Microbiology

(6) From the **University of Toronto** (January 27, 1995): "...At the highest dose (18 mg/300 gram rat) there were **no observed adverse effects** within the treatment period; the data does not permit us to make a statement regarding the metabolic fate of the silver. If these data can be extrapolated to the human scale, then a 60 kilogram individual would have to be given 3,600 mg (3.6 gram) to receive an amount equivalent to the test animals (rats). This corresponds to the injection of 1 ml of a solution containing 300,000 ppm of Mild Silver Protein."

John Barltrop, M.A., D.Phil, D.Sc.

(7) **On tests conducted on *Escherichia coli (E. coli)* and *Staphylococcus aureus (Staph)* using the Mild Silver Protein:** "Three different experiments were performed...to determine the bactericidal activity of (Mild Silver Protein): ...Direct application of test specimen at 1500 ppm and 150 ppm onto sheep blood agar plates seeded with *E. coli* and *S. aureus*...The test specimen (Mild Silver Protein) inhibited growth of *E. coli* and *S. aureus* at a concentration of 1500 ppm..."

(8) **On tests conducted on *Streptococcus pneumoniae (Strep)* (resistant to Penicillin) and *Pseudomonas aeruginosa* (resistant to ampicillin, tetracycline, trimethyoprim, cefazolin, cefoxitin, cefuroxime, and cephalothin) using**

Mild Silver Protein:

"Direct application of Test Specimen A (Mild Silver Protein) at 1500 ppm...and 300 ppm onto sheep blood agar plates seeded with *S. pneumoniae* and *P. aeruginosa*...Test Specimen A (Mild Silver Protein) inhibited growth of *S. Pneumoniae* at concentrations of 1500 ppm and 300 ppm...Test Specimen A (Mild Silver Protein) inhibited growth of *P. aeruginosa* at concentrations of 1500 ppm and 300 ppm..."

Note from Dr. Farber: The latter two studies (on Staph and Strep)are very significant because Staph and Strep are responsible for approximately 90% of common colds!

Note from Dr. Farber: The Mild Silver Protein Formula was recently re-engineered to be 100% free of Nitrates and Nitrites. Thus it will now do at 10-30 ppm what previously required 1,000-2,000 ppm to accomplish. Dr. Henderson agrees totally that the study below is evidence that Nitrates and Nitrites (which most colloidal silver contain) inhibit the action of the silver significantly. This new formulation will be the basis of the Mild Silver Protein. The following study shows final results:

Mild Silver Protein (Dietary Supplement)	10^{-1}	10^{-2}	10^{-3}	10^{-4}
3 ppm	+	+	0	0
0.3 ppm	++	++	+	+
0.03 ppm	+++	+++	++	+
None	+++	+++	++	+
AZT (10mm)	0	0	0	0

Taken as a whole these experiments show an in-vitro effect with Mild Silver Protein (Nitrate and Nitrite Free) as well as HIV replication in the human T cell line, Supt

1. This inhibition of HIV-1 replication is dependent on the concentration of Mild Silver Protein. I trust these preliminary in-vitro results using very low concentrations of Mild Silver Protein will interest you.

CONTENTS

Introduction

In everyone's life, certain events stand out as special. In most cases, each of these marks a turning point - the cusp where the momentum of life circumstances rushes toward a crescendo declaring the end of one era and the fresh beginning of another, forging in a different direction.

Your first serious love forever overshadowed "puppy love," which you had thought was the height of intensity. The college of graduate course where you first had to develop a totally original work suddenly brought into focus your earlier studies as just "preparatory." Such events serve as milestones by which your life is charted on its course.

"Twenty-twenty hindsight" makes these past events stand out so clearly. We can muse at having missed the significance of some of them while they were happening day-by-day. Events that are readily acknowledged by our community – such as graduation, marriage, baptism, promotion – are easy to "spot" as critical junctures. But what about the less obvious ones?

I am honored to write the introduction to this literary work. You see, this is one of those critical events for me – less obvious than many, but highly significant in the context of my lifetime.

Dr. Paul Farber has invited me into his thought processes. He has shared with me the twists and turns of his viewpoints, as he struggled to find the forms to participate, albeit vicariously, in the advancement of a scientific paradigm that embraces both knowledge and experience.

A scientific theory emerges as an attempt to explain a set of facts. The process is one of trying to "get a handle on" the reality that is "Mother Nature." Man's imperfect understanding means that every theory is flawed by not taking into account every possibility in nature. As new observations and facts arise, new theories are proposed to accommodate both the older knowledge and the more recent data as well. Thus, science marches on.

Biological sciences include the study of how human beings "work" and how they survive in an environment of real dangers. Invention of the microscope enabled us to see the microbiological world existing within our world – no longer would "humors" or "vapors" be needed to explain the transmission of illness from one person to another. With Pasteur's demonstrations of bacteria able to cause human illness, the world was set for some of the most miraculous advances of the 20th Century: *antibiotics*. His work in the 1860's was not readily accepted by the scientists of his day. As late as 1888, eminent French surgeons argued that performing operations with gloves (to protect the patient from the surgeon's germs!) was needless and foolish. Indeed, not until 1925 did the last American hospital require the use of protective gloves.

Despite the magnificence of his discoveries, Pasteur in later life questioned whether he had missed the target. Bernard and others had maintained that the condition of the biological animal – whether beast or human – was more important than the actual microorganism in whether an infection would occur...and that would be the effects of such an infection. Indeed, as our understanding of infectious diseases has advanced, we have seen clearly what Bernard was saying. Viruses that cause minor symptoms in one population can be deadly for others. Bacteria capable of causing devastating damage in some people are carried harmlessly in the bodies of others.

Thus, we enter into an interesting phenomenon in medical science. As our knowledge develops, we strive to unify our world view by contriving theories to explain what we see. Those who cling to "the old school" will challenge our new proposals, despite an overwhelming logical argument. As their resistance finally caves in to an obviously better way of explaining nature, new methods of treatment emerge to address problems that were insoluble before. But then...we find exceptions that can't be explained even by the new theories. What we thought was neat and tidy now has a growing number of loose ends.

The irony, though, is that adherents to the newer viewpoint often blindly pursue the course laid out in their training and practice. In their rigidity, they become "the old school," overlooking inconsistencies and blaming treatment failures on factors other than shortcomings of their own perspectives.

Pasteur set the stage for the "one bug - one drug" mentality that has predominated in the treatment of infectious diseases for the past sixty years, since the discovery of sulfa antibiotics. Recent elegant research in the mechanisms of immunity, however, has shown that Bernard offered a more expansive view. Nutritional repletion often enables a body to defeat microbiological infection when the fanciest of antimicrobial treatments have failed. Indeed, many modern drugs -- both therapeutic and recreational – have serious side effects in that they damage or stall immune functions. In many respects, our "modern" thinking has led to the fascinating contradiction that "the cure is worse than the illness."

A sideline to the modern medical viewpoint is that illnesses difficult to quantify with current laboratory methods are somehow not as "real" as others that can be "scientifically" diagnosed. Thus has arisen the pejorative concept of "fad diseases." Examples of this group are "hypoglycemia" and "chronic fatigue" and "the yeast syndrome." Lyme disease escaped inclusion because infection shows obvious signs as well as vague symptoms.

But the "fad" label is so easy to apply when great numbers of patients, anxious to find some explanation for undiagnosed and continuing ill health, request for their physicians to test for this "new disease."

This brings us face-to-face with another major limitation in medical practice: those whose job is to treat illnesses often fall behind with regard to the explosive technical advances in diagnostic testing. Practitioners who do not appreciate the limits of a test or the implications of its results begin to confuse the "test" with "reality." The patient suffers when his physician wrongly tells him "Your tests are all fine, so you have nothing to worry about - perhaps you should see a counselor or even a psychiatrist."

The assumption made is that the doctor has ordered all the right tests. And that the tests can actually tell the doctor what, really, is going on inside the patient. And that the test was done at the right time to show the result that matters. And that no repeat testing is needed to show any changes. And so on. Here we come squarely to the art of medical practice. The physician who seeks to understand "why" and who continues to ask that question despite the apparent finality of any answer is the one who elevates the science to a fine art. Intuition is not so much a matter of "playing hunches" as it is maintaining an open mind and inviting - indeed, seeking - a different answer than one has "come to expect" based on past experience.

At some point, every physician is "stuck" with having to believe his patient. For example, we have no scientific measurement that will demonstrate a "headache." And we have no way to quantify the degree of pain that one person expresses as "tolerable" while another considers "unbearable." But beyond these circumstances, many physicians have stumbled into the error of "treating the tests, not the patients." Numbers that can be plugged into a computer program and checked off on some government "standard of care" checklist are much easier to deal with than patients who "just won't get better."

Into this era of medical practice comes Dr. Paul Farber. Perhaps the most obvious excuse that self-appointed critics will use to attempt to dismiss the significance of this book is that he is "not a real doctor." By this is meant that he is "just a chiropractor," not an "M.D. or D. O." They may even ignore the fact he has a Ph.D., two M.A. Degrees, two Bachelor Degrees, and Doctor of Naturo-pathy, N.D. Degree. One tragic note of our time is that healthcare has become stratified with "real doctors" claiming an "all-seeing" position at the top of a pyramid, imagining themselves to be standing on the shoulders of all others. The logical extension of this image, though, is that all practitioners are ultimately standing on the backs of all patients, who would occupy the very lowest base of the pyramid.

A more enlightened view is that each different practitioner of the healing arts stands equal, on a broad flat plain. And alongside each can stand his patient, both being partners in an effort to resolve problems presented by the patient. So long as a particular practitioner provides guidance and assistance that enhances the wellbeing and furthers the goals of the patient, they remain partners. At every instant, the patient is free to wander over to form a partnership with a practitioner offering a different set of of perspectives. Or even to wander back and forth, benefitting from the advice offered by each of several specialists, each with his own unique training and experience.

More immediately, with regard to this fine book, we must remain aware that Dr. Farber wrote it first from the perspective of a patient. The tragedy is that he wrote it as a patient who had not been able to find help from "conventional" physicians, "the old school" practitioners who purport to have the solution for "whatever ails you" that is "worth fixing." Perhaps starting from the patient's perspective is what gives Dr. Farber's book such a special appeal.

This represents the first efforts of a patient who happens to have advanced training in medical science, to put down in words not just the experience of his illness but also the exhilaration of his discovery of recovery.

Much like a Caribbean pirate's treasure map, this book sketches out for you the general plan of "how to get from here to healthy." Still, the journey is one that must be made with faltering steps, trying at each turn to confirm that you have reached the correct landmark shown on the map. As more patients and their physicians travel this route, more details will emerge. More surety will result as more understandings evolve.

Undoubtedly Dr. Farber himself will be offering more major contributions to the process of "fleshing out" the salient features of his theories. I have had the honor and pleasure to be present with him at this time, to ask questions, to begin to share the vision that is uniquely his. Not a month goes by without several public magazines and scientific or medical journals carrying articles summarizing the latest information on Lyme Disease, the Yeast Syndrome, and Multiple Sclerosis. Unfortunately there will be practitioners who misinterpret these current reports as "the last word" in how to diagnose and treat these problems. Happily, Dr. Farber will be writing more, to stimulate thinking and research, so that true solutions can emerge.

I challenge you to mount the springboard that he has provided. How far can you push the limits by building on his theories?

John Parks Trowbridge, M. D.
President, Great Lakes Association
for Clinical Medicine
Author, **The Yeast Syndrome**

Mild Silver Protein Nutritional Program For Achieving Homeostasis

You cannot overdose on mild silver protein! Drinking the whole bottle will produce no harmful effects but could cause a healing reaction.

ORAL: Normal Dosage: **1 Teaspoon for 7 days, then 1/2 teaspoon daily.**

Children: **1/4 to 1/2 of adult dose.** Pregnant women should consult their doctor.

Severe illness: **2 (two) Tablespoons daily.**

Optimum dose may require more or less mild silver protein depending on individual body chemistry and weight. Kinesiology testing or muscle testing can be an effective way to determine dosage. (**Remember, this is a safe mineral element and there are no known negative side effects.**)

Some people may feel achy and sluggish on the third or fourth day after they begin taking Silver on a daily basis. This is called a "Herxheimer Reaction" which is a healing reaction and it not harmful but may be somewhat uncomfortable. The reaction usually lasts one or two days BUT CAN LAST 2-3 WEEKS. Consume several additional glasses of water and take The Peoples' Doctors' brand Neutra Herx. Take 1 capsule with every dose of silver which contains molybdenum.

We have found that the Neutra Herx which contains molybdenum neutralizes the herxheimer reaction about 95% of the time.

External: Apply directly to cuts, scrapes and open sores. A Q-tip makes a good applicator. Put a few drops on a band-aid and wear over affected area. A colloidal silver salve is now available.

Atomizer/Inhaler: Spray into nose/lungs while inhaling.

Eyes: Put a few drops in the eye 2-3 times per day. Safe even for baby's eyes.

Nose: Put a few drops up the nose 2-3 times a day. Will rapidly open sinuses.

Ears: Put a few drops up to a teaspoon in the ear 2-3 times per day. Safe even for baby's ears.

Colonics, Douches: Add 2 (two) Tablespoons to one quart of distilled water.

To Purify Water: Add one ounce per gallon, shake well, wait six minutes, shake again, wait six minutes and drink.

For Animals: Use 6-8 drops per 20 lbs. of body weight.

Veterinarian: Use 4-10 drops per 20 lbs. of body weight once or twice daily depending on condition. Reduce or increase quantity as condition warrants. Horses and cows can be given the same dosage with no harmful effects. Expect results within 24-48 hours.

Disclaimer: Neither the manufacturer, seller, nor author of this book makes any claim as to any specific benefits accruing from the use of Mild Silver Protein.

Protocol for Respiratory Infections

Maintain a maintenance dosage of 1 Teaspoon of Mild Silver Protein a day: This should prevent the majority of common colds.

If already infected take 2 to 3 Tablespoons of Mild Silver Protein a day until infection ends and then take for 3 more days followed by a maintenance dosage of 1 Teaspoon a day.

If you are put into a social situation with a large number of people infected with a cold or flu, follow the same protocol as if already infected. You could very well be the only individual out of a thousand people who does not become ill.

Protocol Foreign Travel

When you travel to a foreign country, you usually feel the need to receive vaccinations either singular or multiple. In some instances it may be required by law. You should follow your own conscience as well as your physician's advice. You should also do some research to see if any of the vaccinations have side effects that could make you ill.

When I, the author, traveled to South Africa to meet with Nelson Mandela's top officials, I chose to not receive any vaccinations. Instead I took 2 tablespoons of Mild Silver Protein 4 times a day followed 3 hours before and after with the 7 Strain Probiotic. Fortunately I did not become ill and when I was also exposed to an African virus by a fellow traveler sitting next to me on the plane, I not only did not become ill but I also gave this person the same protocol of Mild Silver Protein and she became well within six hours of this 14-hour flight. I also had her snort the Mild Silver protein to stop her sinus and nasal drip. The positive results were immediate. It turned out that her husband was the pilot of this South African Airways flight and I got him started on the Mild Silver Protein also. What a wonderful testimonial!

Use your own judgement, but there does exist an alternative if you so choose.

Mild Silver Protein Nutritional Program
HIV PROTOCOL
FOR ACHIEVING HOMEOSTASIS

First Month	1 Tablespoon	Five times a day sublingually
Second Month	1 Tablespoon	Four times a day sublingually
Third Month	1 Tablespoon	Three times a day sublingually
Fourth Month	1 Tablespoon	Three times a day sublingually
Fifth Month	1 Tablespoon	Three times a day sublingually
Sixth Month	1 Tablespoon	Three times a day sublingually

Sublingual (under the tongue) instructions – Hold under the tongue for 1 minute. Swish around mouth for 10 seconds, gargle for 10 seconds, and then swallow. The tissues under the tongue and in the oral cavity are the most absorptive tissues in the body.

7 Strain Probiotic – Should be taken 3 hours after each dose of mild silver protein. Dosage: 1-2 capsules depending on body weight. Less than 100 lbs. – 1 capsule; 100 lbs. plus – 2 capsules.

If experiencing Herxheimer Reaction from accompanying yeast die off, take 1 tablet of Neutra Herx Molybdenum 2-3 times daily or as needed.

__Disclaimer: Neither the manufacturer, seller, nor author of this book makes any claim as to any specific benefits accruing from the use of Mild Silver Protein.__

Mild Silver Protein Nutritional Program

LYME DISEASE AND CANDIDA YEAST INFECTION
FOR ACHIEVING HOMEOSTASIS

First Month	1 Tablespoon	Twice a day (upon arising and before retiring) sublingually
Second Month	1 Tablespoon	One a day (upon arising) sublingually
Third Month	1 Tablespoon	Once a day (upon arising) sublingually
Maintenance	1 Teaspoon	Once a day sublingually

Children 3-12 Years Old

Same program as adult substituting **1 Teaspoon** instead of tablespoon.

Children 3 Year Old or Younger

Same program as above substituting **1/2 Teaspoon** instead of 1 teaspoon.

For the Common Cold or Flu – If already infected, **1 Tablespoon** 2 to 3 times per day sublingually until symptoms are gone. Then, **1 Teaspoon** per day for maintenance dosage.

Sublingual (under the tongue) instructions – Hold under the tongue for 1 minute, swish around mouth for 10 seconds, gargle for 10 seconds, and then swallow. The tissues under the tongue and in the oral cavity are the most absorptive tissues in the body.

A general maintenance dosage to act as a preventative for colds, flu, or any infectious illness is **1 Teaspoon** a day for adults, **1/2 Teaspoon** for children 3-12, or **1/4 Teaspoon** for children less than 3 years old.

7 Strain Probiotic – Should be taken 3 hours before and 3 hours after each dose of mild silver protein. Dosage: 1-2 capsules depending on body weight. Less than 100 lbs. – 1 capsule; 100 lbs. plus – 2 capsules.

Neutra Herx – Take one tablet with each dosage of mild silver protein during first 3-4 weeks to neutralize possible herxheimer reaction.

Animal Protocol for 10 PPM Liquid Silver

(Things that have worked)

Kirk Reynolds AAWT

This protocol is a starting point. Feel free to adjust dosages as the situation requires. Liquid Silver (Colloidal Silver) works as a catalyst not a chemical and does not interact with other medication or organ function in your animals. (There are no ill effects recorded when using Liquid Silver and no maximum dosage; dosages are not critical except that more is usually better than less.)

Small bird (117 grams) fluffed on the cage floor: Given 1/4 cc 3 times a day for a week the bird showed signs of recovery the first day. This was a large dose for this size bird, the bird recovered with no ill effects.

Eye and Ear Infections (all animals): 1 to 4 drops, depending on the size; should clear in 24 hrs.

Fish Aquarium Water: 1 teaspoon to 10 gallons to keep the water clear.

Colloidal Silver used in the drinking water or formula will not affect digestion, It will keep fungi from growing in the crop and stomach. Digestion occurs as a result of acid and enzyme action. Bacteria are in the large intestine and work to break down fiber, Colloidal Silver does not normally effect the large intestine, but as with any other infection, after the treatment, the reintroduction of friendly bacteria would be advised.

Birds

1) Conjunctivitis: 1 drop in the eye for 2 days.

2) Sinus: Use a syringe to inject Liquid Silver through the nostril openings into the sinus. Dosage: small amounts (1 drop) for finches to 1 cc for larger birds like Amazons and Macaws a couple times a day until the infection clears up. Give an equal amount orally.

3) Cuts, Scrapes, Cracks: Clean the area with Colloidal Skin Cleaner, dry and apply Liquid Silver or Liquid Silver Salve. Reapply daily until wound completely heals.

4) Fluffed Birds: 1 drop to 2 cc (finches to large parrot respectively) Liquid Silver orally 3 times a day for 3 days minimum.

5) Egg, Infection in the: (In a warm environment.) Clean the egg thoroughly with warm Liquid Silver Skin Cleaner of all foreign matter, warm rinse and wipe dry with sterile cotton ball. Next moisten a sterile cotton ball with warm Liquid Silver and wipe the egg. Then place the egg on top of the cotton ball so that the liquid will soak through the egg shell into the embryo, moisten the cotton ball in the incubator as needed to keep it damp during incubation. Adjust humidity accordingly.

6) Tail Bobbing: 1 drop to 2 cc Liquid Silver orally twice a day until bobbing stops.

7) Enlarged Liver (canary): 1 drop Liquid Silver orally once a day until the liver recovers.

8) New Bird Arrival (Quarantine): 1 cc Liquid Silver per day for large birds for 7 days; for smaller birds (finches), 1 drop per day for 7 days.

9) At the present time there is a study being done on AIDS patients using colloidal silver with a very positive preliminary findings. HIV is the virus that causes AIDS and polyomavirous is a virus that kills birds. Neither has responded very well to other treatments and maybe it's time for someone to look at colloidal silver for a cure.

Warts: Apply Liquid Silver Salve to the wart until it goes away.

COLLOIDAL SILVER IN A CANARY AVIARY

Saturday while talking to my friend, Ramon mentioned that he had a number of canaries (He raises fancy canaries) that were sick and he didn't think they would recover. I told him about Colloidal Silver and its antiseptic qualities, its ability to kill all bacterial, fungal and viral infection. With this Ramon purchased a bottle and left.

The next Saturday I was at Ramon's house and he showed me the birds that he had been treating with Colloidal Silver. He had six birds to show me; all were setting on their perches, one male was aggressively singing to its mate. Another bird Ramon was told to put down (mercy killing) as its condition was untreatable and the bird would die, was quietly sitting on its perch. It had had an enlarged liver that could be seen through the skin as an indication of a massive infection (disease unknown) as diagnosed by a mutual friend, Alphonse, who has been breeding canaries for the past 22 years and has seen this condition before. That evening in my presence when Alphonse came to Ramon's house he reinspected this bird, was amazed and remarked that the liver had returned to its normal size. Ramon told Alphonse that the bird had received one drop a day of Colloidal Silver for seven days. Altogether Ramon saved birds valued at approximately $400.00.

E. coli is another serious disease for canary breeders that will stop reproduction if the birds become infected. When canaries drink water they also wash food off their beaks. In a day's time this water and food can become a clouded "soup" of bacterial growth. By using Colloidal Silver in the water, Ramon told me the water in the water bottles stays clean even after two days even with food in them. The water can be a source of infection. Colloidal Silver kept the water clear. He had started using one teaspoon Colloidal Silver per gallon, treating all his water for the birds at this concentration.

Reported by Kirk Reynolds
Garden Grove, CA

GRAY-CHEEKED PARAKEET (Brutogeris) RECOVERY

Monday afternoon when I came home there was a cage on the counter with an inferred heater on the side and a Gray-cheeked parakeet fluffed up sitting inside on the bottom. When asked, my wife Donna told me she brought it in from the outdoor aviary because it didn't look well; I agreed. Then I asked if she had given the bird any Colloidal Silver (C/S) 10 ppm. She replied no. I then gave 1/4 cc (C/S) to the bird orally with a syringe, by 10 p.m. the bird was on the side of the food dish eating but still didn't look good. Donna didn't think it would survive the night, it got another 1/4 cc (C/S) orally.

Tuesday morning the bird was still sitting on the side of the food dish and got another 1/4 cc (C/S) before I went to work. That afternoon when I got home the bird was sitting on a perch (a good sign) but it was still fluffed, it got another 1/4 cc (C/S) orally and again that evening.

Wednesday morning the bird was on the perch and looking much better and not sitting as close to the heater. I gave it 1/4 cc (C/S) and again when I got home that afternoon.

That evening the bird demanded and got a piece of apple from Donna when she was preparing some fruit for the other birds; then spent the evening on her shoulder for company. When left behind on the chair for a commercial break it flew after her. It got another 1/4 cc (C/S) that evening.

Thursday morning the bird got another 1/4 cc (C/S), another 1/4 cc (C/S) that afternoon and again that evening. The bird now sets high on the perch, is eating good and is tight feathered. All signs of a well bird.

The bird weighs approximately 117 grams.

Bird breeders have a little different situation than do most pet owners. Their birds hide their symptoms until they can sit on their perch, then it's usually too late to do much to help. There are costs that have to be considered when dealing with disease in our livestock, too. Colloidal Silver is a tool that can help keep those costs to a minimum as most infections are bacterial or fungal in nature and it works on these inffections effectively.

Documented by Kirk Reynolds
13192 Siemon St.
Garden Grove, CA

No man may see the Father and live. However, I was in my spirit body looking through my spirit eyes instead of my physical body.

Dr. M. Paul Farber

At this time I would like to tell the story of what happened in the hospital chapel on Rosh Hashanah Day which is the day of the Jewish new year which comes right before Yom Kippur which is the Jewish High Holiday called the Day of Atonement. I got permission to go down to the chapel from the nurses as it was located on the first floor and there was no scheduled service for this day.

A few days before I was praying and chanting out loud in both Hebrew and English during an unscheduled service when two women later entered into the chapel. I apologized for praying and singing out loud and welcomed them in telling them I would be finished in a few minutes. One of the women who I later ended up counseling for about an hour because she had just recently lost her daughter in a murder rape attack told me not to stop and the other woman was in agreement. They said that the reason that they had come into the chapel was because they heard and were drawn by the singing, chanting, and prayers. I honored their request and conducted a service for about 30 minutes for the three of us. They did not know that I was studying to be ordained as a Messianic Jewish Rabbi as well as a Christian minister as I was in hospital robe and patient's pajamas and hardly looked like a pastor or rabbi. They said that their souls were just attracted to the prayers. I took this as a compliment from God and perhaps a confirmation of my ministry which is to come in the future after this book is published.

Now let us go back to Rosh Hashanah Day, this time I was completely alone except for God the Father, Jesus Christ and the Holy Spirit. The chapel was small and capable of seating about 50 people. In the front of the seats was a speaker's podium with a Bible on it. It was from there that the ministers would give their sermons. However the most significant part of this lovely chapel as it ultimately proved so to be to me was a large stained glass window about 25 feet tall and 20 feet wide. It was extremely beautiful with the rays of the sun shining through its rainbow of multitudinous colors.

I began praying and singing and chanting praise songs to the Lord in both English and the ancient language of Hebrew which was Jesus's native tongue as well as the original tongue of the inspired word of God which we call the Holy Bible which includes the Jewish Old Testament from the time of Moses as well as the Christian New Testament beginning with the works of Jesus Christ and completed through the Holy Spirit through the Apostles.

This included John through the inspiration of an angel which was sent to him by Jesus Christ wrote Revelations which proved to be very significant and confirmative of the beautiful heavenly and divine experience that layed right before me. As my voice began lifting up to heaven in ancient Hebrew, I was suddenly slain in the Holy Spirit and fell prostrate on the ground in front of the beautiful rainbow-colored stained glass window. My face was down with my eyes covered in reverence and my body layed in a prone position in spontaneous prayer to the Lord God of heaven and earth and His Son, the Messiah. I layed upon the ground for perhaps 10 minutes while the Spirit of God the Father and Jesus Christ came upon me. It says in the Bible "that your young men will have visions" and believe me from first-hand experience that this is a true statement and not merely a metaphor. "Thus Sayeth the Lord."

My head raised up off the ground and my eyes beheld the stained glass window come alive and become filled with the Holy Spirit and the presence of God. The images turned into a burning bush which was not consumed as Moses had seen on Mt Sinai when Jehovah God first spoke to Moses and revealed to him how he was to be the instrument through which God the Father would keep his promise to Abraham and free the children of Israel from the pits of slavery in Egypt and bondage to Pharoah. I then saw within this burning bush an image of a long white bearded Moses saying unto God, "Henene" which in Hebrew means here I am, but who am I Lord that I might break the bondage of Pharoah and free the children of Israel from slavery unto freedom." The Lord responded "That not by his, Moses' hand, but by the rod of God these things would come to pass and that he should have no concern or worry for I, the Lord, will tell thee what thou wilt say and do."

Through my heart and soul the magnanimous question arose and entered into my mind as to what this vision meant to me, Little Paul, down here on planet earth, who am I and of what relevance is a mighty vision of Moses to this little unknown doctor to the twentieth century. At that moment, I lost my normal consciousness and I felt my spirit being lifted out of my body through my heart and then the top of my head in exactly the same manner which it had done over $2^1/_2$ years ago when I died for a five-minute period and was taken into the Kingdom of Heaven and the throne of God.

However, this time I was not dead but merely unconscious from a physical point of view although my mind and spirit were awake, alive, and fully aware of every event that was about to be revealed to me. I then felt and saw the same three glorious angels with Gabriel at the rear and the other two angels, one on each side of me, holding and supporting my arms for a return visit to heaven and the throne of God where all of my questions and much more would be revealed to me with divine understanding, gentleness, love and authority. These three angels were beautiful and magnificent creations of God supported by white heavenly feathered wings but possessing the arms, legs, body and head of a glorified humanlike form all shining with the radiance of the sun. These angels with Gabriel as their leader, as there is a hierarchy in Heaven as I have come to learn, are the divine ministers of God the Father and His Son Yeshuah Hamassiach. In Psalm 91 it is stated "and the angels shall lift you up in their hands less you dash your foot against a stone." They were also my example of the legions of angelic beings which in a perfect and divine order and harmony surround the throne of God in Heaven singing glorious praises and hymns to honor their Creator and Father who "was and is from everlasting to everlasting."

It was revealed to me that there is a geography to the heavens in relationship to the earth. Heaven is actually a place which although it exists on another dimension than the physical, occupies both time and space in God's created universe. This was logical to my rational mind as how could God, the creator, be separate from his creation. After passing through the atmospheres of the earth, lifted up by the power and hands of the angels there appeared in the heavens among the glorious stars within the firmament a large golden rectangular door extremely tall and less wide with round chain-like circular handles of mother of pearl on each side of the central crevice about a third of the way up from its cloud-like base. I felt like the size of an ant in comparison to its dimensions, yet it radiated a peace which allowed me to feel humble to this awesome sight but not insignificant and certainly not unimportant to the creator. After all I was here through a spontaneous invitation and in answer and response to my heartfelt sincere prayers. The golden door was adorned also with white mother of pearl. Truly this was the "Pearly Gates of heaven."

It was not of a physical nature and substance but of a glistening etheric substance of light, energy and archetypal type patterns including the six pointed star of David and the raised cross of Jesus Christ within this star to show the completion and the fulfillment of the Messianic biblical promise. Engraved upon the door by the divine craftsman himself this star of David with the cross of Jesus Christ in its center and placed both sides of the door with smaller patterns going in vertical lines and in many rows from the bottom of the door to its top for as far as the spirit eyes of my spirit body could see was the same pattern which was revealed to me when the Lord with authority requested and led me to write this book over $2^1/_2$ years passed.

This door was the entrance to a magnificent palace with a stature beyond anything conceivable by the human mind. The Lord God of heaven and earth is truly the greatest architect in all the universe. This palace which seemed to go on forever although it did have boundaries was truly located in the center of the highest heaven, the heaven of all heavens for as Jesus said, "In my Father's house there are many mansions."

The doors were then opened in an outward direction by the angels and as I entered my spirit eyes beheld a magnificent and wondrous sight. In the distance and in the center and toward the rear of the palace sat the golden throne of the Lord God Adonai, the creator of both heaven and earth. My spirit man beheld the Father seated in majesty upon His throne. I was privileged to experience this sight that I might reveal it to my fellowman. God is not some amorphous blue dust or merely a pattern of energy as many new age people incorrectly profess. He is a divine being and person with both shape and form which is independent of his environment.

He is the ultimate person. He is a being beyond human comprehension or imagination. He is composed of light and energy like millions upon millions of glorious suns for his cells and the rays of those many suns for his countenance. The image of God the Father creating man which was revealed to Michaelangelo as he painted this revelation on the top of the Sistine Chapel in Rome was not far in image and form from what my spirit eyes beheld before me. His eyes were like glowing stars sitting within a divinely wrinkled brow. His divine mouth sitting beneath his jubilant, happy and peaceful cheeks was truly the lips through which the "word was spoken" and all creation came into being.

His long well-groomed and artistic beard and hair were as white as the whitest snow and his glorious white and flowing robes inlaid with gold, silver, and glorious jewels of all sorts and fashions were a sight glorious to behold. His countenance, authority, kindness, and gentleness were beyond human comprehension or understanding. Upon his head was the crown of crowns befitting the king of all creation. It was made up of the light of many suns interwoven with the first mother of all jewels emitting a glorious radiance of all the colors of the spectrum.

There is furniture in this divine palace of incredible craftsmanship. The Lord sits upon a mighty chair, a throne with golden crafted arms and legs where he sits upon and rules and judges all of his creation, on the right hand side of the Father seated upon his own chair and throne sits our Lord and Savior, Jesus Christ, the only begotten Son of the living God. I can best describe Jesus in his glorified body by quoting from Revelation 1:12-16. This is what I saw although I did not study this in detail in Revelations until the Holy Spirit told me to read and study it after my experience in heaven. after reading and studying these passages I knew that what the Lord had revealed to me was indeed the truth as well as a privileged and divine vision.

Revelation 1:12-16:

Then I turned to see the voice that was speaking to me, and upon turning I saw seven golden lampstands, and in the midst of the lampstands one like the Son of Man, clothed with a long robe and with a golden girdle around his breast; his head and his hair were as white as wool, white as snow; his eyes were like a flame of fire, his feet were like burnished bronze, refined as in a furnace, and his voice was like the sound of many waters; in his right hand he held seven stars, from his mouth issued a sharp two-edge sword, and his face was like the sun shining in full strength.

After reading these passages I realized how fortunate I had been to have personally seen this same vision. I then had no doubt that the explanation of the vision which I had of Moses while observing the Lord in the burning bush of that stained glass window in that small chapel in the hospital in Dallas, Texas.

Joel 2:28 of the Holy Bible states:
And it shall come to pass afterwards, that I will pour out my spirit on all flesh; your sons and your daughters shall prophesy, your old men shall dream dreams, and your young men shall see visions.

This Biblical prophesy of the prophet Joel certainly proved to be true and fulfilled for myself. What he didn't add was what a privilege and a joy this vision experience would be. It was revealed to me and I then came to understand what my vision of Moses meant. I obviously was not chosen to lead my people out of the land of Egypt as these events had already been fulfilled. However, there are other types of slavery other than being in physical bondage to the ruler of a nation like Pharoah. In our modern day age of the 20th century, man both Jew and Gentile find themselves in bondage to a new set of taskmasters no less cruel, harsh, oppressive and destructive. These are the taskmasters of disease, early and unnecessary death, sickness and extreme pain and suffering debilitation, economic oppression as a result of illness, as well as the unnecessary fear, anxiety, worry, and loss of loved ones which accompany all of these modern day plagues. Being both a scientist as well as a physician as the Apostle Luke was a physician as well as a lover and a disciple of the Lord and a Jewish believer in Jesus Christ the Messiah, perhaps my mission was to help lead the people, both Jew and Gentile, from the modern day slavery of these cruel and harsh taskmasters and oppressors. I then came to understand that this is why I had personally become afflicted by Lyme Disease, Systemic Candida Yeast Infection, and Multiple Sclerosis. It also became extremely clear why I was led to the answers for these diseases as well as over 650 other afflictions through the rediscovery of Colloidal Silver as well as the Aids Virus which is affecting literally millions of people around the world.

The Vision Continues

In my spirit, my eyes continued to see the Father seated in the midst of a rainbow of colors surrounded by many glorious angels of many diversities and shapes each possessing a unique and different personality singing and playing divine instruments to praise and glorify their Lord and Father and His Son. The angels were singing Holy, Holy, Holy, Lord God Almighty.

Seated on each side of the Father's and Son's throne were 12 other thrones glorious in themselves but of a stature lesser than that of the Father and the Son arranged in a dynamic yet living and vibrant semicircular fashion. On these thrones sat the 24 elders of heaven. To the right and on the side of Jesus revealed to me sat the 11 disciples of Jesus plus the disciple Paul in replacement of Judas who unfortunately did not make it to heaven. On the left hand side of the Father I recognized through revelation Abraham, Isaac, Jacob, Joseph, Moses, King David and King Solomon, as well as the prophets Samuel, Isaiah, Jeremiah, Ezekiel, and Daniel. Each of them had white flowing robes and golden crowns. Surrounding all things and persons was the Holy Spirit who individualized himself as a glowing radiance from each personage. It was as if the Holy Spirit consisting of the glistening of the glorious rays emanating from the Father and the Son had the ability to match the forms of the patriarchs, the kings, the prophets, the disciples as well as the angels. I became aware that the glorious halo and a shining presence around the the saints of God like the rays of the sun was actually the presence of the Holy Spirit which in Hebrew is pronounced the "Ruach Hakodesh." This same Holy Spirit reaches into all corners of God's universe even to those believers of mankind who choose the Father God and His Son over the world. I became aware that the words which Pastor Benny Hinn, who knows the Holy Spirit well, spoke were true. Paraphrased: "If one for example perceived the Father God as the sun then His Son would be the rays, and the Holy Spirit would be as the warmth of the rays.

Also before the throne of God I perceived and saw seven golden torches each as a spirit within itself. All of these personages and things existed within an ocean of clear energy with waves and patterns giving all things a dynamic and living presence. It was as if my vision of the burning bush in that stained glass window was multiplied millions upon millions of times yet allowing the central creation of all creations to exist within it. God is truly an alive dynamic force of life, light and energy that is individualized yet at the same time maintaining His omniscience, omnipotence, and omnipresence.

There are many other great wonders. However, my spirit man was saturated and absorbed with these magnificent sights which I was privileged to witness.

I had to fight the adversary, Satan and the powers and principalities exceedingly when I went to put these experiences down in words to share with my fellowman. I was then referred by the Holy Spirit to Revelation 4:1-11.

Upon reading this I knew that what I had seen in my spirit body was true and unlike Thomas the disciple I should have no doubt of what the Lord revealed to me in my vision.

Upon winning the battle by the Grace of God I gathered the courage to write these words down and present them to the world regardless of the waves and consequences that might and will be initiated. I only pray that this vision can glorify God and the Son and bring a greater understanding to my readers that there is truly a spiritual force to draw upon for their healing as well as a mental and physical.

Any of my brother Christians who doubt Holistic Healing only because like many other things of it have been stolen through the new age movement by the grand liar deceiver, and cheater and thief himself, Satan, should read the words of Paul inspired by the Holy Spirit in the Bible:

1 Thessalonians 5:23

"May the God of peace himself sanctify you wholly; and may your spirit, and soul, and body be kept sound and blameless at the coming of our Lord Jesus Christ. He who calls you is faithful and He will do it."

As one can see Holistic Health belongs biblically to the Judeo-Christian lineage. We need only to reclaim it and use it. The word soul is equated to the word mind historically and biblically. Thus Holistic Health consisting of the health of the spirit, mind, and body is our biblical inheritance in Genesis 1:29:

"And God said, "Behold I have given you every plant yielding seed which is on the face of all the earth, and every tree with seed in its fruit; you shall have them for food.

In some version of the Bible it says "Every herb bearing seed." In Holistic Health Care we equate food and herbs with medicine. It should be noted that 60% of all modern pharmaceutical medicines have their origins in herbs.

Revelation 4:1-6   Copyright 11-4-94

After this I looked, and lo, in heaven an open door! And the first voice, which I had heard speaking to me like a trumpet said, "Come up hither, and I will show you what must take place after this. At once I was in the spirit, and lo, a throne stood in heaven, with one seated on the throne! And He who sat there appeared like Jasper and Carneluian. And round the throne was a rainbow that looked like an emerald, round the throne were twenty-four thrones, and seated on the thrones were twenty-four elders, clad in white garments, with golden crowns upon their heads. From the throne issue flashes of lightning and voices and peals of thunder and before the throne burn seven torches of fire, which are seven spirits of God; and before the thrown there is as it were a sea of glass, like crystal."

Finally, with this scripture from Revelation and this vision of heaven, this book comes to its conclusion. I sincerely pray both as physician and a servant of the Lord God almighty, God's only begotten Son Jesus Christ to whom this book is dedicated, and to the Holy Spirit in heaven and on earth for the Holistic Health of all my readers. May you be blessed with a pure and vibrant spirit, a sound mind, and a healthy body. If my efforts in the writing of this book helped you to achieve these goals, then my life would have proven to be worthwhile and worthy of glory to God.

In addition, I must add as Dr. John Parks Trowbridge, M.D., stated in the introduction:

"Be prepared for much more to come."

Truly, I say unto you; this is not the end but rather the conclusion of one phase of my work and the new beginning of
THE NEXT PHASE
FOR TRULY I AS AN AUTHOR HAVE JUST BEGUN.
When I experienced a Taste of Death
for a five-minute period and had an opportunity to visit the
THRONE ROOM of the KINGDOM OF HEAVEN
I asked the Lord Jesus Christ, "Am I DEAD?"
He answered, "You are; but you are going to go back
and I, JESUS, and the HOLY SPIRIT
WITH THE BLESSINGS OF MY FATHER
that we might give GLORY AND HONOR
TO MY FATHER'S NAME
Will lead you to the CURE for the
EPIDEMICS which
Satan and the Powers and Principalities
Have AFFLICTED THE WORLD
So that Our Children May Be Of
HEALTHY BODIES and SOUND MINDS
That They May Wisely Choose Me,
JESUS CHRIST
AS THEIR LORD and SAVIOR and
ENTER INTO THE KINGDOM OF HEAVEN
For We Are Approaching the
END TIMES — MY SECOND COMING IS NEAR
When GABRIEL and his two ANGELS Returned MY SPIRIT to my
Physical Body, I was Back in Pain and No Closer To An Answer. Six
Months Later the PROPHECY Which JESUS CHRIST PROPHECIED
To Me WAS FULFILLED And
I REDISCOVERED
THE DEAD SEA SCROLLS OF MODERN MEDICINE.

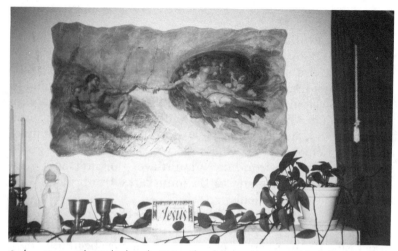

God creating man by Michaelangelo, Sistine Chapel, Rome, the picture of the father is very near to the vision seen by Dr. Farber in his near death experience.

Genesis 1:26 And God said, Let us make man in our image, after our likeness.

Genesis 1:27 So God created man in his own image, in the image of God created he him; male and female created he them.

Daniel 7:9 As I looked, thrones were set in place, and the Ancient of Days took his seat. His clothing was white as snow, the hair of his head was white as wool. His throne was flaming with fire, and its wheels were all ablaze.

Daniel 7:10 A river of fire was flowing, coming out from before him. Thousands upon thousands attended him, ten thousand times ten thousand stood before him. The court was seated, and the books were opened."

This book is dedicated to Yeshua HaMashiach, Jesus Christ The Messiah, and "His Father Who Art In Heaven, Hallowed Be Thy Name."
Designed by Dr. M. Paul Farber

> **In the field of scientific research**
> **when you find three examples**
> **that prove a truth,**
> **the truth is considered a truth.**
>
> Dr. M. Paul Farber
> B.A., B.S., M.A., M.S., N.D., Ph.D., D.C.

Dr. M. Paul Farber

B.A., B.S., M.A., M.S., N.D., Ph.D., D.C.

("The People's Doctor")

A Physician, Scientist and Researcher with over 30 years of experience in the Holistic Healthcare field, Dr. M. Paul Farber has developed **"THE FARBER METHOD"** for victory over Lyme Disease, Candida Yeast Infection and HIV Virus through the utilization of Mild Silver Protein derived from a natural inorganic substance, pure silver found in nature. His NEAR DEATH EXPERIENCE and ultimate personal triumph over Lyme Disease, Yeast Infection and Multiple Sclerosis adds drama and authenticity to his research and intensifies his efforts to get this extraordinary and enlightening information into the hands and bodies of those tens of thousands who suffer from many dread diseases, unnecessarily.

THE DEAD SEA SCROLLS OF MODERN MEDICINE
(THE LOST SILVER PUBLICATIONS)

Dr. M. Paul Farber has discovered the medical answer for Lyme Disease, Candida Yeast Infection, HIV Virus and over 650 other diseases caused by bacteria and viruses. Mild Silver Protein prevents pleomorphic forms, "mutations" of viruses and bacteria from re-emerging. This could spell an end to epidemics of Biblical proportions, when coupled with the application of natural holistic, non-invasive knowledge and methods.

And Now The Story Begins…

Some important information on
7-Strain Acidophilus
Living Acidophilus
and
Nutritional Sabbath

7-STRAIN ACIDOPHILUS
LIVING ACIDOPHILUS

I have made my readers aware throughout this book, THE MICRO SILVER BULLET, of the necessity and importance of replacing the GOOD LIFE-GIVING FRIENDLY BACTERIA after any form of Antibiotic Therapy including the use of Mild Silver Protein. Health Care Suppliers and Pharmaceutical Companies tend to shy away from any wording in their labeling and advertisements which appears to have a negative connotation. It is my contention that the statement that an Antibiotic or even a Natural Silver Product are plagued by this shallow and what I believe to be deceptive thinking due to the FACT that they kill the Friendly as well as the Disease Causing Bacteria.

The BY-PRODUCT of this thinking has created the THIRD LARGEST EPIDEMIC in the world, SYSTEMIC CANDIDA YEAST INFECTION, which crosses the barriers of sex and age. Both males and females as well as children and the elderly are susceptible to this Modern Day Plague.

I, the author, have made what I pray will be considered by Medical History a BOLD STEP. THE MILD SILVER PROTEIN in which I was influential in designing a New Protocol for through the FARBER METHOD is the FIRST LABEL on a Natural Antibiotic or any antibiotic to state, "Take acidophilus in capsule form or by eating yogurt 3 hours before and 3 hours after you take the Mild Silver Protein. I feel that this BREAKTHROUGH of replacing the GOOD FRIENDLY BACTERIA after taking substances which can kill them will improve the OVERALL HEALTH of the Whole Population that is fortunate enough to become aware of this Simple yet Most Important Fact by reading the MICRO SILVER BULLET.

NOW, comes the NEXT REVELATION which I feel will have as Big An Impact as the fact that we have not been told to consume Friendly Bacteria after the usage of antibiotics whether Natural or Conventional and I pray you the Reader have made the transition to the NATURAL, MILD SILVER PROTEIN because there are No Side Effects or Toxicity.

It is MY OPINION after careful Research and Personal Experience of over 30 Years that NINETY-FIVE PERCENT (95%) OF ALL THE ACIDOPHILUS taken by the PEOPLE is DEAD ACIDOPHILUS consisting of not more than One Strain of Friendly Bacteria, the Lactobacillus bacteria. Why is this so? If Friendly Bacteria are NOT REFRIGERATED after opening, which should be done soon after receiving, they will DIE in less than a month. The Bottom Line is that unrefrigerated acidophilus has a SHELF LIFE of less than a month after opening. Also if yogurt is not from a Natural Source and is left out too long or exposed to strong sunlight or heat, it can die also. Perhaps a BIGGER DANGER than not taking FRIENDLY BACTERIA is thinking that you are taking it when you really are not.

The next BIG REVELATION is that there is more than one strain of Friendly Bacteria. In FACT there are SEVEN MAIN STRAINS, each serving a Different Function in the body. It is not important that you memorize these different strains although I will list them below. WHAT IS IMPORTANT is that you GET THEM INTO YOUR BODY IN A LIVING FORM.

A PERSONAL EXPERIENCE

After coming across the above understandings and revelations I made arrangements to obtain a 7 STRAIN Acidophilus that I knew had been kept refrigerated and was LIVING ACIDOPHILUS. My wife and partner in life Marie began taking 2 capsules twice a day. The next morning we had a healthy bowel movement as usual and normal. What then amazed both of us was that throughout the day we then had 4 to 5 MORE HEALTHY BOWEL MOVEMENTS and this continued to repeat itself, Thank GOD. A person with a Healthy Colon and Stomach will have a Healthy Life. I suggest that my READERS put behind them any kindergarten thinking about Bowel Movements and even Urination. After being a Physician for 30 years and seeing people with colostomies (a dissected colon with a bag) and people on dialysis because they cannot urinate you gain an appreciation for the WONDERFUL FLOW OF NATURE WHICH THE LORD GOD HAS PROVIDED. The Orthodox Hebrew Faith has a PRAYER which is said before EACH ELIMINATION thanking GOD for one's HEALTH AND ABILITY TO ELIMINATE.

The following lactobacilli are normal inhabitants of the human intestinal tract, 7 of which are essential.

L. acidophilus

L. casci

L. salivaroes

L. leishmannil

L. cellobiosus

L. bifidus

L. fermentum

L. brevis

L. platnarum

AGAIN, DON'T, WORRY ABOUT MEMORIZING THEM, JUST GET THEM INTO YOUR BODY.

CONCLUDING REMARKS CONCERNING "LIVING 7 STRAIN ACIDOPHILUS"

Based on the many Thousands of Reports Flooding in from all-round the Nation and all over the World, we are in the Process Of Ending the THIRD LARGEST EPIDEMIC in the WORLD, SYSTEMIC CANDIDA YEAST INFECTION. Now we will begin the NEXT

PHASE of REBUILDING A HEALTHY HUMAN BODY. The 7 STRAIN LIVING ACIDOPHILUS will prove to be one of the Methods to Accomplish This Goal along with the diets, holistic methods, and protocols listed and expounded upon in THE MICRO SILVER BULLET. MY PRAYER is that you the READER can use this KNOWLEDGE, WISDOM, and UNDERSTANDING to restore and improve the HEALTH of yourselves, your children, and your grandchildren for generations to come. Last weekend was the weekend of EASTER, the RESURRECTION OF JESUS CHRIST, THE MESSIAH, I pray that EACH DAY IN EVERY WAY the HEALTH OF THIS NATION AND THE WORLD can also be resurrected.

The Nutritional Sabbath

In Exodus 31:12-17 – And the Lord said to Moses, "say to the people of Israel, 'You shall keep my sabbaths, for this is a sign between me and you throughout your generations, that you may know that I, the Lord, sanctify you. You shall keep the Sabbath, because it is holy for you; every one that profanes it shall be put to death; whoever does any work on it, that soul shall be cut off from among his people.Six days shall work be done, but the seventh day is a Sabbath of solemn rest, holy to the Lord; whoever does any work on the Sabbath Day shall be put to death. Therefore the people of Israel shall keep the Sabbath, observing the Sabbath throughout their generations, as a perpetual covenant. It is a sign forever between me and the people of Israel that in six days the Lord made heaven and earth, and on the seventh day he rested, and was refreshed.' "

The last phrase of this verse states, "on the seventh day he rested and was refreshed." In the same manner we need to rest and be refreshed from all of the Nutritional Efforts which we have engaged to restore our health. This allows our body to have an opportunity to absorb and assimilate all the wonderful nutrients which we have wisely put into it following The People's Doctor's Recommended Formulations.

The Lord God's commandment to Keep The Sabbath is perhaps one of the WISEST HOLISTIC FORMULAS which has ever been handed down since the Beginning Of Time. In this commandment we are told to rest. This is a complete rest for the Body, the Mind, and the Spirit. In I Thessalonians 5:23 the Apostle, Paul the Author's Namesake, states: "May the God of peace himself sanctify you wholly; and may your SPIRIT, and SOUL, and BODY be kept sound and blameless at the coming of our Lord Jesus Christ. He who calls you is faithful, and he will do it." In Biblical Studies the SOUL is many times referred to as the MIND. Thus the HOLISTIC FORMULA of BODY, MIND, and SPIRIT had its beginnings all the way back to both the OLD and NEW TESTAMENTS. In man's so-called New Age Arrogance, he should not be conceited in the belief that Holistic Health is a modern day new idea. Instead, we should draw upon the Wisdom Of The Ages and apply it to improving our health today.

We are also commanded in the Bible to let our fields rest every seven years so that they might renew themselves. Why, we might ask, is there all this emphasis on the word REST? The answer lies in the Medically Correct Fact that it is only through rest that our body can reach a Point Of Homeostasis and RENEW itself. Everyone has at one time or another had a Sleepless Night. How did you feel the next day? Perhaps you felt fatigued, irritable, grumpy, had difficulties in digesting, and were unclear in your thinking. You were Holistically in an Imbalanced State of Homeostasis. Thus one should take advantage of keeping a Sabbath Day for himself. If you are of the Jewish Faith this would be on a Saturday and if you are of the Christian Faith, this would traditionally be on a Sunday. Since the Author is of the Messianic Jewish Faith, which is a Jewish Christian, I take both Saturday and Sunday as my Sabbath. If for any reason you have not chosen a Faith, then merely for Health Reasons, pick any day of the week to REST and RENEW your BODY, MIND, and SPIRIT.

Thus we now get back to the Author's Original Idea of a "NUTRITIONAL SABBATH." The Author believes that if you will follow this idea and make it a formula for your Nutritional Life you will have increased Vitality, Strength, and Peace Of Mind. In the Old Testament it states "that whoever does work on the Sabbath will suffer death." Fortunately we are relieved from this pronouncement by The New Testament. However the idea that working continually without a rest does lean one more toward Death than Life still holds true. If we take one and possibly two days a week out without overloading our bodies, we will give our bodies a chance to absorb and assimilate all the Good Nutrition which we have wisely put in it throughout the rest of the week. Even THE LORD GOD OF ALL HEAVEN AND EARTH rested on the 7th Day after Creating All Creation Including Man and Woman as recorded in Genesis of the HOLY BIBLE.

Take One Day At A Time

Help me believe in what I could be
And all that I am.
Show me the stairway I have to climb.
Lord, for my sake; teach me to take
one day at a time.

Jamie Carter

INCH BY INCH, LIFE IS A CINCH.
YARD BY YARD, LIFE IS HARD.
MILE BY MILE, LIFE IS A TRIAL.

Arnie Farber

Dr. M. Paul Farber
Myca, Inc.

Dr. Farber:

This letter is to update you on my wife's progress. As you will recall, she has psoriasis to the point our traditional medical Dr. was considering surgery. It affected the lower half (below the knees) on both legs. The skin was red and "lumpy" with abrasion-like sores.

We tried the traditional treatments as offered by MD's. They had little or no effect for any length of time. When they did appear to work at the outset of treatment, we were soon disappointed by a return to the same condition or worse. With no relief in sight we thought surgery was all that was left.

At that point you made an appearance as a guest on my national Talk Radio Network program. During the show you mentioned to a caller that your new salve product of the COLL/AG-40 was effective against psoriasis. I responded immediately with an order for this product. Upon arrival I commenced treatment as you prescribed.

Over the first few hours after treatment she noticed itching as it began to heal for the first time. Over the first few days the surface sores began to close up and fade away, This top layer took several weeks to disappear. After the first month the surface of the skin was like skin with redness underneath. Over the next three months of daily treatments the COLL/AG-40 salve began to eliminate the redness a layer at a time. This is the best way I can describe it.

The COLL/AG-40 has eliminated all but the outside edges (about an inch wide all the way around) on both legs, with natural skin color in the center for the first time in years! The doctor was quite surprised on her last visit, without any medication from traditional sources. She, of course, asked how we did it. I'm giving her your book to explain.

Your Fellow American, Randy Johnson
Talk Radio Network Host
P.O. Box 633, Medford, OR 97501-0043

PERSONAL HOLISTIC DIARY

CHAPTER 1
A WALK IN THE WOODS...

What a super day. It was Saturday, July 17, 1992 and the sun was shining brightly, the pine-scented air was clean and blowing gently...and the animals of the forest were out and about doing what they always do. A perfect day for taking a leisurely walk and getting away from the telephone, the FAX machine and the everyday stress that comes with the package of making a living.

I live on 20-acres of wooded pine forest in Cut n' Shoot, Texas, (next to Conroe, a suburb of Houston). If you haven't heard of Cut n' Shoot don't worry about it because it's out in the sticks and away from all the hassle and confusion. If you ever drive through it inadvertently, you are totally lost and in dire need of direction.

If I had to guess, I would have to say that the Republicans or Democrats are definitely not considering bringing their Presidential Convention to Cut n' Shoot anytime soon (neither is anybody else). But that's o.k. with me. I kind of like it the way it is.

As I began my walk into the woods, my dogs followed me and we eventually spent the entire day observing the white-tail deer, the squirrels, the rabbits and the owls. What I didn't notice, however, was the presence of *ticks*. Physically, I felt great and had no indications of impending illness. Little did I know.

On a Sunday morning several weeks later, I awoke and greeted the day and then proceeded to get out of bed. But as my feet hit the ground, I began to sense that I had virtually no lower extremity sensations to tell me that I was in fact "getting up." When I transferred my weight to my legs in order to stand, they *collapsed* beneath me. Very surprised, I then attempted to walk, only to find that I was unable to move my legs or support my body. My surprise then began to turn into concern and semi-panic. If you have not experienced this for yourself...trust me, you don't want to. When something of this nature happens this quickly and in this devastating a manner, it knocks the wind out of your body and out of your spirit.

But I've never been a quitter. So I found that with a great deal of concentration, I could slowly and gradually *move* and cautiously support myself. Initially, my mind drew a blank because this was all new to me. What in the world was going on?

After a while, I came to the realization that I was 85% paralyzed from the diaphragm down and, being a physician, began to formulate a possible diagnosis. I concluded that I had severely misaligned my lower back and was experiencing *nerve root compression* which should be easily corrected by a chiropractic adjustment. I found out soon enough that that didn't work and I was then wisely referred to a medical doctor (a neurologist) for further evaluation and diagnosis. I was stumped.

I received a complete neurological and orthopedic examination, plus a Magnetic Resonance Scan (MRI). The doctor confirmed the numbness and lack of sensation in the sensory nervous system and indicated that the motor nervous system was also involved. He eventually concluded that I either had **A.**) Guillian-Berea Syndrome; **B.**) Multiple Sclerosis; or **C.**) that I had suffered a stroke. Bad news is bad news, whether it's *multiple choice* or not.

In my opinion, Lyme Disease is the great medical imposter and impersonator...too often being *diagnosed as something else*, thus allowing it time to strengthen and proliferate in the body.

During the first few days of this disease of yet unknown origin, I got so sick that I almost died. My colon, abdomen and stomach locked up and shut down so totally that I was completely bent over like a crippled old man of 80 with Rheumatoid Arthritis. I spent a considerable amount of time curled up on the floor in the fetal position, and in addition I could not move my bowels, causing pressure to build up in my colon from an inability to eliminate.

As if that weren't enough, I was beginning to have problems *breathing*. So, I began administering oxygen to myself an hour at a time, from a couple of oxygen tanks that I had in my possession. Thank God it worked and kept the paralysis from spreading into my lungs. Had the paralysis crept into my lungs while I was asleep, I would have suffocated to death and simply not awakened the following morning. What a gruesome thought.

But as things got worse, I began thinking about *death*. More specifically, I was evaluating the potentially short period of time I might have left on this earth (I sensed that something very serious had invaded my body). I began thinking about who I was, what I had accomplished in my life...and *where I might be going* from here. I surprised even myself, because although I am of Jewish background and was familiar with the concept of an all-powerful Creator (along with considerable religious tradition), I was not a particularly "spiritual" person. I wasn't even sure what that term meant. But I am convinced that when *eternity* is staring you in the face (no matter who you are), you think about these things a lot.

I was already physically down and out, but now I was succumbing to *mental and emotional submission* to whatever this thing was that attacked my body. Obviously, this made things a lot worse and my downhill descent was greatly accelerated.

Then at one point in the early morning hours I slipped into a state of outer unconsciousness...but on the "inside" I was completely aware of what was going on. Somehow I knew that if I had been connected to *medical monitors* at that point in time, my life signs would have shown me as **clinically dead**. My inner consciousness (my soul)began to concentrate in the center of my brain and then exited through a portal, at which point all of the pain and suffering which I had been experiencing *stopped*.

I didn't understand any of this because I had never been prone to this sort of thing. But all I know is that *it didn't hurt anymore*...and I was being transported to somewhere I had never been before. This was as strange and bizarre to me as it might now seem to you. But it happened.

I felt a great sense of peace and joy as I was drawn through an incredible "kingly" doorway opening into a hall of light and then an ascending crystalline pathway of stairs (wider at the bottom and then smaller at the top) leading to a magnificent Palace. I was enjoying this so much and was in such a state of *awe* that never once through this entire experience did I think to "pinch myself" to see if it was real. I didn't need to. It was.

I both saw and felt the presence of angelic beings during this timeless journey as I was drawn upward through this magnificent vortex to a grand Palace of light. What I saw...and *Who* I saw inside that place is virtually beyond description...and probably too much for the reader to ingest and comprehend at this time. But for now, that's o.k.

Suffice it to say that I was in a state of ecstasy and wanted with all my heart, soul and mind to *stay* and become a citizen of this Kingdom (Heaven is an incredibly large place and occupies a distinct geographical location). But I was told that it was *not yet time* because I had an assignment to complete in which my knowledge as a scientist and physician would be put to critical use in the alleviation of suffering in the world. This would be done through the application of God's own natural laws of health, and through the use of His own organic and inorganic substances. This was all to be accomplished in *perfect order* and to happen through professional adherence to scientific procedure and with empirical evidence to back it up. What a powerful thing to attempt to comprehend.

I was disappointed to have to come back, and although I had a choice, the matter had apparently already been settled.

Then in an instant, I felt myself lifted up as I retraced my previous journey back to where all of this beautiful strangeness had all begun. I awoke in my bed and became conscious, but although I kept the great sense of peace and joy, *the physical pain returned.* I was back to square one...but I knew now what I had to do and how I was to do it. I felt really *privileged* and frankly didn't know quite how to react.

Needless to say, I was totally overwhelmed by all of this. I am a physician, scientist and researcher who has been involved in the healthcare field for over 30 years. Had someone told me that all this incredible stuff would happen in the manner that it did, I would have laughed, too, and skeptically disregarded it. But I'm not laughing anymore. I'm thinking more and more about things that have *eternal significance.*

During the first couple of weeks after being hit by this devastating disease that nobody could definitively diagnose (it was Lyme Disease), I was still paralyzed in excruciating pain. I was very sick but I didn't know why. I applied every known natural Holistic cure which I had knowledge of in order to survive. I had made the difficult decision, after my "near death" experience, not to admit myself into a hospital but to stay home and effectively treat myself (I do not recommend that anyone else do the same thing). I had a lot of *resolve*, I had an ample supply of *oxygen* in my tanks... and I also had almost a quarter century of practical experience in helping people to get well.

But gnawing at me constantly was the idea that I was now *personally* living this nightmare of unknown origin, this disease that had so quickly put me under. I wasn't on the *outside looking in*, dispassionately observing and recording the ordeal. Instead, I was on the *inside looking out* ...and most of the time the outlook was bleak. But I also knew that there was a reason for it.

During the times when I was unable to eat, I did not resort to intravenous feeding, but instead made raw juices (in my juicer), alternating between vegetable juices such as carrot or combinations of carrot, celery, and parsley in the afternoons and evenings. In the mornings, I would have either raw apple juice or apricot juice.

Although I was still quite ill, this "liquid diet" did much more to help heal my body and ultimately sustained me in a much stronger manner than any intravenous saline nutrient solution could ever have done (I highly recommend *juice fasting* as a part of the Holistic regimen not only to sustain you through Lyme Disease but also to help rebuild your overall health and strength).

But then one day as I was listlessly bathing, I noticed a lump on my head, underneath my silver-tinged and dark, thick hair. Upon closer examination, I discovered that it was a TICK embedded deeply in my scalp. I carefully extracted it, making sure that the head did not remain. I then took the tick to the local veterinarian who advised me to have it analyzed for disease. It was at this point that the puzzle began to come together.

I sent the tick to Dr. Thomas Craig, D.V.M., Ph.D., head

of the Department of Veterinary Microbiology and Parasitology at Texas A&M University. Sure enough, the verdict was that the tick was Ixodes scapularis, which as we know may carry the spirochete found to be the causative agent of Lyme Disease.

So now I knew that I had Lyme Disease, although I didn't know what it was (up to this point I thought that Lyme Disease was something miners got because they were around *lime* all the time). But what now?

Still tolerating vicious symptoms and in excruciating pain, I went to a doctor who prescribed intravenous antibiotics, specifically Penicillin and Rocephin (two weeks on Penicillin and two 30-day treatments of Rocephin). This helped, but not a whole lot. My overall improvement was minimal, but worst of all, I developed chronic side effects, including systemic Candida Yeast Infection caused by the destruction of the "good bacteria" in my body by the antibiotics (I discovered this when I went to visit my good friend Hanna Kroeger in Colorado).

I found myself between the proverbial "rock and a hard place." The more antibiotics I took, the worse the yeast infection got. It was the trap that most Lyme victims find themselves in today. And even when I felt better, I knew the Lyme would re-emerge because the antibiotics characteristically kill only about 80% of the spirochetes, the remainder of which either hide in the fibroblast of deep muscle tissue...or they mutate and become resistant to antibiotics. I first learned this at the Lyme Disease Conference in Atlantic City, New Jersey in 1993.

This was a *roller coaster ride* going back and forth between Lyme Disease and Candida Yeast Infection, but with a one-way ticket: once you get on, you can't get off. I didn't want any part of it. No way. Neither do multiple tens of thousands of others in this country and around the world.

I had to find something better. Being a physician,

scientist and researcher I began a meticulous search for an answer for this great *imposter and impersonator,* Lyme Disease. Through a series of events, I was led to what I call **"The Dead Sea Scrolls of Modern Medicine,"** the "lost" Silver Publications of the early 20th century...which includes all microbiological research done between 1900 and 1938 by the top medical doctors, university scientists and pharmaceutical companies of that time.

I again felt *privileged,* because I was able to rediscover Mild Silver Protein, an extremely potent broad-spectrum natural antibiotic that kills spirochetes, bacteria, viruses, and fungus responsible for over 650 diseases. It was discovered and used by the Medical Profession over 90 years ago, but was eventually "shelved" due to the inordinately high cost of producing it (over $400 an ounce), coupled with its extremely short shelf life of a week or less.

Today, however, through advanced space-age technology Mild Silver Protein can be produced at a reasonable cost ($55 for a 4-ounce bottle, with a 5-year shelf life)...making it *accessible* to the multitudes who are hurting.

While everyone seemed to be struggling on the *confusing* treadmill of synthetic antibiotics, the answer (Mild Silver Protein) was there "in front of our face" all the time. Sometimes it's hard to see the tree for the forest of confusion that surrounds it.

So...I began taking specific dosages of Mild Silver Protein (I call it "The Silver Micro-Bullet") as soon as I could, and the results were *dramatic.* In fact, I am totally free of Lyme Disease as determined through a spinal tap at the Neurological Department of Parkland Hospital in Dallas (I'm also free of Candida). And I know it *will not reoccur* because Mild Silver Protein is 100% effective against the spirochetes that cause Lyme. It kills them all, including spirochetal mutations. The spirochetes can run, but they can't hide.

This natural antibiotic really get the job done! And fortunately, since it is a pre-1938 antibiotic, it has had FDA approval for almost a century (it is now classified as a *dietary mineral supplement*). There are absolutely no side effects recorded in decades of use and recent studies at the University of Toronto concluded that no toxicity, even in high dosages, results from using Mild Silver Protein.

This antibiotic is attenuated silver that has been broken down, electrically charged and suspended in colloidal solution, having been reduced to microscopic silver particles smaller than .001 microns in diameter (smaller than a virus or bacteria). Mild Silver Protein interferes with the metabolism of oxygen by microorganisms, causing them to suffocate. Recent testing at the Fox Chase Cancer Center in Philadelphia described the following: "Preliminary studies on Borrelia burgdorferi spirochetes revealed that mild silver protein solutions reduce the growth rate of these cells significantly and eventually lead to cell death."

I have done considerable additional research on this potent antibiotic, conferring frequently with knowledge-able people in the field, including two years of interaction with Dr. Willy Burgdorfer, the world-renowned scientist who discovered and pinpointed the spirochete as the causative agent of Lyme Disease. He encouraged me to get this information which I have discovered to the population as soon as feasible, and he is optimistic about the program. Dr. Burgdorfer is currently contemplating additional research on the effect of Mild Silver Protein on spirochetes in animals.

I feel a heightened responsibility to get the information on Mild Silver Protein to as many Lyme Disease and Candida Yeast Infection victims as possible and as quickly as I can because I believe it can bring a revolutionary, long-awaited solution to pain and suffering, both here and around the world. *It certainly worked for me*, and I don't want anyone to go through the pain and suffering that I went through now that I know the potential answers that are detailed in this book. But the communication process must be a very careful one, based on providing responsible, quality information and encouraging natural, non-invasive Holistic healthcare procedures.

It is critically important to be totally informed in order to make an intelligent decision on the intake of a medicine or other healing agent. It is also vital to understand that Mild Silver Protein is a specialized, proprietary formulation and that Mild Silver Protein in any lesser and inferior form *may not work* effectively.

Well...I was now free of Lyme Disease and I thank God for His kindness and His mercy. I was also free of Candida which was caused by the conventional antibiotics that were administered in order to combat Lyme. Let me say again that most people don't understand this *connection* and that in the final analysis, they will have traded one disease for another...which is just as bad or worse.

CHAPTER 2
WHAT IS LYME DISEASE?

The Origin and Development of the
Second Largest Epidemic in the World

A disease is normally described and identified in medical literature as a grouping of symptoms which either occur simultaneously or in a certain order and progression of events. It may also be a grouping of symptoms that occur in a specific stage or order. These diseases are normally recorded in medical literature with a given name which represents the knowledge and the thinking of the times.

The disease and illness which we now call *Lyme Disease,* discovered in 1975 in Lyme, Connecticut, is a perfect example of this phenomenon. The disease is transmitted to humans usually through the bite of a *tick (or flea)*, generally found in forested, woody, marshy areas. Lyme Disease itself is caused by the spirochete Borrelia burgdorferi (named after its discoverer, Dr. Willy Burgdorfer) and is prevalent on the East Coast of the United States, as well as the Midwest and coastal or wooded areas of California, Oregon, Colorado, Nevada and Utah. However, it has been reported in virtually the entire country, as well as many parts of the world.

The adult, spirochete-carrying tick does bite humans, but prefers to feed on animals such as deer, birds, raccoons, etc. During the feeding process, the spirochetes are transmitted to the host and once inside the body, they proliferate and spread rapidly through the bloodstream and to potentially every organ in the body. Lyme Disease has been reported throughout the year but is most prevalent during the warm summer season. In its early stages, it is known to cause an expanding red rash termed Erythema Migrans, and common symptoms of early disease include headache, chills, fever, fatigue, stiff muscles and joints. In its later stages, Lyme Disease manifests itself through neurological, cardiac, or musculoskeletal abnormalities. Subsequent conditions may include shortness of breath, loss of memory, eye disorders, Bell's palsy, tingling and numbness in arms and legs and arthritis.

We now know (thanks to the marvelous scientific discoveries of Dr. Burgdorfer) that the very tiny microorganism called *spirochete* is the infectious agent in Lyme Disease, and it is carried by ticks and probably fleas.

Can Lyme Disease kill you? Most emphatically *yes!* If left untreated, the spirochetes will attack and overtake and destroy vital organs, including the brain. One might wonder what the future years will bring in terms of long term effects of this dreadful disease. I personally believe that there are four simple possibilities:

1. Both a *wrong diagnosis*, coupled with improper treatment (or no treatment at all) could result in a continual debilitating and downward spiral, until death eventually occurs. For example, if the treating physician did not know that a patient had Lyme Disease, that person may never receive *any* antibiotic therapy to combat the spirochetes.

2. Conventional antibiotic treatment of either Penicillin or cephalosporins would result in a destruction of 85-95% of the spirochete population of the body and would also create mutant and pleomorphic forms. It is the mutant forms, as well as 15% of the spirochetes that hide from the antibiotics, which would

cause recurrent infections and symptomatology, perhaps for the rest of the patient's life.

3. Treatment with conventional antibiotics, with no replacement of the friendly acidophilus, would result in a full-blown Candida Yeast Infection, even though the spirochetes are under control. This yeast infection is the *second greatest impersonator* and perhaps rivals Lyme Disease in its manifest systems and mocking of major diseases. The treating physician, thinking that his patient still suffers from Lyme Disease, prescribes more antibiotics without acidophilus replacement, perpetuating and worsening the yeast infection. The patient then ends up on an endless roller coaster of disease for the rest of his life.

4. Most importantly, the Lyme Disease patient learns (through this publication) that there is an answer to this disease and that the roller coaster ride from Lyme Disease to Candida Yeast Infection can finally be stopped.

Mild Silver Protein (I call it the *Silver Micro-Bullet*) can indeed stop the Lyme Disease in its tracks. Then a Candida Yeast treatment program can be implemented. Eventually, the patient can experience a *complete recovery* and perhaps enjoy even better health, due to the new health programs and wellness practices which he has adopted in order to get well in the first place.

The last two decades of understanding Lyme Disease (as stated earlier) began in 1975. This occurred when a surprising and statistically abnormal medical phenomenon was detected in many children in the town of Lyme, Connecticut. These children, in large groups, began experiencing arthritic-like symptoms and joint inflammations, common mostly to middle age, upper middle age and older geriatric populations, and for no apparent reason. Who would even conceive of a child acquiring and suffering from the symptoms of *arthritis?* Perhaps one, maybe two or three "freak instances" was understandable...but certainly not in large numbers. A medical puzzle was at hand which cried out and demanded to be unraveled.

Perhaps someday it will become historically correct to state that it was not a doctor or a scientist who first became aware that there was a major epidemic brewing. It was the God-created invention called a *mother* who first realized that there was a serious health problem beginning to plague not only her children, but also the children of her friends and neighbors. This mother's name was Polly Murray, who eventually became known as "the mother of Lyme Disease" and who also fell victim to the disease. Her intuition that the cause of her severe illness was associated with the prevalence of deer ticks eventually proved correct.

Unfortunately, Ms. Murray received no antibiotic treatment and eventually became a victim as well as a martyr to what would become known as Lyme Disease. Her entire family of three daughters and two sons became stricken with arthritic, flu-type symptoms, rashes, as well as other disorders associated with the disease. It was diagnosed as Juvenile Rheumatoid Arthritis. Polly Murray would not accept this diagnosis and like the proverbial "voice crying out in the wilderness" brought the beginning pandemic to the attention of Dr. David Snydman of the Connecticut State Health Department, who in turn invited Dr. Allen Steere of the Yale University School of medicine to investigate. Dr. Steere and his associates initially thought they had a new disease which they called *Lyme Arthritis*, a term changed to Lyme Disease when it was realized that arthritis was only one of several clinical manifestations.

Some of the patients, prior to the onset of arthritis, had an erythemorfous papule thought to be an insect bite and developed an expanding annular lesion similar to Erythema Chronicum Migrans discovered in Europe at the beginning of the century. There the lesion was associated with the bite of the sheep tick, Ixodes ricinus.

This rash was sometimes found preceding a case of

Spinal Meningitis, which is an inflammation of the brain and spinal cord, often striking children for no apparent reason. I have memories of fellow classmates in grade school, high school and college being stricken with this dread disease. At that time, there was no one around to question the diagnosis. They simply had Spinal Meningitis because the doctors said so and *that was that.* I have to believe that many of them had Lyme Disease, which at the time was unheard of. Now we know that the symptoms of Spinal Meningitis are also caused by the spirochetes that are associated with Lyme Disease.

One needs to stop and reflect upon how many years of misdiagnoses have taken place for literally thousands and perhaps tens of thousands of unsuspecting people. How many people have lived and arranged their life (and perhaps their death) around the thought that they had incurable Multiple Sclerosis or Spinal Meningitis, to name but a few of the misdiagnosed diseases that what we now know to be Lyme Disease?

Many times the rash occurs and goes unnoticed due to the part of the body on which it may appear. For example, if it were to appear on the sole of one's foot, on one's buttocks (or in the creases of the buttocks), on the back of one's neck, or under one's hair...it could easily go unnoticed. Most researchers don't make note of the fact that the rash most usually appears within a 1 to 3-inch radius from the site of the tick bite. Therefore, as was in my case, it can go completely undetected. Also, there can be times when it does not appear, or it appears and leaves within a relatively short period of time so as to be missed and go unnoticed. It may also appear on a person and be dismissed as just a *heat rash,* since they also are reddish in color and seem to disappear quickly. Obviously, then, one cannot always depend upon this objective symptom for diagnosis. Just to reiterate, in my case this identifiable rash was never seen, even though the guilty tick was found on the back of my head. How many people ever take the time to examine their own scalp, especially if their hair is thick and curly, as is mine?

It is also possible that the tick itself may go unnoticed, which is quite unfortunate since it can be removed and analyzed for a positive diagnosis. However, in my own case I discovered the tick only after weeks of severe and debilitating symptamology and partial paralysis. But thank God I found it.

Because of my training as a physician, I knew immediately how to remove it. I then sent it immediately to Texas A&M University, for a positive analysis and identification. As previously noted, it turned out to be Ixodes scapularis, a tick which is found in Texas on the white tail deer. This makes sense, since deer are abundant in the area of Texas where I have a ranch and retreat.

It is also conceivable–in fact it is the case in most instances–the patients are bitten by immature nymphal ticks that because of minute size (not larger than a typewriter period) are easily overlooked and engorge more quickly (3-5 days) than the adults (6-10 days). It is also possible that when an unknowledgeable victim discovers a tick for the first time, it is removed incorrectly and then quickly discarded because it is considered *unimportant* or just something ugly to be gotten rid of immediately (thus throwing away crucial evidence that should be investigated).

These few examples aptly demonstrate the need and importance for a greater *awareness* through health education in the schools, as well as through the media concerning Lyme Disease, the second largest epidemic in the world (and also its resulting counterpart Candida Yeast Infection which occurs as a result of incorrectly administered antibiotic treatment with no regard for replacing the friendly bacteria of the body which are necessary for life to exist). Candida Yeast Infection rarely receives notice or publicity, with the possible exception of the writings of men like Dr. Truss, Dr. Crook and Dr.

Trowbridge.

The amount of research and importance which has been given to this most devastating and unwelcome illness is tragic but not unusual. Historically, many diseases such as Scurvy have gone unnoticed for long periods of time with only a few crying unheard in the wilderness of opinion.

It is difficult to determine how many people have been stricken with Lyme Disease because there is no way to know if all of the cases which have occurred have been correctly diagnosed and reported. As of the present time, to the best of our knowledge Lyme Disease has been reported on the continents of Africa, Asia, Australia, Europe, as well as more than 20 foreign countries. In the United States, it is documented in approximately 38-45 of the states. Louis Reik, Jr., M.D., in his book *Lyme Disease and the Nervous System* states the following:

In North America, Lyme Disease occurs in both the United States and Canada. Within the United States, it is now the most commonly reported tick-transmitted infection (4,507 cases reported to the Centers for Disease Control in 1988) and it has been acquired in 43 states in all. The disease is endemic along the East Coast from Maryland to Massachusetts, in the upper Midwest in Minnesota and Wisconsin, and on the Pacific Coast in California and Oregon. Increasing numbers of cases have also been reported from mid-Atlantic, south-eastern, mid-western, and south-central states. But the illness remains most common from the states from which it was originally reported: In 1987-1988, 92% of the reported cases were from New York, New Jersey, from Pennsylvania, Connecticut, Massachusetts, Rhode Island, Wisconsin, and Minnesota. New York reported the most cases

(57% of the national total in 1988), while the incidence in Rhode Island was 9.9 cases/100,000.

The usual vector in the Northeast and Midwest is the deer tick, Ixodes dammini. This species ranges along the Atlantic coast from southern Delaware to Massachusetts, and it is common in Wisconsin, Minnesota, and Southern Ontario, Canada. The tick has also been collected in upstate New York, New Hampshire, Maine, Ohio, Illinois, and Manitoba, Canada and it is likely that the population is continuous from the Atlantic to Manitoba. In some areas as many as 80% of the ticks are infected with spirochetes, explaining the very high attack rate of Lyme Disease in these localities.

Ixodes dammini develops in a two-year life cycle, and all three of its stages may bite humans. However, immature ticks usually feed on a variety of wild birds and small mammals, especially the white-footed mouse, Peromyscus leucopus, while adult ticks feed on larger mammals, particularly the white-tailed deer, Odocoileus virgianus. Larger domestic animals are parasitized also, and Lyme Disease has been reported in dogs, cattle and horses. In all, the ticks have been found to parasitize at least 31 mammalian species, and 49 species of birds.

However, it is the presence of both deer and especially mice in the environment that is critical for the maintenance of the disease transmission. The importance of white-footed mice as a reservoir of B. burgdorferi is apparent in their high rate of infection. In some areas, almost 90% of the mice harbor spirochetes. The deer, on the other hand, probably serve no reservoir or natural infection, but are a preferred host for adult ticks, as they are critical for the tick's reproductive success. The elimination of deer in an established focus is followed by reduced abundance of immature Ixodes dammini. Consequently, Lyme Disease is most frequent in forested and suburban areas where both ticks and mice are common.

On the Pacific coast, the main vector is the Ixodes pacificus, the western black-legged tick. The vectors in other parts of the United States where Lyme Disease has been acquired is less certain. One possible carrier is the common black-legged tick, Ixodes scapularis. This widespread tick ranges from Florida, west to Texas, and north to Kansas, Missouri, Iowa, Illinois, Indiana, Ohio, West Virginia, and Maryland.

Lyme Disease is both widespread and common in Europe, where thousands of cases are estimated to occur each year. The disease is most common in Austria, Germany, France, Sweden, and Switzerland. But it also occurs in the other three Scandinavian countries, Belgium, Czechoslovakia, Hungary, Italy, the Netherlands, Romania, Spain, the United Kingdom, the USSR, and Yugoslavia. The main European vector is the sheep tick, Ixodes ricinus. Lyme disease has also been found in Africa, Asia, and Australia.

One may ask how Lyme Disease can spread so quickly and get into so many different parts of the world. One possible theory is that birds pick up the tick and carry it from state to state and from country to country. This could account for the tens of thousands of cases over the last few decades.

It was the tick Ixodes scapularis that I was bitten by in Texas. Little did I know that one little isolated creature would change my life dramatically and thrust me into the adventure and mission of discovering an *answer* for Lyme Disease, writing this book, and ultimately making the results known to the world. Little did I realize that it would launch me into rediscovering the early 1900's antibiotic Mild Silver Protein, which could also be instrumental in bringing AIDS under control and revolutionizing the way we think about antibiotics. In the past, as a society we have always turned to our trusted antibiotics such as *Penicillin* for cures. In my own experience with Lyme Disease, Penicillin helped but did not cure the disease. And now I also know that this antibiotic, while offering temporary help, has been instrumental in creating mutant forms of spirochetes as well as causing systemic Candida Yeast Infection.

CHAPTER 3
THE CANDIDA ALBICANS CONNECTION

A Visit With Hanna Kroeger, Herbalist
And With
Dr. John Parks Trowbridge, M.D.

It had been several months since I began this unplanned journey of severe illness and a search for an answer after that eventful Sunday morning when I work up almost paralyzed from the waist down, with little or no feeling in my legs. It was only after three false diagnoses that I discovered the engorged black tick hidden beneath my hair, which would prove to be responsible for causing the Lyme Disease, devastating my body. It took me...a man who has had over 30 years of training in The Natural Holistic Healthcare Field...a long time to unravel the truth surrounding this great medical imposter and impersonator called Lyme Disease and to find a safe and effective answer. It is little wonder that the average lay person in a similar situation and with no medical training is in such a state of confusion and perplexity.

During the time that I was fighting Lyme Disease with antibiotics (before discovering Mild Silver Protein), I had this feeling inside of me that I was suffering from more than just the Lyme Disease. The antibiotics had helped somewhat, but *something else* was coming against me and having good success. But I didn't know what it was.

So, in August of 1993, I visited Hanna Kroeger, a venerable herbalist who lived on a peaceful meadows retreat in Boulder, Colorado. Full of knowledge and wisdom, Hanna Kroeger has over 60 years of experience helping people recover from medically diagnosed so called "incurable diseases." She is descended from a family of 1800's missionaries who worked and lived among the American Indians. In her beautiful and unorthodox manner she observed me carefully, including my eyes and the redness on the tips of my fingers around the nails. It took her only a short period of time and then she pronounced "Candida" in a high, but affirmative voice. "You have a severe yeast infection. You have yeast everywhere in your body. Bad yeast."

I was taken aback. But I couldn't help but trust this experienced voice of authority as she expressed what she knew to be true. My only experience with yeast up to this point was *athletes' foot* or female patients stricken with vaginal yeast infection.

I never dreamed that a male or female could have a full-body systemic yeast infection. And I never would have believed that this new severe illness (which I have dubbed *The Second Greatest Medical Imposter*) had been iatrogenetically caused (doctor-induced) by both oral and intravenous antibiotics which had initially been prescribed for Lyme Disease. I was shocked, but the truth of the matter was that I had *traded* the first medical imposter and impersonator (Lyme Disease)...for the second greatest medical imposter and impersonator: *Candida Albicans* systemic yeast infection...and ended up with both. Who could have predicted that an accepted, prescribed medical treatment with antibiotics would open the door for another disease that was possibly worse than the first? Let me emphasize at this point that this Candida Albicans yeast epidemic among Lyme Disease patients is certainly not an intentional act on the part of the established medical profession. To the contrary, most medical doctors are a very sincere and dedicated group of professionals interested only in being a help to their patients and applying medical knowledge to bring healing.

I had the privilege of meeting with and speaking to over 500 medical doctors at the Lyme Disease Conference in Atlantic City, New Jersey in 1993 at Dr. Willy Burgdorfer's invitation. These doctors were great and I know that they were doing their best at the time that their knowledge and training made them capable of. But my prayer is that the information contained in this book will be quickly embraced by the medical profession and that these same doctors will become consciously aware of these vital connections in nature, as well as the great gift from their medical ancestors known as Mild Silver Protein. Armed with this natural antibiotic and an understanding of the roller-coaster ride their patients are on due to the onslaught of the yeast infection (caused by antibiotics prescribed for Lyme Disease), medical doctors as well as physicians of Chiropractic and Naturopathy can now become the much needed medical salvation to the multitudes of hurting people. The treatment program for these two great medical imposters can now be formulated and be effectively administered.

It's an old story which has repeated itself many times in the history of the medical profession: the disregarding of known and accepted natural health care methods due to lack of understanding. It is the story of overlooking the obvious and simple laws of nature by which all human beings are governed and have been since man began to walk the earth. It is the old story of thinking that some medication created synthetically in a laboratory somehow works independently of these laws and will therefore not conflict with its checks and balances. The example which I have just discussed is the relationship between the *friendly* bacteria of the body and *other bacteria* that can cause disease, when this friendly bacteria which the body does not produce is *destroyed* and *not replaced* from outside the body.

The truth of the matter is that synthetic medications created in the laboratory are not independent of the laws of nature. The side effects that result are actually a disruption of the harmony which is brought about by following these laws.

This does not mean that synthetically produced medications are all bad. In fact, there are times when they can become lifesavers. The wisdom comes in knowing when this is the case and proceeding with caution. It is unwise to trade one disease for another which may be worse than the one you are trying to cure.

It really does not matter whether a person is killed by a gun or a knife, because the ultimate result is death. Synthetically produced substances are usually not bio-degradable, which means that they cannot be absorbed back into nature. And substances which cannot be absorbed usually create residues which interfere with the normal functioning of body metabolism.

In my opinion, a *prescription of wisdom* for a person's health upon becoming ill should be as follows (in order of importance):

Medicinal Substances

1. Natural herbal medications, homeopathics and/or vitamins and mineral substances
2. Scientifically applied dietary regimens
3. As close to natural, proven herbally-based prescription drug formulas and over the counter drugs
4. Synthetically produced prescription drug (if all else fails)
5. Surgery (as a last resort)

Therapeutic Techniques

1. Chiropractic treatments, acupuncture, therapeutic massage and colonic irrigations
2. Psychological counseling, biofeedback, and non-drug related mental therapies
3. Non-invasive medical methodologies
4. Surgery (as a last resort)

In all instances, one must first place his trust in God through the guidance of a Pastor, Priest or Rabbi. I sincerely believe that a person who is disturbed in his soul may not respond to any kind of therapy.

The remainder of my visit to Hanna Kroeger's seminar was extremely rewarding, having gained much additional naturopathic information concerning herbs and natural treatments for a multitude of diseases. In gratitude, I offered my services and treated many people with a unique, holistic chiropractic regimen which I had created in order to solve difficult problems which normally did not respond to the average chiropractic adjustments. These techniques were developed to help partially paralyzed patients walk again and involve realigning the whole body, including the extremities. A demonstration of this technique was given to a group of about 250 people and recorded on videotape for future use by the Kroeger Institute.

A VISIT TO DR. JOHN PARKS TROWBRIDGE, M.D.
(author of *The Yeast Syndrome*)

Upon returning to Houston from my journey to Colorado, I was then referred to a Houston-based physician, Dr. John Parks Trowbridge, M.D. (and his book *The Yeast Syndrome*) by my lovely wife Marie. This proved to be a stroke of good fortune as not only was Dr. Trowbridge knowledgeable of yeast infections, but he was also a licensed medical doctor who could legally prescribe the safe prescription drugs *Nystatin* and *Nyzorol* (he was not yet aware of Mild Silver Protein), as well as prescription doses of certain vitamins, some of which are injectable. Again, this was before I discovered and used the Mild Silver Protein which made the use of Nystatin and Nyzorol no longer necessary.

To my surprise, there were a whole lot of forms to fill out by new patients, which covered just about every aspect of my personal history. This would all lead to a diagnosis of Candida Yeast Infection if the answers proved positive. The bottom line was that since in these cases laboratory tests (blood and urine samples were taken) were often inconclusive, this analysis of subjective symptoms on the part of the patient was essential to correct diagnosis.

Another section of the new patient information inquiry led to a commitment by the patient on how much he or she were willing to do in order to get well. For example, would the patient be committed to altering his *entire diet* and actively thinking about how to improve it? This was essential. Apparently, a *partial commitment* would only lead to *partial results*. Also, since the likelihood of having to take Nystatin and possibly Nyzorol was prevalent, there were different additional commitment levels that the patient had to face in order to accomplish the goal of ridding himself of this yeast infection.

Dr. Trowbridge proved to be a very competent, caring, and knowledgeable physician. After a careful analysis of all the information (including conclusive lab reports), I was diagnosed as indeed having a full-blown systemic Candida Albicans Yeast Infection. It was clearly noted that the cause of the infection was both the oral and intravenous antibiotics which I had taken for the Lyme Disease, previous to my discovery of Mild Silver Protein.

He also agreed that the symptoms from this infection could be easily interpreted as a continuance of Lyme Disease and that the roller coaster effect of additional antibiotics (which most unknowledgeable physicians would prescribe)...would simply aggravate and perpetuate a person's illness.

Although I felt badly about having the Candida Yeast Infection, psychologically I felt great and quite reassured that a physician and noted authority such as Dr. Trowbridge could substantiate and reaffirm my own personal suspicions (on which I had done much research).

THE LYME DISEASE ROLLER COASTER

After all of my firsthand experience in this matter, I must conclude the following:

1. Lyme Disease is treatable and can be conquered through the use of the natural antibiotic that I have discovered called Mild Silver Protein, and that the holistic supportive methods in this book can carry the victim of Lyme Disease through this most difficult challenge.

2. Conventional oral and intravenous antibiotic treatment without the replacing of the body's normal friendly acidophilus bacteria does indeed lead to a systemic Candida Albicans Yeast Infection.

3. This Candida Yeast Infection can be wrongly diagnosed as a continuation of the original Lyme Disease which will be 70-80% over, although it would eventually return, if conventional antibiotics were used...and 100% over if Mild Silver Protein was used as a method of treatment.

4. That if a yeast infection is wrongly diagnosed as Lyme Disease and further antibiotics are prescribed, this will only perpetuate a more severe yeast infection (which is assumed to be Lyme Disease).

THE CANDIDA ALBICANS CONNECTION

There are four major "modern day plagues" which are devastating mankind and destroying his health, as we move toward the 21st Century. Each disease has graduated to epidemic proportions, bringing to mind visions and fears of a Biblical nature and magnitude. These epidemics have become just as frightful as a swarm of hungry locusts or the rotting away of human flesh with Leprosy. At least one, AIDS, carries the same social stigma and tendency towards isolation as Leprosy did.

These four major plagues are running rampant through almost every state in the union and over 30 foreign countries, recognizing no geographical boundaries, religious beliefs or political ideologies. And each one has perplexed modern scientific medicine, which sees no immediate or magical cure in sight. Each one of these diseases is mutating and multiplying at rates totally alarming to our physical stability and mental security. Most importantly of all, I believe that each was created by upsetting the normal balances of nature, which have been with mankind since the first humans walked on the earth...and even before then when the first microbe of organic life appeared and began to multiply.

This disruption of the balance of nature is just like the tragic fate of the humpback whales, which for millions of years reigned undisturbed in our great oceans. Then man, whose Biblical purpose according to Genesis was to rule over all other forms of creation, destroyed this delicate ecological balance with his ignorance, indifference, greed and total disregard and disrespect for all life forms and the organic vegetable material and mineral foundations which support that life.

The four epidemics or modern-day plagues are:
1. AIDS - Auto immune deficiencies
2. Lyme Disease - Spirochete tick-borne diseases
3. Candida Albicans - Yeast fungus infections
4. Retroviruses - Iatrogenic born viruses

In this chapter, I will discuss in great detail the Candida Albicans connection to Lyme Disease, which perpetuates the illusion that Lyme Disease cannot be conquered but only hopefully controlled. I will say again that I firmly believe that I have found an answer for Lyme Disease through combining prevention, Mild Silver Protein antibiotic treatment, holistic restorative treatments and maintenance... plus Candida Albicans eradication through an understanding of the relationship of yeast infection to Lyme Disease.

The other epidemics listed will be discussed in lesser detail due to the lack of time and space, as I feel a tremendous urgency to get the valuable information on Lyme Disease out into the hands of hundreds of thousands of people who are hurting, but worse than that, don't even know why.

Candida Albicans are yeast fungus related diseases which are exploding in epidemic proportions and are a direct result of nature's reaction to imbalances caused by man-made cultured and synthetic medicinal substances. Again, let me emphasize that modern day scientists and physicians did not purposefully intend to disrupt these sensitive ecological balances of nature, but instead in their zeal to cure, overlooked the inescapable laws of nature and became blind to the repercussions of their actions. An example of *purposeful intent* would be germ warfare. However, the one similarity common to both actions is that the D.N.A. and R.N.A. are chemically or genetically altered through man's intervention with the basic genetic codes and natural balances which govern all life.

However, just as in the popular motion picture "The Andromeda Strain," the solution to killing a dangerous and unwanted living organism was by understanding the balances which govern the laws of nature. In this movie (I use this only as an example) all man-made methods failed in destroying a very virulent microorganism. Finally, the answer was found when it was realized by the "scientist" that the microorganism could live only within a certain range of PH or acid alkaline balance. When it was forced into an atmosphere where this range did not exist, it died and succumbed to the laws of nature. In this particular story, the threat to society came about because the scientist failed to respect the powerful laws of nature and began to manipulate them. Although fictional, this same threat is now a reality due to modern techniques of gene therapy which can both help and harm human beings.

Without proper safety checks, the results could prove as devastating as Hitler's futile attempts to breed a master race. On the other side of the spectrum, if genetic disorders such as Muscular Dystrophy could be eliminated, then it would be a tremendous blessing. Let me reiterate that what we are dealing with in terms of Candida Albicans is the power with which nature rebounds when its balances are disrupted or destroyed.

The question that may be arising in your own mind is this: "Why I have I not heard of this Candida Albicans Infection before?" Well, perhaps you have, but under a different name and different circumstances. The average individual has probably heard of *vaginal yeast infections,* which almost every woman has experienced at one time or another in their adult life. What almost every man has probably heard of is a related type of yeast fungus called *athlete's foot* and also *jock itch,* both commonly picked up in locker rooms or gymnasiums. Of course, the common term to both men and women is "yeast." Actually, this is the same substance that is used in baking almost all breads and cakes in order to make them rise. Yeast is a living microorganism from the vegetable kingdom.

There are three major kingdoms of matter, those classified as **animal, vegetable** and **mineral**. All matter on earth, both living and non-living, must fit into one of these three categories. Bacteria and viruses are living organisms which belong to the animal kingdom. Yeast is a living one-celled, potentially colonizing microorganism which belongs in the vegetable kingdom. Calcium is a mineral which all life must have to build bones (among other purposes) and is from the mineral kingdom.

In the animal kingdom one could be dealing with a ferocious wild lion or tiger from Africa...or a tame, domestic dog or cat that is free to run through your neighborhood with no thought of malice or harm. In the microscopic world of the vegetable kingdom, one could be dealing with a friendly or unfriendly germ, depending upon its effect when introduced or activated within the human body. Does it promote health or does it promote illness and disease in the body when exposed to it? This choice between health and illness is the criteria as to whether a specific family of bacteria such as Lactobacillus Acidophilus or vegetable microorganisms such as yeast are friendly or unfriendly.

Yeast in very small amounts is native to the human body and is basically dormant and would not fall into either category. However, when nature's beautiful balance is destroyed by natural phenomena or man's intervention, it can grow into much larger and uncontrolled amounts which then become antagonistic and cause disease.

There was another motion picture which was produced many years ago called "The King of Hearts," in which a group of insane people in an asylum in Europe (during World War II) were accidentally released into the mainstream of society during an invasion of enemy forces. While under lock and key, these people were kept under total control. However, when inadvertently released into the "healthy body of society," it didn't take long before their uncontrolled actions began causing havoc in their small community. They were like a cancerous disease which began infecting everything around them. Just as a cancer cell can and will infect the healthy cells with which it comes in contact, so also can the so-called "bad guys" in the bacteria chain infect healthy cells in their vicinity. In this same manner, yeast when free to grow uninhibited will also cause great harm until its growth is brought back under control.

The two major categories of friendly and unfriendly microorganisms with which we will concern ourselves in relation to the Candida connection to Lyme Disease are these:

Friendly bacteria - Lactobacillus Acidophilus, if constantly present in the body (it should be noted that there are actually six strains that need to be present and may at times be replaced)

Unfriendly yeast - Candida Albicans (when the growth is out of control)

It is the upset in the delicate balance of nature between these two foes which can create symptoms in the human body which are in many ways as devastating as Lyme Disease. It can also give the false impression that one is not over Lyme Disease, which can initiate more broad spectrum antibiotic treatment, which again in repetition kills off the friendly bacteria, the Lactobacillus Acidophilus, bringing about uncontrolled growth of the Yeast Candida Albicans. The cycle can be endless.

Candida Albicans has been around for millions of years since the beginning of microscopic life. Man has always carried it in his body and has peacefully coexisted with it, up until the time modern man created broad spectrum antibiotics, both *cultured* like Penicillin and *synthetic* like the cephalosporins which kill friendly and unfriendly bacteria. The purpose of Candida in nature is to initiate biodegradability of the body after death.

Every living thing has a purpose in nature or our Creator would not have created it. It was once thought by the medical profession less than 25 years ago that the appendix and the tonsils were superfluous organs which had no purpose in the body and should be taken out when they became infected. It is now known that *tonsils* are a part of the immune system and that the *appendix* is an appendage which keeps the colon lubricated for digestive purposes. Statistics now show that the rate of colon cancer is much higher when the appendix has been removed and that individuals with no tonsils have less resistance to infections and throat cancers. The tonsils are as much a part of the immune system as the lymphatics which they are family to. Men who have had vasectomies are having them reversed because of the higher rates of prostate cancers which have been recorded.

It is important that we recognize these purposes and *do not tamper with them.* Again, this is not to say that antibiotics are bad, as they have saved many lives. However, in my 47 years of existence, not one medical doctor who prescribed antibiotics for me ever warned me or my family about the potential harmful and perhaps devastating effects of killing off the friendly bacteria or the need to replace these bacteria through dietary methods which can prevent side effects. And not one physician ever warned me about the potential side effects of any prescription drug or told me about "The Physician's Desk Reference," a book which can be purchased by lay people as well as the medical profession. It meticulously lists all the potential as well as the probable hazards of prescribed drugs. Perhaps the overemphasis on disease and death-causing factors, rather than *health and life* causing factors (which include balances in nature)...is the culprit. In listening to Dr. Andrew Weil, M.D. lecture on this, I got the distinct impression that the medical mind can become so focused on illness that it can lose track of what it really takes to have and maintain health and *wellness.* As an addendum, I personally feel that every prescription for antibiotics should carry a *warning label* on the bottle, making the consumer aware of the potential hazards of not replacing the friendly bacteria which are killed off when these drugs are used.

With proper education, warnings and correct

restorative programs, antibiotics can maintain their throne as a medical miracle which can cure disease and save many lives. Without these important cautions, the question can accurately be raised as to whether physicians are doing more harm than good (as pertains to this scenario) and breaking the *Hippocratic Oath*, which states as its basic tenet "Do No Harm." Are we, as the old saying states, "Throwing the baby out with the bathwater?"

I would suggest that all physicians *throw caution to the wind* and seek to abide by the oath, and add to it "Do Good!" It is time to practice both preventive and protective medicine and to use procedures and medications which can only *help* the patient, not *harm* him.

WHAT IS CANDIDA'S CONNECTION TO LYME DISEASE?

All individuals who have Lyme Disease and who have been treated both orally and intravenously with broad spectrum antibiotics, have without a doubt a Candida Yeast Infection, if the antibiotic did it's job and destroyed the good bacteria in the body (as well as the bad spirochetes). If these same individuals have not been educated and informed that the helpful bacteria (Lactobacillus Acidophilus) has to be replaced through dietary supplements or by eating fresh yogurt culture or both, then the "yeast tiger has been let out of the cage." It is beginning to colonize and multiply out of control and is beginning to attack every living, healthy organ, tissue and cell in the body, releasing toxins and interfering with the nervous system and cellular metabolism, just like the spirochetes in Lyme Disease do. As mentioned earlier, I have dubbed Candida "the second great medical imposter," since the symptoms are almost identical to that of Lyme disease (and, like Lyme Disease, mimic many other diseases).

WHAT IS ACTUALLY GOING ON IN CANDIDA INFECTIONS WHICH MAKE YOU FEEL SO BAD?

Imagine a finely-tuned computer with all its working parts exposed and sitting on a beach full of white sand, vulnerable to the wind and the elements. Then suddenly picture a slight sea breeze as it begins blowing the fine grains of sand into the inner workings of the computer. The fan becomes frozen, the mechanisms become sluggish and the circuitry becomes polluted to the point that the computer is diminished in efficiency and capability, and eventually quits performing due to malfunctions and electronic chaos. The sand, as an unwelcome intruder who was not included in the design of the system, has "gummed up the works."

Now, simply imagine this same scenario as you visualize a similar kind of thing happening to the human body as the tiny microscopic cells of the Candida begin multiplying and "gumming up the works." This is a graphic example of how something which is extremely small can become a mighty force when literally billions of units are grouped together and behave as one. In the original *Star Trek* series, there was a story of an alien organism which looked like a one-celled creature. However, there turned out to be tens of thousands of them which were mentally connected and acted as one mind. Spock and Kirk eventually had to change their way of perceiving and treat them as *one mind*, even though the parts were not physically connected.

Similarly, in order to understand a one-celled microscopic yeast, one must understand how this one-celled microorganism thinks and acts when it becomes a colony of billions acting as one, like a well trained army. Each of these individual cells, just as every soldier in an army, must eat in order for the army to keep moving. The dissimilarity lies in the fact that each individual soldier in the attacking force of an army is incapable of reproducing himself. On the other hand, a one-celled yeast can reproduce itself by a process of budding, just like a rose is reproduced from a rose bud that forms and then begins to blossom (this reproductive process is, not surprisingly, called "budding").

In the yeast example, each bud then breaks off the mother cell and becomes a new yeast cell capable of now reproducing itself. But the real problem occurs because of the accelerated rate of speed at which all this occurs. It happens very quickly, similar to the mushroom (also a fungus) growing from a tiny spore and *overnight* becoming a large mushroom an inch or more in diameter. You can compare it to time-lapse photography in a Disney movie.

The yeast victim eventually realizes the power of what these tiny cells can do to the human body when they act with one mind: to eat, to survive and to colonize. But what you need to know is that the cells they are eating are *yours.* You are the *main course.* The yeast cells desperately need the healthy cells in your body, which contain and metabolize life-giving substances, in order to carry on with the goal of contamination.

At this point comes the greatest danger and folly which causes chronic, perpetuating infection in the victim of Lyme Disease. The treating physician acknowledges that the patient's symptoms have not subsided and perhaps have even gotten worse. Another round of antibiotics is then prescribed, which ensures that any remaining "friendly bacteria" are destroyed (even that which has been inadvertently replaced by eating yogurt, etc.). This causes the

Candida Albicans yeast to go even more out of control. It has been proven by the scientific community that these broad spectrum antibiotics do not kill all of the spirochetes, as they hide in the deep fibroblast (muscle cells). Again, it has also been shown that mutant pleomorphic strains of spirochetes are created by the drugs, ensuring the continued proliferation and reoccurrence of spirochetes (and thus Lyme Disease) in the human body..

The patient now finds himself on that proverbial roller coaster of illness and disease, with debilitating symptomatology, both from Lyme Disease and yeast infection. And with no end in sight. The chronic yeast infection is usually not fatal, but can make a person extremely sick.

When I was a young boy of about ten, I read a children's book entitled: "Leninger Versus the Ants." In this story, a man who owned a farm discovered that a large colony of ants was moving toward his farm and house, consuming everything in the way. At first, of course, the man thought little about it because he could not conceive of a possible danger or threat coming from such a small creature. Maybe just a sting or two. However, as this incredible mass of billions of ants came closer, he noticed the devastation behind them and he quickly began to change his mind. The rest of the story deals with a multitude of defenses he attempted to put up in an almost futile attempt to stem the tide of destruction. The ants literally crossed over barriers of water by floating upon each other. And even when fire consumed their bodies, their mass was so great that they just kept marching on, eating and destroying. They were miniscule, but they wielded great power in numbers.

Just like the tiny sand particles attacking the mechanisms of the exposed computer on the beach, these small yeast cells get into the workings of the healthy cells, tissues and organs (in enormous numbers) and become *the monkey wrench in the machinery*. This is done by creating inflammation through cell irritation, which then interferes with the metabolic workings of the healthy cells. Since these cells make up tissues and organs, metabolic functions are interfered with and eventually disrupted. The end result to the yeast victim is the appearance of bizarre symptoms. You are now "headachy," irritable, tired, to name only a few of the symptoms. You are generally "sick all over" and both physically and mentally fatigued. In fact, you may be down and depressed to the point of not being able to carry on your normal activities. You may also have arthritis-type joint pains with feelings of pressure and bloating. The reason you are affected mentally as well as physically is because the yeast attacks the brain and nervous system, disrupting normal endorphin production which are hormones that keep you feeling good when they are in abundance.

In simple terms, your brain is not working at its full capacity because its works are also "gummed up." Just like a joint of the body would feel terrible if it were saturated with sand and causing great friction, so also do those same joints feel constrained and not being able to move freely because of the tens of thousands of yeast cells in its inner workings. That is not difficult to understand. It's important to realize that just as Lyme Disease infects every major system of the body, so also does Candida Yeast Infection. At this point, the friendly bacteria needs to be replaced in order to offset the growth of the renegade yeast cells.

Just imagine eating Hot peppers without any bread or water to balance the effects of the peppers. It would burn the palate of the mouth, the esophagus and virtually overwhelm the lining of the stomach. Eating hot peppers ("solid fire") has got to be tempered with bread or a tortilla in order to lessen the impact. The meal has to be balanced.

There are also balances of nature which allow the body to live and thrive. Again, when they are removed, life is disrupted and a person can become deathly ill to the point of entertaining suicidal thoughts. A person can come under such painful attack that he or she loses the desire to go on. Before this happens, treatment and therapy must begin. The good news is that there are effective non-invasive treatments that actually work so that there is *hope* as well as an answer. "Giving up" is no longer the most attractive option.

HOW DO YOU KNOW IF YOU HAVE A YEAST INFECTION?
(more specifically, Candida Albicans)

There are two marvelous and informative books available through your local book store or health food store which proved to be valuable to me in understanding and treating Candida Albicans yeast infection. I highly recommend that those afflicted with Lyme Disease and subsequent yeast infection read and study these publications:

1. *The Yeast Syndrome* - Dr. John Parks Trowbridge, M. D. and Morton Walker, D. P. M. (Bantam Books, publisher)
2. *The Yeast Connection* - Dr. William G. Crook, M. D. (Professional Books, publisher)

These two books should prove sufficient for the detailed information which a person will need to fully understand and treat a "full blown" Candida infection which is more than likely present if the patient has received oral or intravenous antibiotic treatment for Lyme Disease. And unless the patient has received the Mild Silver Protein therapy, he probably is suffering from both diseases.

It would seem that the degree of severity depends upon the length of time and the form in which the antibiotics were taken. At this present time in history, almost all doctors prescribing antibiotics do not inform and educate their patients about how to prevent systemic Septicemia from yeast infections. This can be prevented by moderate and cautious use of antibiotics, but most importantly, while at the same time replacing the friendly bacteria (Lactobacillus Acidophilus) through eating fresh, high-quality plain yogurt and taking fresh, powdered capsule supplements during and immediately following antibiotic therapy. In this case, the old saying "An ounce of prevention is worth a pound of cure" definitely holds true, except that yeast infections can be so severe that we are actually talking about a "ton of cure."

It has been determined that birth control pills can bring on a systemic yeast infection just as easily as antibiotics. If you think you might have a yeast infection, then male prophylactics should be the birth control method of choice, which will also accomplish keeping the yeast infection from spreading to your sexual partner (and then back and forth). All sexual partners should be checked for systemic yeast infection by a qualified physician specializing in the diagnosis and treatment of this disease. Again, the severity of an infection is directly proportional to the type and amount of antibiotic treatment given. The following list gives four levels of this type/amount relationship:

1. Oral Antibiotics - Mild to moderate yeast infection
2. Intravenous Antibiotics - Moderately severe to severe yeast infection
3. Combination oral, followed with one to three

months intravenous antibiotic therapies - Severe "full-blown" Candida Albicans Yeast Infection
4. Short-term use of birth control pills - Mild to moderate yeast infection
5. Long-term use of birth control pills - Moderately severe to severe yeast infection

The yeast infection will only continue to get worse without a proper treatment program, including a revision of your entire diet. This includes not only what you eat, but when and how you eat your food and drink your fluids. Also, you may have to discontinue taking certain medications which you are presently on and you may also have to alter your physical environment and how you interact with it.

CONFIRMING A CANDIDA ALBICANS YEAST INFECTION

Candida Yeast infections can be further confirmed and diagnosed by your physician, utilizing laboratory blood work to do a yeast count, as well as a thorough blood profile to look for the effects of the infection. Since Candida is always present in the human body, confirmation of its presence only illustrates that you are a human being. What is truly important is its *population*. Is the amount of yeast in your system relatively normal or does it moderately or severely exceed the normal limits? If the yeast count falls into the latter two categories, it is further objective confirmation that the cause of suffering is Candidiasis.

One of the easiest and most effective ways of determining the presence of a yeast infection can be accomplished by taking the *health quiz* for the yeast syndrome as designed by Dr. Trowbridge (pages 100-103 in his book *The Yeast Syndrome*). I'll quote it directly:

"RATE YOUR HEALTH" QUIZ FOR YEAST SYNDROME

There are several ways you can privately determine at home whether you have been affected by Candida Albicans. The most important question that you might ask yourself or that you may be asked by your doctor is: "When is the last time that I (you) really felt well?"

Circle the number of the question in which you must answer "yes." If you have four or five "yes" answers, you may suffer with yeast related illness; if you have six or seven "yes" answers, you are probably a Candida infection victim; if you have eight or more "yes" answers, you almost certainly need medical treatment for chronic, generalized Candidiasis or for unusual illnesses that occasionally mimic the condition and for which proper medical diagnoses and care should be sought.

QUESTIONS FOR ADULTS AND TEENAGERS

Have you suffered with:

1. Frequent infections, constant skin problems - or taken antibiotics (or cortisone medications) often for long periods?

2. Feelings of fatigue, being drained of energy, drowsiness - or the same symptoms on damp, muggy days in moldy places such as a basement?

3. Feelings of anxiety, irritability, insomnia - or cravings for sugary foods, breads, alcoholic beverages?

4. Food sensitivities, allergy reactions - or digestion problems, bloating, heartburn,

constipation, bad breath?

5. Feeling 'spacey' or 'unreal,' difficulty in concentrating, or being bothered by perfumes, chemical fumes, tobacco smoke?

6. Poor coordination, muscle weakness, or joints painful or swollen?

7. Mood swings, depression, or loss of sexual feelings?

8. Dry mouth or throat, nose congestion or drainage, pressure above or behind the eyes or ears, or frequent headaches?

9. Pains in the chest, shortness of breath, dizziness, or easy bruising?

10. Frustration at going from doctor to doctor, never getting your health completely well - or being told that your symptoms are "mental" or "psychological" or "psychosomatic"?

FOR WOMEN ONLY

Do You Suffer With:
1. Vaginal burning or itching, discharge, infections - or urinary problems?

2. A difficult time getting pregnant - or been pregnant two or more times - or taken birth control pills?

3. Premenstrual symptoms: moodiness, fluid loading, tension - or irregular cycles, other menstrual or sexual problems?

ESPECIALLY FOR CHILDREN

Do You Suffer From:
1. Frequent infections particularly of the ears, tonsils, bronchitis, history of frequent diaper rash?

2. Continuous nasal congestion or drainage?

3. Dark circles under the eyes–or periods of hyperactivity, poor attention span?

There is now an answer to the dreaded symptoms of Candida Yeast Infection: Mild Silver Protein.

PERSONAL HOLISTIC DIARY

CHAPTER 4
MILD SILVER PROTEIN
THE COMPLETED SOLUTION
With References From The Lost Silver Publications

"THE DEAD SEA SCROLLS OF MODERN MEDICINE"

WHAT IS MILD SILVER PROTEIN?

It is a very powerful natural prophylactic and antibiotic/antifungal. It is a catalyst that dissolves an enzyme that all one-celled bacteria, fungus and viruses use for their oxygen metabolism. They suffocate. It does no harm to human enzymes or any part of the human body chemistry. It kills all disease-causing organisms on contact, even those pleomorphic, no matter how they mutate; resistant strains, therefore cannot develop, and the body does not develop a tolerance. Mild Silver Protein is both a remedy for and a prevention of infections of *any kind*. Having sufficient Mild Silver Protein in the body is like having a superior second immune system. Great Grandma put a silver dollar in her milk crock to keep it fresh longer at room temperature.

Mild Silver Protein, contains the metal silver in a

colloidal form (def: colloid - a substance composed of particles that are extremely small but larger than most molecules, actually 0.001 microns in diameter...currently referred to in scientific jargon as *atomic microclusters*). The particles in Mild Silver Protein do not actually dissolve, but remain suspended in distilled water. Many materials associated with ordinary life such as soap, most plastics, rubber and glass are produced from colloids. Colloids also play an important part in organic functions such as digestion and excretion. The color of the pure Mild Silver Protein solution is largely dependent on the manner of its preparation and the presence or absence of minute quantities of electrolytes. A "goldish" color usually indicates purity and balance.

Silver is an element which occurs naturally in the earth. It is a silvery-colored metal that, upon heating, is malleable and therefore can be shaped into different objects. It has been regarded both Biblically and historically (along with gold) as one of the most precious metals in and on the planet. It has been a source of beauty as well as an inspiration to writers and poets throughout the ages. No other element needs to be added to it or mixed with it in order to enjoy its many attributes and qualities. In fact, it is most beautiful and useful in its pure form. This proves to be true both for artwork, as well as *healing methodologies.*

Silver has been considered a source of *wealth*, with great value and usually in the possession of the kingly and the prosperous...which is very true in the material level. But now with the rediscovery of Mild Silver Protein and its development, silver has become a *new source of wealth* called HEALTH, and a restorer of long life as promised in the Bible. It is a foundation for renewed vigor and strength which, coupled with the right attitude and *positive thinking,* leads to prosperity.

Mild Silver Protein's future as a backbone for the re-established and continued health of mankind shall become the inheritance of our children and grandchildren. Just imagine with me a world for both the rich and poor *free of all diseases* caused by microorganisms. Imagine a renewed second immune system whose silver content protects it from degenerative diseases such as cancer and the devastating effects of AIDS.

SOME ESTABLISHED USES

Mild Silver Protein should be taken as directed by your holistically-minded physician who has both studied and read the contents of this book, which I pray will become a *standard text* for medical schools, chiropractic colleges and all institutions of higher learning in the healing arts. In this manner our physicians will be armed with this most potent healing tool.

Mild Silver Protein can be applied directly to cuts, scrapes, and open sores. Also a few drops on a small band-aid can be worn over warts, cuts, abrasions, or any open sore. It can be dabbed directly onto eczema of any kind, acne, mosquito bites or a multitude of skin problems. It is also an ideal food preservative and can be used in canning at one-eighth teaspoon per quart. Those who use Mild Silver Protein report that they catch milder and fewer, if any, colds or flu. The emphasis, of course, is on the prevention of all infections.

THERE ARE NEVER ANY SIDE EFFECTS

It never does any harm to the liver, kidneys or any organ or system of the body. No one has ever overdosed and it is not an allopathic poison.

When prepared under suitable conditions and properly "protected," Mild Silver Protein solution is quite stable even in the presence of salts and normal constituents of the blood. Its destructive action on toxins is very marked so that it will protect laboratory rabbits from ten times the lethal dose of tetanic or diptheric toxin.

Unlike certain organic compounds of silver, the colloidal metal is not *organotropic* (definition: organotropic - organo = organic, tropic = a tendency to turn or change in a manner or in response to a stimulus. Hence organotropic = a tendency to change a response to an organic stimulus) and does not cause *necrosis* (definition: necrosis - localized death of living tissue) of the underlying tissues. Hence it has been used for several months consecutively without staining the conjunctiva (definition: conjunctive - the mucous membrane that lines the inner surface of all the eyelids and is continued over the forepart of the eyeball).

Taken internally, the particles of Mild Silver Protein are resistant to the action of dilute acids and alkalies of the stomach, and consequently continue their catalytic action and pass into the intestine unchanged.

T. H. Anderson Wells reports in *Lancet*, February 16, 1918, that years ago a preparation of Mild Silver Protein was used *intravenously* in a case of Puerperal Septicemia without any irritation to the kidneys and with no pigmentation to the skin. This physician has found that a series of intravenous injections, each of Mild Silver Protein every forty eight hours, produce no outward effects and that recovery is rapid.

Sir Malcolm Morris reports in the *British Medical Journal* (May 12, 1947) that Mild Silver Protein is free of the drawbacks of the other preparations which cause pain and the discoloration of the skin. Indeed, instead of producing irritation, it has a distinctly *soothing effect*. It rapidly subdues inflammation (anti-inflammatory) and promotes the healing of the lesions. He had remarkable results in enlarged prostate with irritation to the bladder, in Pruritus Ani and Perineal Eczema, and in hemorrhoids. It can be used in the form of suppositories while a solution is simultaneously applied to the irritated skin. In Bromidrosis in the axillae and feet, it quickly gives relief. It causes a rapid disappearance of warts and, being non-toxic, it can be given internally in urticaria and other forms of dermatitis which are suggestive to toxemia. In such cases it is quickly beneficial.

In Ophthalmology, Mild Silver Protein has now largely replaced silver nitrate. For Eye, Ear and Nose specialists, the following will prove interesting. J. Mark Howell writes in the *British Medical Journal* (December 15, 1917) that Mild Silver Protein has also been used successfully in septic conditions of the mouth (including pyorrhea alveolzris - Rigg's Disease); throat (including Menier's symptoms and closure of Valsava's inflation), and in generalized septicemia, leucorrhea, cystitis, whooping cough, and shingles.

OTHER USES OF SILVER

Silver appears in colloidal form or in various other forms and is once more receiving widespread attention in the medical community. For example, most antibiotics kill only six or seven different disease organisms, but silver is known to kill more than 650, almost 100 times more. Further, resistant strains fail to develop and silver in the colloidal form is non-toxic and in other forms virtually non-toxic. Says a pioneering silver researcher, Dr. Henry Margraf of St. Louis: "Silver is the best all-around *germ fighter* we have."

SOME SPECIFIC INSTANCES OF SILVER'S USE

Swimming Pool Water - Silver is widely used to purify pool water and it doesn't sting your eyes as chlorine does. A dramatic demonstration recently took place in Nebraska. Fifty gallons of sewage was pumped into a pool without any disinfectant. With the standard measure of contamination being the count of E. Coli (an organism found in the human intestinal tract), the count in the swimming pool soared to 7,000 E. Coli cells per milliliters of water. When the water was subsequently flushed through silver electrodes - within three hours it was completely free of E. Coli.

Fighting Deadly Poisons - Japanese firms have announced five startling technologies which use silver to purify air. One company converts 50 parts per million of carbon monoxide by passing the gas through a stack of screens coated with silver compounds. Another uses silver compounds to remove vinyl cyanide, methyl cyanide, and hydrocyanic acid from its discharges. A gas chemical company removes all the 200 parts per million of nitric oxide by passing the gas through its silver compounds.

Combatting Waterborne Diseases Such as Dysentery - More than half the world's airlines now use silver water filters. For instance, British Airways, Swissair, Scandinavian Airlines, Lufthansa, Olympic, Air France, Canadian Pacific Airlines, Alitalia, KLM, Japan Airlines and Pan AM. The Swiss government has approved silver water filters and they are used in homes and offices throughout the country. After testing 23 methods of purifying water, NASA selected a silver system for the Space Shuttle.

Historical Uses - The currently increasing interest reflects a kind of revival in the public health sector. In ancient Greece and Rome, people used silver containers to keep liquids fresh. American settlers traveling across the West, often put a silver dollar in milk in order to delay spoiling.

SOME CANCER RESEARCH

Dr. Gary Smith (a pioneer in cancer research) in an unpublished article writes that: "Success depends on the amount of silver in the person's body and *failures* result from the *lack* of silver in the body. When silver was present, the cancer cell redifferentiated and the body was restored. When silver levels are low or non-existent, the cancer growth rate slows or continues to grow because the cells cannot redifferentiate.

"At various times I have thought about the ability of silver to destroy bacteria but have never been able to do anything about it because silver is not available in supplemental form. I believe the residual silver in the body has a big effect on the killing power of the immune system to destroy viruses and bacteria."

HOW DO WE GET SILVER IN THE BODY IN THE FIRST PLACE?

We get silver and all minerals in the body through the food we eat. How does silver get in the food? It gets in the food through living soil organisms in humus soil of which there are billions in a handful of dirt, and breaks down the soil so that plants are provided minerals in a form assimilable to the plant. By assimilating the plant nutrients, the minerals are transferred in our digestive tract where our bodies utilize the captured organic (chelated) minerals, through the blood system to the various organs of the body. Hence, we get silver from plants.

If we cannot assimilate silver for some reason or as the tissues age, we develop a silver deficiency and thus an impaired immune system, which can lead to cancer. I suspect a silver deficiency is possibly one of the main reasons cancer exists and is increasing at such a rapid rate.

Mild Silver Protein is the only substance that can safely be used as a silver supplement. A teaspoon a day is the recommended dosage. There is a book printed by a naturopathic doctor in Colorado called *AG - THERAPY DOCTOR'S DESK REFERENCE* which lists the treatment dosages for a multitude of different diseases which have shown to be helped through the use of Mild Silver Protein. It is a marvelous piece of pioneering literature.

RECOGNIZED REMEDIES

Research indicates the following as a partial list of the more than 650 diseases that Mild Silver Protein has been used successfully against: Acne, Acne Rosacea, Allergies, Athlete's Foot, Tuberculosis, Bladder Inflammation, Blood Parasites, Blood-poison Boils, Bubonic Plague, Burns, Candida Albicans Yeast Infection, Chillblanes, Cholera, Conjunctivitis, Cystitis, Diabetes caused by Infection, Indigestion, Keratitis, Leprosy, Leukemia, Lupus, Lymphangitis, Lyme Disease, Malaria, Meningitis, Multiple Sclerosis, Neurasthenia, Parasitic infections (both oral and fungal), Pneumonia, Pleurisy, Prostate, Priritis Ani, Psoriasis, Purulent Ophthalmia, Rhinitis, Rheumatism, Ringworm, Scarlet Fever, Septic Conditions of the Eyes, Ears, Mouth and Throat, Sevorrhes, Shingles, Staph Infections, Syphilis, Thyroid, Tonsillitis, Toxemia, Trachoma, Trench-foot, Dermatitis, All forms of Virus, Warts, Whooping Cough, Yeast Infections, Viral Stomach Ulcer, AIDS, as well as Parvovirus and other veterinary uses.

THERE HAS NEVER BEEN A DRUG INTERACTION WITH ANY OTHER MEDICATION

Mild Silver Protein has been found to be both a remedy and prevention for all colds, flu, all infections and all fermentation due to any bacteria, fungus or virus, including staph and strep. Mild Silver Protein is the useable form of *the most effective disease fighter known.* The body needs it to fight disease-causing organisms and to aid healing. Older people using it feel younger because their body energies are used for other than fighting disease, and digestion is improved. Medical research has proven that silver promotes rapid healing with less scar tissue in the case of severe burns. Silver aids the developing fetus in growth, health, and eases the delivery and recovery for the mother. It is tasteless and it does not upset the stomach. Mild Silver Protein is not a chemical containing silver. It is microscopic clusters of pure silver held in suspension in pure distilled water by an electric charge on each atom. It is non-toxic (except to one-celled plants and animals) and non-addicting. Mild Silver Protein is a remedy for all infections, even the non-apparent low-grade infections all people have.

Dr. Henry Crooks found that silver in the colloidal state is highly *germicidal*, quite harmless to humans and he also concluded that it is absolutely non-toxic. There is no known microbe that is not killed by the Mild Silver Protein.

The Environmental Protection Agency's *Poison Control Center* reports no toxicity listing for Colloidal Silver. They consider it harmless in any concentration. Dr. Robert Becker ("The Body Electric") recognized a correlation between low silver levels and sickness. He noted that a silver deficiency was responsible for the improper functioning of the immune system. Dr. Becker's experiments conclude that silver works on the full spectrum of pathogens without any side effects or damage to any cells of the body (being tissue and not single cells).

Just imagine a hospital setting completely *free* of all virulent microorganisms which can cause disease as well as antibiotic treatment programs with no side effects.

Dr. Becker also concluded that silver was doing something more than killing disease-causing organisms; it was also bringing about *major growth stimulation of injured tissues.* Burn patients and elderly patients notice more rapid healing.

ALL STRAINS OF PATHOGENS RESISTANT TO OTHER ANTIBIOTICS ARE KILLED BY MILD SILVER PROTEIN

Dr. Bjorn Nordstrom, of the Karolinska Institute, Sweden, has used silver as a component of his *cancer cure* method for many years.

An article in Science Digest, March 1978 ("Silver, Our Mightiest Germ Fighter"), states:

As an antibiotic, Silver kills over 650 disease-causing organisms and resistant strains fail to develop. Silver is absolutely non-toxic. Silver is the best all around germ fighter against syphilis, cholera, malaria, some diabetes and severe burns." Richard L. Davies, Executive Director of the Silver Institute, which monitors silver technology in 37 countries, reports: "In four years we've described 87 important *new* medical uses for silver.

WHAT DOES THE F.D.A. SAY ABOUT MILD SILVER PROTEIN?

In a letter written on September 13, 1991, Harold Davis (Consumer Safety Officer) writes:

Colloidal Silver is considered to be a pre-1938 drug. These products may continue to be marketed without submitted evidence of safety and effectiveness (required of all prescription drugs marketed after 1938) as long as they are advertised and labeled for the same use as in 1938." Because of the F.D.A. policy; Colloidal Silver could be purchased off the shelf from any store that carries such products.

Mild Silver Protein has traditionally cost about $400 per ounce. Recently, however, a breakthrough in process engineering has made it possible to drop that price by more than 90% bringing the price to approximately $14 per ounce.

A HISTORY OF MILD SILVER PROTEIN'S DEVELOPMENT
(and its safe use)

The following article on the safety of silver colloids is by Stephen A. Levine, Ph.D. and Paris M. Kidd, Ph.D., Allergy Research Group:

Silver has been used medicinally for more than 1200 years. The germicidal action of the silver colloids was probably discovered by Carey Lea in the late 1800's. Their applications were further refined by Crede around the turn of the century, the later commercialized by a Doctor Henry Crooks. The use of these products lasted into the '30s before they disappeared from the medical literature. Mild Silver Protein is a modern version of the traditional colloidal. Its acceptance as a broad spectrum antimicrobial preceded the 1938 Federal regulation of Food and Drugs, so we are able to offer this product without incurring the prohibitive expense of government-mandated drug approval requirements.

Special aspects that define colloids are that the molecules are in Brownian motion, that free ions exist only in small extent, and that the colloid molecules are able to selectively pass through gelatin filters. They were produced by either electrification or chemical activation. Their intense molecular activity may be related to the broad antimicrobial activity of such colloids, and suggests some possible relationships to homeopathics.

Mild Silver Protein contains trace amounts of silver and protein in distilled water, as a colloidal dispersion. One teaspoon of Mild Silver Protein supplies levels of silver comparable to those consumed in the diet. It was not uncommon during the 40 to 50 years of colloid use, for doctors to inject very febrile patients, many suffering from life-threatening infections, with 250 mg. of a silver colloid or even much higher dosages. This was often repeated for only two or three days. Prolonged use was rarely necessary.

Common silver colloids preparations were initially very concentrated - Argonin 4.25% silver, Collargol 85-87%, are examples (Compilation, 1912-1). We can take one gram per day by injection to be a historic dosage. Our preparation contains about 90 micrograms per teaspoon, about 1/10,000th of one gram historic use. Also, we are dealing with the oral route of dosing and historically these agents were given by injection. We are suggesting 2 tsp. for 3-7 days. This roughly amounts to 1-3 times the highest estimated weekly dietary intake of 700 micrograms per week - Browning, 1969 (Toxicity of Industrial Metals, Chapter 35).

In 1907, Crede employed 3 grams of silver colloid at a time intravenously, but later increased the dosage. The harmlessness of these injections was confirmed by Muller. One observation stands out prominently, and that is the innocuousness of these bodies when injected into the veins and muscles, or into the spinal canal (Compilation 1012-3).

Being non-organic, the dosage can be increased from 1 or 2 or more drachms twice or thrice daily" (Compilation, 1919-2) (One drachm equals 4 grams). There can be no doubt from the foregoing experiment, that colloidal silver in the form of collosal is an active germicide. We understand that the colloids are non-poisonous and have been administered internally (Compilation, 1914-1). Concerning its use in ophthalmology, I have used it many thousands of times and have never known it to cause the slightest irritation, and it may be used for many months without staining the conjunctiva (Compilation, 1915-3).

HOW DO SILVER COLLOIDS KILL PROKARYOTIC CELLS?

From a read-through of the early literature on silver colloids, it is apparent that the colloids were important as safe and effective medicines. We discovered twelve years ago, while writing our book on antioxidants, that fundamentally toxic heavy metals of all varieties will cause oxidative toxicity, either directly via free radical production of, or indirectly via diminution of antioxidant defenses; and that antioxidants would protect against their toxicity. However, if the silver colloids were killing microorganisms via free radical/oxidative mechanisms, we would have seen enormous toxicity associated with injection of one gram or greater: red cell lysis, liberating iron and copper which encourage radical formation via Haber-Weiss mechanisms, further amplifying the free radical pathology.

"Silver as the metal has very minimal oxidative-action. We think that Mild Silver Protein, our product, must not be working via free radicals: the doctors who have been having success with it surely are giving antioxidants to their patients, and the concentrations of silver from Mild Silver Protein are low (micrograms per dose) that antioxidants would be expected to mitigate its effects."

SO HOW MIGHT SILVER COLLOIDS BE WORKING?

There is speculation that the silver binds to the microorganism, and by so doing somehow causes it to be eliminated from the body. Activation of phagocytes may be involved; orally ingested silver becomes localized in Kuppfer cells of the liver, and leukocytosis often is observed following dosing. Practitioners may find that the Herxheimer reaction is less severe with silver, because the bacterial cells may not be lysed prior to being cleared from the body. Alternatively or in addition, the Brownian motion of the colloid may contribute to the selective destruction of microbes.

If the silver colloid material were retained and stored in the body, as with other heavy metals, we would expect to have seen many deaths of injection and thereafter, yet in the literature we see just the opposite. We see dramatic statements indicating that the colloids are non-toxic or of very low toxicity. There are mentions of a few deaths from silver colloids, but only after injection of large doses (Hill and Pillsbury, 1939, Argyria, the Pharmacology of Silver, Chapter IV).

The *overriding message* is that silver colloid Mild Silver Protein is quite safe.

Thus ends the chapter on Mild Silver Protein, but this ending is nothing more than a new beginning and a new era for the world. I sincerely pray that it will be a *new beginning of freedom* from disease as we have known it. Let the practical usage of Mild Silver Protein and the significant healings for some of the worst diseases to have ever hit the world be Mild Silver Protein's testimonial.

PERSONAL HOLISTIC DIARY

CHAPTER 5
THE END OF MIRACLE DRUGS

The Post Antibiotic Era

As mentioned previously, Mild Silver Protein has been researched and proven to kill all strains of pathogens resistant to antibiotics. Silver kills over 650 disease causing organisms. It is the best all around germ fighter against syphilis, cholera, malaria, some diabetes and conditions associated with severe burns. Silver is absolutely non-toxic and resistant strains will not develop as a result of its use. And new medical applications for Mild Silver Protein are being constantly discovered.

All of this is amazingly significant and the fact that Mild Silver Protein has been *rediscovered* and once again brought to the forefront is absolutely vital. But the crucially important aspect of the resurgence of Mild Silver Protein is the *timing* of its comeback. It is *right on.*

It seems that all of a sudden there is a growing understanding and more acute awareness of what could perhaps be the worst medical disaster to ever confront mankind...the *post antibiotic era.* A time when it is becoming obvious that we are losing the war against bacteria and infectious diseases.

Everyone seems to be talking about it. The front cover of **Newsweek** flatly asks: "Antibiotics: The End of Miracle Drugs?" The front cover of **Time** also predicts: "Revenge of the Killer Microbes: Are We Losing the War Against

Infectious Diseases?" Also, newspapers, the electronic
media and spokesmen for the medical profession are
forecasting gloom and doom. And rightfully so because
"New viruses and drug-resistant bacteria are reversing
human victories over infectious disease (*Time Magazine*,
September 12, 1994)."

In an article appearing in *The Rocky Mountain News* in
Colorado (dated Sunday, February 20, 1994) the
following is stated:

BACTERIA BECOMING UNTREATABLE
Organisms Evolving Into Forms
Resistant To All Known Medicines

SAN FRANCISCO - Common bacteria that
cause pneumonia, children's ear infections
and many other diseases are evolving into
forms untreatable by all known medicines,
threatening a chilling Post-Antibiotic Era that
would be nothing short of a medical disaster, a
researcher said Saturday.

"In the post-antibiotic world, the simplest
infections could quickly escalate into fatal
illnesses," said Alexander Tomasz of
Rockefeller University of New York City.

The first antibiotic, penicillin, became
widely available in 1940. For 50 years most
bacterial infections have been treatable.

But certain uncommon bacteria already
have developed untreatable strains. And
laboratory experiments have proved that the
same thing can happen with common
bacteria, Tomasz said.

Tomasz sounded the alarm at the annual
meeting of the American Association for the
Advancement of Science. He is a leading
authority on bacteria that are resistant to
treatment by antibiotics. His concerns are

shared by doctors at the national Centers for Disease Control and Prevention in Atlanta.

"It's potentially an extremely serious problem," said Dr. Mitchell Cohen of the CDC. New drugs that might be developed to cope with the deadly bacteria are at least five years away, and drug companies are not pursuing them eagerly, Cohen said, because of belief that there is little market for them because existing drugs are successful.

Certain strains of pneumococcus which cause pneumonia, are treatable with only one antibiotic, vascimycin, the researchers said. If those bacteria become resistant to vascimycin, there will be no treatment.

Doctors are concerned about drug-resistant strains of tuberculosis. But the diseases caused by pneumoccus and staphylococcus are far more common than tuberculosis.

Certain strains of enterococcus which cause wound and blood infections, already have become resistant to vascomycin and all other known antibiotics. Researchers know that such resistant bacteria can cover the globe in a matter of years. They have seen what happened with Penicillin.

That's the *bad news*. The good news, according to Dr. Joe Cardot, N. D., Ph. D., a doctor who has expertise in Mild Silver Protein, is that "Mutation will not protect viruses, bacteria or Fungi from a 30-parts per million solution of Mild Silver Protein."

The following article appeared in the "Health Brief's" section of the *Houston Chronicle,* one of the largest newspapers in the country on Sunday, February 20, 1994:

MEDICAL DISASTER SEEN

San Francisco - Common bacteria that cause

pneumonia, children's ear infections and many other diseases are evolving into forms untreatable by all known medicines, threatening a chilling era that would be "nothing short of a medical disaster," a researcher said Saturday.

"In the post antibiotic world, the simplest infections could escalate quickly into fatal illnesses," said Alexander Tomasz of Rockefeller University in New York.

Certain uncommon bacteria have developed untreatable strains. "Experiments have proven the same thing can happen with common bacteria," Tomasz said.

"It's potentially an extremely serious problem," said Dr. Mitchell Cohen of the Centers for Disease Control and Prevention in Atlanta.

"Drugs that might be developed to cope with the bacteria are five to seven years away, and drug companies are not pursuing them eagerly," Cohen said.

According to many of the experts, as I view it, we are sitting on a *time bomb* that could easily outproportion AIDS, Lyme Disease, and Candida Yeast Infection. The Candida Yeast Infection is a perfect example of this warning already having become a reality and is now the world's third largest epidemic with AIDS being the first and Lyme Disease the second largest epidemic. It should be noted again that the Candida Yeast Infection was iatrogenically caused (doctor-induced).

Even further evidence of this pending and present disaster was made public on Sunday, December 19, 1993. Again, the Houston Chronicle ran the following revealing and shocking article in its *Metropolitan News and Features* section by Ruth Sorlle, medical writer:

DISEASE–CAUSING BACTERIA
BECOMING MORE VIRULENT

A bacteria that causes ear infections, pneumonia and meningitis is becoming increasingly more resistant to common antibiotics and harder to treat, say specialists in Houston and Atlanta.

"The pneumoccus bacteria is one of a host of organisms - including tuberculosis - that is becoming less susceptible to the drugs commonly used against them," said Dr. Sheldon Kaplan, professor of Pediatrics at Baylor College of Medicine and also chief of infectious diseases at Texas Children's Hospital.

"We could have real problems like in the pre-antibiotic era when we had all these germs and nothing to treat them with," he said. The increase in cases of resistant disease–coupled with the threat posed to the elderly and chronically ill–makes vaccination important.

Right now there is a vaccine that works in adults, and the voluntary *Hospitals of America*, a non-profit hospital group that includes the Memorial Hospital System locally, is working to get more elderly people immunized. Only about 15 percent of those for whom the vaccine is recommended have actually received it.

And said Dr. Kaplan, "More work needs to be done to develop a vaccine to prevent the disease in children under the age of two for whom the current immunization is ineffective." Before 1986, neither Kaplan nor his colleague Dr. Edward O. Mason had seen evidence of resistant Streptococcus pneumonia bacteria at Texas Children's (this is different from the Strep infection).

And until 1989 only two or three of the children treated at the hospital failed to respond to Penicillin, the drug most commonly used to treat the infection. But in 1992, 45 children had the resistant strain - 21 percent of all such infections that were scrutinized in the hospital labs.

"It is a growing problem," said Dr. Jeff Duchin, a physician epidemiologist at the Federal Centers for Disease Control in Atlanta. However, the CDC does not know how large it is because it is not a reportable infection. "We have a suspicion that there are high levels of the drug-resistant strain in some parts of the country," Duchin said in a television interview. "We are establishing mandatory reporting of drug-resistant strains."

Kaplan and Mason are heading a multi-center study to determine how frequently drug resistance occurs in children. Dr. Edward Septimus, infectious disease expert at the Memorial Hospital System, is attempting to do a similar study to determine how many Houston adults have drug-resistant disease. A CDC team has been monitoring resistant bacteria at 13 hospitals in 12 states.

In a recent report at a meeting of infectious disease experts, CDC team members said they found 6.6 percent of the samples, submitted in 1991-1992, were resistant to bacteria. By comparison a study conducted in 1979-1987 indicated that only 4.8 percent of isolates were resistant. But the increase was in isolates that were resistant, he said.

Duchin and Houston Doctors said that routine testing to determine if patients with pneumoccal infections have resistant disease is needed. Duchin said such results must be reported to the CDC so that the problems can be monitored.

One culprit in the rise in resistance could be the cure itself. As Penicillin attacks the bacteria, the bacteria finds a way around that attack by changing its structure. For that reason Kaplan warned that antibiotics should be used carefully. He said patients frequently expect antibiotics when they go to the doctor, even though their viral infection may not warrant such treatment.

"Foreign countries have high levels of resistant organisms," said Kaplan. For example in Spain, Hungary and South Africa, as many as 70 percent of the samples tested are resistant to Penicillin.

Right now, resistant infections are treated with a form of the cephalosporin–an antibiotic. But the cephalosporins are extremely expensive, and some of the organisms are becoming resistant to those drugs, Mason said.

In Memphis, Tennessee, for instance, physicians now routinely use a two-drug combination to fight the disease. The CDC has in recent years investigated major outbreaks in Memphis, a rural area of Kentucky...and also Alaska, said Duchin. "It's a relatively recent issue for the United States," said Septimus.

Memorial facilities are making the pneumoccus vaccine available at no cost to people over age 65 who have Medicare Part B coverage. Other at-risk people can receive the vaccine for $25. Funds are available to cover the cost of people who are unable to pay. Septimus said that pneumoccal disease is sixth among the top 10 killers of the elderly in the

United States, a total of 150,000. And 270,000 will develop the infection in the United States this year.

"The emergence of resistant strains of the bacteria make it more important that the people receive immunizations," he said. "We have no good handle on how diffusely spread it is," he said.

Many newspaper and magazine articles are reporting a new and virulent strain of tuberculosis bacteria which is causing a new resurgence in the disease around the world. Again, this is merely one example of what is to come if we do not alter our methods of treating disease.

There are further reports of a new and mutated form of the AIDS virus. It goes on and on. The basis problem is that we as a medically-oriented society seem to be creating more new diseases that we cannot control by the use of our chemical medicines. I believe that any substance which is inorganic and not naturally found in nature, carries within it this potential threat of creating new, mutated, virulent forms of disease.

Who knows what the chemicals of modern science have done to the insect and microbiological populations which are part of the whole chain that supports life on this planet and which man is dependent upon for his very existence? How many mutant bacteria and viral organisms have we as mankind created and set loose upon ourselves? Just look at the Ozone Layer as another example of this abuse and ignorance toward nature.

The balances within nature are intricate and many times fragile as well as interconnected. Man cannot go on indefinitely upsetting these balances through ignorance and greed without reaping the disastrous results. I will say again that I firmly believe that many of the modern-day plagues *were brought upon man by himself* and the misuse of science. We must be very careful lest we commit an epidemic of slow and gradual planetary suicide by going against the natural laws which govern God's creation.

To me it is apparent from these revealing articles that a *major medical problem* has erupted and is further brewing. Is it possible that *man* in his attempt to cure disease...coupled with impatience, arrogance and perhaps lack of proper information on the long-term effects of drugs...has created a *medical disaster?* From the ever-emerging evidence, it seems that there can be no doubt that this is indeed the case. In addition, I do not feel that the vaccines mentioned in the articles are the answer. How many times in our history, including but not limited to the Swine Flu Vaccine and the original Salk Vaccine for Polio...has this proven to have not been the case? The Swine Flu Vaccine actually caused worse short and long term symptoms than the actual flu (which never really happened) could have ever caused. And history records that the Salk vaccine, until replaced with the Savin Vaccine, actually caused the symptoms of polio rather than curing them. I remember experiencing the disastrous effects of the Swine Flu shot and I personally watched my brother get *worse* from Polio as a result of the Salk Vaccine.

Are we as a society in such a hurry to find a *knight in shining armor* cloaked in medical science as a cure for medical diseases which do not work (or at best, work for a season) but yet are heralded as miracles? Fortunately medical science *did find* an actual knight in shining armor in its original discovery of Mild Silver Protein. However, just like the knights of old, its armor has grown rusty *sitting on the shelf.* Is it not time to wake up and take this magnificent discovery off the shelf, polish up its Silver Armor, and give it back to the masses of people who are crying for relief?

I think it is.

VERTEBRAL SUBLUXATION AND NERVE CHART

A Vertebral Subluxation Complex (VSC, Bio-Mechanical Lesion) has numerous components, i.e., osseous (bone), neurological (nerve), connective tissue (muscles, ligaments and discs), lymphatic, circulatory, biomechanical alterations (curvatures, etc.) and somato-visceral (tissue, organs, etc.), which may cause irritation and/or compression of nerve roots and affect these components.[1] The nervous system controls and coordinates all organs and structures of the human body. Many nerves come from the spinal cord, pass through foramina (holes) formed by notches of 24 vertebrae in the movable spinal column, and innervate or supply specific areas and parts of the body.[2] Whenever specific areas or parts of the body are malfunctioning, generalized and/or specific symptoms are possible.[3]

SPINAL VERTEBRAE	Spinal Nerves	Areas and Parts of Body	Possible symptoms
CERVICAL SPINE (NECK)	1C	Back of the head	Headaches (including migraines, aches or pains at the back of the head, behind the eyes or in the temples, tension across the forehead, throbbing or pulsating discomfort at the top or back of head) Jaw muscle or joint aches or pains Dizziness, nervousness, vertigo Soreness, tension and tightness felt in back of neck and throat area Pain, soreness, and restriction in the shoulder area Bursitis, tendonitis Pain and soreness in arms, hands, elbows and/or fingers
	2C	Various areas of the head	
	3C	Side and front of the neck	
	4C	Upper back of neck	
	5C	Middle of neck and upper part of arms	
	6C	Lower part of neck, arms, and elbows	
	7C	Lower part of arms, shoulders	
THORACIC SPINE (MID-BACK)	1T	Hands, wrists, fingers, thyroid	
	2T	Heart, its valves and coronary arteries	Chest pains, tightness or constriction Asthma, difficult breathing Middle or lower mid-back pain, discomfort and soreness
	3T	Lungs, bronchial tubes, pleura, chest	
	4T	Gall bladder, common duct	
	5T	Liver, solar plexes	Various and numerous symptoms from trouble or malfunctioning of: Thyroid Heart Lungs Gall bladder Liver Stomach Pancreas Spleen Adrenal glands Kidneys Small and large intestines Sex organs Uterus Bladder Prostate glands
	6T	Stomach, mid-back area	
	7T	Pancreas, duodenum	
	8T	Spleen, lower mid-back	
	9T	Adrenal glands	
	10T	Kidneys	
	11T	Ureters	
	12T	Small intestines, upper/lower back	
LUMBAR SPINE (LOW BACK)	1L	Iliocecal valve, large intestines	
	2L	Appendix, abdomen, upper leg	
	3L	Sex organs, uterus, bladder, knees	
	4L	Prostate gland, lower back	Low back pain, aches and soreness Trouble walking Leg, knee, ankle and foot soreness and pain Sciatica, pain or soreness in the hip and buttocks Rectal Trouble
	5L	Sciatic nerve, lower legs, ankles, feet	
SACRUM & COCCYX (PELVIS)	SACRUM	Hip bones, buttocks	
	COCCYX	Rectum, anus	

For further explanation of chart, ask your Doctor of Chiropractic.
[1] Murkowski, K.S.J., Collected Works — Vertebral Subluxation Complex, 1988-1990.
[2] Gray's Anatomy, 29th Edition. Page 4. Note: Neurological innervation of the spinal nerves of the human body overlap in its supply to different areas and parts of the body as well as differ somewhat in different persons. This chart is a simplification of actual innervation. It has been designed for ease of layman's understanding and general edification and is not meant and should not be construed as anatomically accurate in its specific sense.
[3] Leach, Robert A: The Chiropractic Theories—A synopsis of scientific research, 2nd Edition. Baltimore, Williams & Wilkins, 1986©.
Note: The possible symptoms listed on this chart are not meant and should not be construed to mean that all these possible symptoms are produced whenever there is a vertebral subluxation complex at a specific vertebral level or that chiropractic care will correct all of these conditions.

#1300090

TIME

Articles and information from Time Magazine are reproduced with written permission.

The question ceased to be, When will diseases be gone?

known in the U.S., emerged from mice to kill 30 people in as many as 20 states.

All this bad news is undoubtedly having a cumulative impact on the human psyche. The age of antibiotics is giving way to an age of anxiety about disease. It's getting harder to enjoy a meal, make love or even take a walk in the woods without a bit of fear in the back of the mind. No wonder people pay an unreasonable amount of attention when tabloids trumpet headlines about "flesh-eating bacteria." And no wonder Stephen King's *The Stand*, a TV mini-series based on his novel about a "superflu" that ravages the world's population, earned some of the year's highest ratings.

The odds of contracting a life-threatening infectious disease are still very low—at least in the developed world. But the threats are real and frightening enough to spur medical researchers to redouble efforts to learn more about how the many kinds of microbes cause disease—and how they can be kept at bay.

MICROORGANISMS

IT IS TEMPTING TO THINK of the tiny pathogens that produce such diseases as malaria, dysentery, TB, cholera, staph and strep as malevolent little beasts, out to destroy higher forms of life. In fact, all they're trying to do is survive and reproduce, just as we are. Human suffering and death are merely unfortunate by-products.

Plasmodium, a protozoan responsible for malaria, flourishes in the human body, growing inside red blood cells until the cells burst. And without enough red cells to carry oxygen through the body, humans become anemic and can die from renal failure or convulsions. Bacteria, which are considerably smaller than protozoans, generally do their damage indirectly, producing toxins that stimulate the body to mount an immune response. Ideally the immune cells kill the bacteria. But if the bacteria get out of control, these cells can either kill cells or generate a huge immune reaction that is itself toxic.

In an illness like tuberculosis, the immune system kills the body's own cells in the localized areas where TB germs have taken hold, including the lungs or the bones. With staph or strep, the sheer volume of disease-fighting immune cells can overload blood vessels, ripping tiny tears in the vessel linings; toxins can also damage the vessels directly. Plasma begins to leak out of the bloodstream; blood pressure drops, organs fail, and the body falls into a state of shock. In cholera, bacterial toxins attack intestinal cells, triggering diarrhea, catastrophic dehydration and death.

Before the coming of penicillin and other antibiotics, bacterial diseases simply ran their courses. Either the immune system fought them off and the patient survived or the battle was lost. But antibiotics changed the contest radically: they selectively killed bacteria without harming the body's cells. For the first time, potentially lethal infections could be stopped before they got a foothold.

The World's Deadliest Scourges

Infectious disease	Cause	Annual deaths
Acute Respiratory Infections (mostly Pneumonia)	Bacterial or Viral	4,300,000
Diarrheal Diseases	Bacterial or Viral	3,200,000
Tuberculosis	Bacterial	3,000,000
Hepatitis B	Viral	1,000,000 to 2,000,000
Malaria	Protozoan	1,000,000
Measles	Viral	880,000
Neonatal Tetanus	Bacterial	600,000
AIDS	Viral	550,000
Pertussis (Whooping Cough)	Bacterial	360,000

Unfortunately, as Columbia University's Dr. Harold Neu observed in the journal *Science*, "bacteria are cleverer than men." Just as they have adapted to nearly every environmental niche on the planet, they have now begun adjusting to a world laced with antibiotics. It didn't take long. Just a year or two after penicillin went into widespread use, the first resistant strain of staph appeared. As other antibiotics came along, microbes found ways to resist them as well, through changes in genetic makeup. In some cases, for example, the bacteria gained the ability to manufacture an enzyme that destroys the antibiotic.

BY NOW NEARLY EVERY DISEASE organism known to medicine has become resistant to at least one antibiotic, and several are immune to more than one. One of the most alarming things about the cholera epidemic that has killed as many as 50,000 people in Rwandan refugee camps is that it involves a strain of bacterium that can't be treated with standard antibiotics. Relief agencies had to scramble for the right medicines, which gave the disease a head start in its lethal rampage.

Tuberculosis, too, has learned how to outwit the doctors. TB is an unusually tough microbe, so the standard therapy calls for several antibiotics, given together over six months. The length and complexity of the treatment have kept underdeveloped nations from making much progress against even ordinary TB. But now several strains have emerged in the U.S. and other developed countries that can't be treated with common antibiotics.

Even such seemingly prosaic but once deadly infections as staph and strep have become much harder to treat as they've acquired resistance to many standard antibiotics. Both microbes are commonly transmitted from patient to patient in the cleanest of hospitals, and they are usually cured routinely. But one strain of hospital-dwelling staph can now be treated with only a single antibiotic—and public health officials have no doubt that the germ will soon become impervious to that one too. Hospitals could become very dangerous places to go—and even more so if strep also develops universal resistance.

One of medicine's worst nightmares is the development of a drug-resistant strain of severe invasive strep A, the infamous flesh-eating bacteria. What appears to make this variant of strep such a quick and vicious killer is that the bacterium itself is infected with a virus, which spurs the germ to produce especially powerful toxins. (It was severe, invasive strep A that killed Muppeteer Jim Henson in 1990.) If strep A is on the rise, as some believe, it will be dosed with antibiotics, and may well become resistant to some or all of the drugs.

Microbes' extraordinary ability to adapt, observes Harvard microbiologist Fields, "is a fact of life. It's written into evolution." Indeed, the end run that many organisms are making around modern antibiotics is a textbook case of Darwin's theory in action (anti-evolutionists, take note). In its simplest form, the theory states that new traits will spontaneously appear in modern members of a given species—in modern terms, mutations will arise in the organisms' genetic material. Usually the traits will be either useless or debilitating, but once in a while they'll confer a survival

TIME, SEPTEMBER 12, 1994

and became, Where will the next deadly virus appear?

advantage, allowing the individual to live longer and bear more offspring. Over time, the new survival trait—camouflage stripes on a zebra, antibiotic resistance in a bacterium—will become more and more common in the population until it's universal.

The big difference between animals and bacteria is that a new generation comes along every few years in large beasts—but as often as every 20 minutes in microbes. That speeds up the evolutionary process considerably. Germs have a second advantage as well: they're a lot more promiscuous than people are. Even though bacteria can reproduce asexually by splitting in two, they often link up with other microbes of the same species or even a different species. In those cases, the bacteria often swap bits of genetic material (their DNA) before reproducing.

They have many other ways of picking up genes as well. The DNA can come from viruses, which have acquired it while infecting other microbes. Some types of pneumococcus, which causes a form of pneumonia, even indulge in a microbial version of necrophilia by soaking up DNA that spills out of dead or dying bacteria. This versatility means bacteria can acquire

useful traits without having to wait for mutations in the immediate family.

The process is even faster with antibiotic resistance than it is for other traits because the drugs wipe out the resistant bacterium's competition. Microbes that would ordinarily have to fight their fellows for space and nourishment find the way clear to multiply. Says Dr. George Curlin of the National Institute of Allergy and Infectious Diseases: "The more you use antibiotics, the more rapidly Mother Nature adapts to them."

HUMAN BEHAVIOR JUST MAKES the situation worse. Patients frequently stop taking antibiotics when their symptoms go away but before an infection is entirely cleared up. That suppresses susceptible microbes but allows partially resistant ones to flourish. People with viral infections sometimes demand antibiotics, even though the drugs are useless against viruses. This, too, weeds out whatever susceptible bacteria are lurking in their bodies and promotes the growth of their hardier brethren. In many countries, antibiotics

are available over the counter, which lets patients diagnose and dose themselves, often inappropriately. And high-tech farmers have learned that mixing low doses of antibiotics into cattle feed makes the animals grow larger. (Reason: energy they would otherwise put into fighting infections goes into gaining weight instead.) Bacteria in the cattle become resistant to the drugs, and when people drink milk or eat meat, this immunity may be transferred to human bacteria.

Because microbial infections keep finding ways to outsmart antibiotics, doctors are convinced that vaccines are a better way to combat bacterial disease. A vaccine is usually made from a harmless fragment of microbe that trains the body's immune system to recognize and fight the real thing. Each person's immune system is chemically different from everyone else's, so it's very difficult for a bacterium to develop a shield that offers universal protection. Diphtheria and tetanus can be prevented by vaccines if they are used properly. A vaccine against the pneumococcus bacterium has recently come out of the lab as well, and scientists expect to test one that targets streptococcus A within a year.

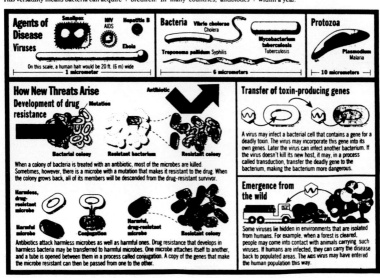

When bacteria began to outwit antibiotics, doctors found

breaks were rare in that part of the world before the breakup of the Soviet Union, but collapsing health services and worsening sanitary conditions have fostered the disease. Shortages of vaccines, meanwhile, have led to an upsurge in diphtheria in Russia, and health experts have encountered cases of typhoid, hepatitis, anthrax and salmonella in neighboring Ukraine.

■ The notorious flare-up in Gloucestershire, England, of what the press dubbed flesh-eating bacteria alerted people to the dangers of streptococcus-A infections. The common bacteria that cause strep throat generally produce no lasting harm if properly treated, but certain virulent strains can turn lethal. Strep-A infections claim thousands of lives each year in the U.S. and Europe alone.

■ Newspaper accounts publicized a startling flare-up of tuberculosis that was first detected last year at a high school in Westminster, California, a middle-class suburb of Los Angeles. The disease was apparently brought in by a 16-year-old Vietnamese immigrant who contracted it in her native country. Nearly 400 young people, or 30% of the school's students, have tested positive

for the infection, and at least 12 have a variety of the TB bacterium that is resistant to standard antibiotic treatment. One student has lost part of her lung.

■ The *New England Journal of Medicine* reported that the children of Cincinnati suffered an epidemic of pertussis (whooping cough) last year. There were 352 cases (none fatal), compared with 542 cases in the 13 years from 1979 to 1992. The alarming part was that most of the children had been properly vaccinated, suggesting that an unusually hardy strain of the pertussis bacterium might be emerging. Another disturbing statistic: there were more than 6,500 cases nationwide, the largest number in more than 26 years.

■ In many parts of the U.S., especially the Northeast, people are already leery of strolling in wooded areas for fear of encountering ticks carrying Lyme disease, a potentially chronic, arthritis-like condition. Now the *Journal of the American Medical Association* has reported on another tick-borne disease, which struck 25 people in Wisconsin and Minnesota, killing two. It is caused by a new variety of the *Ehrlichia* bacterium, which was first de-

tected in humans in 1954. Doctors are concerned because life-threatening *Ehrlichia* infections may be misdiagnosed as Lyme disease or even a bad cold.

A GENERATION AGO, NO ONE HAD ever heard of Lyme or Legionnaires' disease, much less aids. Back in the 1970s, medical researchers were even boasting that humanity's victory against infectious disease was just a matter of time. The polio virus had been tamed by the Salk and Sabin vaccines; the smallpox virus was virtually gone; the parasite that causes malaria was in retreat; once deadly illnesses, including diphtheria, pertussis and tetanus, seemed like quaint reminders of a bygone era, like Model T Fords or silent movies.

The first widespread use of antibiotics in the years following World War II had transformed the most terrifying diseases known to humanity—tuberculosis, syphilis, pneumonia, bacterial meningitis and even bubonic plague—into mere inconveniences that if caught in time could be cured with pills or shots. Like many who

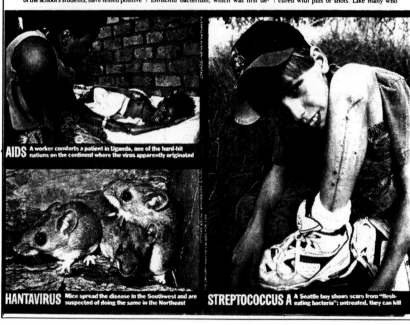

AIDS A worker comforts a patient in Uganda, one of the hard-hit nations on the continent where the virus apparently originated

HANTAVIRUS Mice spread the disease in the Southwest and are suspected of doing the same in the Northeast

STREPTOCOCCUS A A Seattle boy shows scars from "flesh-eating bacteria"; untreated, they can kill

TIME

themselves retreating in the battle against the germs

went through medical school in the 1960s, Dr. Bernard Fields, a Harvard microbiologist, remembers being told, "Don't bother going into infectious diseases." It was a declining specialty, his mentors advised—better to concentrate on real problems like cancer and heart disease.

The advent of AIDS demolished that thinking. The sight of tens of thousands of young people wasting away from a virus that no one had known about and no one knew how to fight was a sobering experience—especially when drugs proved powerless to stop the virus and efforts to develop a vaccine proved extraordinarily difficult. Faced with AIDS, and with an ever increasing number of antibiotic-resistant bacteria, doctors were forced to admit that the medical profession was actually retreating in the battle against germs.

The question ceased to be, When will infectious diseases be wiped out? and became, Where will the next deadly new plague appear? Scientists are keeping a nervous watch on such lethal agents as the Marburg and Ebola viruses in Africa and the Junin, Machupo and Sabiá viruses in South America. And there are uncountable

threats that haven't even been named: a virus known only as "X" emerged from the rain forest in southern Sudan last year, killed thousands and disappeared. No one knows when it might arise again.

A U.S. Army lab in Frederick, Maryland, faced a terrifying situation in 1989 when imported monkeys started dying from a strain of the Ebola virus. After destroying 500 monkeys and quarantining the lab and everyone in it, officials found that this particular strain was harmless to humans. But the episode was dramatic enough to inspire an article in the *New Yorker* magazine—now expanded into a soon-to-be released book called *The Hot Zone*—and work on two competing movies (one of which seems to have collapsed before production).

The Ebola affair and the emergence of AIDS illustrate how modern travel and global commerce can quickly spread disease. Germs once confined to certain regions may now pick up rides to all parts of the world. For example, the cholera plague that is currently sweeping Latin America arrived in the ballast tanks of a ship that brought tainted water from Asia. And the

New England Journal of Medicine has reported two cases of malaria in New Jersey that were transmitted by local mosquitoes. The mosquitoes were probably infected when they bit human malaria victims who had immigrated from Latin America or Asia. Writes author Laurie Garrett in a book to be published next month called *The Coming Plague:* "AIDS does not stand alone; it may well be just the first of the modern, large-scale epidemics of infectious disease."

The latest bulletins from the germ front come on top of a long series of horror stories. For years now people have been reading about—and suffering from—all sorts of new and resurgent diseases. As if AIDS were not enough to worry about, there was a rise in other sexually transmitted infections, including herpes, syphilis and gonorrhea. People heard about the victims who died in the Northwest from eating undercooked Jack in the Box hamburgers tainted with a hazardous strain of *E. coli* bacteria. They were told to cook their chicken thoroughly to avoid food poisoning from salmonella bacteria. And last year they saw how the rare hantavirus, once un-

LEGIONNAIRES' Contamination on the cruise ship *Horizon* led U.S. officials to consider new safety rules

CHOLERA A Rwandan child is treated in a Zaire hospital; drug-resistant strains have turned up in refugee camps

TUBERCULOSIS A victim of the California school outbreak; many thought TB had been conquered

TIME

MEDICINE

THE KILLERS

New viruses and drug-resistant bacteria are reversing human victories over infectious disease

By **MICHAEL D. LEMONICK**

THEY CAN STRIKE ANY-where, anytime. On a cruise ship, in the corner restaurant, in the grass just outside the back door. And anyone can be a carrier: the stranger coughing in the next seat on the bus, the college classmate from a far-off place, even the sweetheart who seems perfect in every way. For wherever we go and whatever we do, we are accosted by invaders from an unseen world. Protozoans, bacteria, viruses—a whole menagerie of microscopic pests constantly assaults every part of our body, looking for a way inside. Many are harmless or easy to fight off. Others—as we are now so often reminded—are merciless killers.

Humanity once had the hubris to think it could control or even conquer all these microbes. But anyone who reads today's headlines knows how vain that hope turned out to be. New scourges are emerging—AIDS is not the only one—and older diseases like tuberculosis are rapidly evolving into forms that are resistant to antibiotics, the main weapon in the doctor's arsenal. The danger is greatest, of course, in the underdeveloped world, where epidemics of cholera, dysentery and malaria are spawned by war, poverty, overcrowding and poor sanitation. But the microbial world knows no bound-

TIME

ALL AROUND

aries. For all the vaunted power of modern medicine, deadly infections are a growing threat to everyone, everywhere. Hardly a week goes by without reports of outbreaks in the U.S. and other developed nations. Some of the latest examples:

■ A Royal Caribbean cruise ship on a trip to Baja California returned early to Los Angeles last week after more than 400 passengers came down with an unidentified intestinal ailment. It may have been the reason one elderly man died. And just a few weeks ago, 1,200 disgruntled passengers were evacuated from the ocean liner *Horizon* in Bermuda because of the threat of Legionnaires' disease. Among customers on previous *Horizon* voyages this summer, there have been 11 confirmed cases of the potentially fatal pneumonia-like illness and 24 suspected cases. At least one victim died.

■ A Yale School of Medicine researcher is recovering from a rare and potentially lethal disease called Sabiá virus. Before 1990, the illness was unknown to medicine. Then a woman in the town of Sabiá, Brazil, died from a mysterious virus that had evidently been circulating in local rodents for years before making an assault on humans. Brazilian doctors sent samples to Yale, and a month ago the scientist became infected when he accidentally broke a container holding the virus. Health officials point out that it is not easily passed between humans, but some 80 people who came into contact with the man have been under observation.

■ More than 850 people have come down with cholera in southern Russia, and officials fear the disease could erupt into an epidemic. Cholera out-

TIME

Some microbes can reproduce in just 20 minutes

VIRUSES

UNLIKE BACTERIA AND PROTOZOANS, WHICH are full-fledged living cells, capable of taking in nourishment and reproducing on their own, viruses are only half alive at best. They consist of little more than a shell of protein and a bit of genetic material (DNA or its chemical cousin RNA), which contains instructions for making more viruses—but no machinery to do the job. In order to reproduce, a virus has to invade a cell, co-opting the cell's own DNA to create a virus factory. The cell—in an animal, a plant or even a bacterium—can be physically destroyed by the viruses it is now helplessly producing. Or it may die as the accumulation of viruses interferes with its ability to take in food.

It is by killing individual cells in the body's all-important immune system that the AIDS virus wreaks its terrible havoc. The virus itself isn't deadly, but it leaves the body defenseless against all sorts of diseases that are. Other viruses, like Ebola, kill immune cells too, but very quickly; the dead cells form massive, deadly blood clots. Still others, hantavirus, for example, trigger a powerful reaction in which immune cells attack both the invading virus and the host's healthy cells.

Unlike bacteria and protozoans, viruses are tough to fight once an infection starts. Most things that will kill a virus will also harm its host cells; thus there are only a few antiviral drugs in existence. Medicine's great weapon against viruses has always been the preventive vaccine. Starting with smallpox in the late 1700s, diseases including rabies, polio, measles and influenza were all tamed by immunization.

But new viruses keep arising to challenge the vaccine makers. They may have

---

Counterattack: How Drugmakers Are Fighting Back

By LEON JAROFF

DOCTORS AND THE PUBLIC WERE NOT ALONE IN FEELING cocky about infectious disease a decade ago. The drug companies did too. More than 100 antibiotics were on the market, and they had most bacterial diseases on the run, if not on the verge of eradication. So rosy was the outlook that U.S. government funding for antibiotic research was declining, and many pharmaceutical firms were focusing on cancer and viral diseases, especially AIDS.

Observes George Miller, a microbiologist at the Schering-Plough Research Institute in Kenilworth, New Jersey: "What we in the pharmaceutical industry had been doing was to take existing classes of antibiotics and modify them to stay one step ahead of the bacteria." But that approach seems no longer able to stem the spread of drug-resistant bacteria.

Instead, researchers are employing several new strategies that they hope will put medicine ahead, at least temporarily, in the battle against the bugs. One approach is "rational" drug design, based on new understanding of how bacteria function at the molecular level. Using the techniques of biochemistry and crystallography, scientists are identifying bacterial genes and enzymes that confer drug resistance, and are creating antibiotics that will act specifically against a targeted microbe.

By discerning the molecular structure of an enzyme used by a drug-resistant bacterium to fight off that drug, for example, scientists can design a molecule that fits precisely into the active site of the enzyme. That neutralizes the enzyme, depriving the bacterium of a crucial element of its defense and making it susceptible once more to the original drug. "It's like sticking a wad of gum into a keyhole and binding it up," says

Fred Cohen, professor of pharmacology at the University of California, San Francisco.

Scientists are pursuing a similar line of attack against viral diseases. In their AIDS research, for example, some are concentrating on a protein called CD-4, which resides on the surface of immune-system T cells where the AIDS virus attacks. Before the virus can enter T cells, it must join with a receptor site on the CD-4 protein. Here, too, a properly designed molecule might block that site and protect the T cell.

Some companies are delving into "combinatorial" chemistry, which involves making Lego-like blocks of chemicals that can be joined in hundreds of thousands of combinations, one or a few of which might create molecular havoc with a particular bacterium.

"Chemists have conceived of ways to build vast libraries of these wonderful combinations of building blocks, concepts that did not exist five or 10 years ago," says Barry Eisenstein, a vice president of the Eli Lilly research labs in Indianapolis, Indiana. Roboticized testing has helped make this approach practical by enabling researchers to screen hundreds of thousands of compounds in just a few months.

CLOSE LOOK Trying to find the chink in a deadly germ's armor, an Eli Lilly scientist studies bacteria that cause cardiac infections

Prevention is even better than cure, and scientists are also experimenting with new vaccines that will ward off infections by alerting and arming the body's immune system against the invaders. One such vaccine is already on the market. It is designed to prevent the ills brought on by pneumococcus, which include sinusitis and ear infections as well as pneumonia.

Scientists are sanguine about regaining the upper hand against infectious disease but now realize that no strategy will work forever. As long as microbes have the ability to neutralize medicine's weapons, the drug companies will have to keep adding to the arsenal. —**Reported by Lawrence Mondi/New York**

TIME

The price of doing nothing will be millions of lives

gone undetected for centuries, inhabiting animal populations that have no contact with mankind. If people eventually encounter the animals—by settling a new part of the rain forest, for example—the virus can have the opportunity to infect a different sort of host.

Scientists believe Ebola virus made just that kind of jump, from monkeys into humans; so did other African viruses such as Marburg and the mysterious X that broke out in Sudan. And many more are likely to emerge. "In the Brazilian rain forest," says Dr. Robert Shope, a Yale epidemiologist, "we know of at least 50 different viruses that have the capacity of making people sick. There are probably hundreds more that we haven't found yet."

Viruses like Ebola and X are scary, but they're too deadly to be much of a threat to the world. Their victims don't have much of a chance to infect others before dying. In contrast, HIV, the AIDS virus—which may have come from African primates as early as the 1950s—is a more subtle killing machine, and thus more of an evolutionary success. An infected person will typically carry HIV for years before symptoms appear. Thus, even though HIV doesn't move easily from one human to another, it has many chances to try. Since the first cases were reported in the late 1970s, HIV has spread around the world to kill perhaps a million people and infect an estimated 17 million.

It isn't just new viruses that have doctors worried. Perhaps the most ominous prospect of all is a virulent strain of influenza. Even garden-variety flu can be deadly to the very old, the very young and those with weak immune systems. But every so often, a highly lethal strain emerges usually from domesticated swine in Asia. Unlike HIV, flu moves through the air and is highly contagious. The last killer strain showed up in 1918 and claimed 20 million lives—more than all the combat deaths in World War I. And that was before global air travel; the next outbreak could be even more devastating.

Vaccines should, in theory, work just as well for new varieties of disease as they do for old ones. In practice, they often don't. An HIV vaccine has proved difficult to develop because the virus is prone to rapid mutations. These don't affect its deadliness but do change its chemistry enough to keep the immune system from recognizing the pathogen.

Creating a vaccine for each strain of flu isn't exactly simple either. "First," says Yale's Shope, "we have to discover something new is happening. Then we have to find a manufacturer willing to make a vaccine. Then the experts have to meet and decide what goes into the vaccine. Then the factory has to find enough hens' eggs in which to grow the vaccine. There are just a lot of logistical concerns."

People are partly to blame for letting

KILLER FLU Seattle police wore protective masks during the pandemic of 1918-19, in which 20 million died

new viruses enter human populations. Says Dr. Peter Jahrling, senior research scientist at the U.S. Army Medical Research Institute of Infectious Diseases: "If you're a monkey imported from the Philippines, your first stop when you hit this country is a quarantine facility. If you're a free-ranging adult human being, you just go through the metal detector and you're on your way."

Sometimes environmental changes help microbes move from animals to humans. Lyme disease, a bacterial infection, was largely confined to deer and wild mice until people began converting farmland into wooded suburbs—which provided equally good habitats for the animals and the bacteria-infested ticks they carry and also brought them into contact with large numbers of people. The mice that transmit the hantavirus often take refuge in farmers' fields, barns and even homes. Air-conditioning ducts create a perfect breeding ground for Legionnaires' dis-

ease bacteria. Irrigation ditches and piles of discarded tires are ideal nesting spots for the *Aedes aegypti* mosquito, carrier of dengue and yellow fevers; imported used tires have already brought the Asian tiger mosquito, also a carrier of dengue, into the U.S.

Clearly there is no way to prevent human exposure to microbes. But the risks can be reduced. To minimize bacterial resistance, for example, doctors can be stingier with antibiotics. "We've been careless," says Dr. Robert Daum, a University of Chicago pediatrician. "Every childhood fever does not require antibiotics." Nor does a healthy farm animal.

Most important is increased vigilance by public-health authorities. The faster a new microbe can be identified and its transmission slowed, the less likely a small outbreak will turn into an epidemic. Unfortunately, the trend has been in the other direction. "Even in the U.S.," says Thomson Prentice of the World Health Organization in Geneva, "disease-monitoring expertise has been lost, either through cost-cutting or reduced diligence. If some of the edge has been lost in the U.S., just imagine how poorer countries have reacted."

American health officials are convinced that their information-gathering network must be strengthened. That has begun to happen under a new program that will, among other things, increase the surveillance of new microbes and educate both health workers and the public about how to deal with emerging diseases.

An all-out effort to monitor diseases, vaccinate susceptible groups, improve health conditions around the world, develop new drugs and get information to the public would be enormously expensive. But the price of doing nothing may be measured in millions of lost lives. Doctors are still hopeful but no longer overconfident. "I do believe that we're intelligent enough to keep ahead of things," says epidemiologist Shope. Nonetheless, neither he nor any of his colleagues will ever again be foolish enough to declare victory in the war against the microbes. —*Reported by J. Madeleine Nash/Chicago, Alice Park/New York, Mia Schmiedeskamp/Washington and Andrew Purvis/Nairobi, with other bureaus*

TIME

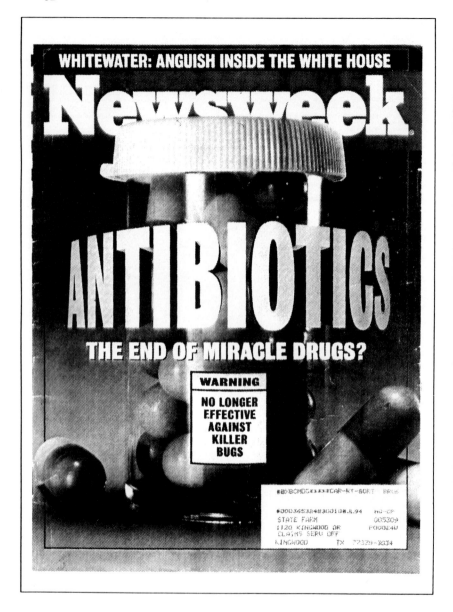

Newsweek

Articles and information from Newsweek Magazine are reproduced with written permission.

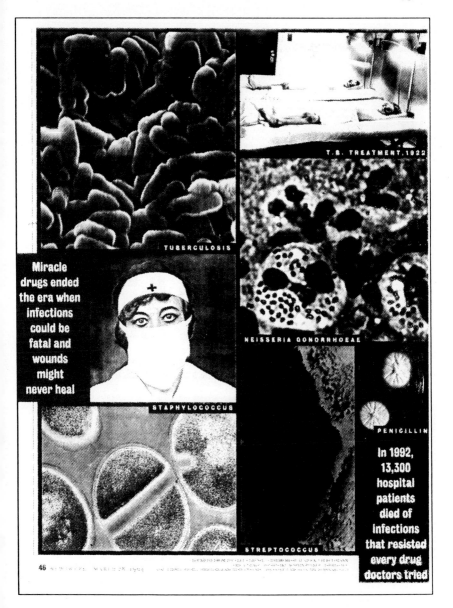

TUBERCULOSIS

T.B. TREATMENT.1922

NEISSERIA GONORRHOEAE

Miracle drugs ended the era when infections could be fatal and wounds might never heal

STAPHYLOCOCCUS

PENICILLIN

STREPTOCOCCUS

In 1992, 13,300 hospital patients died of infections that resisted every drug doctors tried

Newsweek

84

S O C I E T Y

NOTHING WORKED. FOR NINE MONTHS DR. CYN-
thia Gilbert desperately tried one antibiotic after
another on her 57-year-old kidney patient, but no
matter which tablets, capsules or even IVs she
gave him – from plain-vanilla ampicillin to fancy
experimental teicoplanin – the man's blood was
still flooded with enterococcus bacteria, which
were slowly poisoning his red blood cells. "We
tried six or seven different medications. Some
alone. Some in combination. Some we didn't think would work.
But we had nothing else to try," says Gilbert, an infectious-disease
specialist at the Veterans Affairs Medical Center in Washington.
Sometimes her patient's blood tested clean, but within days the
infection came roaring back: a few rogue bacteria, no more
threatened by the antibiotics than an urban gang by a pop gun.

pneumonia, septicemia (blood poisoning), syphilis, gonorrhea and
other bacterial infections that hark back to a time of high-button
shoes were vanquished. Yes, people died – and still die – from these
ills, but not so many, and not those who began antibiotics before the
microbes wrecked some vital system. "The perception [in the 1980s]
was that we had conquered almost every infectious disease," says
Dr. Thomas Beam of the Buffalo, N.Y., VA Medical Center. Science
was sure the real challenges would lie in the conquest of cancer,
heart disease and other chronic ailments. Instead, "medicine's
purported triumph over infectious disease has become an illusion,"
writes Dr. Sherwin Nuland in his best-selling "How We Die."

Indeed, it looks like medicine declared victory and went home
too soon. Every disease-causing bacterium now has versions that
resist at least one of medicine's 100-plus antibiotics. Some resist
all but one (chart, page 48). Drug-resistant tuberculosis now ac-

The End of Antibiotics

SCIENCE THOUGHT IT HAD VANQUISHED INFECTIOUS DISEASES. BUT NOW THE BUGS ARE FIGHTING BACK.

bided their time until their more vulnerable cousins had been killed. Then
they multiplied by the billions. So one
morning last year, Gilbert gathered her courage and walked softly
into the man's room. "I guess you're coming to tell me I'm dying,"
he said. Nothing had worked, she explained, they had run out of
options. Antibiotics, the miracle drugs of the 20th century, had
been bested by bacteria, the most primitive organisms on earth.
Several days later the man died of a massive bacterial infection of
the blood and heart

Ever since 1928, when Alexander Fleming serendipitously discovered penicillin oozing out of mold in a laboratory dish, "man and
microbe have been in a footrace," says Dr. Richard Wenzel of the
University of Iowa. It's a race in which the lead keeps changing. In
1946, just five years after penicillin came into wide use with World
War II, doctors discovered staphylococcus that was invulnerable to
the drug. No problem: smart pharmacologists invented or discovered (often in samples of soil they collected like souvenirs whenever
they visited exotic locales) new antibiotics. The drugs pounded the
microbes into submission once again. But the bacteria regrouped,
and mutants capable of fending off the latest drugs appeared. New
drugs, newer mutants. And so it went. Overall the drugs retained a
slight lead and, slowly, scourges such as tuberculosis, bacterial

BY SHARON BEGLEY

counts for one in seven new cases; 5
percent of those patients are dying.
Several resistant strains of pneumo-
coccus, the microbe responsible for infected surgical wounds and
some children's ear infections and meningitis, appeared in South
Africa in the 1970s, spread to Europe and now are turning up in the
United States. In January the federal Centers for Disease Control
and Prevention (CDC) reported an epidemic of resistant pneumococcus in rural Kentucky and in Memphis. The bugs had spread
through day-care centers like a chain letter, leaving toddlers with
ear infections, pneumonia and, in six cases, meningitis. In 1992,
13,300 hospital patients died of bacterial infections that resisted
the antibiotics doctors fired at them, says the CDC. It was not that
they had infections immune to every single drug but rather that, by
the time doctors found an antibiotic that worked, the rampaging
bacteria had poisoned the patient's blood, scarred the lungs or
crippled some other vital organ

The financial toll is steep, too. Because the first antibiotic
prescribed often fails, the patient has to try several; this adds
some $100 million to $200 million to the nation's health-care tab.
"Right now the microorganisms are winning," says Iowa's Wenzel.
"They're so much older than we are – and wiser."

They are indeed wise, especially in the ways of evolution. Bacteria

MARCH 28, 1994 NEWSWEEK **47**

Newsweek

Since then, resistance has spread.

DRUG-RESISTANT MICROBES

Only a few years after penicillin came into wide use with World War II, strains of staph had emerged that were immune to the drug. Since then, resistance has spread.

MICROBE	DISEASES CAUSED	ANTIBIOTICS THAT NO LONGER WORK
Enterococcus	Blood poisoning, surgical infections	Aminoglycosides, cephalosporins, erythromycin, penicillins, tetracycline, vancomycin
Haemophilus influenzae	Meningitis, ear infections, pneumonia, sinusitis	Chloramphenicol, penicillins, tetracycline, trimethoprim/sulfamethoxazole
Mycobacterium tuberculosis	Tuberculosis	Aminoglycosides, ethambutol, isoniazid, pyrazinamide, rifampin
Neisseria gonorrhoeae	Gonorrhea	Penicillins, spectinomycin, tetracycline
Plasmodium falciparum	Malaria	Chloroquine
Shigella dysenteriae	Severe diarrhea	Ampicillin, chloramphenicol, tetracycline, trimethoprim/sulfamethoxazole
Staphylococcus aureus	Blood poisoning, pneumonia, surgical infections	All but vancomycin
Streptococcus pneumoniae	Meningitis, pneumonia	Aminoglycosides, cephalosporins, chloramphenicol, erythromycin, penicillins, tetracycline, trimethoprim/sulfamethoxazole

develop resistance to antibiotics for the same Darwinian reason that gazelles evolved speed in response to lions. When a colony of bacteria is dosed with, say, penicillin, most die. But a few lucky microbes, by chance, harbor mutant genes that make them immune to the drug. They survive, just as speedy gazelles lived to romp another day, while their slower-footed herd mates became dinner. The mutants pass on their resistance genes to their progeny – one bacterium can leave 16,777,220 offspring within 24 hours. Even more insidious, the mutants gladly share their resistance gene with unrelated microbes. In one version, a microbe exudes a come-hither chemical, attracting another bacterium; when the two touch, they open pores and exchange a loop of DNA called a plasmid in a process that can only be called unsafe bacterial sex (diagram, page 49). Through this sort of coupling, cholera bacteria picked up resistance to tetracycline from plain old *E. coli* in the human intestine. So while antibiotics did not create resistance genes, the drugs fast-forwarded their spread. "Antibiotic usage has stimulated evolutionary changes unparalleled in recorded biologic history," writes Dr. Stuart Levy of Tufts University in his 1992 book "The Antibiotic Paradox."

Even more ominous, there are signs that bacteria are "clever little devils," as microbiologist Stanley Falkow of Stanford University puts it, in ways scientists never suspected. It turns out that the germs can become resistant to antibiotics they never even met. In women receiving tetracycline for a urinary-tract infection, for instance, E. coli developed resistance not only to tetracycline but to other antibiotics, too. "It is almost as if bacteria strategically anticipate the confrontation of other drugs when they resist one," says Levy. How did we get into this bind? In their eagerness to finish off the old diseases, doctors and patients have,

paradoxically, given them new life. Patients demand antibiotics for viral infections, like colds, that antibiotics cannot touch; every dose of antibiotics makes it that much easier for resistance to spread. Also, doctors sometimes dispense antibiotics without knowing whether the sore throat, or even the pneumonia, is indeed caused by bacteria (page 50).

For sheer overprescription, no doctor can touch the American farmer. Farm animals receive 30 times more antibiotics (mostly penicillins and tetracyclines) than people do. The drugs treat and prevent infections. But the main reason farmers like them is that they also make cows, hogs and chickens grow faster from each pound of feed. Resistant strains emerge just as they do in humans taking antibiotics and remain in the animal's flesh even after it winds up in the meat case. Many salmonella strains in turkey, for instance, are resistant to several common antibiotics. Although high heat kills them, the superbugs spread from animals to people through raw or undercooked meat. (People on antibiotics are particularly vulnerable: the drugs kill off susceptible strains in the intestinal tract, leaving the field wide open for infection by resistant strains.) At least 500 people in the United States die annually from microbes present in meat and poultry; among them were the three children who ate E. coli-infested hamburger at Jack-in-the-Box restaurants last year. An additional 6.5 million people fall ill.

The threat could be even greater to those who down a milkshake with their burger. Milk is allowed to contain a certain concentration of 80 different antibiotics all used on dairy cows to prevent udder infections. With every glassful, people swallow a minute amount of several antibiotics. The U.S. Food and Drug Administration sets limits on how much of the 80 antibiotics milk can contain, and insists that the less than 1 percent of milk that violates these limits is dumped. But a 1992 study by Congress's General Accounting Office found that states test for only four of the federally regulated antibiotics. The GAO's own tests discovered traces of

TUFTS' LEVY EXAMINES THE ENEMY

The rise of drug-resistant germs is 'unparalleled in recorded biologic history'

Newsweek

86

64 antibiotics at levels "that raise health concerns"; they could produce resistant germs in milk drinkers. That may be understating the case. In a recent study at Rutgers University, antibiotics at levels deemed safe by the FDA increased the rate at which resistant bacteria emerged by 600 to 2,700 percent.

The drug residues are likely to increase now that genetic engineering has taken hold on the back 40. The FDA recently approved bovine growth hormone (rBGH), which is produced through gene splicing and increases milk production. But BGH also raises the incidence of udder infection and, with it, the need to give the cows antibiotics. And the FDA is about to hold hearings on whether the biotech company Calgene may market a tomato containing a gene that confers resistance to the antibiotic kanamycin. The announced benefit: a tomato that will stay fresh longer. But environmental groups warn that the resistance gene will be taken up by bacteria in people's stomachs and intestines, breeding still more invulnerable bugs.

If there is a lurking Andromeda Strain in all this, it is *Staphylococcus aureus*, the bacterium responsible for some pneumonias and, most worrisome, for blood poisoning in surgical wounds. Some 40 percent of staph in hospitals are resistant to every antibiotic but one, vancomycin. "We know at some point vancomycin will succumb and the bacteria will grow and proliferate unrestrained," worries the VA's Beam. "It will be like the 1950s and 1960s, when we had nothing to treat this infection, and the mortality rates were as high as 80 percent." In those decades, thousands of people each year died of staph infections.

Researchers even have a good hunch how that supermicrobe will be created. The culprit will likely be enterococcus, the blood-poisoning microbe that killed Gilbert's patient. About 20 percent of enterococcal infections in hospitals are resistant to vancomycin, says Barry Kreiswirth of New York's Public Health Research Institute. The number is rising: in 1989, only one hospital in New York reported vancomycin-resistant enterococcus; in 1991, 38 did. The following year, a British researcher showed that the gene for this resistance can travel from enterococcus to S. aureus. The finding was so terrifying that the researcher immediately destroyed all his stocks of vancomycin-resistant staph – but microbiologists have no doubt that the transfer of vancomycin resistance will happen in some hospital, somewhere, soon. "Bacteria have their own Internet," says Stanford's Falkow, swapping plasmids the way humans exchange E-mail. Once staph gets the gene for vancomycin resistance, warns Dr. Richard Roberts of Cornell Medical School, "we will really, really have a problem. Vancomycin is the last line."

Won't the next miracle drug save us? Until the mid-1980s, pharmaceutical companies always had another antibiotic in the wings. But then it began to look as if most bacterial infections were fading away with the millennium. The domestic antibiotic market was saturated and the only emerging market seemed to be in the developing world, with its cholera and dysentery and other ills that modern sanitation had banished elsewhere. Comparatively few Third World citizens can lay out $100 for the latest pill. Many of the big pharmaceutical firms stopped looking for the next penicillin. Even the government got complacent: federal funds for antibiotics research dwindled. "There hasn't been any support of [basic antibiotic research] by the government in the last 20 years," says Dr. George Miller, head of infectious-disease research at Schering-Plough. As a result, in 1990, the FDA approved one new antibiotic; in 1991, five; in 1992, three; last year . . . one.

Some companies, at least, are scrambling to catch up with a race of microbes that has sprinted at least five years ahead of the ability to control them. One strategy is to better understand how bacteria fight off antibiotics. The microbes defend themselves in several ways (diagram). They can secrete an enzyme that dismembers the drug, as staph does to neutralize penicillins. They can change their cell walls so antibiotics cannot get in, or alter some other site that the drug attacks. Enterococcus does this to foil erythromycin. Or, the microbes simply pump out the drug, which is how E. coli resist tetracycline. The first oral antibiotic to foil a superbug is Smith-Kline Beecham's Augmentin. Along with a form of penicillin, it contains a chemical that knocks out the enzyme that resistant

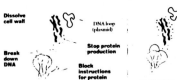

LIVES OF A BUG

Antibiotics attack bacteria in several ways, such as dissolving cell walls. But sometimes, by chance, a bacterium acquires a trait that fights back against the antibiotic, making the microbe resistant to the drug.

Dissolve cell wall

Break down DNA

DNA loop (plasmid)

Stop protein production

Block instructions for protein synthesis

Ordinary cell   Resistant cell

Resistance gene

Antibiotic attack: When it works, the drug can destroy the germ's cell wall, or wreck its ability to produce life-sustaining proteins.

Superbug: If a bacterium develops a genetic mutation, it can strengthen its cell wall to keep the antibiotic out, break apart the drug or protect its genes and protein-making machinery.

filament

Breeding resistance: The resistant bacterium sends out a filament to another bacterium, pulling it in.

The resistant microbe makes a copy of the loop of DNA that contains the gene for resistance.

When the two bacteria touch, the resistant one transfers the extra loop of DNA through its cell wall, into the other microbe.

The second bacterium is now resistant to the antibiotic, and can transfer that resistance to its own progeny and to other bacteria.

SOURCE: STUART LEVY, TUFTS UNIVERSITY MEDICAL SCHOOL   DIAGRAM: BUMRICH, NEWSWEEK

bacteria deploy to neutralize the drug. But three years ago a strain of E. coli learned to make a new penicillin-slaying enzyme. This left Augmentin ineffective against those E. coli (though it still kills other bacteria) and raised the specter that E. coli might transfer its resistance to other bacteria. That's why trying to cripple bacteria's defenses, says Miller, "will not do much more than buy us five to 10 years."

In the past, pharmaceutical companies typically found new antibiotics by chance. Employees traveling to exotic climes were asked to bring back samples of dirt, which chemists back at headquarters would screen for antibiotics churned out by the soil microbes. In the 1980s, the companies adopted a new approach: with "rational drug design," they would build antibiotics from the bottom up, molecule by molecule. But now it's back to nature. The companies are searching everywhere from the bottom of the sea to the jungles of Borneo for the next bacteria-killing compound.

Newsweek

S O C I E T Y

A better strategy might be to abandon antibiotics altogether in favor of different kinds of drugs. Resistance can affect a bacterium's ability to make a living, rendering it more vulnerable to temperature extremes or to acidity, for instance. "A drug-resistant bacterium is always at a competitive disadvantage," says Dr. Lee Green, a family practitioner at the University of Michigan. Maybe researchers can hit some bugs where they hurt through a drug that, say, increases the acidity in the intestine. Researchers are also looking for chemicals that can prevent the multiplication of plasmids, those E-mail messages of the microbial world, and for decoy molecules that can lure away the bacteria's killer enzyme and so allow the antibiotic to sneak in. Alternatively, vaccines might work against bacteria – there is already a vaccine against pneumococcus. But research on vaccines against strep and staph is nearly nonexistent. Why? "My gut feeling is vaccines aren't really big revenue generators," says Thomas Salzmann, vice president of chemical research at Merck.

Or maybe what we need is not more technological fixes, but some plain common sense. Like not tossing the hand grenade of powerful antibiotics at the mosquito of a minor infection. Like

Too Much of a Good Thing

FROM OVERPRESCRIBING TO SATISFYING PATIENTS WHO COMPLAIN TOO MUCH, DOCTORS ARE NOW PART OF THE ANTIBIOTIC PROBLEM

BY GEOFFREY COWLEY

LIKE ANY INTERNIST, DR. Robert Moellering of Boston's Deaconess Hospital has felt the pressure to hand out antibiotics on demand. When he served as director of student health services at Emerson College, he saw a steady stream of students with colds and flus, and many knew just which drug they wanted. Instead of dashing off prescriptions, Moellering would dutifully explain that their ailments were caused by viruses, and that no antibiotic — however new or expensive — can kill a virus. His campaign didn't get very far. As he now recalls, the kids would return days later waving bottles of pills in his face. "They'd tell me, 'My doctor said I almost had pneumonia'."

If the golden age of antibiotics is ending, the reasons should be no mystery. Bacteria gradually adapt to any antibiotic, and when one is misused, its power to heal is squandered. "If I give my patient too much hypertensive medicine, I might hurt that patient but there's no way I'm going to hurt the next patient," says Dr. Frank Rhame, director of infection control at the University of Minnesota Hospital and Clinic. "If I use an antibiotic too much, I'm making it less useful for everyone." Unfortunately, doctors have been slow to act on that

insight. Confronted with a miserable patient, they tend to write a prescription. Antibiotic sales are a result (sales have nearly doubled since the mid-1980s), and so are drug-resistant infections.

The misuse of antibiotics isn't a new problem. Since the 1970s, various studies have concluded that 50 to 60 percent of all outpatient prescriptions are inappropriate. Other studies have found that seven in 10 Americans receive antibiotics when they seek treatment for common colds. "Essentially," says Dr. Lee Green, a family practitioner at the University of Michigan, "we have a tradition of prescribing antibiotics to anybody who looks sick."

ANTIBIOTICS SALES

To drugstores and hospitals*

IN BILLIONS OF DOLLARS					5.6
			5.4	5.2	
		4.7			
	4.2				
$3.7					
1988	1989	1990	1991	1992	1993

*EXCLUDING SALES TO HMOS, CLINICS, ETC.
SOURCE: IMS AMERICA

There's plenty of blame to go around. As Moellering has learned in Boston, Americans like quick fixes, and when a doctor doesn't offer one, they look for a doctor who will. Patients aren't the only culprits. When insurance companies fail to cover bacterial tests, they encourage sloppy prescribing. Drug companies, for their part, promote the use of their products by advertising them widely and supplying doctors with free samples. Experts in health policy agree that the latest patented medications, which can cost 10 times as much as older generics, should be reserved for uniquely stubborn infections. "The more widely you use these newer antibiotics," says Dr. David Kessler, commissioner of the U.S. Food and Drug Administration, "the greater the chances that [bacteria] will develop resistance." But when a manufacturer touts a new product as a high-octane alternative that every patient deserves, doctors can feel duty-bound to prescribe it. "It's another form of defensive medicine," says Dr. Thomas O'Brien of Harvard.

Even when doctors dispense antibiotics properly, there is no guarantee they'll be used that way. Studies suggest that a third of all patients fail to use the drugs as prescribed. Many stop taking their medication after just a few days, when it has killed the most susceptible invaders but left hardened survivors to flourish. Besides being

harder to treat, those resistant germs can then spread through the community. Besides quitting treatment early, some patients save unused drugs to take later, or pass them around

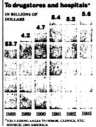

LOOKING FOR SIGNS OF INFECTION

Americans like quick fixes. When a doctor doesn't prescribe an antibiotic, they look for one who will.

like vitamins. "I've heard of people on trips who take a fellow traveler's antibiotic, thinking it will protect them from illness," says Dr. Stuart Levy of Tufts University. "It just causes widespread resistance."

Drug-resistant microbes don't threaten us all equally. A healthy immune system easily repels most bacterial invaders, regardless of their susceptibility to drugs. But when resistant bugs take hold among the

Newsweek

otating antibiotics to roll back resistance by allowing weaker germs to re-establish themselves. Like limiting the use of antibiotics in agriculture. Like insisting that doctors and nurses and even orderlies use antiseptic on their hands before treating or touching a patient, a sheet, a gurney. Like giving some antibiotics a well-deserved rest: "If we do, we know we'll see a re-emergence of vulnerable strains," says Dr. Richard Duma, head of the National Foundation for Infectious Diseases.

Antibiotics, more than anything else cooked up in biomedical labs, have led 20th-century medicine out of an era when women died during childbirth because of blood poisoning, when children's ear infections metamorphosed into fatal meningitis, when simple wounds turned lethally septic. Modern sanitation and better understanding of disease ensure that we will not return to those days. But already patients are suffering and dying from illnesses that science predicted 40 years ago would be wiped off the face of the earth. The scientists were wrong. Before science catches up with the microbes, many more people will die.

With MARCUS BRANT in New York and PAT WINGERT and MARY HAGER in Washington

weak, the sick or the elderly, they're hellishly hard to control. "I believe resistant infections are present in every hospital and nursing home," says Dr. Thomas Beam of the Buffalo, N.Y., VA Medical Center. The only question is whether he institution is releasing that information." In the past 18 months alone, Beam has seen il patients stricken with drug-resistant *Staphylococcus aur-*

already," says Dr. David Shlaes of Cleveland's Case Western Reserve University, "the only way to keep it out is to screen patients and keep [carriers] in some kind of holding center until you treat them." Last month officials at the VA nursing home in Sioux Falls, S.D., quarantined half of the facility's 42 residents to control an outbreak of drug-resistant staph. Two of

whose infections were confined to the urinary tract, where drugs can be used in high concentrations. Though they're concentrated in hospitals and nursing homes, the superbugs aren't confined to such settings. Out in the community, many bacterial diseases are becoming ever harder to treat. Some 20 percent of the nation's gonorrhea is now resistant to one or

lating in their communities the Centers for Disease Control and Prevention now encourages local health officials to conduct regular surveys for drug resistance. Meanwhile the World Health Organization is funding a global computer database that doctors can use to report drug-resistant outbreaks. Surveillance alone won't stop the erosion of the wonder drugs. "The

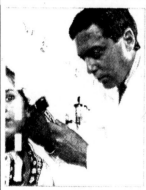

WORKING TO CONTAIN DRUG-RESISTANT TB

Antibiotic sales have soared in recent years, but the drugs that doctors prescribe are often inappropriate

us, a microbe that infects surgical wounds and can cause pneumonia and systemic blood infections. Twelve of those infections have been lethal.

Penicillin and tetracycline lost their power over staph back in the 1950s and '60s. Another antibiotic, methicillin, provided a backup for a while, but methicillin-resistant staph is now common in hospitals and nursing homes worldwide. If it's not in your hospital

them are still in isolation. Like staph infections, bugs known as enterococci flourish among weak and elderly hospital patients. Shlaes recalls that when a resistant strain of enterococci took hold in a Pittsburgh liver-transplant unit, 50 people were infected over the course of two years. The only survivors were patients whose infected tissues could be removed surgically (a trick from the pre-antibiotic era), or

more antibiotics. A similar proportion of TB now resists the drug isoniazid. As any doctor who has spent a winter throwing one drug after another at a toddler's ear infection can tell you, resistance is common in other bugs as well. But because the government doesn't track drug resistance, clinicians rarely know when to expect it.

To give doctors a better sense of what germs are circu-

classic response has been to develop new and more powerful antibiotics," says Moellering. With luck and perseverance, scientists will discover unimagined new weapons. But the immediate challenge is to get doctors, and patients, to stop abusing the weapons we still have.

With JOHN F. LAUERMAN in Boston, KAREN SPRINGEN in Chicago and MARY HAGER and PAT WINGERT in Washington

Newsweek

CHAPTER 7
MILD SILVER PROTEIN
AND THE AIDS EPIDEMIC

Ever since the early 1980's, both Americans and people all over the world have been bombarded with horror stories concerning the AIDS Epidemic. We've not been able to pick up a newspaper or magazine, or turn on the evening news or listen to the radio without being *frightened out of our wits* by the news of the imminent and impending disaster which has befallen mankind with this scourge called AIDS (Acquired Immune Deficiency Syndrome). Some of the information has been true, some has been false, and much has been exaggerated. But the fact remains that as many as 1.02 million people could be infected; and since the early 1980's, over 202,000 people have died.

There have been numerous scientific studies which indicate that we may have brought this disaster upon ourselves through our own manipulation of nature. Perhaps it is true that the virus came from our research on vaccinations with the Simian green monkey or perhaps not. At one time scientists thought it was only those with a homosexual lifestyle or the Haitians or drug users that spread the disease. Now we see on the cover of

LIFE Magazine (and many other publications) that no one is safe, from a little baby to a heterosexual. I could write an entire book on AIDS and perhaps someday in the near future, by the Grace of God, I will. I think I'll title it "The Forest For The Trees". However, for now let us not concern ourselves whether the green monkey or one's lifestyle brought on the epidemic. The fact of the matter is *that it is here, spreading, people are dying and many have died.* The fact remains that in spite of all the attempts by the greatest of scientific institutions and the medical profession, no cure has been found and we are *not able to kill the AIDS virus* or stop the destruction of the immune system which allows opportunistic diseases to kill.

With all of our computers, research laboratories and modern technology we have been found lacking and helpless. It is no wonder that the world is in a state of shock and fear. At the present time we find ourselves subject to a disease which we cannot cure, stop or prevent. From a psychological point of view, this all adds up to a state of *helplessness, confusion and despair.* And dwelling on this dilemma can only lead to further despair and hopelesssness. How marvelous it would be if the answer was right under our noses and we have not been able to "see the forest for the trees," because we have been looking everywhere except in our own back yard.

There is a story about a man who left his secure yet humble home to go off to Africa in search of diamonds. He left with youth, vigor and enthusiasm in search of his fortune. However, many misfortunes happened to him along the way. He ended up losing his wife and family as well as almost all his wealth...and his mind. Finally at 80 years old and in a state of despair and defeat, he decided to return to his home. He was by now very lame and crippled, hardly being able to move about. All his vigor and strength had been sapped out of him in this fruitless search for the precious gems. He never found the diamonds and was now a decrepit and poverty-stricken old man.

Finally, by sheer effort he reached the stairs to the porch of his old house, just to see it one more time, though he no longer owned it. The years and the elements had taken their toll and the wood was rotten and weak. As he reached the peak of the steps and climbed onto the porch, it collapsed and he fell into the shaft of an old mine which he did not know existed. When he recovered his balance, he looked around in *utter amazement*. He had discovered an old, abandoned diamond mine and he could see the gems glittering in the sunlight as it rushed through the holes which he had made in the porch floor.

He became so excited and was so overwhelmed at his discovery and all the *wealth* it could bring, that his blood pressure rose too rapidly. He had been so weakened by the years of struggle and defeat, that he had a heart attack and died. He had finally discovered his diamond mine but it was *too late* and couldn't do him any good.

Had he simply looked in his own yard before taking off in various directions in his fruitless pursuits, he might have enjoyed his wealth, along with his wife, his family, his youth and his health. This is what I feel about Mild Silver Protein and the scourge of AIDS.

I'd like to quote an article on AIDS which appeared in the Houston Post on Tuesday, December 14, 1993. It is a reasonably accurate assessment on the impact of this dreaded invader on the world. I will then explain what I believe is the *ANSWER* to the eradication of the AIDS epidemic, a solution which has been "under our noses" since the early 1900's, followed by scientific documentation to prove that my assertions are well founded. Finally I will present a potential *methodology* to end the epidemic.

AIDS SURVEY REDUCES ESTIMATE OF INFECTION
550,000 Carry Virus, CDC Figure
Likely Too High, Study Says
(The Houston Post, Tuesday December 16, 1993)

ASSOCIATED PRESS, WASHINGTON - The first nationwide survey of AIDS infections conservatively estimates about 550,000 Americans carry the virus, which is considerably less than previous government estimates.

The new figures, released Monday, represent the first attempt to estimate the scope of AIDS infection in the United States by directly testing ordinary Americans. They were based on a randomly chosen sample of 7,992 households and compiled by the National Center for Health Statistics.

The most widely accepted estimate of AIDS infections has been compiled by the U. S. Centers for Disease Control and Prevention. It projects that about one million Americans are infected, a number that remained virtually unchanged since the mid-1980's. In fact, the researchers who conducted the latest survey said theirs is a conservative estimate because it covered only people who live at home, not prisoners, the homeless or hospitalized patients. In addition, young men in the study were slightly less likely than other participants to allow their blood to be drawn for AIDS testing, and this too could have led to an underestimation of the infections.

Dr. Geraldine McQuillian, a well known epideminologist with the center who presented the new data at a medical meeting, said the CDC figures have overestimated the extent of the epidemic in the past, but they might not be far off because of the size of the new survey's margin of error. The true number, based on the new survey, could range anywhere from 300,000 to 1.02 million, she said.

The data came from a massive, ongoing survey of every aspect of American Health, called the National Health and Nutritional Examination Survey, which is scheduled to end next December.

High-risk people at drug clinics or prisons, as opposed to the general population, have been studied extensively, but the center did not include those previous studies in the calculations. That means the 550,000 estimate probably "is on the low side," said center spokeswoman Sandra Smith.

"The new study," McQuillian said, "implies the epidemic is slowly increasing in the general population. It is not exploding."

McQuillan's interpretation suggests that earlier estimates were inflated.

As of September 1, almost 400,000 AIDS cases have been reported to the CDC since the epidemic began in the early 1980's and about 202,000 people have died of the disease.

Of the early 8,000 tested, 29 people were found to carry HIV, the AIDS virus. This works out to just over one third of one percent of all Americans.

Blacks were four times more likely than whites and three times more likely than Mexican Americans to be infected, according to the sample. The highest infection rate was among black men between ages 18 and 39. The survey found that 2.5 % of them carried the virus.

I sincerely believe that the latest facts indicate that

we are involved in a full-blown AIDS EPIDEMIC that is on a gradual increase and shows no sign of subsiding. It has probably killed more than the 202,000 estimate, as there are probably many cases that have not been reported or been misdiagnosed. We must also realize that these figures are based only upon surveys in the United States. It is possible that if we were to have accurate data from around the world, including Third World Countries, that possibly five times that amount (a million people) have died a horrible, painful, agonizing and humiliating death. The amount of emotional loss to the family members, as well as the loss of human resources and the loss of money used *unsuccessfully* to treat these people (and to try and find a cure), is staggering to the imagination.

It is estimated that $15-20 billion is spent on AIDS related treatment and research in the United States *annually*, with *totally negative results*. In addition to all of this, there is not an *inkling of hope* nor a hint of a possible cure despite the best of efforts and intentions. This staggering amount of human suffering and loss seems inconsistent to a modern, highly technical society with the degree of *scientific resources which we have at our disposal*.

THIS IS TRULY A PLAGUE OF BIBLICAL PROPORTIONS

It was not my original intent in this publication to find and publish an answer for AIDS. I was specifically searching for a potential answer for both Lyme Disease and systemic Candida Albicans Yeast Infection, from which I was suffering. Fortunately, I have never been afflicted with AIDS. However, prior to being bitten by the tick which carries the spirochete which causes Lyme Disease, I was (for humanitarian purposes) vigorously researching for the AIDS cure (please read the section on the *AIDS letters* which I wrote while searching for a cure; in fact, at that time the answer that I found involved *supersaturating* the body with oxygen, which is still theoretically correct, as demonstrated by reported cases in which this type of treatment has been successful). The AIDS virus is anaerobic, which means that it cannot live in the presence of *oxygen*.

In the final analysis, after having been bitten by the tick and contracting Lyme Disease and becoming *deathly ill* from this and the subsequent yeast infection, my time, energy and attention were diverted to this most pressing situation. It is said that "The Lord works in mysterious ways," and I believe it. Little did I realize that while I was finding an answer for Lyme Disease and Candida Albicans Yeast Infection (the second and third largest epidemics in the world), that I would simultaneously be led in the direction of a *potential answer* for the largest epidemic in the world which is AIDS, if only the establishment and the people can see and acknowledge this discovery and put it into usage.

When, in my scientific research, I was fortunate enough to come across the "Dead Sea Scrolls of Modern Medicine (a compilation of the lost and forgotten Silver research from 1900-1938)," I was also fortunate to discover a more recent study which was conducted on December 30, 1992 at perhaps one of the most renowned Medical Research facilities in the world. The study is copyrighted by Academic Press, Inc. and can be obtained for a minimum fee (its copyright number is 0006-291X/92).

This *impeccable scientific study* only served to confirm my own theory that since Mild Silver Protein kills all viruses as well as bacteria, then it would have to kill the HIV virus also (by suffocating it). It should be noted that *until now there has been no known antibiotic or substance that will kill a virus*. All previous antibiotics can kill many bacterial organisms, but there is no known cure for viruses for humans or animals.

It must also be remembered that the ability to kill the

HIV virus is only the *first step* in the healing process. For individuals who truly have the virus and are not ill, such as Magic Johnson, the Mild Silver Protein would completely prevent the possibility of this becoming an illness. In the event that a person is treated with AZT or some other harsh drug, recent research demonstrates that this type of treatment could lead to the symptoms of AIDS and even death (if left untreated, they may never have gotten ill to begin with).

In cases where people are already ill and are suffering from the symptoms of AIDS, killing the HIV virus is *only the first step.* It then becomes necessary to *rebuild the immune system,* utilizing methods discussed in this book (this subject will be pursued at length in the aforementioned upcoming book "The Forest For The Trees").

The following study is extremely enlightening:

SILVER CYSTEINE KILLS (HIV) VIRUS

Vol. 189, No. 3, 1992
December 30, 1992 Pages 1444-1449
Biochemical and Bioresearch
Communications

Cysteine Protects Na, K-ATPase and Isolated Human Lymohocytes from Silver Toxicity

Saber Hussain 1, Rolf M. Anner 2
and Beatrice M. Anner

1 Laboratory of Experimental Therapeutics, Division of Clinical Pharmacology, Geneva University Medical Center, CH-1221, Geneva 4, Switzerland

2 Laboratory of Hematology, Maternite, Geneva University Hospital

CH-1211 Geneva 14, Switzerland

Received November 12, 1992

Metal-binding proteins are important components of retroviruses such as human immunodeficiency virus (HIV). Therefore, metals could be used as ANTIVIRAL AGENTS. However, most metals are toxic for humans with the exception of SILVER, which is toxic only to prokaryotic cells and viruses. In addition, HIV infection causes a decrease in body Cysteine. We formed a complex of silver and Cysteine, named silver Cysteine.

Silver inhibition of isolated Na,K-ATPase was easily reversed by Cysteine. Thus, NON-TOXIC SILVER CYSTEINE COULD BE USED AS AN ANTI-VIRAL AND CYSTEINE REPLENISHING AGENT.

Attention has been paid recently to the important regulatory roles of metal proteins in macromolecular interaction in gene expression (1,2).

Human Immunodeficiency Virus (HIV) contains Cysteine-rich or metal binding proteins essential to its expression. Demineralization could be important for virus replicability. Metal Chelators have been shown to reduce virus replication in vitro (5,6).

The above findings clearly indicate the importance of metals for expression of HIV. Metals have indeed been used as chemotherapeutic agents before as antibiotics. The Therapeutic use of most of the metals has been abandoned due to the general toxicity. However, *Silver is a highly active bactericidal with little toxicity for humans* (8). Silver has also been shown to be a potent inhibitor of HIV Protease (9).

Low levels of Cysteine are found in the plasma of AIDS patients (11) suggesting a major role of cysteine for Lymphocyte activity. Cysteine and Cysteine-rich proteins protect cells from aggression and stress present, therefore, important defense systems.

MIHM ET AL. (12), for instance, reported that N-Acetyl L Cysteine (NAC) blocks the replication of HIV. The Cysteine Analogue D Pencillamine inhibits HIV replication in vitro (13). Thus drugs and chemicals that deliver Cysteine or glucothione to deficient cells are potentially useful. Therefore, we decided to combine the protective role of Cysteine with the potential anti-viral effect of silver. Silver-Cysteine may increase the Thial concentration in deficient cells and at the same time inactivate the metal sensitive HIV proteins.

RESULTS

Apparently, silver Cysteine complex protects the cells from the toxicity exerted by silver by an unknown mechanism. The results indicate that Na, K-ATPase is a highly silver sensitive enzyme. The isolated renal NaK-ATPase is more silver-sensitive than the human lymphocytes, since we are dealing with a highly purified protein, which is no longer protected by membrane embedding. Complete reversal of silver inhibition was obtained by 1mM Cysteine. Thus, in contrast to mercury, silver found in Na,K-ATPase has still strong affinity to free Cysteine (14). Thus, in contrast to mercury, silver found in Na,K-ATPase has still strong affinity for free Cysteine. This phenomena of reversibility suggest the possibility of removal of silver from Eukaryotic metal binding proteins by cysteine or Cysteine analogues.

DISCUSSION

This low toxicity of the silver-Cysteine complex opens interesting possibilities for the use of *silver* as a potential antiviral agent. Kariston et al (18) reported that the HIV protease is highly sensitive to mercury and copper. Inactivation by copper is rapid and not reversed by subsequent exposure to EDTA. They have tested a series of metals on protease activity and found mercury and copper to be active. Thus Karlston et al (18) suggested that mercury and copper could be used as therapeutic agents to block HIV growth, since the protease enzyme is essential for HIV replication. However, mercury is more toxic on lymphocytes (unpublished data) than silver. Further, Cysteine is unable to reverse mercury action on the Na,K-ATPase activity (15), in contrast to silver which can be removed from the enzyme by Cysteine.

Since AIDS patients contain very low levels of Cysteine (11), supply of exogenous Cysteine is *expected to render cells more resistant to HIV* (19). The silver-Cysteine complex is taken up by the isolated lymphocytes (Hussain, S. Anner, R.M., Volet, B. and Anner, B.M., manuscript in preparation). Thus, agents which deliver Cysteine to deficient cells are potentially useful in vivo.

In conclusion, the newly designed silver-Cysteine complex is not very toxic for human lymphocytes and possibly for euaryotic cells in general. On the basis of our results and information available from the literature (9, 20), *Silver is expected to interact potently with HIV proteins* and to interrupt thereby the cellular replication of HIV at various stages such as interaction with surface receptors, gene expression or cellular biosynthesis of viruses. Possible therapeutic forms of silver-Cysteine and evaluation of this new compound in cells from patients with HIV remain to be investigated.

It can clearly be seen from this study that Silver in the form of *Silver-Cysteine* has a terminal effect on the HIV virus. It is also found that Silver is non-toxic in this form, in stark contrast to other heavy metals.

Mild Silver Protein, in contrast to Silver-Cysteine, has about 100 proven years of usage with no known recorded side effects. It appears that since Mild Silver Protein *kills all viruses,* its usage for patients infected with HIV is indicated. It also appears that either supplementation with Cysteine or the combining of Cysteine with Mild Silver Protein would be ideal and most effective anti-viral formula for the annihilation of the HIV virus. Since Mild Silver Protein has no known side effects, it would seem wise for additional studies on HIV patients to be conducted in order that the people as well as the practitioner's *faith* in its usage could become more widespread and mainstream.

I believe that the use of Mild Silver Protein to kill the HIV virus, along with holistic methods to rebuild the immune system (including use of Cysteine) will have the ultimate result of *annihilating and removing this plague called AIDS from the face of the Earth!*

*Please note preliminary study on Mild Silver Protein and its effect on the AIDS virus at beginning of book.

CHAPTER 8
THE MOST EFFECTIVE HOLISTIC NATURAL SUPPORTIVE TREATMENTS

At this point, I am going to outline and further explain the holistic methods and techniques which I utilized for a 2 1/2 year period of time in order to survive and overcome the devastating symptoms of Lyme Disease, Candida Yeast Infection and Multiple Sclerosis. If it were up to me, early detection and treatments as described in this publication would reduce the healing time from 1-3 months, as opposed to the 12-15 months it took me to reach total healing. But whatever the situation, I am also outlining these methods into an easy reference guide which can be effectively used. What makes these suggested natural supportive treatments so valuable is that I have tried them all and *they worked.* As is true with most of the material in this book, I write from a perspective of *having gone through* Lyme Disease, Candida Yeast Infection, and Multiple Sclerosis...and not just *observing* other victims and their reactions. I LIVED IT. I was not on the outside looking in, but on the inside looking out...and feeling the terrible pain, the debilitating paralysis and the frightening *internal loneliness* and desolation of not knowing what would happen next as I forced myself through uncharted territory. This allows me to speak and write with authority and credibility.

Colonic Irrigations - As I have mentioned earlier, when I was first hit with the Lyme Disease, my intestines locked up so completely that oftentimes I was doubled over in the fetal position with severe cramps, gas, and pain. I chewed up "Mylanta" tablets two at a time, which brought me some temporary relief from the gas. I consulted a gastroenterologist for an opinion because the condition was so severe. His advice to me was to admit myself to a hospital in order to run a battery of barium dye and x-ray tests in order to determine whether the colon was blocked. At that point in time, he would then surgically perform a colostomy in which he would cut my colon in half and then put a bag on the end. Needless to say, I wasn't very impressed and not at all enthusiastic to get started. I had seen this procedure performed on many of my own patients, as well as my own father, who died within two months of his surgery. There had to be a better way.

I decided to pay a visit to an old friend and colleague of mine Joseph Vargas, a Certified Colonic Therapist who regularly performs colonic irrigations (a procedure endorsed by the expert author on colonics, Dr. N. W. Walker). Colonic irrigations are a method of high enemas administered in one-hour sessions utilizing a colonic irrigation machine. It consists of an apparatus with a sterile, throw-away plastic speculum attached with a small plastic tube coming off the unit, carrying fresh water. An exhaust tube is also used to carry out fecal waste matter.

The speculum is inserted into the bowel while the patient is in a reclining position, lying on a specially designed table. Through a series of valves on the machine, fresh water (alternating between 75 degrees Fahrenheit on the cool end and 104 degrees on the warm end) is pumped into the colon through the bowels at between one and a half and two pounds of pressure. When the pressure builds up in the colon it is released so it may pass out through the exhaust tube. This is usually a couple of minutes of fill, followed by three to five minutes of emptying. It is a very soothing, relaxing and pressure-releasing process which is extremely effective. The relief from extreme pain caused by pressure and blocked bowels is dramatic as well as instantaneous.

If your colonic therapist is as good as mine was, then you will also receive a gentle acupressure treatment to the colon, causing moving of the fecal matter through the ascending, transverse and descending colon, accompanied by relaxing music and positive affirmations. On some machines, you can actually observe the built-up waste and feces passing from your unhealthy colon on the way to the sewer, where they belong. You then begin to realize that your colon can become as filthy as a *toxic waste dump*. It is these built-up toxins, waste and impacted fecal matter, undigested residues and poisons which are literally strangling the life out of you and bringing you ever closer to disease and a very young death.

Thank God the colonics worked dramatically. The pressure and pain was released in my colon and the impacted and constipated bowels cleared out. I was able to stand up-right again. The gas also passed out through my bowel, relieving me of even more pressure. I had a new lease on life and I could sense that fresh blood and oxygen was now getting back into my system and that the healing process was again moving forward. Over the entire course of the Lyme disease, I had fourteen colonic irrigations over a ten month period. I plan, for the purposes of preventative care, on having at least one every three to six months or as needed. It is important to remember that a clean colon is a key to a disease-free life. Colonic irrigations bring undeniable *positive results*, despite all the prejudice and misunderstanding surrounding the procedure. Actually, historically speaking, at one time between 1940-1950, colonics were utilized as a very sound and effective medical procedure. In fact, they were so effective that they began replacing more *expensive* medical procedures involving the gastroenteric system. But, in my opinion, greed eventually won out and the medical profession, hospitals, and drug companies saw to it that the use of this most natural and effective treatment was eliminated for public use. What a terrible loss to the suffering of mankind. I pray that this miraculous, effective method will be brought back to the mainstream of healthcare. It would easily replace ineffective fleet enemas now performed in hospitals. Colonic irrigations provide a dynamic cleansing system geared at not only relieving pain and suffering, but also at restoring a person's health and vitality. This procedure can also prevent much unnecessary gastrointestinal surgery.

Chiropractic Adjustments - The most immediate and powerful pain reliever and nervous system healing agent which I had at my disposal during my bout with these diseases was chiropractic adjustments. I can honestly calculate that without the dramatic relief which the adjustments offered to me, it would have been twice as hard to make it through. Fortunately, I had three marvelous chiropractic doctors: Dr. Mike Davis from Conroe, Texas; Dr. Richard Dean Golden from Houston and Dr. Robert Sones from Conroe. Their exceptional talents utilizing their hands in the application of a chiropractic adjustment would not allow extreme pain to exist long within my body. It was the *periods of relief* which gave me the energy...the strength to endure and keep moving forward with my healing program. In fact, it was the wisdom of Dr. Davis which concluded that what I was suffering from was more than just a chiropractic problem, prompting him to refer me to a neurologist. It was his wife that advised me to send the tick that I had found on my scalp to Texas A&M to be analyzed.

Chiropractic was rediscovered by Dr. B.J. Palmer in Davenport, Iowa over 100 years ago. While in chiropractic college I saw photos of paintings dating all the way back to ancient Greece and Rome, depicting chiropractic type manipulations being delivered to ailing people. Since that time, chiropractic has grown to the second largest healing profession in the world, next to the medical profession (however, it is the number one *natural* largest healing profession). There are over 40,000 Doctors of Chiropractic who are practicing licensed physicians and over 20,000 in 25 countries throughout the world. The Doctor of Chiropractic has over two years of undergraduate training and four years of formal chiropractic education at one of the 27 accredited colleges in the United States and 5 chiropractic colleges in other countries.

To many people's surprise, the Doctor of Chiropractic has over 4,500 hours of formal education in comparison to 3,876 for the medical doctor. In the area of *Neurology*, a Medical Doctor has 112 hours, versus 320 hours for a Doctor of Chiropractic. In *Orthopedics*, a Medical Doctor has 156 hours in comparison to 225 hours for the Doctor of Chiropractic. Needless to say, the chiropractic physician is a highly skilled diagnostician and practitioner.

The question was once posed: "What would be the best type of doctor to be stranded on a desert island with?" The answer: "A Doctor of Chiropractic because as long as he had his hands, he would have all the tools he needed to still be able to help his fellow man."

The spinal column is made up of 24 moveable vertebrae. In the neck there are 7 cervical vertebrae, in the upper and mid back 12 thoracic vertebrae, and in the lower back, 5 lumbar vertebrae. There are 24 spinal pairs of nerves innervating from these vertebrae, going to every major organ, gland and muscle group in the entire body. There are visceral nerves which emanate from the lateral horn of the spinal column and motor and sensory nerves from the anterior and posterior horns which go to even the most minute nerve in the most distant part of the body which is connected into this system.

When two vertebrae come together it creates a *hole* called an intervertebral foramen, through which the spinal nerves pass. When the vertebrae which are moveable become misaligned in relationship to one another, the hole becomes smaller and it creates a *pinching* on the nerve. When this pinching occurs, the nerve impulses are cut off to the areas which the nerve goes to, much like the water passing through a water hose is cut off when the hose becomes pinched. If the water from that hose went to a garden, this garden (which is a living organism much like the human body) would eventually become sick and diseased from lack of nourishment.

In the same light, when the nerve supply (as well as the blood flow) becomes pinched off, the organ, gland, tissue, or muscle group that it goes to becomes dysfunctional and the person becomes diseased. Historically in medical circles, the chiropractic profession believed that it was the pinching of the nervous system which caused illness. On the other hand, the osteopathic profession believed that it was the impedance of the circulatory system which caused illness. In my own experiences and research efforts, I have found that *both were correct* and that both the interrelated nervous system and the circulatory system are involved when a misalignment occurs in the spinal column. This pinching can be caused by an accident such as a fall or on-the-job injury, everyday stresses and strains, and visceral illnesses all the way from the common cold to heart disease or gastrointestinal disease. An infectious attack such as Lyme Disease will take hold more quickly and spread faster because of the *lack of resistance,* a result of diminished nerve supply to the immune system, organs and glands of the body.

The bottom line is that chiropractic works and gets excellent, many times dramatic results where medication and surgery are ineffective (although there are times when they are necessary). Drs. Jim and Karl Parker of the Parker Chiropractic College in Fort Worth, made the following statement: "Chiropractic first, drugs second, surgery last." It is important to reiterate that this does not discount the importance of surgery or medication when it is truly needed. It is wiser, however, to utilize non-invasive treatments whenever possible and as long as they are effective. This understanding, that the health care profession must recognize and use the unique talents of all the different specialties, has not become a reality. One can see chiropractors on the staffs of many major hospitals throughout the nation, doing the job of removing disease and pain-causing subluxations, which is their unique talent and one which they are highly trained and skills to do well.

I feel that the words of the Hippocratic oath are now due for an addendum. In addition to the words "Do No Harm" as stated by Hippocrates, the following words should be added: "Do Good...Do That Which Is Best For The Patient, Not The Doctor, Without Prejudice." Along these same lines, it is interesting that the final and most important link in the answer for my Lyme Disease (before discovery of Mild Silver Protein) turned out to be a synthetic compound created in a laboratory. Being that I am a holistic and natural-minded physician, this further emphasized that all doctors should be open to any philosophical viewpoint (even if it is contrary to their own) so long as it works and does no great harm while saving lives and relieving suffering. Medical physicians should be willing to utilize natural holistic therapies in addition to their normal regimens of treatment. This attitude will require a certain level of humility on the part of doctors of all the different professions. I feel personally that humility should be considered one of the vital qualities of an outstanding physician, in addition to skill, knowledge and compassion. If this unbiased and caring attitude became a part of the mainstream of healthcare, the true winners would be the patients. And the doctors would achieve success along with the self-satisfaction that they have indeed done the very best they could do for their patients. (See Chiropractic Chart on page 72.)

Physical Therapy - Physical therapy is an art and a science in itself, which when practiced by itself, gets excellent results. However, when it is practiced in conjunction with chiropractic adjustments, the results become magnified and many times phenomenal. The reason for this is that the application of physical therapy modalities to aid the tissues in their healing process, as well as to speed up this process, become accelerated when aided by a more complete nerve supply to that tissue and muscle group. It would be analogous that in addition to improving the quality of a light bulb in a lamp in order to get better light, one would also see to it that the rheostat on the light switch was turned up completely so that the lamp could receive a full supply of electricity...maximum power. Therefore, to merely aid the tissues in the healing process by the direct application of various physical therapy modalities (which will be outlined in this section) without *switching on the power* of the nerve supply which runs these tissues, would not achieve the desired result of healing the area of the body which is injured or diseased. Without the chiropractic adjustment which *turns this nerve supply on*, one is limited to the amount of nerve supply being received by the tissue during the time of illness, which can be diminished anywhere from 10 to 90 per cent.

Imagine that your leg "falls asleep" while having your legs crossed while sitting in a chair for a prolonged period of time. Obviously, one would want the feeling in the leg to "wake up", so you proceed to apply direct electrical stimulation to the leg, accompanied by hot packs, ultrasound, massage, traction, and trigger-point therapy, all of which are physical therapy modalities in common usage in hospitals, medical doctors' offices, and with Chiropractors and Physical Therapists. However, how much more dramatic the results become when the person *simply stands up,* allowing the nerve and blood to return to the leg. In a matter of minutes, everything's o.k. because you had the *voluntary* conscious ability to uncross your legs.

However, when there is a misaligned vertebrae pinching on a nerve and blood vessel, one does not have the voluntary ability to remove this pressure. At that point, a person needs to seek out the skills of a chiropractic physician who can (through the application of the chiropractic adjustment) remove these pressures on both nerves and blood vessels from the spinal column. Then, coupled with physical therapy, a perfect marriage is achieved in the healing arts. In over 30 years of holistic practice, I have seen *incredible* results. this is the wave of the future because it is the best for the patient, not the doctor, According to Drs.

Jim and Karl Parker of the Parker Chiropractic Research Foundation: "Chiropractic works, it gets the results, and that is what counts."

Physical therapy (along with a chiropractic adjustment) helps to alleviate pain, improve movement and function, thus attempting to attain the highest functional level of physical independence. This combination treats the existing condition of the Lyme Disease and at the same time provides preventative care to avoid aggravation or injury to the affected areas.

The use of physical therapy, like chiropractic, is as ancient as the first man who had a physical body and who experienced pain. When early man stumped his foot or banged his head, he rubbed it with an early form of massage in order to make it feel better. The early Chinese, Romans and Greeks used physical methods such as heat, water and therapeutic massage to relieve pain, restore movement and to relax the body. The first health spas were built in ancient Rome and Greece, and were an integral part of a healthcare program.

In Lyme Disease, posture and movement are affected because of the arthritic-like symptoms caused by the inflammation to the joints from the effect of the spirochetes. The joints become stiff and tight and muscle strength, range of motion and flexibility are all affected. To help reduce the pain which can be immobilizing and which can lead to stiffness, inflammation and swelling, *physical therapy modalities* such as heat, cold, electrical stimulation, therapeutic massage, traction and therapeutic exercise will all be used in order to reduce pain. The results can be outstanding.

When proper movement has been interrupted, one may need to re-learn basic movements for daily living. The goal, of course, is to improve movement and coordination following the neuritis of the nervous system caused by the disease. Through neuromuscular re-education, the body can be taught to respond. Muscle tone is reduced or strengthened in order to correct imbalances in the muscles through exercises and specific positioning of the body. To improve the range of motion (ROM) of the joints which become stiff and compromised during this illness, physical therapy methods such as soft tissue mobilization or stretching exercises may be utilized to restore function and movement. The muscles can become weak due to non-use, a result of stiffness and pain. They can be strengthened by exercises and electrical stimulation. The exercise program is designed to improve coordination, strength, endurance and circulation.

Physical therapy should be prescribed by your chiropractic physician and built into a program which will get you out of pain and also maintain, so that you *stay out of pain* throughout the course of the disease from its initial stages to any possible long-term effects. Remember that there can be exacerbations even years later with Lyme Disease, especially during the changes of seasons (due to atmospheric conditions such as barometric pressure, temperature and subsequent fluctuations). This serves to shake loose the toxins in the body which were stored in the liver during the course of the disease. Remember that the *colonics* are also very helpful during these periods.

One form of therapy which I created in order to help stimulate circulation and joint mobility in the hands is what I have dubbed "Bongo Therapy." Start by putting on one of your favorite albums of music that has a good drum beat. Proceed to play the bongos for 20 to 30 minutes, with the bongos placed between your legs. This works! In addition to the fun and entertainment and stress reduction, your hands get a good stimulation. Plus, your circulation and mobility is improved.

Therapeutic Massage - Therapeutic massage is

performed by a licensed and experienced practitioner, usually a *Massage Therapist* working on his or her own, or under the direction of a physician or physical therapist who is familiar with both the anatomy and physiology of the body. Special emphasis is placed on the muscle groups of the body and how they interact with each other and how they react to specific physical problems. Like its counterpart and ancestor *physical therapy*, therapeutic massage has also been around for thousands of years. It was the choice of the elite of the Pharoahs of Egypt, the Senate of Rome and the Royalty of Greece...for the relief of stress, burdens and the tension associated with their positions of authority. It was used to both nurture and promote healing by relieving muscle fatigue, relaxing the muscles and enhancing and restoring life function by improving circulation and breaking up waste congestion within the cells of the muscles.

In addition to the muscular problems which accompany Lyme Disease (resulting in tightness, fatigue and pain) one must also contend with the complexity and tension of the modern world with all of its hustle and bustle and confusion. There are many pollutants, stresses, and daily tensions which make it difficult for us to stay physically well, relaxed, vibrant, and full of energy. Our muscles also react to psychological pressures as we tend to tighten up and become stiff and immobile. Thus, these psychological pressures eventually lead to pain and immobility, leaving us distressed and unsatisfied with life. We become literally "all wound up," as the old saying goes.

In Lyme Disease, the spirochetes as well as toxins emitted in the mucosa of the tick, disrupt cell metabolism and create stagnation, causing the muscles to tighten, become fatigued, painful and sore. A full body therapeutic massage should be performed at least once a week to break up these spasms and restore the proper circulation in the body (and also to relieve pain). Combining massage with chiropractic and other physical therapy modalities is both a powerful and effective combination which I have used in my holistic chiropractic clinic for many years in Houston.

The American Massage Therapy Association, along with state licensing bureaus, is a national organization which effectively organizes and coordinates *education*, to insure that the standards maintained for licensing massage therapists are on the highest level. I salute and applaud their efforts in giving credibility to this marvelous science and art.

The predominant effects of therapeutic massage are listed as follow:

1. Relieving tension and relaxing muscle spasms
2. Improving muscle tone
3. Reducing effects of stressful living
4. Energizing the body for more effective functioning
5. Stretching and loosening tightened joints
6. Increasing circulation
7. Relieving headaches and pain in the lower back, in the neck and in the shoulder
8. Helping balance body, mind and emotions

A good massage therapist will consult with you concerning many aspects of your lifestyle and will discuss with you diet, exercise habits, mental attitudes, stressful life situations and family medical history, including specific problems such as Lyme Disease. A massage program will then be coordinated with your chiropractic and physical therapy into a complete holistic program. During your massage, your therapist will use information gathered from the consultation, plus your appearance, as well as how your body feels...in order to select the most beneficial therapeutic techniques. While the therapist is working with your muscles, he or she may also give you mental suggestions for relaxing and shifting your thought patterns to a more effective and life-enhancing mode. All the patient has to do is relax and allow the skilled therapist to finely tune and relax the body.

In addition to the therapeutic and health benefits, massage is an extremely relaxing and enjoyable experience. And again, when combined with chiropractic manipulation and physical therapy, the results are significant. It should be noted that massage should be performed *prior* to the chiropractic adjustment in order to ensure that the cervical area, especially the atlas and axis (the top two vertebrae which are like the master circuit breaker of the body's electrical nervous system)remain in proper alignment. Working with the muscles can often *misalign* them. If the upper cervicals are not aligned, it is possible that you may not feel any better, even though your muscles are relaxed.

This is a natural law which I have discovered through trial and error over the last 30 years. I absolutely will not let a patient leave my clinic unless their *cervicals* as well as the rest of their vertebrae are in perfect alignment. This is extremely important and has proven to be most effective. In looking back, I have to personally thank my wife Marie, Allen Boxman and Viviana Rojas (all licensed Massage Therapists) for their crucial and excellent care during the course of my illness.

Traditional and Electrical Acupuncture - Acupuncture is an important component to traditional Chinese medicine, involving the prevention and treatment of disease by using specific body points and sterile needles in order to alleviate symptoms. Traditional Chinese Medicine is a comprehensive system of healthcare that is more than 5,000 years old. It works with vital energies inherent within all living things in order to promote the body's ability to heal itself. It is still used extensively throughout the orient and is rapidly gaining acceptance in the West.

The methods used in assisting with assessment are:

1. Inspection - observation of expression, color and texture of the tongue, vitality and color of the eyes, circulation under fingernails and toenails, overall degree of alertness and vitality.

2. Traditional reading of the six pulses - this reveals the overall strength or weakness of the different major organ systems.

3. Auscultation and olfaction - listening to body sounds and evaluating the sense of smell.

4. Inquiry - consulting with the patient concerning related signs or symptoms like chills, fever, perspiration, thirst, appetite, sleep, etc.

5. Palpation - goes along with reading the pulse and the different channels and meridians of energy.

According to Chinese theory, there are natural mechanisms (both neurological and biochemical) built into the body that should keep it in harmony. Acupuncture is used to mobilize these mechanisms and to promote natural normalizing in case of an imbalance. When a problem occurs in the internal organs or in the parts of the body, there are immediately one or more points in the ear or body that respond to the problem. Generally, the number of acupuncture points are directly proportional to the intensity of the illness. They are sensitive to pressure and/or low intensity electrical stimulation.

An example is a "tension headache." Acupuncture works directly on spastic muscles by inhibiting neural transmission of pain messages. This is done by limiting stimulating messages coming to the muscles under tension and by biochemical repression of pain responses. When these functions are balanced, the muscle tension dissipates and tends to come back less and less, until eventually the noxious response is unlearned. Those who undergo such treatment find it rewarding and effective and completely free of undesirable side effects.

One of the primary advantages of acupuncture treatment is that it does not alleviate a symptom or problem by putting artificial substitutes into the body. Instead, it prompts the body to produce the required substances naturally. For example, *endorphins* to ease pain, or in the case of "allergy" acupuncture suppresses the chemicals causing it, like histamine.

The question that many times comes up in the discussion of acupuncture is whether acupuncture is a *placebo*. A placebo is defined as an inactive substance or treatment given to satisfy the patient's symbolic needs for drug therapy (most of them are "empty"). Acupuncture is certainly not a placebo for conditions which are appropriate and when applied in accordance with the principles of Chinese medicine. Acupuncture has the highest success rate as a clinical modality. Alterations in pain perception and reactions have been consistently demonstrated even in laboratory animals, which are not led to "expect" a particular outcome. Tam Thai, who helped to prepare this section on acupuncture, has proven this in very difficult cases with horses.

Tam Thai is from Vietnam and is a tenth-generation acupuncturist, a man I have known and worked with and studied with since 1989. He has made a tremendous contribution toward making acupuncture an accepted part of Western medicine. This blending of East and West is proving extremely beneficial to modern society and is the wave of the future as exemplified by the

March 1993 PBS special with Bill Moyers: "The Body/Mind Connection," which featured acupuncture, Chinese medicine and herbs, meditation techniques utilized by professional psychologists for quieting the mind and healing the body. Also included were various other natural therapies, including nutrition.

Dry Brush Massage - Few people realize that the skin is the largest organ of elimination of the body. When we're unable to sweat properly because of disease or improper hygiene, we are opening ourselves up to a greater level of disease. Bathing in itself, especially with commercial soap, may end up clogging pores rather than opening them. There are soaps available at the health food stores such as Dr. Bronner's Castille Soap that is more healthy for us than commercial soaps that contain many harsh chemicals. Body lotions should also be of a natural origin and free of chemicals. This also holds true for women's cosmetics, as well as deodorants. Cotton clothing is also preferable to synthetic fabrics.

When one is experiencing extreme itching, it could be a sign of a fungal infection from Candidiasis. In addition, individuals who have Multiple Sclerosis can have extraordinary itching.

I was first introduced to dry brush massage by one of my mentors, Dr. Paavo Airola...and I have been practicing it for over 15 years. It's hard to imagine now living without this healing tool which really works and is extremely relaxing as well as *stimulating*. It can stop itching, improve circulation, increase the waste and toxin elimination process, as well as improving your overall health. The optimum time to perform this procedure is directly after bathing in the morning and/or evening.

You should purchase three separate boar bristle hair brushes of a medium texture, getting three different styles so that you can distinguish them one from another. For purposes of hygiene, one *smaller brush* should be used solely for the genital area, one for the bottom of the feet (preferably round), and one (the largest) for the scalp as well as the skin on the rest of the body such as the arms, legs, abdomen and back, as well as the face.

Do about 10-minute brushings, using very vigorous short strokes. It may take from 3-6 times for the skin to adapt and not be overly sensitive. Be patient, as you will become used to it and eventually desire it.

Dry brush massage is a very useful and effective tool which you should integrate into your overall health program, as well as when your body is experiencing mild to extensive itching. Every time you brush you will literally be removing tens of thousands of dead cells, bacteria, funguses and viruses.

This non-invasive technique has absolutely no side effects.

NUTRITIONAL RECOMMENDATIONS FOR SPECIFIC CONDITIONS

(The following information is reprinted from "PRESCRIPTION FOR NUTRITIONAL HEALING," by James A. Balch, M.D. and Phyllis A. Balch, C.N.C., (c) 1990, $16.95, Published by Avery Publishing Group, Inc., Garden City Park, New York, 1-800-548-5757. Reprinted by permission."

CANDIDIASIS

Candida Albicans is a type of yeast-like fungus that inhabits the intestine, genital tract, mouth and throat. Normally this fungus lives in healthy balance with the other bacteria and yeast in the body; however, certain conditions can cause this fungus to multiply, weakening the immune system and causing an infection known as

Candidiasis. Because this fungus travels through the bloodstream to many parts of the body, various symptoms may develop.

When this fungus infects the oral cavity, it is called *thrush.* Hite sores may form on the tongue, gums, and inside the cheeks. When the fungus infects the vagina, it results in *vaginitis.* The most common symptoms include a large amount of white, cheesy discharge and intense itching. Very often allergies to foods are present. Allergy testing is advised. Oral thrush, athlete's foot, ringworm, jock itch, and even diaper rash can develop as a result of food allergies and Candida Albicans.

Because Candidiasis can infect various parts of the body – the most common being the ears, nose, gastrointestinal tract, and bowels – it can also be characterized by many symptoms. These include constipation; diarrhea; colitis; abdominal pain; canker sores; persistent heartburn; muscle and joint pain; sore throat; congestion; nagging cough; numb hands, legs, or face; tingling sensations; acne; vaginitis, kidney and bladder infections; arthritis; depression; hyperactivity; hypothyroidism followed by adrenal problems; and even diabetes. Some afflicted with Candidiasis may develop a sensitivity to the environment. Many cannot tolerate the smell of rubber, petroleum products, tobacco, exhaust fumes, and chemical odors .

Candidiasis may affect both men and women; however, it is rarely transmitted sexually. An infected mother may pass the fungal infection known as thrush to the newborn. Most often the baby's tongue will appear red and be covered with white spots that resemble milk spots. Thrush may also infect the baby's buttocks, appearing as a rash. Because there is no simple, accurate test, this infection is difficult to detect.

Women diagnosed with a yeast infection should also be checked for diabetes. Because their vaginal environment is more conducive to the growth of yeast, diabetics are at greater risk of contracting a yeast infection such as Candidiasis.

NUTRIENTS

SUPPLEMENT	SUGGESTED DOSAGE	COMMENTS
Very Important		
Capricin from Professional Specialties or Caprystatin from Arteria (caprylic acid)	4 capsules 3 times daily with meals. 1st week: 1 tablet twice daily. 2nd week: 2 tablets twice daily. 3rd week: 3 tablets twice daily.	Destroys the Candida fungus.
Dioxychlor from American Biologics or Aerobic 07 from Aerobic Life Products	5 drops in water twice daily.	These stabilized oxygen products destroy the fungus, while preserving the "good" bacteria.
Garlic capsules (Kyolic)	2 capsules 3 times daily.	An odorless form of garlic that inhibits the infecting organism. Kyolic vaginal suppositories also effectively treat Candida vaginitis.
Maxidophilus or Megadophilus or Non-Dairy Neo-Flora or DDS Extracts or Prime-Dophilus from Klaire Laboratories	Use as directed on label. Send for Superdophilus: Natren Inc. 10935 Camarillo St. N. Hollywood, CA 91602	Eugalan Topfer, a form of mother's milk from Germany, is the best form. A vegetarian form is also available for anyone who cannot tolerate dairy products.*

Omega 3–6 with evening primrose oil from Arteria or primrose oil or salmon oil	Use as directed on label.	A good source of essential fatty acids.
Vitamin B complex with extra biotin	100 mg 3 times daily.	Malabsorption is common in candidiasis.
Vitamin B$_{12}$ lozenges	1 lozenge (2,000 mcg) under the tongue 3 times daily, taken between meals. Vitamin B injections may be necessary.	Important for digestion. Needed for metabolism of carbohydrates, fats, and proteins. Candida prevents the absorption of nutrients from the intestinal tract.

Important		
Germanium	100–200 mg daily.	Improves tissue oxygenation.

Helpful		
Coenzyme Q$_{10}$	100 mg daily.	Improves tissue oxygenation.
L-Cysteine (amino acid)	500 mg on an empty stomach twice daily.	A potent antioxidant and free radical destroyer.
Multivitamin and mineral complex (zinc, iron, and yeast free) with	Daily as directed on label.	Nutrients are needed for proper immune function.
vitamin A and	25,000 IU	
selenium	200 mcg	
Orithrush from Cardiovascular Research	Use as a mouth rinse or as a douche.	Destroys Candida.
Protein supplement (Free Form Amino Acid Complex from Cardiovascular Research)	¼ tsp. under the tongue between meals on an empty stomach.	Rebuilds damaged tissue.

RECOMMENDATIONS

■ Do not use corticosteroids or oral contraceptives until condition improves. Oral contraceptives can upset the balance of Candida Albicans.

■ Avoid aged cheeses, alcohol, chocolate, dried fruits, fermented foods, all grains containing gluten (wheat, oats, rye, barley, ham, honey, nut butters, pickles, raw mushrooms, soy sauce, sprouts, sugars of all forms, vinegar, and all yeast products. Also eliminate citrus and acid fruits (e.g., oranges, grapefruit, lemons, tomatoes, pineapple, and limes) from your diet for one month; then add back only a few twice weekly. These fruits are alkaline-forming and Candida thrives on them.

■ Your diet should be fruit free, sugar free, and yeast free. Candida thrives in a sugary environment, so your diet should be low in carbohydrates. Eat vegetables and meat instead. Eating live yogurt or applying it directly to the vagina can help inhibit the growth of the fungus. Consume also brown rice, millet, and acidophilus. Acidophilus capsules help to restore the normal balance of the bowel and vagina. This diet program has been used for years with good results. Take only hypoallergenic food supplements.

■ Avoid chemical household products and cleaners, chlorinated water, moth balls, synthetic textiles, and damp and moldy places, such as basements.

■ To prevent reinfection, use a new toothbrush every thirty days. This is a good preventive measure against both fungus and bacterial infections of the mouth.

Considerations

■ For vaginal disorders use Yeast-gard vaginal suppositories from Wakunaga of America company.

■ Candida-Forte from Nature's Plus is good for mild cases of Candidiasis.

■ All persons on long-term antibiotics or

chemotherapy are at high risk for severe cases of Candidiasis.

■ Most doctors no longer us Nystatin or antibiotics because they weaken the immune system and can damage certain organs. When prescribed, they are usually only for short-term treatment. Occasionally the antifungal drugs Nizorol and amphotericin B are also used for treatment. Stronger strains of yeast can develop, becoming resistant to the drugs. Higher dosages are then required, further weakening the immune system.

■ High mercury levels can result in Candidiasis. Mercury salts inhibit the growth of necessary "friendly" bacteria in the intestines. You may want to have a hair analysis done to determine the levels of toxic metals.

■ You might want to try pau d'arco herb tea. This tea contains an antibacterial agent. It does have an alkaloid base and a small percentage of people may not benefit from its use. Those that do not benefit from this tea should try clove tea instead. It is a good idea to alternate between the two teas because clove tea has some benefits that pau d'arco does not have and vice versa. To make pau d'arco tea, boil one quart of distilled water with two tablespoons of tea for five minutes. Store it in the refrigerator with the tea leaves in. Strain as much as you need. Drink three to six cups daily.

■ Candidiasis may be related to hypoglycemia and allergies. Consult these sections for additional suggestions.

■ Fiber is an important part of the diet. Oat bran is more easily digestible than wheat bran.

Note from Dr. Farber: We now have evidence that Mild Silver Protein kills all Candida Yeast organisms. Take grapefruit extract to assure all yeast in the *digestive system* is destroyed, as Mild Silver Protein may be absorbed too quickly before it reaches that area of the body.

MULTIPLE SCLEROSIS

Multiple Sclerosis (MS) is a progressive, degenerative disorder of the central nervous system. The disease is variable in its progression and affects various parts of the nervous system by destroying the myelin sheaths which cover the nerves, causing an inflammatory response. Its symptoms include a staggering gait, blurred vision, dizziness, numbness, breathing difficulty, weakness, tremors, slurred speech, bladder and bowel problems, emotional problems, sexual impotence in men, and paralysis.

There is no known cure for MS, primarily because the underlying cause is unknown; however, stress and malnutrition often precede the onset of the disease.

As in so many of the degenerative disorders, a strong immune defense system is essential in the treatment of MS. A strong immune system helps avoid infection, which can trigger this disease. Dr. Murray Bornstein, from the Albert Einstein College of Medicine in New York City, finds the drug Copolymer 1 to be an entirely new approach to the treatment of MS. It appears to present no risk to the patient, whereas the drugs currently used sometimes depress the immune system. This drug may prevent MS attacks.

MS usually occurs in persons between the ages of twenty-five and forty. The disease progresses slowly and may disappear for periods of time but usually returns intermittently, often in a more severe form. Long-term sufferers of MS may not benefit as well from supplements, but in the young patient just starting to exhibit symptoms, supplements may possibly slow or even stop the progress of the disease.

NUTRIENTS

SUPPLEMENT	SUGGESTED DOSAGE	COMMENTS
Very Important		
DMG (Gluconic from DaVinci Labs)	Dissolve 1 lozenge under tongue twice daily.	Enhances oxygen utilization by tissue. Reduces amount of free radicals in the body.
Kelp	5–10 tablets daily.	Supplies needed minerals and iodine.
Sulfur tablets from DaVinci Labs	500 mg 2–3 times daily.	Found in eggs, garlic, onions, and the amino acids L-cysteine and L-cystine.
Important		
Acidophilus or Megadophilus or Maxidophilus	1 tsp. twice daily on an empty stomach.	Replenishes "friendly" bacteria destroyed by stomach acid.
Calcium and magnesium	2,000–3,000 mg chelate. 1,000–1,500 mg chelate.	Chelate form offers best assimilation.
Inositol and choline	300–600 mg 150 mg	
L-Leucine, L-isoleucine, and L-valine combination from Carlson Labs	¼ tsp. twice daily on an empty stomach.	These amino acids should be taken together for correct balance. Aids in absorption of nutrients by the muscles.
Multidigestive enzyme	Take after meals.	
Potassium	300–1,000 mg	
Primrose oil	2 capsules 3 times daily.	Contains linoleic acid, which is needed.
Protein (free form amino acids)	¼ tsp under tongue between meals.	Free form amino acids are absorbed and assimilated quickly. (Ecological Formulas are good.)
Selenium	150–300 mcg	

Vitamin A plus beta-carotene	25,000 IU 15,000 IU	Use emulsion form for easier assimilation.
Vitamin B complex	100 mg 3 times daily.	Hypoallergenic form is best.
Vitamin B$_6$ (pyridoxine)	100 mg 3 times daily.	Hypoallergenic form is best.
Vitamin B$_{12}$	100 mcg twice daily.	Consider injections for all B vitamins. Consult your doctor.
Vitamin C	3,000–5,000 mg	Use buffered ascorbic acid form or esterified form.
Vitamin D	800–1,200 IU	
Vitamin E emulsion	Begin with 400 IU. Increase slowly to 1,800 IU.	Important for circulation, destroys free radicals, and protects the nervous system.
Vitamin K (alfalfa tablets)	200 mcg with meals.	Alfalfa tablets are helpful or take in liquid form.

Helpful		
Brewer's yeast	Start with a small amount and increase slowly.	
Coenzyme Q$_{10}$	30 mg twice daily.	Needed for improved circulation and tissue oxygenation. Strengthens the immune system.
Germanium Ge-132	200 mg	Strengthens the immune system.
Kyo-Green from Wakunaga of America Company	1 tsp. in liquid 3 times daily.	A good source of organic chlorophyll, live enzymes, vitamins, and minerals plus amino acids.
Lecithin	1 tbsp. 3 times daily or 1 capsule 4 times daily before meals.	Protects the cells. Needed for normal brain function.
Manganese	25 mg	
Multimineral formula (high potency)		
Phosphorus	900 mg	Needed for transfer of energy within cells.

| Proteolytic enzymes | Take between meals 3 times daily. | Needed for digestion. |
| Raw thymus extract | 500 mg twice daily. | Enhances immune function. |

RECOMMENDATIONS

■ A well-balanced diet is of great importance. All food eaten should be organically grown (no chemicals) including fruits, vegetables, grains, seeds (raw) and nuts, fertile eggs, and cold-pressed oils (never rancid). Plenty of raw sprouts, wheat, rye, and alfalfa are good, as are lactic acid foods such as sauerkraut and dill pickles.

Massage, exercise (especially swimming), and keeping mentally active are extremely valuable in bringing about remission of symptoms. Exercises that may increase body temperature can decrease the function of the nerves involved, and make symptoms worse. Exercises in cool water help by supporting the body's weight. Stretching exercises help to prevent muscle contractures.

■ The family of an MS sufferer must learn about the disease. Emotional support is essential. Contact Multiple Sclerosis National Society by writing to 205 E. 42nd Street, Manhattan, NY 10017 or phone (212) 986-3240. Physical therapy is often needed.

Considerations

■ Fiber is important for avoiding constipation. Periodically take warm cleansing enemas with the juice of a fresh lemon.

■ Avoid extremely hot baths, showers and overly warm surroundings, as these may trigger an attack.

■ According to the New Jersey College of Medicine, x-ray irradiation to the lymph glands and the spleen has halted the progress of MS in 25 percent of the patients treated. However, radiation depresses the immune system.

■ A two-year multicenter study reported in the

Archives of Neurology showed that exacerbations of MS can be relieved by spinal injections of natural human fibroblast interferon.

■ Do not consume sugar, coffee, chocolate, salt, highly seasoned foods, spices, or processed, canned, or frozen foods.

■ Short fasts are helpful

■ Lyme disease often mimics the symptoms of multiple sclerosis.

Note from Doctor Farber: I have found that Bee Venom (Serum) Therapy is extremely effective.

LYME DISEASE

This disease takes its name from the town of Lyme, Connecticut, where it was first discovered. It is seen more often in Europe, although in recent years its prevalence in the United States has grown, especially in the areas where white-tail deer are found. Ninety percent of all known cases have occurred in California, Massachusetts, Minnesota, Connecticut, New York, Rhode Island, Wisconsin, and New Jersey. If you live in white-tail deer areas, you must use precaution when going near wooded areas. A tiny tick (Ixodes dammini) carried by the deer transmits the disease. Household pets like dogs and cats can carry the tick into the home where it can be transmitted to humans. In the eastern United States, the main host is the white-footed field mouse. In the West, lizards and jackrabbits carry the disease.

Tick bites often go undetected. The first sign of Lyme Disease may be the appearance of a rash a few days after the tick bite, following a red papule on the skin. If this appears, see your doctor. Left untreated, Lyme Disease can lead to arthritis and damage the cardiovascular and the central nervous systems.

Symptoms that accompany a tick bite include fatigue, flu-like symptoms, headache, stiff neck and backache, nausea, and vomiting. Enlargement of the spleen and lymph nodes, irregular heart rhythm, arthritis, and brain damage occur with the disease. Some of these symptoms slowly subside over two to three years. Often symptoms leave and recur without another tick bite.

Because tick bites are usually painless, Lyme Disease may go unrecognized for weeks or even months. Doctors may fail to diagnose the disease before it is in its advanced stages. The disease resembles Multiple Sclerosis, gout, and epstein Barr virus (chronic fatigue syndrome).

A test has been developed to identify Lyme Disease. A blood sample is used to determine the number of specific antibodies present, which increases from three days to three weeks after infection. In addition, a urine test that may be more accurate will soon be made available. It will detect Borrelia burgdorferi bacteria, which cause Lyme Disease.

Lyme disease usually occurs in three stages, although not everyone experiences all three:

1. Small raised bumps on the skin and/or a rash appears and may cover the entire torso for a day or two or several weeks and then fade. If a rash appears immediately, it may be a reaction to the tick bite and not to the bacteria itself. Fever, chills, nausea, and vomiting may also occur.

2. Facial paralysis may occur weeks to months later. Enlargement of the spleen and lymph gland, severe headaches, enlargement of the heart muscle, and abnormal heart rhythm occur frequently.

3. Backache, stiff neck, joint pains that attack the knees, swelling and pain in other joints, and even degenerative muscle disease have been linked to Lyme Disease.

The following nutrients help in the treatment of Lyme Disease by strengthening the immune system. As yet, there is no specific antibiotic therapy for this disease.

Note from Dr. Farber: Mild Silver Protein completely destroys all the spirochetes that cause Lyme Disease. MILD SILVER PROTEIN PROTOCOL FOR LYME DISEASE AND CANDIDA YEAST INFECTION
1st month - 1 tablespoon 2 times a day sublingually
2nd and 3rd month - 1 tablespoon 1 time a day sublingually
Take acidophilus by capsule form or by eating yogurt 3 hrs. before and after taking the Mild Silver Protein.

Definition of Sublingual – Hold under tongue for 1 minute, swish around mouth for 10 seconds, gargle and then swallow. The tissue under the tongue which is called sublingual is the highest absorbative tissue in the body.

NUTRIENTS

SUPPLEMENT	SUGGESTED DOSAGE	COMMENTS
Helpful		
Chlorophyll ("green drink")	Take daily.	A potent detoxifier.
Garlic capsules (Kyolic)	2 capsules 3 times daily.	A powerful immune system stimulator that acts as a natural antibiotic.
Germanium	100-200 mg. daily.	Stimulates immune function.
Kelp	5 tablets daily.	Contains essential vitamins and minerals and aids in detoxifying the body.
Multivitamin and mineral complex (high potency)		For necessary vitamins.
Selenium	200 mcg daily.	A free radical scavenger (antioxidant).
Vitamin A	50,000 IU daily.	An important antioxidant.
Vitamin C	6,000-10,000 mg daily in divided doses.	Needed for adequate immune function.
Vitamin E	600 IU daily.	An important antioxidant.
Zinc gluconate lozenges	1 lozenge every 3 hours for 4 days. Dissolve under the tongue.	Necessary for immune function Do not repeat lozenge regimen for at least 30 days.

HERBS

■ Echinacea, goldenseal, milk thistle extract, red clover, and suma are good for treating Lyme Disease.

Recommendations

■ The following are precautionary measures to help prevent tick bites. Remember: time is crucial because the longer the tick is attached, the greater the risk of Lyme Disease.

■ When near or in wooded areas, wear long pants tucked in socks, long sleeved shirts with high necks or a scarf, and a hat.

■ Use Deet (N-diethyl metatoluamide) on clothing, neck, or any exposed area except the face. Deet lasts longer and is safer to use on clothing than on exposed skin, so cover as much of the body with clothing as you can.

■ Do not use excessive amounts of Deet. Wash off as soon as you go indoors. Note: Deet could be fatal if ingested, so watch small children.

■ Check yourself for any small raised bumps and ticks that may appear as pinpoint size specks on clothing.

■ Check pets after they have been outdoors and remove any ticks that you find.

■ Check your children before going to bed during summer if they spend a lot of time outdoors.

■ Put suspicious clothing in the dryer for a half hour to kill ticks by dehydration. Washing clothes, even in hot water and bleach, will not necessarily kill ticks.

■ In an overgrown area, try to stay near the center of the trails and out of wooded areas.

If you find a bite, do the following:

1. Remove the tick with a pair of tweezers. Put the tweezers as close to the skin as possible and pull straight out. Don't twist as you pull and don't squeeze its bloated body or the bacteria may be injected into the skin. Thoroughly wash your hands and the bite area and

apply rubbing alcohol to the bite area. Don't use a match or try to burn the tick out or any other home remedy like kerosene or petroleum jelly. If you suspect it is a deer tick, call your doctor. He may want to identify the tick.

2. Apply a topical antiseptic (rubbing alcohol).

3. For the next three weeks look for any of the symptoms listed in this section. See your doctor.

Considerations

Heat relieves joint pain. Take hot baths or whirlpool treatments.

Note from Dr. Farber: When using Mild Silver Protein, add some form of acidophilus daily.

AIDS
(Acquired Immune Deficiency Syndrome)

AIDS is an immune system deficiency disorder that suddenly alters the body's ability to defend itself. The AIDS virus invades the T-cells and multiplies, causing a breakdown in the body's immune system, eventually leading to overwhelming infection and/or cancer, with ultimate death. Many of those who die from AIDS have respiratory illnesses that the immune system is not able to fight (e.g., pneumocystis carinii pneumonia, a parasite found in about 60 percent of AIDS patients). At this time, there is no cure for AIDS. Eighty percent of those diagnosed with full-fledged AIDS since 1984 have already died.

The virus that causes AIDS is called HIV, which stands for human immunodeficiency virus. The origin of this virus is unknown. The earliest documented case of AIDS appeared in 1981, but doctors acknowledge that there were probably unidentified cases in the 1970's.

Many people who are carriers of the HIV virus are not

even aware that they have it. They spread the virus primarily through sexual contact or through the sharing of needles during intravenous drug use. Those who abuse drugs should never share a needle. Those who engage in sexual intercourse (anal or vaginal) with persons whose sexual history is unknown or with multiple partners should consider the consequences. Adequate precautions should be taken by those who continue to practice anything but monogamy. Condoms, along with spermicide, should be used if a monogamous relationship cannot be maintained; they are about 90 percent effective against transmission of the HIV virus.

It is conservatively estimated that about 30 percent of those who are infected with HIV contract AIDS. People who are infected with this virus are more likely to contract AIDS if their immune systems are severely suppressed. When the immune system is working properly, a virus is taken into the white cells and destroyed. When a person has a full-blown case of AIDS, the AIDS virus is taken in, but the white cells can't kill it, and the virus reproduces unchecked.

The risk of developing AIDS is proportional to the degree of immune suppression and, of course, the amount and duration of exposure to the AIDS virus. With an optimal functioning immune system, AIDS can be avoided, even in high risk groups. Studies have repeatedly shown that the "immune compromised person" is at greatest risk to succumb to AIDS. Because of a weakened immune system, resistance to many viruses and bacteria results in an increased susceptibility to infections, a rare skin cancer called Kaposi's sarcoma, Epstein Barr virus (EBV), cytomegalovirus (CMV), herpes simplex virus (HSV), candidiasis, salmonella, *Mycobacterium aviumintracellulare*, tuberculosis, and toxoplasmosis.

Besides sexual contacts, AIDS is spread primarily

through the sharing of needles by intravenous drug users and blood transfusions. In the United States, as well as in many other parts of the world, blood is screened for HIV and discarded if found to contain the virus. Occasionally, however, the HIV-infected blood does pass through, because the virus does not always show up in tests if it has been recently contracted. AIDS is also passed from mothers with the virus to children during birth. It is also possible for dentists and medical workers who come into close contact with bodily fluids of infected persons to become infected if they fail to use extreme caution. Many wear rubber gloves to avoid possible contact with blood products or saliva. While there are varying points of view, we believe that the virus may live for many days, even in a dried inactive state, and then become infectious again.

It takes two to five years (or longer) after infection for symptoms of the AIDS virus to appear. When the virus becomes active, some of the symptoms are non-specific and variable. They include fever, fatigue, loss of appetite and weight, swollen lymph nodes, diarrhea, night sweats, skin disorders, and enlarged liver and/or spleen. The first sign may be a tongue that is coated with white bumps. This is oral candidiasis, or thrush. Candidiasis indicates a compromised immune system.

The immune system is the most important single factor in disease prevention. At this time, building up the immune system is the best defense for the potential AIDS victim. Correct diet, appropriate supplements, exercise, proper environment, and correct mental outlook all play significant roles in keeping the immune system working adequately at all times.

The fundamental approach in treatment is to eliminate all known causes of immune suppression and to implement the use of all therapies that stimulate immune function.

The AIDS victim and those at risk to contract AIDS can be helped through the following program:

NUTRIENTS

SUPPLEMENT	SUGGESTED DOSAGE	COMMENTS
Very Important		
Aerobić 07 from Aerobic Life Products or Dioxychlor from American Biologics	9 drops in water 3 times daily.	For tissue oxygenation. Kills harmful bacteria.
Egg lecithin	20 g on an empty stomach, divided throughout the day.	For cellular protection.
Garlic tablets (Kyolic)	2 capsules with meals 3 times daily.	A powerful immunostimulant.
Germanium	200 mg daily.	For tissue oxygenation and interferon production.
Protein supplement (free form amino acids)	As directed on label.	Protein in this form is readily available for the body's use and more easily metabolized.
Selenium	200 mcg daily.	Free radical scavenger.
Superoxide dismutase (SOD) from Biotec Foods	As directed on label.	Free radical scavenger.
Vitamin B complex plus B_{12} and B_6 (pyridoxine) or liver	100 mg 3 times daily in tablet form or receive injections under doctor's supervision. Injections are the most effective.	Antistress vitamins, especially important for normal brain function.
*Vitamin C plus bioflavonoids	10,000 mg in divided doses through day.	Use buffered, powdered ascorbic acid. *See* ASCORBIC ACID FLUSH in Part Three.

Acidophilus	3 times daily. Take a high-powered form.	Supplies essential "friendly" bacteria for intestinal tract.
Coenzyme Q_{10}	100 mg daily.	Supports immune system.
DMG (Gluconic from DaVinci Labs)	As directed on label.	Actively stimulates the immune system, increasing the T-cell population.
Kyo-Green	As directed on label.	Supplies nutrients needed for repair. Important in immune response.
Multimineral formula (high potency) with		Hypoallergenic form is best. Omit iron supplements if fever is present. Do not exceed 100 mg zinc at any time.
zinc	50 mg daily.	
plus copper	3 mg daily.	
Proteolytic enzymes	6 tablets between meals.	Destroys free radicals and aids digestion.
Quercetin plus bromelin	As directed on label.	Aids in preventing reactions to certain foods, pollens, and other allergens. Increases immunity.
Raw thymus plus multiglandulars including spleen from Arteria	As directed on label.	Best from lamb source. Enhances T-cell production from thymus and spleen.
Vitamin A emulsion	50,000 IU daily.	Reduce dosage if known to have liver disease, and use caution if using pill form.
Vitamin E emulsion	200 IU daily increasing to 800 IU. Emulsified form is readily and rapidly assimilated.	Both vitamins A and E destroy free radicals and enhance immune function.

Aloe vera	As directed on label.	Carrisyn from the aloe plant may work as the drug AZT without the side effects.

Essential fatty acids	As directed on label.	Unsaturated fatty acids are most important in the diet. Some sources are primrose oil, black currant oil, salmon oil, and linseed oil.
L-Carnitine plus L-cysteine and L-methionine and L-ornithine (amino acids)	As directed on label, taken on an empty stomach with 500 mg vitamin C and 50 mg vitamin B₆.	Improves immune function. Do not give children L-ornithine.
Multiple enzyme digestive formula	Take with meals.	Improves digestion.
RNA-DNA complex		

---

*Massive IV doses of vitamin C (100–200 grams daily) have been used safely, often with dramatic improvement, in the treatment of AIDS.

HERBS

■ Silymarin (extract of milk thistle weed) aids in repairing the liver. Also helpful are cayenne, echinacea, Chinese ginseng, shiitake mushroom extract, and suma.

■ An extract from a mushroom known as somastatin may bolster the immune system and improve liver function in AIDS patients.

■ Echinacea, goldenseal, mullein, and suma are good for cleaning the blood and lymph systems, for viral and bacterial infections, and for boosting the immune system.

■ Ginkgo biloba extract is good for the brain cells and circulation.

■ Pau d'arco is a natural antibiotic, and potentiates immune function.

■ Red clover is a good blood cleanser.

The AIDS *Treatment News* of San Francisco, California, reported that a chemical compound called hypericin, which is found in the herb St. Johnswort, may inhibit retroviral infections, which may be useful in the treatment of AIDS patients.

■ Black radish and dandelion help cleanse the liver.

■ Chapparal aids in the destruction of free radicals.

■ Garlic and rose hips aid in digestion, endurance, and strength, and reduce the risk of blood clotting. Garlic is a natural antibiotic.

■ Siberian ginseng helps bronchial disorders and endocrine gland function, and boosts energy.

■ Bee propolis is good for bacterial infections invading the lungs, mouth, throat, and mucous membranes.

RECOMMENDATIONS

■ Increase your intake of fresh fruits and vegetables. Juicing is beneficial. "Green drinks" and carrot and beet root juice should be consumed on a daily basis, with garlic and onion added. Kyo-Green is excellent three times a day, and contains chlorophyll, protein, vitamins, minerals, and enzymes.

■ The diet should consist of 75% raw foods plus seeds, nuts, and grains. Obtain as much fresh air, rest, and sunshine as possible. A lack of quality protein and adequate calories in the diet is a common reason for immune deficiency.

■ Do not smoke, and stay away from those who do. Eliminate alcohol, caffeine, colas, sugar, and sugar products, as well as red meat.

Note from Dr. Farber: Preliminary studies have shown that Mild Silver Protein not only inhibits the replication of the HIV Virus, but also kills it in vitro (see report at the beginning of book).

CHAPTER 9
NUTRITIONAL THERAPY

In this section, I will cover the basic principles and methods of nutritional therapy as it pertains directly to Lyme Disease and will give an outline of what to take, how much, and why. For a more in-depth treatment of this field, the author recommends "Health and Healing" by Dr. Andrew Weill, M.D., graduate of Harvard University. He is a medical researcher and a practicing physician in the field of complimentary alternative methods of holistic medicine. He currently teaches medical students at the University of Arizona College of Medicine in Tuscon. I had the privilege of studying with Dr. Weill at an intensive seminar and found him to be a pioneer in his field but also the most knowledgeable and objective expert in nutritional and herbal medicine.

PURPOSE OF NUTRITIONAL THERAPY IN RELATION TO LYME DISEASE

While living in Colorado, I had the opportunity to become a licensed General Contractor, building chalet cedar homes as well as holistic health facilities in the mountains. During that period of time, it became very clear that in addition to a good blueprint of what one wanted to build, the next most important concept to consider were the materials which were to be used to build with. Regardless of how great an idea and plan one had to work with, the finished product would only be perfect if the materials used were of the highest quality. There is a lesson to be learned here.

The human body (when free of disease) is an outstanding example of a perfectly designed machine. This is not surprising, since He who designed the blueprint is the Creator of the universe and we all carry God's genius in our D.N.A. However, just as a seed attracts the elements from the earth around it in order to grow and create a new life organism, so also do the cells of the human body grow from the materials which we eat and then assimilate. And *what* we assimilate is a direct result of our *diet*.

BASIC RULES FOR GOOD HEALTH

Eat Fresh, Raw Fruits and Vegetables, Nuts, Seeds, Sprouts and Herbs.

Meals should consist largely of these. Drink only pure water, fresh or natural fruit and vegetable juices and herb teas between meals. If a snack is desired, limit to fresh fruits or vegetables, and possibly a small amount of cheese or nuts. Natural vitamin supplements should be taken with meals, unless otherwise directed.

DO NOT OVEREAT

Small meals eaten only when hungry are the most healthy practice. Breakfast is considered by many to be the most important meal of the day. If you are one of those who does not feel hungry in the morning, a very simple rule to follow is this; never eat more at dinner than you ate at breakfast, i.e., if you ate no breakfast, eat no dinner. We can guarantee you will be hungry the next morning! "Feast," do not eat, and always feast in as calm and peaceful environment as possible. It is better not to eat when you are upset or uptight. It is also better not to eat while watching television, and if you must eat in a hurry, eat a very small meal. While you are feasting, do so slowly and allow your appetite to catch up with your mouth. Stop when you are full.

COMBINATIONS OF FOODS

There are certain limitations to the efficiency of our digestive enzymes. When our eating overrides these limitations, we are asking for digestive trouble. Undigested foods have no nutritional value. In fact, undigested food spoils in the digestive tract producing poisons or congestion which may be injurious. The proper digestion of starches and sugars are assimilated as monosaccharides, while the fermentation of starches and sugars produces carbon dioxide, acetic acid and alcohol which are poisonous. Protein, properly digested, yields amino acids, while the putrefaction from improperly digested protein yields ptomaines (ptomaine poisoning), and leucomaines–both toxic. Consequently, proper food combinations enhances nutrition and provides protection against poisoning. Allergies are a form of protein poisoning, whereas indigestion is a form of putrefaction poisoning. Allergic reactions can usually be prevented by complete digestion afforded by proper food combinations.

ACIDS AND PROTEINS SHOULD NOT BE EATEN TOGETHER

Remembering that pepsin (the protein digester) acts favorably in an acid medium, one might suppose that the addition of more acid, such as citrus fruits, might enhance digestion. Quite the contrary happens. The addition of acids, citrus or other, inhibits the secretion of the gastric juices necessary for the digestion of proteins. Either the gastric juices will not be secreted in the presence of an acid or the acidic environment will destroy pepsin. Any acid eaten on a salad, for example vinegar or lemon juice, eaten in combination with a protein meal inhibits the production of hydrochloric acid by pepsin and thus interferes with protein digestion. There is an exception to this rule. Acids may be combined with nuts, cheese and avocados because the high fat content of these foods will postpone gastric secretion until the acids have been assimilated.

ACIDS AND STARCHES SHOULD NOT BE EATEN TOGETHER

The digestion of starches begins in the mouth with an enzyme called ptyalin. The body works sequentially. Saliva, high in ptyalin, is secreted by the salivary glands, reducing starches to maltose which is later reduced in the intestine to dextrose. Actions in the mouth are preparatory and ptyalin will not act in a mildly acidic or strong alkaline environment. The axiom, chew your food 100 times is not solely to masticate. Lemons or other sour fruits will completely arrest the action of ptyalin, resulting in a poorly digested meal which will most likely putrefy, yielding low nutritional value.

SUGAR AND PROTEINS SHOULD NOT BE EATEN TOGETHER

All sugars, sweet fruits, and even honey undergo digestion in the intestine. If they are delayed in the stomach, they quickly ferment, producing acids. To our mutual dismay, the addition of jams, jellies, honey, molasses, etc. to breads, cereals, or even pancakes produces fermentation. Date bread, raisin bread, or any other sweet fruit bread will most likely ferment. What happens is that the mouth is fooled by the sweet disguise of starch and will not secrete the ptyalin which is necessary for starch digestion, so none will occur. The starch will then delay the sweets in the stomach where they will ferment.

FATS AND PROTEINS SHOULD
NOT BE EATEN TOGETHER

Fat, present in the stomach, lessens the activity of gastric juices by as much as 50%. It does this by actually depressing the gastric secretion of pepsin in addition to protecting the food you have eaten with a protective fatty shield. Green vegetables, especially raw ones, will counteract the effect of fat. So the consumption of greens with a fat-protein meal may offset the imbalance.

PROTEINS AND CARBOHYDRATES
SHOULD NOT BE EATEN TOGETHER

Gastric juices contain three enzymes which act upon proteins, fats, and milk. They are pepsin, lipase and rennin respectively. The digestion of protein requires an acidic environment initiated by the secretion of pepsin into the digestive tract. Pepsin splits the protein molecule forming hydrochloric acid. As the stomach gains in its acidity, while digesting protein, starch digestion comes to an abrupt end. We may say that those conditions which are optimum for protein digestion exclude starch digestion and, worse than that–the introduction of the starch almost neutralizes the acid, deactivating both enzymes, yielding once more, the beginning of putrefaction. Beets, potatoes, cauliflower and other starchy vegetables make a poor combination with proteins.

EAT ONE HIGH PROTEIN FOOD AT A TIME

Man's digestive system is expressly organized and timed. If two distinctly different high proteins are eaten together, the amount of digestive secretions for each may serve to nullify the action of the other. The body modifies its digestive process to the requirements of each food. Suppose milk were eaten jointly with meat. Rennin would initiate a highly acidic reaction which would upset the proportion of pepsin and lipase acting upon the meat. Both proteins would be incompletely digested. Non-starchy vegetable and succulent vegetables make the best combination with protein foods.

MELONS SHOULD BE EATEN ALONE

Melons are one of the most simple foods to digest. So simple, in fact, that they proceed directly to the intestine. If they are held up in the stomach by other foods, they will decompose quickly and ferment. It is very good to make a meal of a melon. Fresh berries with melons are acceptable.

DRINK MILK ALONE

Man is the only animal in the animal kingdom who drinks milk beyond the age of weaning. Milk often causes mucus in the colon and should be eliminated from the diet. However, if you must drink milk, it should be natural raw milk from a certified source, and follow these tips: because milk is high in protein and fat, it stimulates the secretion of pepsin and rennin which coagulates the milk. These coagulated particles insulate other foods from gastric juices by clinging to them. Milk may combine with acid fruits, but its use with grains, cereals or starches foster putrefaction.

LIMIT PROTEIN

Especially animal protein and, in particular, red muscle meats as they are very hard to digest and certainly overrate in quality of protein. Most authorities agree that the egg is the perfect protein and we recommend 2 per day. It is generally agreed that the required amount of protein that a normal adult needs is between 65-95 grams per day. The average American eats 2-3 times that amount. It is generally considered healthier to limit animal protein to only 3 or 4 times per week and then primarily fish and poultry.

CHEW YOUR FOOD WELL

Chew until you think it is chewed enough...then chew some more. You can't overdo it.

EAT NATURAL FOODS WHENEVER POSSIBLE

If the food you eat will not spoil when left out overnight on your kitchen counter top, it probably is not a live food and, therefore, will contribute little to your health. Almost all canned, frozen and otherwise processed foods contain additives for color, taste or preservation, and are considered to have potentially deleterious effects on human health. In the years to come, due to consumer pressure, most of the over 10,000 food additives which the FDA has on the GRAS (generally regarded as safe for human consumption) list will be removed due to more extensive research showing their potential danger, especially when ingested in combinations. In the meantime, it is recommended that you avoid foods with these products in them. Learn to read labels carefully.

REST AND RELAXATION

Learn to get complete relaxation and rest to allow the body its required time to recuperate from the daily stress we place it under. A good course in prayer mediation is strongly recommended.

EXERCISE, FRESH AIR AND SUNSHINE

Daily exercise is probably the one single missing ingredient after poor diet that causes poor health in our society. Make a contract with yourself today to get into a daily habit of exercise and, if possible, combine it with fresh air and sunshine. If you set any kind of a priority on your health, then set your highest priority on regular, daily exercise and START NOW!

POSITIVE THINKING AND MEANINGFUL ACTIVITY

Get a good book such as Peale's "Power of Positive Thinking" or Carnegie's "How to Win Friends and Influence People," and begin to develop a good positive image. Couple this with a meaningful activity such as participation in church, civic or youth activities, and you will find a new look on life and your health will improve.

FOODS TO AVOID

Avoid refined sugar or refined sugar products such as jams, jellies, preserves, marmalade, ice cream, sherberts, jello, cake, candy, cookies, chewing gum, pastries, pies, soft drinks, tapioca puddings, sugared fruit juices, fruits canned in sugar syrup.

Also catsup, mustard, Worcestershire sauce, pickles, green salted olives.

Avoid salted foods, such as potato chips, salted nuts, pretzels, salted crackers and popcorn.

Avoid white rice and pearled barley.

Also commercial dry cereals such as cornflakes and others.

Don't eat fried foods.

Avoid saturated fats and hydrogenated oils...enemies of your heart.

Avoid foods which contain cottonseed oil. When a

product is labeled *vegetable oil...*find out what kind it is before you use it.

In all vegetable oils found in a grocery store, Lecithin and Vitamin E have been removed to give a long shelf life. Substitute cold-pressed or unrefined oils found in health food stores.

ALSO AVOID...

Oleo and margarines...saturated fats and hydrogenated oils.

Peanut butter that contains salt, hydrogenated oils and corn syrup.

Coffee, decaffeinated coffee, commercial tea and alcoholic beverages.

Tobacco.

Fresh pork and pork products.

Smoked meats, such as ham, bacon and sausage.

Lunch meats, such as hot dogs, salami, bologna, corned beef, pastrami and meats containing sodium nitrate or nitrite.

Dried fruits which contain sulfur dioxide (preservative).

Chickens that have been injected with stilbestrol, or fed with chicken feed that contains any drugs.

Canned soups (read labels, look for sugar, starch, white or wheat-white flour and preservative).

Food that contains benzoate of soda, cream of tartar (preservative).

White-flour products such as white bread, and wheat and rye bread that has a mixed wheat-white flour in it: dumplings, biscuits, buns, gravy, noodles, spaghetti, pizza, ravioli, sago, prepared & commercial puddings, and ready-mix bakery products.

Bleached and unbleached white flour products.

Wheat flour, a mixed white-wheat flour. If you use wheat, it should be whole wheat, thus you know it contains no white flour. However many people are allergic to the gluten in wheat.

Day-old cooked vegetables, pre-mixed salads, warmed-over potatoes.

Self drugging...no aspirin, buffered aspirin, antihistamines, milk of magnesia, tranquilizers, sleeping pills, pain killers, strong catharics or fizzing bromides. These are all potentially harmful and all medication should only be taken at the direction of a holistic physician.

GOOD FOOD SUBSTITUTIONS

If you must use a sweetener, raw unprocessed honey is an excellent one. Honey may be used in place of refined sugar for jams, jellies, preserves, homemade ice cream and all pastries. If there is a glucose problem, granulated fructose is a perfect substitute. Honey or sucrose may be used as you would sucrose.

USE...

Condiments such as catsup, mustard, etc., may be used in moderation if they contain natural ingredients with no preservative, such as those found in health food stores.

Cayenne pepper replaces black pepper.

Kelp or "Vegit" replaces the desire of salt (found in health food stores).

Make your own pickles or green olives, or look for those containing "all natural" ingredients. Commercial pickles/green olives are loaded with chemicals, preservative and other additives and, therefore, should be avoided.

Raw nuts for snacks.

All natural brown rice (long or short gain) or wild rice.

Granola containing natural ingredients (no sugar or preservative).

Millet (hot cereal), 100% oatmeal, wheat germ, raw bran and many others.

Bake, broil or steam your foods instead of frying.

"Crude" or "cold-pressed" vegetable oils which are high in poly-unsaturated fats: safflower, corn, peanut, soy, all-blend, etc. (from a health food store). They should be refrigerated to prevent rancity.

Butter used in moderation. Raw, unsalted is best.

100% peanut butter and other nut butters. Grind your own or shop in a health food store. Look for unsalted, no hydrogenated oils.

Coffee substitutes: Sano-Caf, Pero, Postum and others taste very similar to coffee and contain all natural ingredients. Also, there is a great assortment of herb teas available to replace commercial tea which contains tannic acid.

Fresh, raw juices are a great substitution for alcoholic beverages. Not only are they healthful, but they give you a natural high with no hang-over. Fresh or frozen fish (unbreaded and not smoked).

Meat (beef, lamb, chicken): If you wish to include meat in your diet, it should be free of hormones, chemicals and other injections.

Good substitutions for lunch meats might include avocado, cheese, a good quality tuna, fresh natural poultry, etc.

Try making your own homemade soups. They are much more delicious and nutritious. Natural food cookbooks have numerous recipes.

Use 100% whole grain breads to replace white bread. Whole wheat flour or whole wheat pastry flour can be used for all baking.

Always try to eat fresh vegetables, salads and fruit. When food is re-cooked, warmed over, or has been sitting in the refrigerator for a few days, enzymes are destroyed as well as many vitamins and minerals. Therefore, you are consuming food with little or no nutritive value.

There are numerous herbs available in capsule form and bulk pack which aid in providing relief from any common ailments. Keep an open mind and acquaint yourself with these. Your local health food store can be of great help in this area.

Use leafy lettuce (i.e., red, romaine and butter) in place of head lettuce which is very difficult to digest and causes gastral intestinal stress.

Sprouts are an excellent source of vitamins, minerals and enzymes plus being fun to grow (its like having a mini garden in your kitchen). See your local health food store for supplies and directions. Also cookbooks for recipes and ideas on using them.

Experiment with herbs as seasoning in your foods. They contribute variety and promote good health. Most health food stores have fresh herbs, and books to guide in their use.

Natural salad dressings are becoming popular and are much more healthy and flavorful than the old traditionals found in supermarkets.

SEVEN DAY DETOXIFYING FEAST

When an automobile is full of carbon, it has no pep. It is clogged up. You may put in the very best gas and oil, but the speed is not there. The sensible and logical thing to do is to take the car to a mechanic and have the carbon cleaned out. After that is done, what happens? The car seems like new. There is plenty of power.

Your body is comparable to the car. When the cells, of which you have millions, are clogged up with acid, sugar, mucus, pus, etc., you have no pep, your appetite is poor, you do not sleep well, your complexion is bad, your eyes are dull, you suffer from aches and pains, you are nervous and irritable, you feel indifferent...everything seems wrong. Life is not so great as it once was; in fact, you are really ill.

The sensible and logical thing to do is to CLEAN OUT, not just the bowels but the CELLS. Purge these cells—get all this accumulated toxic material out. But how? Well, that's easy if you observe this detoxifying feast.

It will do it every time.

For seven short days you will be on a FEAST, not a fast. You will be filling your body with Nature's life-giving foods--fruits and vegetables that contain all those precious vitamins and minerals. When a sufficient amount of these live substances reach the cells of your body, there will be a flushing and a cleansing such as you have never experienced before. You will eliminate toxic material that has been with you for years, toxic material that has robbed you of your vitality. When this is all out, you will be like the car which has been cleaned of the carbon. You will have plenty of energy—your complexion will undergo a marvelous transformation—you will sleep like a baby—aches and pains will disappear—your nerves will be at ease and you will feel so good that life will be a joy.

That is what this detoxifying feast will do. Follow directions carefully.

BREAKFAST FOR EACH OF THE SEVEN DAYS

Fifteen minutes before you are ready to eat breakfast, squeeze the juice of a lemon in a medium glass of hot water and drink it.

BREAKFAST

Orange or grapefruit juice: 8 ounces. You can take more if you desire, but be sure that you take eight ounces at least.

Cottage cheese: 5 level tablespoonfuls. No more—no less.

Fresh fruit: one-half pound. You may eat more, but be sure to eat at least one-half pound. You can eat only one kind of fruit or you may mix (no bananas or avocados).

Herb tea: one cup, if desired. Sweeten lightly with

honey, if desired.

Between breakfast and lunch you should drink all the fruit and vegetable juice you can hold. Also eat fresh raw vegetables and fruit. The more live food you put down, the more thorough will be the cleansing. If you cannot get the fresh juices, then use the canned variety. Make up a lot of vegetable juices. Drink lots of this broth. It is full of minerals.

LUNCH FOR EACH OF THE SEVEN DAYS

Vegetable broth: drink two cups during the meal.

Salad: make a chopped salad of fresh raw vegetables. Use a dressing of olive oil, lemon juice and salt. Eat at least eight level tablespoonfuls of salad, more if you desire. Use four of the vegetables listed below:

artichokes, asparagus, beans, beets, brussels sprouts, cabbage, carrots, cauliflower, cucumbers, celery, dandelions, endive, egg plant, fresh green corn, fresh green peas, green peppers, kale, kohlrabi, lettuce, Lotus, okra, onions, parsley, parsnips, pumpkin, radishes, rutabagas, salsify, spinach, squash, swiss chard, tomatoes, turnips (you may use the leaves or tops also).

Dessert: fresh fruit dessert with a little pure honey.

Herb tea or water.

Between lunch and dinner drink all the fruit and vegetable juice you desire. Eat all the fresh fruit and vegetables you want. Fill up, it's medicine for you. Remember; the purge comes from the vitamins and minerals in the food, so be sure and eat plenty.

DINNER FOR EACH OF THE SEVEN DAYS

Vegetable broth: drink two cups during the meal, more if you desire.

Cooked vegetables: select two or three of the different kind listed above and cook them with butter. Eat a generous helping of each (no potatoes).

Dessert: baked apple with cream or a salad of fresh fruits. A little honey may be used.

Herb tea or water

If you feel hungry after dinner, eat fresh fruits and drink fruit or vegetable juice–ALL you want.

RECIPE FOR VEGETABLE BROTH

Take 7 carrots and 1 small bunch of celery and cut fine. Place in 2 quarts hot water and boil for 15 minutes. Add one-third bunch of parsley and a large handful of fresh spinach, cut fine. Boil 10 minutes more. Drain off the juice or broth. Flavor with salt of onion, okra, tomatoes, green peppers or garlic.

The above recipe makes about one day's supply. You can make more if you desire and place in refrigerator. It can be used hot or cold. The purpose of this broth is to FLUSH. Drink lots of it during the seven days. It is full of minerals from the vegetables.

WHAT TO EXPECT FROM THE DIET

The first day you may feel slight discomfort by having changed your regular mode of eating, but do not allow this to disturb you, for it is natural. About the third or fourth day the bowels and kidneys will begin to move freely. Much toxic material will be passed. There may be symptoms of headache, perhaps nausea, gas, a few aches and pains but do not become alarmed. Nature is merely cleaning you out. These symptoms are quite natural and to be expected. About the fifth day you will feel a surge of energy. You will be surprised at yourself. Your complexion will probably have cleared up, your eyes will begin to brighten, you will feel wonderfully clean inside. The little cells that were so full of toxins are now clean and they begin crying out for other food. Continue on until the end of the seventh day; then combine your meals.

P.S. If you start this diet—STICK TO IT. Don't try it one day then quit. Follow instructions and reap a wonderful reward of HEALTH again.

COMMON FOOD ALLERGIES

The discussion of food allergies is included in nutritional planning due to growing awareness by many hundreds of clinicians that this phenomenon is occurring in a substantial number of patients and that the percentage of patients affected is increasing from year to year. In 1932 when Warren T. Vaugn, M.D. began to make his studies of the problem, he discovered that 61% of individuals queried had food allergies. By 1956 when Arthur F. Coca, M.D. wrote *The Pulse Test* he estimated that 90% of the American public were experiencing the manifestations of common food allergies. That is to say that almost all of us are allergic to many of the foods we are eating every day.

The list of possible conditions associated with food allergies may be more impressive than the numbers of people involved. The list includes such conditions as recurrent headaches, nervousness and emotional complaints, heart attacks, epilepsy, obesity, gastro-intestinal disorders of all types, diabetes, and many, many others.

Why is the problem growing in numbers affected and why are the conditions involved becoming more serious as the years go by? There are may reasons. Many of the potential excitants are symbiotic with each other; they combine to create an enhanced effect more serious than could be done alone. The list of excitants includes not only foods but airborne pollutants from industrial pollution, the automobile, odors from cleaning products, perfumes, shaving lotions, rubber and soft plastics, as well as what Thermon G. Randolph, M.D., calls "chemical contamination" of our food. These contaminants include EDTA in frozen vegetables, chemicals from the lining of tin cans, softening agents, emulsifying agents, food coloring, preservative, and many others whose use increases from year to year. Also, refined white sugar and white flour, complex foods that are difficult for the body to assimilate, are a major part of the problem. As you know, the amounts of these substances consumed has grown greatly since the turn of the century.

Researchers have conclusively proven that these products are a major factor in the common chronic disease states of "civilized Western man". In 1966 and 1969 Doctors Cleve and Campbell wrote the first and second editions of a book entitled *Diabetes, Coronary Thrombosis and Saccharin Disease.* They discovered in extensive travels around the world that societies that do not consume white sugar and flour simply do not experience dental decay and pyorrhea, gastric or duodenal ulcers, and other forms of indigestion, obesity, diabetes, coronary disease, and constipation. In 1963 Dennis Burkitt, M.D., also stated similar findings based on his experience as a surgeon in Africa for many years.

To combat the effect of these allergy states we must strive to discover what foods, "food contaminants," and airborne odors we are sensitive to. There are several methods we can use.

It has been observed by Coca and others that the pulse rate will rise when we are exposed to an allergen. This can be used to discover food allergies. Take your pulse before you get up in the morning, then again before breakfast and thirty, sixty, and ninety minutes after breakfast and each meal throughout the day. Carefully record all foods consumed. During this time you must stop smoking. If your pulse rate is higher laying in bed then when you get up, you can suspect you are allergic to "house dust" in your bedding. If the pulse rate is higher before breakfast than it was lying in bed, you can suspect toothpaste, perfumes, or deodorants.

Consult your holistic physician.

Another method is the fast for four days consuming only distilled water, and then eating one food at a time, carefully recording how you feel and any elevation in pulse rate. You may notice many chronic symptoms disappearing if they are caused by food allergy. If you become very ill during this time, it is a sign of food allergy-addiction, or of glucose intolerance.

These methods are not easy and should be utilized if other nutritional measures have not sufficed. It should be remembered that the nutritional program you have been placed on by your holistic doctor is designed to combat food allergies by greatly enhancing your body's ability to handle these allergy-producing substances through supplements and to eliminate many of those substances from your diet.

Note from Dr. Farber: There is material quoted in this chapter that I have collected over many years and from unknown sources. My sincerest thanks to any and all who may have contributed to this chapter unknowingly.

CHAPTER 10
UNDERSTANDING AND CONQUERING THE COMMON COLD

(Through the use of Mild Silver Protein
and Supportive Holistic Methods –
including Chronic Infection, Flu, Grippe,
Tonsillitis, Sinusitis, Bronchial Catarrh,
Chronic Colds, Virus Type Infections)

COMMON MISCONCEPTIONS

Before you can conquer something you must first understand what you're up against. The common cold is probably one of the most deluding and least understood phenomenon in medical symptomatology. Everything from the change in the weather to bacteria have been named as its cause.

It's the old story of the Indian wise man who asked (separately) a group of blind people to describe what an elephant looked like. One man who touched the elephant's tail said that it looked like a rope. Another who touched its leg said that it looked like a tree trunk...while yet another who touched its ear described it as a large leaf. In this story each man was correct from his own point of perspective; however, each one of them missed the holistic picture which involves putting all these parts together.

This same phenomenon is true of the *common cold.* One person describes it as congestion, another as an inflammation, another as a fever, while another describes it as a cough. They're all correct but they're all wrong in that they have failed to see the whole.

We need to dispel the myths about what the common cold is and also describe the necessary steps which can be taken to conquer it and relieve much unnecessary suffering.

The prevention and immediate answer to the common cold is Mild Silver Protein, which attacks and destroys either the bacterial or viral cause of the microorganism which initiates the common cold when one has allowed his resistance to become weak by a depleted or improperly working immune system.

WHAT IS THE COMMON COLD?

Nature, in its divine wisdom, has provided man with the perfect healing tool for detoxification, which is implemented automatically when the body gets to a point where more serious disease may develop. This *healing tool,* which is a very positive process in nature, is the *common cold,* although most people consider it a negative process out of ignorance. Its purpose as outlined by nature is as follows, by tracing the positive aspects of its symptoms.

1. FEVER–is an adaptation of nature which the body implements in order to burn up toxic waste and disease-causing bacteria.

2. CONGESTION–is a result of the body's attempt to clear itself of excess mucous and lymph which has built up in the body.

3.COUGH–is the body's tool for bringing excess

mucous and phlegm up from the lungs and throat to the outside of the body. This is also true of sneezing.

4. INFLAMMATION–occurs in the throat, lungs, and throughout the body in order to burn up toxic waste products.

5. DIARRHEA–occurs sometimes in order to purge the colon of toxic waste materials, unfriendly bacteria, and mucous plugs.

6. HEADACHE–occurs along with body ache as a result of toxins running through the blood stream. Its purpose , through its pain, is to make the person aware that something needs correction so that the body can be put to rest in order to seek out relief.

7. PAIN–is a warning signal, and its purpose has never been to punish the individual. It is an *alarm* of nature that signals that something is wrong and needs correction. Without pain receptors in the nervous system, man would not survive as a species because any small injury could kill him if unattended.

Pain should be respected and not hated. Everything possible should be done to remove and alleviate it by affecting a cure, but it should never be covered up by medication such as pain pills, muscle relaxants, or tranquilizers. This would be analogous to turning off a fire alarm while allowing the fire to grow in strength and eventually rage out of control.

All of the symptoms of the common cold should be respected and *accelerated* through natural methods rather than blocked or covered up. It is easy to see that the common cold is a holistic process of nature, which if allowed to persist without dealing with the *cause,* can eventually lead to more serious complications. It should be viewed a *natural elimination process.* With this philosophy it will be much easier for an individual to implement those necessary steps in nature which will speed up this process, rather than to slow it down or hide it.

COMMON QUESTIONS
AND MISCONCEPTIONS

Patient: Is it true that the causes of the common cold are unfriendly bacteria or viruses?

Doctor. The cause of the common cold is not bacteria or viruses, but the *lowered resistance* of the body, which then provides a breeding ground for the bacteria or virus to grow. If one raises the resistance of the body through natural methods, then it will cease to be a fertile breeding ground and environment. Bacteria is not a cause of disease but instead the initiator of the symptoms of this disease called the common cold when it is allowed to take root because of an improperly functioning immune system.

Patient: Is it wise to use conventional antibiotics to cure the common cold?

Doctor: Conventional antibiotics have *never cured anything*. Only nature cures. All an antibiotic can do is kill harmful bacteria. The problem with this is that it also kills all the friendly bacteria in the colon and body, which can lead to further disease while it also lowers the body's resistance. Your body, with the aid of natural substances, produces all the antibodies it needs naturally. Conventional antibiotics should be avoided and Mild Silver Protein should be used instead. It is also important to keep the body's acidophilus level high by eating yogurt and taking acidophiluc supplements.

Patient: Are antihistamines for decongestion harmful to the body?

Doctor: Yes, they are. They cause the lymph and mucous membranes to unnaturally dry up, thus blocking the pathway for excess mucous and lymph-carrying harmful bacteria to get out of the body. Conventional antihistamines and conventional antibiotics defeat the whole purpose for which the body implemented the *cold symptoms* in the first place...and they can only set up the body as a breeding ground for worse diseases at a future time.

Patient: What about using aspirin for alleviating pain and bringing down fever?

Doctor: Aspirin, when used in excess, is a dangerous over-the-counter drug which can cause ulcers as well as irritation to all of the soft tissue linings of the body. To try to cover up pain is like *sweeping dust under the rug.* One should strive to alleviate the *cause* of the pain instead.

It is important to reiterate that the cause of the common cold is not bacteria or viruses or change in the weather...but instead, *lowered resistance of the body.* All a change in weather does is to stimulate the body, like a catalyst, in order to start this process in motion. Thus the word "cold" comes from the change in seasons (hot to cold, cold to hot), nature's way of causing these eliminative processes to be achieved. It follows that changes in seasons strengthens the body. This is why modern man, with his synthetic environment (central heat and air-conditioning), always has a lowered resistance, unless he constantly exposes himself to the elements of nature which will make him strong.

Patient: Is it true that drinking a lot of fluids such as Coca-Cola will help to overcome a cold if done in conjunction with bed rest?

Doctor: Bed rest is many times necessary to use while treating the cause of the symptoms of the common cold. It is also wise to drink a lot of fluids such as natural orange juice, grape juice, spring water, and herb teas. However, the elements in soft drinks such as coke both clog up and lower the body's resistance with white sugar syrup and chemical contents.

Patient: Is it true, then, that one can cure the common cold by natural methods and that the old techniques for dealing with the common cold are illogical and antiquated?

Doctor: A physician using natural methods does not

seek to cure the collective cold but instead seeks to restore the body of the patient to a high state of natural resistance in which the symptoms of the common cold (or natural elimination process) can be accelerated to their natural conciusion as quickly as possible. This restores the bodily environment to a state of *high resistance* in which disease processes cannot manifest. The old techniques are indeed antiquated in that it is illogical to either sweep dust under a rug or turn off a fire alarm without arresting the fire. It is much wiser for one to clean up the dust and put out the fire at its source. A holistic physician seeks not to cure the common cold, but instead to aid nature in curing the patient who has the cold. However, Mild Silver Protein, by immediately killing the virus or bacteria can totally prevent a cold from beginning or end it in a matter of a few days. One then needs to strengthen and rebuild the immune system.

NATURAL HEALING TECHNIQUES FOR CONQUERING THE COMMON COLD

DIETARY CONSIDERATIONS–In the acute stage of disease which is noted by fever, congestion, and inflammation, one should maintain a partial fast, abstaining from all solid foods and "junk" foods. One should drink fresh fruit juices in large quantities . The orange juice seems to cut the mucous best, and herb teas should also be used. A low-calorie raw fruit and vegetable diet with plenty of raw juices and herb teas (sweetened with honey) can be used after the fever subsides. Raw salads provide a roughage which cleanse the body and can contain raw seeds, nuts, and sprouted seeds and grains...with natural oil and apple cider vinegar dressing.

A loss in appetite is the body's message telling the patient that heavy eating would slow down the healing process while partial fasting will speed it up. While experiencing the symptoms of a cold, do not eat mucous-forming foods such as yogurt, milk, cottage cheese, or cheese. One could eat a good vegetable soup and broth made naturally with tamari (soy sauce) and miso (soybean puree) which helps the body counteract the effects of the common cold. After the cold has completed its cycle, one should ask his holistic physician about receiving a functional nutritional balance and analysis and corresponding dietary program to help insure against future disease processes.

SUPPORTIVE HOLISTIC METHODS AND BIOLOGICAL TREATMENTS

First, take one tablespoon of Mild Silver Protein sublingually twice a day. A child should take a teaspoon and a baby 1/2 teaspoon twice a day until any symptoms subside and then for 3-7 days, depending on the severity. Mild Silver Protein can be used all winter as a preventative.

1. *Ginger and Golden Seal Bath*–The first and possible second night of the symptoms, the patient should take a hot ginger bath. Golden Seal Herb can also be added to this bath as it also helps to detoxify the body. It can be added and brewed directly with the ginger. This bath works extremely well and has been known to cut the symptom time of a cold that has been treated with Mild Silver Protein from its normal length of three weeks to about three days. However, this varies with each individual.

2. *Castor Oil Packs*–These packs can be used on the throat and chest area to lubricate these areas for the purpose of removing congestion. This process is quite effective. Method: apply castor oil externally to the throat and chest area and then apply hot towels, as hot as one can take it, directly to the area and then cover

with any towel. This can be done while laying on a table or the floor. Repeat the heat process and reapplication of the castor oil 3-5 times , as the heat is absorbed by the body quickly.

3. *Slippery Elm Lozenges and Hall's Menthol Eucalyptus Cough Drops*–It is wise to constantly keep the throat lubricated. When the throat is extremely raw, use the "Hall's" and when it is mildly sore, use the "Slippery Elm," which can be purchased at a health food store. These relieve the soreness of the throat quite well.

4. *Sea Salt Water Gargle*–Gargle often with sea salt water as this aids the healing of the inflamed linings of the mucous membranes of the throat.

5. *Eating of Raw Garlic*–Garlic is one of nature's most powerful natural antibiotics. It can be eaten by cutting up a clove into small bits and heating them on a toasted piece of whole wheat bread for a short time with a little safflower oil margarine. One side of the bread can be toasted first under the broiler, then turned over to add the chopped garlic cloves, safflower oil margarine, and garlic salt. This should be eaten along with parsley, as this will help to alleviate and absorb the odor of the garlic. Garlic and parsley tablets (although not as strong), can be taken liberally. Please note that the garlic is hot and may burn and sting the mouth slightly, but this will bring no harm to the body and it is this burning quality which destroys harmful bacteria. Garlic, when used correctly in its raw form, is much more powerful than synthetic antibiotics. The mouth odor can be reduced by eating with parsley and also by using a natural mouthwash such as Tom's spearmint mouth wash. Garlic capsules like Kyolic or Arizona Natural can also be used.

6. *Rest, Mild Exercise, Sunshine, Fresh Spring Water, and Walking in the Fresh Air*–These elements of nature are essential if the body is to become healthy and disease resistant. Most Americans get none of these, as their environment has become as synthetic as their diets.

7. *Further Biological Treatments (as recommended by Dr. Paavo Airola)*–In persistent chronic conditions, treated short juice fast from one to ten days (consult your physician); hot epsom salts baths with dry brush massage (consult your physician); barefoot walking in the sand, ground and or wet grass is strengthening; once a week, take a sauna or schlenz-bath.

8. *Apple Cider Vinegar and Honey Drink*--Two tablespoons of apple cider vinegar to one teaspoon of organic honey can be added to a small cup of warm water and drink like a tea. It creates an acid ph level in which harmful or unfriendly bacteria cannot live.

9. *Nasal Irrigation*–For the purpose of cleaning out sinus blockage and nasal congestion, take some cool spring water with a little sea salt in the cup of the hand and "snort" it through the nose. It may burn and sting a little at first, but one will get used to it and it will settle down. Repeat this five minutes later after brushing the teeth and this should clear the sinus and nasal cavities. After the water is snorted, suck it into the mouth and rasp the throat to expel the mucus. Forget about Emily Post and do all of this in private. Please note: do not blow the nose too hard as this may hurt the eardrums and ears. Always blow the nose *with the mouth open*. If the nose becomes raw or irritated, apply some natural Aloe Vera cream several times daily.

10. *Vicks Vapor Rub*–Can be applied to the chest and beneath the nose before going to bed at night. In cases of extreme congestion, a vaporizer with Vicks added may be used. However, be careful not to burn the nasal passages by getting too close.

11. The eyes may become extremely dry. Freely spray a liquid saline solution, such as used by contact lens wearers, into the eyes directly with light pressure. This same technique can also be used for Lyme Disease and Candida Yeast Infection to soothe the eyes and counteract dryness which can be extremely uncomfortable and itchy.

VITAMINS AND SUPPLEMENTS (DAILY)

1. *Vitamin C:* In its time-released form in mega doses of up to 2 tablets (1,000 mg each tablet) or 2,000 mg every third hour, not to exceed 10,000 mg a day. Vitamin C acts as a natural antibiotic. The C should contain bioflavenoids such as rutin, hesperidin, and citrin.

2. *Vitamin A:* Can be taken in tablets of up to 10,000 units (I.U.) two at a time with the vitamin C. From 50,000 to 100,000 I.U.'s can be taken in one day up to a month and then must be reduced to 25,000 I.U.'s a day or it will become toxic. It is also a natural antibiotic and if the dry form is used it will have no toxicity. More vitamin A can be taken in its dry form.

3. *Apripol Bee Pollen:* Two 500 mg tablets can be chewed every three hours along with the VIT C&A. The pollen acts as natural sponges which absorb mucous and toxic materials in the body. It acts as a decongestant.

4. *Lymphatic Drops:* These homeopathic drops can be taken up to six times a day to clear the lymphatic system, 15-25 drops mixed with an equal amount of distilled water under the tongue. Your holistic physician will give you directions on how to take these.

5. *Calcium:* With magnesium, phosphorus, and VIT-D it can be taken every 3 hours with the other supplements. This is in chewable or tablet form and amounts to approximately 300 mgs every 3 hours. This, along with the VIT-C acts as a natural pain reliever.

6. *High B Complex:* Also called Brewer's Yeast, it helps calm the nervous system and acts as an antistress factor. If Brewer's Yeast is not pallitable, then use a high B-complex. Take 2 100 mg capsules twice a day.

7. *Vitamin E:* Can be taken in as much as 10-12,000 I.U.'s a day without harm and improves circulation greatly. More can also be taken in its dry form.

8. *Zinc:* It acts with the C and A to aid in antibiotic action and can be taken at 30-60 mg a day.

9. *Vitamin B6:* 100 mg acts as a natural antihistamine.

10. *Lecithin*: Acts as a natural blood cleansing agent and from 1-3 tablets can be taken a day, consisting of 600 mg each.

11. *Chlorophyll*: Can be taken in droplet form and also acts as a natural blood cleanser and purifier. Approximately 6 eye-dropper full, 6 times a day should be sufficient.

12. *Honey*: Natural, organic, and unfiltered in herb teas soothes the mucous linings.

13. *Multiple Organic Vitamins*: 2-4 a day for the whole system.

14. *Raw Glandular Thymus Tissue*: Prompts lymphatic drainage and can be taken from 6-8 tablets a day of 200 mg. It is important to note that this is a non-vegetarian substance.

This regimen is designed only for the symptoms of the common cold. For everyday purposes, consult your physician concerning the Functional Nutritional Balancing Program and natural diets tailor-made to your specific needs. Chiropractic adjustments should be received on a 3-time a week basis to remove pressures from the nervous system till the symptoms subside.

JUICES WHICH CAN BE USED DURING COLD SYMPTOMS

Lemon, black currant, orange, pineapple, elderberries (particularly for bronchial catarrah), carrot, beet, tomato, green pepper, watercress, plus onion and garlic juice in small doses added to vegetable juices.

HERBS

1. *Comfrey and Pepsin*: To help clean the colon and body of unnecessary mucous. The pepsin is an enzyme which breaks the mucous loose and the comfrey helps to gather it for elimination. It removes toxic waste from the

body. Good for coughs and infections.

2. *Golden Seal:* is a tonic, laxative and detergent, which helps to cleanse the mucous membranes of the body and heal sore tissue. Also for catarrhal conditions. It is very powerful.

3. *Chamomile:* is helpful in the treatment of upset stomach, indigestion, and headaches.

4. *Peppermint:* useful as a mild stimulant, it induces perspiration and prevents spasms and cramps. It also soothes the stomach lining.

5. *Lemon Grass:* is very high in Vitamin A and helps to fight off infection.

6. *Slippery Elm:* excellent diarrhea and nausea remedy which also helps to reduce irritation of colon and small intestine. Also for fever treatment and respiratory infections.

7. *Ginger:* aids in the removal of excess waste from the system and helps prevent griping and diarrhea. It is also used to alleviate cold symptoms centered in the lungs. Good externally as a bath to remove toxins.

8. *Chenchona Bark:* cleanses blood and strengthens the liver. Helps with fever and inflammation and remedy for kidney and bladder.

9. *Sage:* Acts as a tonic for the nerves and helps in stomach problems.

10. *Fenugreek:* recommended for lung problems such as bronchitis. Also good in treatment of throat inflammations and as poultice for external wounds.

NOTE: Your holistic physician will gladly give you one or two herbal combinations in tablet form which will contain almost all of these substances and more. Herbs are one of nature's greatest aids in healing the body and a knowledge of these is very beneficial.

ADDITIONAL NOTES:

1. Vitamins C, A, B6, garlic, bioflavinoids, honey, rose hips, fresh juices, optimum nutrition and repeated short

juice fasts will increase the body's resistance against colds.

2. Garlic, combined with onion juice, diluted with water and drank several times a day has been found in studies to be extremely effective to patients suffering from grippe, sore throat, and sinusitis.

3. In so-called *"intestinal flu,"* in addition to supplements mentioned above, Betaine Hydrochloride (2 tablets after each meal) helps in internal detoxification. Also, Pepsin is beneficial (according to Dr. Airola).

4. Colonic irrigation will clean out the colon and speed the healing process many-fold, as well as helping to restore the body to a high state of health.

5. Sinus Treatments: When congestion persists, then consult your physician about sinus treatments.

SUMMARY

The so-called "common cold" is nothing more than the body's *natural elimination process* for removing toxic waste materials and unfriendly bacteria from the body. Its symptoms should never be "hated" or suppressed, but instead appreciated and accelerated. When people come into harmony in understanding and utilizing these laws of nature, then much unnecessary suffering can be removed from the world.

Mild Silver Protein should be the first line of defense for modern man's prevention as well as alleviation of the common cold or flu. I have now treated many patients, relatives and friends and in every case (if begun soon enough) the cold never happened or took root. If it had already begun, however, it was treated with Mild Silver Protein and was ended within 1-3 days, as opposed to 1-3 weeks.

PERSONAL HOLISTIC DIARY

CHAPTER 11
HOW TO PSYCHOLOGICALLY SURVIVE AND CONQUER PAIN

Many times in life, a person finds himself in a difficult situation which seems impossible to solve. There seems to be no apparent easy answer and one becomes frustrated and possibly pessimistic that one will come. It could be that a person is in a state of physical suffering from a disease, illness or disability. Since up until this point all efforts to relieve the situation have failed, one can usually find himself in a state of *psychological mental pain and suffering*.

This mental pain can many times be more severe to an individual than the physical pain, and is a person's reaction to and interpretation of the actual physical pain they are suffering. We will explore in this chapter how the concept of suffering can be re-interpreted in such a way as to remove it from one's mind. The question then becomes this: is it possible to have no psychological pain, even though one may be momentarily caught in a physical pain situation which the victim is helpless to alleviate?

I have been a Clinical Psychologist in the Natural Health Care Field for the past 30 years. I have a Bachelor of Arts in Psychology from the University of Texas and a

Master of Arts in Psychology from the University of
Missouri. I have also *taught* Psychology at the University of
Texas, the University of Missouri and the University of
Kansas. Over the last 30 years I have had the opportunity
to counsel with and treat literally thousands of
individuals and have learned much. Due to the fact that
all of this was coupled with a Holistic Health Practice in
which physical ailments were treated, I was put in a
unique position to observe how various people respond
psychologically to physical pain.

There are basically three types of pain that an
individual may suffer from. These can occur by
themselves or in combination with each other. I will list
them in order of severity:

SPIRITUAL PAIN
PSYCHOLOGICAL OR MENTAL PAIN
PHYSICAL PAIN

This entire book has already dealt with physical pain,
as well as the holistic methods which I have used to
conquer it. The methods *work* and that's what counts. I
would urge you to read carefully, reread, and then use
this book as a *reference guide* because solutions to many
physical ailments are outlined.

Spiritual pain may be relieved and cured by the
attributes and disciplines of:

Faith, Hope, Positive Thinking and Optimism.

Do not underestimate the concept of spiritual pain
because how to overcome it is of such great importance.
The man or woman who is suffering pain *in their soul* is
indeed in pain. In fact, most suicides are a result of
spiritual pain. Once we have covered this subject of how
to psychologically survive and conquer pain, you will
possess the tools to conquer all three types (spiritual,
psychological, physical).

This very book is a testimony and witness of how, in
Dr. Robert Schuller's words, one can "turn his scars into

stars" and how one can "turn pain into gain." I was faced
with three dread diseases, Lyme Disease, Candida Yeast
Infection, and Multiple Sclerosis...which at the time
could only be controlled and had *no known cure*. I
constantly faced some form of moderate–to–extreme
pain for a period of two and one-half years. I could
control it through the use of holistic methods but it
could not be alleviated until the Mild Silver Protein
answer was found, adapted and utilized for the Lyme
Disease and Candida Yeast Infection and the Bee Serum
Therapy for Multiple Sclerosis.

I will be the first to admit that the *ultimate strength*
which I received to eventually conquer and overcome
this situation came from my deep belief in God and His
Son, Jesus Christ. But, what *avenues* did God use to
channel this strength through my mind? I sincerely
believe that with sincere prayer, both *answers* and *strength*
will come.

There are literally tens of thousands of books which
have been written in the field of Psychology. What I will
seek to do in this chapter is to make this complex
subject simple, in the same manner in which the chapter
on anatomy and physiology was written. I spent four
years of undergraduate school and three years of
graduate master's work in the field of psychology, as well
as 30 years in post graduate practice and study. Keeping
this in mind, I strongly feel that if you can understand
the few simple concepts in this chapter, you will be able
to psychologically handle Lyme Disease, Systemic
Candida Yeast Infection, Multiple Sclerosis and all the
changes which you will go through in conquering them.

Perhaps the three most important words in
psychological health are:

ATTITUDE, INTERPRETATION , OPTIMISM.

The singer Joni Mitchell once had a song in which the
phrase "Changes in attitude brings changes in latitude"

appeared. Take a little time and meditate upon what this phrase might mean. In a physical and geographical sense, to change one's latitude means to change one's specific physical location. On the earth in which latitude and longitude both exist, latitude means to change one's geographical location to either farther *north* or *south*. Even this physical relocation demands a change in attitude as one must mentally decide where to move to.

This concept of changing one's *mental direction* by changing one's *attitude* also holds true. The human mind is made up of literally millions if not billions of neuro-transmitters. Physically, these neuro-transmitters which are made up of interconnected axons and dendrites actually form a *mental circuitry*. Perhaps the easiest way to understand what mental circuitry is would be to look at a very well-known example which the average individual has a knowledge of. This example is the modern-day computer.

Computers have become so sophisticated that they are literally capable of a form of *cognitive thought* and even speech. The advanced computer can even put together new and original concepts by analyzing and re-organizing known concepts. However, this is where the comparison ends because a computer is an inanimate object with no *spirit*. However, the mechanism through which the memory banks of a computer work are similar to the human mind.

A basic concept in computer language and terminology is the concept of "GIGO," which literally means "garbage in, garbage out." All the memory in a computer (no matter how sophisticated) is limited by what information the programmer puts into it. A computer is simply not capable of placing the original ideas into its memory banks. This has to be done by an outside human source. Thus, whatever the programmer puts into the computer, whether considered "good" or "bad," is all that is in there. Since the unit can only analyze and rearrange these ideas, the final arrangement can only be based upon the original ideas. Therefore, if the programmer places a hundred negative ideas into the computer, the only result can be another negative idea. In other words, if a programmer puts *garbage in*, the only result can be *garbage out*.

This concept of *negative* and *positive* is relative to one's belief system and is many times hard to define. For the purposes of this writing in relationship to one's health, I will offer the following simple definitions. We will discuss positive and negative in relationship to ideas that influence one's health either to the *good* or *detriment* of that individual.

POSITIVE - Those ideas and actions which bring about greater health, removal of pain and suffering, and total well being.

NEGATIVE - Those ideas and actions which cause one to lose his health, create greater pain and suffering, and bring about a loss of well being.

I think the most important concept in determining whether one is a positive thinker or a negative thinker is that of *attitude*. Ideas in themselves, and even events, are not inherently negative or positive. A good example would be the writing of this book. I had no original intention of writing it until I was bitten by a tick and became very ill and almost died. To become ill and come close to death, and perhaps even experiencing a taste of death, could hardly be considered a positive experience. If one were to take a poll of opinions on these events, the vast majority of all individuals would interpret these events as a negative experience.

However, because of many years of both psychological as well as spiritual training and study, I chose to interpret these events in a different manner. I sincerely viewed them as a *challenge*, in order to find answers to seemingly impossible problems. I was faced with Lyme Disease, a Systemic Candida Yeast Infection, and Multiple Sclerosis which up until the publishing of this book, would be considered *incurable* diseases. Let me reiterate that these could be controlled but not cured, and most certainly could and would return and cause problems for the rest of the victim's life.

And very importantly, because of my near death experience I took these series of events and interpreted them as a mandate and command from both God and Jesus Christ to complete this publication and to find an *answer* so that multitudes could be spared from the ravages of these modern-day plagues.

So...was this severe illness and a brush with death a negative event or a positive event? To me it was *positive.* Of course I would not have opted for pain and suffering for a prolonged period of time. No one in his right mind would. But I chose to view all of this in a constructive manner from which only *good* could emanate. This interpretation also created a *frame of mind* in which pain and suffering for a divine purpose became a joy rather than a burden.

The key word and concept here is the function of the word INTERPRETATION. As we have already discussed, one cannot always choose what events will have to be faced in the uncertainty of life's experiences. No one ever chooses to be in a car accident or break his leg or witness a death in the family. The only thing that a person has a free will choice to do is to find an interpretation of these events which will formulate into a positive idea, which will then lead to *positive action steps.* This freedom and power of interpretation can be applied to every event in one's life.

If an individual decides to do the following, in my opinion his or her life will be transformed into a very fruitful experience:

1. Find the good in every situation, no matter how seemingly bad it may seem;

2. Interpret this good in such a way as to formulate positive action steps to overcome it;

3. Mentally and physically act upon your situation, using the positive action steps which you have

formulated;

4. Be observant about how your life begins to change and improve.

The very fact that you are reading this book and this very paragraph shows that you are being led to the correct answers in order to heal and restore your life. But, as stated in No. 3, you must of your own free will choose to *apply them* and put them into action.

The next step along the path to good psychological health is OPTIMISM. The author Martin Seligman has a book out entitled "Learned Optimism." It becomes understood that optimism is not a concept which comes naturally to most adult human beings. However, it does come naturally to the baby and the young child, but is usually lost after a series of discouraging events which occur during the growing up process. Eternal optimism is a God-given gift, and perhaps the child would not have lost it if he had been given the training of interpretation.

Thus in order to re-attain optimism and regain one's mental health and stability, a person must go through a *renewed learning process.* For this renewed learning experience, we will use Mr. Seligman's coined phrase *learned optimism.*

You don't have to read 100 books in order to learn optimism. There is the Holy Spirit of God within you that will teach you all you need to know, if you would both pray and then *be still and listen* for the answers. In a book entitled "Power Thoughts" Dr. Robert Schuller defines what he terms *power thinking.*

Positive thinking?.....That's Faith
Possibility Thinking?.....That's Faith That's Focused
Power Thinking.....That's Focused Faith Filled With
Following-Through Power

Faith + Focus = Follow-Through = Success

I feel that all of this together equals the completion of

positive thinking. This comes about through a positive interpretation of events which leads to optimism.

As you read this, you should be very optimistic because regardless of how much pain and suffering you have been through with Lyme Disease, Systemic Candida Yeast Infection, and Multiple Sclerosis I personally feel that you now have the solution and the answers in your very hand, if you would just utilize for yourself the *follow-through power* of "power thinking." One may ask the question: "What is faith?" From a Biblical perspective,

Faith is the substance of things hoped for
and the evidence of things not seen.

Many books have been and could be written on the subjects that I have covered here. But if you would just apply the simple concepts that I have outlined, you will have what you need to both spiritually and psychologically conquer pain.

CHAPTER 12
THE FINAL HEALING CRISIS
"TO HEAVEN AND BACK"

As I was ending this book, I woke up one morning and once again found myself in extreme physical pain and plagued with a multitude of symptoms that I was only too familiar with (it seemed like the "third stage of Lyme Disease"). I didn't understand it.

I had been through an incredible personal journey through Lyme Disease and Candida Yeast Infection and had been totally healed through the utilization of Mild Silver Protein. I *knew* that it had worked, *big time*. So now why were my left arm and hand completely numb and 95% paralyzed? Why had I now lost all feeling in my ankles and the bottom of my feet? Why all the severe musculoskeletal pain? I just didn't understand what was going on. I do remember, also, that the day before all this began to happen I had experienced double-vision and everything seemed *blurred*.

After seeing my ophthalmologist Dr. James Keats, M.D., he determined that my 6th cranial nerve was quite inflamed and he suspected that I had either a brain infection such as *cerebral meningitis* or that perhaps I had suffered a stroke. I was perplexed and a little bit afraid. But fortunately, it was conclusively determined that neither one of these potential diagnoses was correct.

So what was all of this about? As the days progressed, all the symptoms grew worse and my faith in all that had happened to me in the last two and a half years began to wane. Talk about being *tested!* After my victory over the two great medical imposters (Lyme Disease and Candida Yeast Infection) I had sold my clinic in Houston in order to move out to our 20-acre retreat where I planned to practice both chiropractic and nutritional consultation in order to support my family. But now, that was impossible because a chiropractor cannot practice his art with one arm and hand. It's analogous to an attorney without a tongue. Or to a welder without a torch. Or a politician without tact.

After speaking with Dr. Joe Cardot, Ph.D., N.D. we both came to the conclusion that this apparent "third stage of Lyme Disease" and re-infection of my body might have been caused by *flea bites.* Fleas *can* and *do* cause Lyme Disease and can initiate an even more severe case than a tick. I had been aware that fleas can carry the spirochetes that cause the disease but had not given it much thought, and neither had most of the noted authors on this subject. But on further investigation and research, it turns out that fleas carry hundreds of different bacteria and viruses, many of these micro-organisms being disease-laden (including the Borrelia that causes Lyme Disease).

So, following advice given to me, I set out some flea traps in and around my environment which consisted of bowls of *soapy water*, placed approximately 12 inches beneath bright *night lights.* The fleas actually jump into the lights, bounce off and then fall into the water and drown.

It worked. The next morning, much to my surprise, I found the traps full of waterlogged, dead fleas. My house, my yard and practically everything around me was infested with the critters. And in discussing this with

Dr. Cardot, we came to the conclusion that I had been severely bitten (perhaps thousands of times) all over my body...over a several month period...by fleas. All too often, a fleabite will go undetected but the potential damage it can cause can be devastating.

Although it seemed that we had found the answer to these overwhelming, reoccurring symptoms in my body, I decided to get a second opinion...and perhaps even a third. After all, I was partially paralyzed and I was experiencing massive pain.

I got in touch with Joe Burke, who had recently served as the president of the Lyme Foundation and had been in charge of the "Lyme Newsletter" for many years. I had the privilege of meeting him at the same time as I had met Dr. Willy Burgdorfer at the Lyme Conference of 1993 in Atlantic City, New Jersey. Joe gave me the name of a neurologist who specialized in Lyme Disease and who also had knowledge of how fleas can infect an individual. Her name: Dr. Audrey SteinGoldings, M. D., from Dallas. I made arrangements for a consultation and went to Dallas in search of an answer to my dilemma. Since I was unable to drive, my Godson Michael Rodriguez took me in the car, and during the entire, uncomfortable trip I did intensive study on Rheumatoid Arthritis and the "third stage of Lyme Disease." I read from Dr. Louis Reik, Jr.'s book "Lyme Disease and the Nervous System." At the basis of all of this was my uncertainty as to whether my suppositions were correct...or did I have some other disease of an unknown origin and nature that was causing me such great distress?

When I arrived at Dr. SteinGolding's, M.D., office I filled out all the necessary forms and was handed a packet of materials on Lyme Disease and its treatment. But what impressed me the most was a single leaflet warning about acquiring a Candida Yeast Infeciton while on antibiotic therapy, pointing out that a patient should receive *acidophilus* by eating yogurt or taking acidophilus supplementation in order to avoid infection. I couldn't help but think that if the rest of the medical profession would simply follow this doctor's example and inform people about the dangers of destroying and not replacing "friendly bacteria," Candida Yeast Infection (the third largest epidemic in the world) could be stopped in its tracks.

Dr. SteinGoldings had my complete respect as she listened intently to my entire case history, reviewing every major illness which I had had since birth, especially in my early 20's. I had suffered from severe headaches which I thought were related to two separate whiplash accidents. After a careful analysis of all the data, she concluded that I had indeed been subjected to Lyme Disease, as well as Candida Yeast Infection. But her further conclusion was that the courses of treatment that I had selected, including the use of Mild Silver Protein, were the absolute *answer* for the diseases. That only confirmed what I already knew and that's primarily what this book is all about.

But this was the real kicker: Dr. SteinGoldings proceeded to inform me that the core of my problem was that I had a chronic case of *Relapsing and Remitting Multiple Sclerosis*. I had **M. S.**! I wasn't expecting this at all and it floored me.

She explained that this might have been the underlying factor for my many years of headaches as well as fatigue and periods of disorientation during my twenties. She felt that in addition to this, the disease had "hit me again" about 2 1/2 years ago (along with Lyme Disease) in my mid- forties and then again immediately prior to coming in to see her. She felt strongly, however, that I should get *one more opinion* as well as an M. R. I. and a lumbar puncture spinal tap to confirm her diagnosis. This would require hospitalization.

I decided to do it. And to do it quick. So I got in touch with David and Andrea Perkins from a Messianic Jewish Congregation in Dallas, who knew of an M. D. Neurologist/Neurosurgeon. They indicated that he was willing to see me immediately. That was great news! As I have mentioned earlier, my health insurance had been cancelled for over two years, ever since I began making claims on expenses associated with the effects of Lyme Disease. The insurance company rather rapidly found a "technicality" in their favor and cut me off. Andrea and David had to figure a way to get me into the hospital, which they did.

Shortly after arriving at his office in Dallas, Dr. Matwijecky was called out on an emergency. So Andrea, my wife Marie and I decided to go out and grab a bite to eat. I wouldn't mention this except for an extraordinary thing that happened at this point, a *miracle* that clearly set the stage for a series of incredible events that would begin to unfold.

After eating and walking out of the restaurant, Andrea suddenly realized that she had locked her keys in her car, something she had never done before. And if that wasn't bad enough, her automobile had *protective slip locks* which were impossible to open with a coathanger or any other makeshift contraption. But we gave it a shot anyway, because we faced the very real possibility of missing our appointment with a very busy neurosurgeon, and also losing an entire day and a considerable amount of expense. We were desperate and we began to pray for an answer to the dilemma.

Then a gentleman showed up with the proverbial coathanger, but that didn't get it done. But then, while we were fumbling with this, another fellow walked up and announced that he was a *locksmith* and that he would gladly make us a key and that he would only charge us

$5, which he promptly did and then we were on our way (we now call this "the miracle of the key"). As I have mentioned, without this guy's timely intervention, a whole series of important subsequent events would not have come to pass. I sensed that some kind of a "Plan" was in motion here and was greatly elevated in spirit because I had been involved in a similar kind of thing before and it had cost me an entire day and a whole lot more money to resolve. It was virtually statistically impossible in a city the size of Dallas...for a locksmith to appear at the precise right time and in the exact right place with the exact tools he needed...and to do the job for minimum wage. It just doesn't happen.

We made it on time to the doctor's office. He did a complete consultation, case history and neurological exam and his ultimate diagnosis was exactly the same as Dr. SteinGoldings': Relapsing and Remitting Multiple Sclerosis. He also suggested that I enter Parkland Hospital and have a brain and cervical spine M. R. I., as well as a spinal tap.

This was all new territory for me. I had been convinced that I was in the "third stage of Lyme Disease," but it was obvious now that my self-diagnosis was erroneous. I think that it would be wise at this time to delve into this very important subject: the "third stage of Lyme Disease" and its relationship and confusion with Multiple Sclerosis.

I will quote from *Lyme Disease And The Nervous System*, by Louis Reik, Jr., M. D.:

> A number of authors have noted the similarity in neurological appearance and course CNS Lyme Disease and Multiple Sclerosis (MS) and the possibility of mistaking one for the other. Chronic Progressive Encephalomyelitis, and especially the predominantly spinal form, can be confused

clinically with MS because of its remitting and relapsing course and the high incidence of spinal motor signs: ataxia, bladder dysfunction, and less often, optic neuritis. Acute transverse myelitis, when it develops in stage 2 Lyme Disease can also cause confusion. Adding to the similarity between the two illnesses are the presence of oligoclial bands of IgG and increased levels of IgG in the CSF in most patients with severe CNS Lyme Disease, and the presence of periventricular white matter lesions on CT and MRI in many.

But severe CNS Lyme Disease can usually be distinguished from MS by the presence of a more brisk pleocytosis and more marked bloodbrain barrier dysfunction, while an additional clue in some patients is the simultaneous presence of peripheral nervous system abnormalities.

Neurological Abnormalities In Late Lyme Disease

"A variety of neurological abnormalities, both central and peripheral, can develop during the late Lyme Disease, often after an asymptomatic interval. Accumulation of evidence now suggests that these abnormalities result from the persistence of live spirochetes in the nervous system. Once Borrelia Burgdorferi penetrates the nervous system, it can remain there for months to years, either latent or causing disease.

ENCEPHALITIS

Typical signs and symptoms of more diffuse cerebral involvement on which local signs may be superimposed include somnolence, confusion, poor concentration, restlessness and irritability, disorientation, and decreased memory. Occasionally patients have had apraxia, myoclonus, hemiparesthesia, visual field abnormalities, alexia, agraphia, impairment of upward gaze, and skew deviation in addition.

Ataxia, particularly Ataxia of Gait is also common (37% of cases), but it is not clear how often reported Gait Ataxia is caused by spasticity and sensory loss in the legs due to myelopathy and how often it is caused by cerebellar involvement alone. In some cases the cerebellum is definitely involved, as Ataxia of all four limbs, intention tremor in the arms, and hemitaxia, have all been reported also.

PERIPHERAL NERVOUS SYSTEM ABNORMALITIES

As many as 50% of these author's patients with late Lyme Disease (defined by them by disease of greater than four weeks duration) have tingling paresthesias of the extremities. These usually begin months after illness onset (median 6 months; mean 22.5 months), and typically have been present a year or more at the time of clinical evaluation (median 12 months; mean, 27.4 months). The parathesias are often intermittent; can involve the arms, the legs, or both; and are commonly distal but can be patchy in distribution. About 25% of patients with paresthesias have a mild stocking glove distal sensory loss, but motor weakness and reflex loss are rare. The legs are most often the sight of the pain (75%), the arms

THE FINAL HEALING CRISIS

(20%), and the trunk (5%) less often so. The location of the pain is not consistently related to the sight of the initial tick bite.

The Carpel Tunnel Syndrome (CTS) also develops in about 25% of the patients with late Lyme Disease (disease duration 4 months to 9 years; mean 37 months). Affected patients typically have intermittent paresthesias in the median nerve distribution that are exacerbated during sleep or by use of the hands. Symptoms are bilateral in two thirds. Deymelination can occur also, although rarely. Paresthesias almost always improve, as do the many accompanying electrophysiological abnormalities within 3-6 months after antibiotic therapy. The abnormalities detected included blood brain barrier disruption.

So...I was diagnosed with Relapsing Remitting Multiple Sclerosis. And I had no insurance to back me up as I proceeded to undergo various tests and examinations at Parkland Hospital in Dallas. This is the same hospital where President John Fitzgerald Kennedy was taken after he was shot while in a motorcade through this city. As I thought about it, even though I was in great pain and at this point uncertain about my own viability, I felt that I was quite fortunate. God rest his soul.

My friends David and Andrea Perkins told me not to worry about anything, that they would show me how the "system" worked and how the less privileged make it work. I was in for a rude awakening. They took me to the emergency room where I saw multitudes waiting to get into the hospital to see a doctor. Andrea then took the initiative and approached the head nurse and quickly explained that this was truly an emergency and that my left arm and hand were paralyzed and that I was in extreme pain and must see a neurologist immediately. All of us were praying (including the Perkins' kids), and privately I was convinced that this country needs some form of properly administered universal health insurance in order to alleviate suffering.

Our prayers were answered as we miraculously bypassed several hundred people and found ourselves in an examination room, waiting for a neurologist. Eventually two doctors agreed that it was quite possible that I was suffering from Multiple Sclerosis. I was then transported to a private room and both an M. R. I. and a spinal tap (both extremely expensive) were ordered, while I was put on steroid IV twice a day (reluctantly).

The results of the M. R. I. clearly showed that I had sclerotic plaques of areas of demyelination bilaterally in my cerebrum, cerebellum, occipital lobes and in my spinal cord in the upper cervical area. The cerebrospinal fluid also showed positive signs for M.S. and since I am a doctor, the radiologist allowed me to view the results personally. There was no longer any doubt in my mind about the bad news.

But the *good news* was that the cerebral spinal fluid also proved to be *negative* for the Lyme titers. The Mild Silver Protein had done its job as I knew it would and I no longer had Lyme Disease!

Both the nurses and the doctors (who quickly gained my admiration and respect) could not understand my *high spirits* and my positive attitude after receiving a diagnosis of Multiple Sclerosis, a so-called "incurable" disease. I knew what they didn't know, that I was here for a much higher purpose and that the events that were transpiring were part of a supernatural, spiritual blueprint that was beginning to unfold. I truly felt that Jesus Christ, The Messiah, would eventually lead me to an answer to this dread disease, just as he had done for both Lyme Disease and Candida Yeast Infection. I say this with great humility.

I remembered Charlton Heston, my favorite actor, in the movie "Ben Hur"...as he was trapped as a slave in a galley of a Roman warship. Immediately preceeding a great battle, the admiral of the fleet approached Ben Hur and told him that it was his fate to probably die chained to the oars. Hur replied: "I cannot believe that the Lord God of Abraham, Isaac and Jacob has brought me this far to allow me to die chained to this oar in a Roman war ship." I felt exactly the same. And I, too, had met Jesus Christ face-to-face and become a Believer. Only my story is *for real.*

God has a plan...and God's plans don't end in tragedy. There was no way that the God of my Jewish forefathers would let me spend the rest of my life suffering and perhaps dying from some hideous disease. It wasn't in the SCRIPT.

He had allowed me to see through veiled eyes to the other side of the spiritual spectrum...and to recognize his Son as the true Messiah. He had allowed me to visit the Throne Room, making me a welcomed guest in His own House. He had allowed me to follow His leading in order to find a answer for Lyme Disease and Candida Yeast Infection, as well as discovering a potential answer for the AIDS epidemic. He knew that Mild Silver Protein would have to replace conventional antibiotics, as well as taking care of all the mutations created by them.

And now it was Multiple Sclerosis that was staring me *right in the nervous system,* a most devastating disease that affects over 350,000 Americans. But there was no panic or lingering dread inside of me. Somehow I knew that God was in control and that's why I felt a sense of elation. I don't mind being *used.*

An extraordinary thing happened to me during the

rest of my short stay at Parkland Hospital. It was on Rosh Hashanah, the day of the Jewish New Year which comes immediately prior to Yom Kippur (the Jewish high holiday called the day of Atonement). It quite literally blew me away.

I had gotten permission to go down to the hospital chapel which was located on the first floor, there being no services scheduled for that day. I was quite familiar with the chapel because I had been in it *only a few days earlier*, praying out loud in both Hebrew and English, when two women walked in. I immediately apologized for praying and singing out loud, as this was a place where many came to pray privately. I welcomed them in and told them that I would only be a few minutes. They hastened to point out that they had indeed been drawn in by my vocal praises and agreed to join me as I conducted about a 30-minute ceremony. In the final analysis, I ended up counseling one of the ladies, who had just recently lost her daughter in a murder/rape attack. Little did they know that I have been under training to become a Messianic Jewish Rabbi along with being a ministerial student with my wife Marie at Liberty Seminary College in Humble, Texas. God had visited that little room on that day and all three of us knew it.

But this time, I was back in the little chapel and it was Rosh Hashanah Day...and I was all alone. Or so I thought.

The chapel was small, with a seating capacity of about 50 people. It had a podium at the front with a Bible on it. But the most significant part of the little room was a large stained-glass window about 25 feet tall and 20 feet wide. It was incredibly beautiful, with the rays of the sun shining through its rainbow of multitudinous colors.

As before, I began to pray in both Hebrew and English and began to sing praise songs. It was *powerful* in there, a Heavenly presence so strong that I lost control and fell prostrate on the floor in front of the beautiful rainbow-colored stained glass window. My face was down and my eyes covered in reverence as I continued to pray, but this time *spontaneously*. I was in that state for perhaps ten minutes as I felt the Spirit of God envelop my total being. What an *awesome* thing. I was being allowed to look into another dimension as I felt my body become weak with exhilaration. It says in the Bible that "your young men will...have visions," and believe me...it is not a metaphor...it's for real.

As my head raised up off the floor, my eyes beheld the stained glass window *come alive* with the presence of God. My total attention was captive as the images on the window turned into a *burning bush* which was not consumed by the flames. I instantly recalled the same experience that Moses had in the Old Testament on Mt. Sinai, when God spoke and revealed to him that he was to be the instrument through which the Children of Israel would be freed from the pits of slavery in Egypt.

As my mind tried desperately to assimilate all that was happening to me, I then saw within this burning bush an image of a white-bearded man who had to be Moses...saying to God: "Henene," which in Hebrew means "Here I am," but then continued "But who am I Lord, that I might break the bondage of Pharaoh and free the Children of Israel from slavery into freedom?" Then I heard the Lord respond: "That not by his, Moses's hand, but by the rod of God these things would come to pass and that he should have no concern or worry for I, the Lord will tell what to say and do."

What can I say. Here I was again, right smack dab in the middle of something my mind was having trouble accepting and that I totally did not understand. I've had untold years of scientific training, where I was taught that true science (and ultimate truth) revolves around things that "make sense" and can be repeated under similar experimental conditions. But as I have eventually discovered, the Lord was dealing with my spirit and not my head.

As this was happening to me, I had to search my mind and my heart concerning this vision and how it applied to *me*. I'm just a guy, a little-known doctor of the twentieth century. What was going on? What was **Moses** doing in my world? I was overwhelmed.

At that moment, I lost my normal consciousness as I felt my spirit being *lifted out* of my body through my heart and then the top of my head. I was not totally unfamiliar with this part of my experience because the exact same thing had happened 2 1/2 years ago when I *clinically died* for a five minute period of time and was taken into the Kingdom of Heaven and the Throne of God. However, this time I was not dead but merely unconscious physically, although my mind and spirit were awake, alive and fully aware of every event that was being revealed to me.

I then felt and saw three angels around me, one on each side supporting my arms. The third angel, whom I believe to have been Gabriel, was directly behind me, serving as a heavenly rudder and guiding the party of four in the proper direction towards Heaven and the Throneroom of God. I was not afraid. How could I be? These three beings seemed more *powerful* than you could possibly imagine. And they were magnificent and indescribably beautiful creations of God, with white feathered wings but possessing the arms, legs, body and head of a glorified human being, shining with the white radiance of the sun. I felt puny in their presence, although I knew that God had created man on an even higher level than the angels.

The Bible talks consistently about angelic beings and the various hierarchies assigned to them. Among the chief duties of angels is the protection of God's people on the earth. In Psalm 91 it says: "And he shall give his Angels charge over thee and they shall bear you up on their wings lest you dash your foot against a stone." The Bible also talks about legions of angelic beings surrounding the Throne of God in perfect and divine order singing glorious praises to honor their Creator. I can tell you first hand that angels are for real.

As all of this was going on, it was revealed to me that there is a geography to the heavens in relationship to the earth. Heaven is actually a *place* which, although it exists in another dimension, occupies both time and space in the universe. This was logical to my rational mind as I deduced that the Creator could not be separated from his creation.

After passing through the atmospheres of the earth, lifted up by the power of the angels, there appeared in the heavens among the stars a large golden rectangular door, extremely tall and less wide with round, chain-like circular handles of mother of pearl on each side of the central crevice, about a third of the way up from its cloud-like base. I felt like a dwarfed *ant* in comparison, yet it radiated outwardly a peace which allowed me to feel humble to this awesome sight but not insignificant and certainly not unimportant to the Creator. After all, I was here through an *invitation* and an answer to sincere prayer.

The golden door was adorned also with white mother of pearl, thus the common reference to the "pearly gates of Heaven." It was not of a physical nature and substance, but of a glistening etheric substance of light, energy and archetypal patterns, including the six-pointed star of David and the raised cross of Jesus Christ within this star to demonstrate the completion and fulfillment of the messianic biblical promise.

This golden door was the entrance to a magnificent palace with a stature beyond anything conceivable by the human mind. The palace just seemed to go on forever, although it did have boundaries and contained many mansions. And it was truly located in the center of the highest Heaven.

It is intriguing to note that the golden doors were opened by the angels in an *outward direction*, as opposed to opening inwardly as most doors do. This indicated to me that perhaps those already in this beautiful place could *leave freely*, while those first attempting to enter must "pass through the narrow gate," but only with divine permission.

As I was escorted through the gates, my spirit eyes were drinking in sight after beautiful sight as quickly as was necessary. In the distance and in the center and toward the rear of the palace was situated the golden Throne of the Lord God Adonai, the creator of both Heaven and Earth. It was absolutely staggering to experience, while in my spirit body and through my spirit eyes (no *mortal* man can see God and live), I was actually seeing the Father on His Throne, and I was instantaneously reminded on the inside that I was privileged to experience this sight so that I might *reveal it to my fellow man* (it had absolutely nothing to do with my own personal merit or standing). Any stray thought on my part that even hinted at being "more Holy" or deserving of an experience like this would have been instantly eradicated in this atmosphere of immeasurable love, peace and joy. God always has a flawless purpose for everything He does.

As I watched, it became obvious that God is not some amorphous blue dust or mist...or merely a pattern of energy, as many New Age people incorrectly profess. He is a divine being and person with both shape and form which is independent of His environment.

He is the Ultimate Person, a being beyond human comprehension or imagination. I perceived Him as being composed of light and energy, like millions upon millions of glorious suns for His cells, and the rays of those many suns for his countenance. I have seen the Sistine Chapel in Rome...and the image of God creating man, as was revealed to Michelangelo as he painted, was not far in image and form from what my spirit eyes held before me.

His eyes seemed like glowing stars, sitting within a divinely wrinkled brow. His mouth was framed by the divine lips through which the "Word was spoken" and all creation came into being. His long, well-groomed and artistic beard and also His hair were as white as the whitest snow I had ever seen anywhere. It was dazzling! And so were his white and flowing robes, inlaid with gold, silver and spectacular jewels of every kind.

But the most captivating part of Him was the authority in His countenance. There was absolutely no question as to who was in charge of all creation.

Utter kindness, gentleness and compassion radiated from His presence...an awesome **LOVE** that would melt anything it touched into submission.

Upon His head was the Crown of Crowns, made up of the light of many suns interwoven with the first mother of all jewels, emitting a rainbow radiance of all the colors of the spectrum. As I was watching all of this, I couldn't help but wonder how in the world I would ever be able to return to the mundane surroundings and existence that all of us here are used to.

There is furniture in this divine place of incredible craftsmanship. The Lord sits upon a mighty chair, a throne with golden crafted arms and legs. And to His right is yet another throne, occupied by His Son. I can best describe Jesus Christ in His glorified body by quoting from The Book of Revelation 1:12-16 (NIV):

> "Then I turned to see (whose was) the voice that was speaking to me, and on turning I saw seven golden

lampstands, and in the midst of the lampstands (One) like the Son of Man, clothed with a robe which reached to the girdle of gold about His breast. His head and His hair were white as white wool, (as white) as snow and His eyes flashed like a flame of fire. His feet glowed like (bright) burnished bronze as it is refined in a furnace, and his voice was like the sound of many waters. In His right hand He held seven stars, and from His mouth there came forth a sharp two-edged sword, and His face was like the sun shining in full power at midday."

This is what I saw, although I did not study any of this in detail until the Holy Spirit told me to do so *after* my experience in higher places. But now, after studying these passages, I knew that what had been revealed to me was indeed the *truth*, as well as a privileged and divine vision. It made me realize that all of this that was happening to me was not only quite strange and out of the ordinary, but also *quite real.*

In my spirit, my eyes continued to see most wondrous things. As God was seated on His throne, he was surrounded by countless angels of many diversities and shapes. Each seemed to have a different personality, but they were all singing, playing instruments and praising God and His Son. What an unbelievable sight. Seated on each side of the two thrones were twelve other lesser thrones, situated in a semi-circular fashion. On these sat the 24 Elders of Heaven. How did I know who they were? I don't know. I just did.

To the right and on the side of Jesus sat His 11 disciples, plus the disciple Paul who replaced Judas Escariot. To the left and on the side of God I recognized (through revelation) Abraham, Isaac, Jacob, Joseph, Moses, King David and King Solomon, as well as the prophets Samuel, Isaiah, Jeremiah, Ezekiel, and Daniel. Each of them had white flowing robes and golden crowns.

Surrounding all things and persons was the Holy

Spirit, who individualized Himself as a *glowing radiance* from each personage. It was as if the Holy Spirit, consisting of glistening rays of light emanating from the Father and the Son...had the ability to match the forms of the patriarchs, the kings, the prophets, the disciples and the angels. I became acutely aware that the glorious halo and glow that has been associated with devout and committed Godly people throughout the centuries was actually the presence of the Holy Spirit, which in Hebrew is pronounced the "Ruach Hakodesh." It brought to mind something I had once heard, but that now seemed so true: "If one perceives the Father God as the sun, then His Son would be the rays, and the Holy Spirit would be as the warmth of the rays." It was amazing how my memory and thought processes were so greatly enhanced while I was in this place.

Also before the throne of God, I perceived and saw seven golden torches, each as a spirit within itself. It seemed that all of these personages and things existed within an ocean of clear energy with waves and patterns, giving all things a dynamic and living presence. It was as if my vision of the burning bush in that stained glass window was multiplied millions upon millions of times, yet allowing the central creation of all creations to exist within it. God is truly an alive and dynamic force of life, light and energy that is individualized yet at the same time maintaining his omniscience, omnipotence and omnipresence.

I could go on about all of this for some time, because there were many other great wonders that I saw. But my spirit man was virtually *saturated* as I absorbed in awe what was being revealed to me. It's going to take time to recall the totality of my experience. Even today, specific details of much of what happened are coming to me in bits and pieces as my finite brain attempts to sort them out.

Again, throughout all of what transpired, I kept asking the question: "Why me? What does all of this mean? What am I supposed to do?"

Someone subsequently pointed out to me that the Old Testament Prophet Joel may have had at least a partial answer to my dilemma when he stated in Joel 2:28 (NIV):

> "And afterward I will pour out My Spirit upon all flesh, and your sons and your daughters shall prophesy, your old men shall dream dreams, your young men shall see visions."

I would not presume to assign anything of this great a significance to myself. No chance. But the fact remains that I did have a very genuine *supernatural experience* and it is becoming clearer to me as to what it meant. I believe that I now understand why Moses and the burning bush were a part of the vision.

Obviously, I have not been chosen to lead the people out of the land of Egypt. Moses did that. However, there are other types of slavery that humanity has labored under for generations.

Both Jew and Gentile today find themselves in bondage to a *new set of taskmasters* no less cruel, harsh, oppressive and destructive. These taskmasters are *disease,* early and unnecessary *death, sickness,* extreme *pain* and suffering, *debilitation,* economic oppression as a result of illness...as well as unnecessary fear, anxiety, worry and the loss of loved ones.

Being both a scientist as well as a physician, I now see my assigned mission as one of those people helping to lead much of suffering humanity out of this terrible bondage and into the arena of health. I now understand why I had personally become afflicted with Lyme Disease, Systemic Candida Yeast Infection and Multiple Sclerosis. It also became undeniably clear why I was led to the answers for two of these diseases (as well as 650 other afflictions) through the discovery of Mild Silver Protein (I'm still working on M.S.). I am approximately 80-90% recovered from M.S. I am working on the last 10-20% at the present time. Even the AIDS virus is now under assault.

I not only feel privileged...but I am anxious to get started. Even though it took over three years to complete this book and I have served in the Holistic Healthcare Field for over 30 years, I DIVINELY FEEL THAT MY WORK FOR THE LORD AND MANKIND IS JUST BEGINNING.

It says in PSALM 91, "When you call out in times of trouble I will answer thee because you know MY NAME. Praise GOD, I do know HIS NAME, it is ADONOI ELOHENU, ADONOI ECHAD and his SON'S NAME who is the Messiah is YESHUAH HAMASHIACH, JESUS CHRIST THE MESSIAH. And HIS HOLY SPIRIT through which GOD reaches down to Man on Earth is the RUACH HAKODESH.

PERSONAL HOLISTIC DIARY

CHAPTER 13
SOME INSIGHT FROM HAL LINDSEY
EXCERPTS FROM "PLANET EARTH–2000 A.D....WILL MANKIND SURVIVE?"

I have just finished reading the new book by the best selling author Hal Lindsey, which was written 25 years after his best seller *The Late Great Planet Earth*. Time Magazine has referred to Lindsey as the *Jeremiah* for his generation. He is the author of 11 books with combined worldwide sales of over 35 million.

I have seen Hal Lindsey on the Trinity Broadcasting Network and have developed a great deal of respect for this man because after reading his first book, *The Late Great Planet Earth*, over 25 years ago, *my life was changed*. His prophetic works tie in closely with the fulfillment of not only the major epidemics, but also the answer for many of these, which are coming through God's grace and forgiveness. I'm convinced that we are in the "latter days" and feel in my spirit that God wants His children to be of sound mind and body so that they can clearly and wisely choose the gift of *salvation* through the Messiah Jesus Christ...uninhibited by the plagues and epidemics addressed in his latest book. The following are excepts:

BIOLOGICAL EQUIVALENT OF NUCLEAR WAR

Dr. Seale has accurately called AIDS the 'thermonuclear biological equivalent of nuclear war.' And he is shocked at how public health authorities have failed to take appropriate actions to curb the disease and how the media has spread so much disinformation about it.

Today, in our major cities, AIDS has become one of the leading causes of death, and there is no cure in sight. What makes AIDS more horrible than any previous plague is its attack on the immune system, which leaves its victims helpless to defend themselves from every kind of sickness--from the common cold, to tuberculosis, to meningitis.

NO ONE IS SAFE ANYMORE

This is a disease from the pit of hell that affects not only the body, but clouds the mind and judgement of those afflicted with it. And it is spreading to all parts of the world: no one is safe anymore. Dr. Claude Newbury has said that by the end of 1995, there could be as many as 12.6 million South Africans infected with the AIDS virus. The CIA calculates that approximately 75% of Africa's population south of the Sahara could be infected by AIDS by the mid 1990's. This surely will be the worst epidemic the world has ever witnessed.

THE PANDEMIC RANGES

The world has not even begun to grasp the

magnitude of the AIDS epidemic. Even the conservative International AIDS Center at Harvard now predicts that as many as 110 million people worldwide will have contracted HIV by the year 2000.

WHAT WE DON'T KNOW CAN'T HURT US

There is a growing fear that AIDS may be just the tip of the iceberg–the first sign of a wave of diseases in an age of plagues. Medical journals have begun discussing outbreaks of deadly mutant strains of AIDS. There was one horrendous wave of AIDS cases in the west African nation of Ghana in which most of those afflicted tested positive for HIV.

DEADLY MUTANT VIRUSES

But remember folks, AIDS is not just some exotic, tropical plague. The epidemic is growing very quickly in the United States and most other western industrialized nations. In 1993 for instance, the number of Americans with AIDS jumped at a surprising rate–some 35,000 new cases.

"That is higher than expected," admitted Dr. John Ward, Chief of AIDS Surveillance for the Center For Disease Control And Prevention in Atlanta. "Some of the 21% (increase) is a sign that the AIDS epidemic is continuing to grow."

WHAT IT WOULD TAKE TO CHANGE

How, you might ask, does the AIDS disaster

fit into the prophetic scenario? The Bible tells us that there will be several great signals to alert us that the end of the age and the beginning of a new world is near. War, revolution, earthquakes, religious deception, strange appearances in space, famines and plagues are all mentioned.

OTHER PLAGUES

In part due to the spread of AIDS and its effect on the immune system of millions of people, old diseases like tuberculosis are making a comeback–big time. "It's perfectly clear that tuberculosis and HIV-AIDS walk hand-in-hand," explains Dr. David Rogers of Cornell Medical College.

WHATEVER HAPPENED TO MALARIA?

Another disease thought behind us is Malaria. In 1955 the World Health Organization actually announced that the disease would soon be completely eradicated. It once killed more people around the world than any other disease. Well, it may again.

Malarial parasites now infect an estimated 270 million people every year, killing up to 2 million (far more than AIDS right now) and causing at least 10 million cases of acute illness.

People are flooding into Malarial clinics in unprecedented numbers and Dr. Louis Miller, Head of Malarial research at The National Institute of Health in Maryland admits that we're worse off than we were in 1950.

CHOLERA'S COMEBACK

Scientists are also concerned that the world is facing a new cholera epidemic–possibly the biggest in this century. A strain resistant to all known vaccines has appeared in Asia and is already claiming thousands of lives. By the mid 90's it is expected to spread into Africa, the Middle East and the Mediterranean. The number of Cholera deaths is expected to increase 10-fold by that time.

In 1993 an epidemic of a mysterious flu-like disease broke out in the southwestern United States. But it was no surprise to the virologists, who have been predicting for years that humanity's encroachment on nature will eventually unleash on America and other developed nations, exotic diseases previously confined to the poverty-ridden third world.

STRANGE NEW VIRUSES

The Hantavirus or "Four Corners" disease is actually not so mysterious at all, but rather a common wildlife virus. The outbreak, say scientists, is a classic case of what can happen when you keep fumbling around with the environment. Part of the problem in the southwestern U.S. is a population explosion by rats. Rodents are carrying strains related to the bubonic plague, which nearly destroyed Europe. Actually the plague is carried not by the rodents but by the fleas.

SOME OF MY OWN CONCLUSIONS
(Dr. Farber)

It was interesting to me that I did not encounter Hal Lindsey's new book until after I had completed the last chapter of this book. But after reading "Planet Earth..." I felt a most pressing obligation to include the above excerpts because of the kinship of thought and because the scientific findings of my own research and experiences so closely coincide with Lindsey's ultimate conclusions. I have written expansively about the devastating results and complications of man's "fumbling around" with nature with little respect for the consequences. I have also pointed out extensively about the new viruses caused primarily by mutations created by man's chemical warfare on disease. It should be noted here that the Mild Silver Protein *kills the bacillus* that caused the Bubonic Plague, along with other viruses and bacteria which cause hundreds of other diseases.

As mentioned previously, Mild Silver Protein also kills the AIDS virus, also inhibiting its replication and latent formation, which admittedly is a startling statement. However, for many reasons (including F.D.A. restrictions), at this time a cure" for AIDS cannot be announced. However, in good conscience I can point out that under laboratory conditions, Mild Silver Protein did indeed destroy the AIDS virus within 3-4 minutes after coming in contact with it.

Jesus stated: "Let those who have eyes see, and those who have ears hear."

It is interesting that all of the Diseases Hal Lindsey mentions in this section from Malaria to Cholera, to the HantaVirus and also to the E Bola and E Coli viruses are all killed by the Mild Silver Protein. The Lord GOD in Heaven and His Son Jesus Christ's prophecy to me that HE would lead me to the CURE for all these Major Epidemics has definitely come true and have been Scientifically Proven. Biblically, when a Prophecy comes true, it is truly from GOD.

CHAPTER 14
MEDICINES OF THE 21ST CENTURY:
A Quantum Leap Into Effective Healthcare

DHEA – APITHERAPY – AQUA RESONANCE
SHARK CARTILAGE – COENZYME Q-10
RODAKEM-MELLALEUCA – DEPRYNYL
BHT THERAPY – CHELATION THERAPY

In the 20th century, we travelled through an era in modern medicine where pharmaceutical drugs became the ruling principle of the day. Medical advancement and success was evident, even though the observation and recording of myriad and often harmful side effects were commonplace. The predisposition to this mindset has been predominant for over a generation.

Although many beneficial results came from this period in our history, advances in the medical field are now beginning to plateau due to a lot of reasons, including the mutation of bacteria into new and deadly strains that are unaffected by conventional drugs. *Time* and *Newsweek* call it the "post-antibiotic era." And rightfully so, as it seems that we are indeed losing the war against infectious diseases. For example Penicillin, which was previously able to control the majority of bacterial infections, is now estimated to be ineffective against 80% of the new generation of mutants.

This sets the stage for the beginning of a new phase of healthcare in which many of the now outdated medicines must make way for a new family of drugs and treatments that are making a *quantum leap* into the 21st century. These "new medicines" will have little or no harmful side effects; they will be able to reverse the course and effects of disease in a relatively short period of time; they will help rebuild the immune system, the nervous system, and heal the connective and muscular tissue; and they will contribute greatly to bringing the cells, tissues and organs of the body back into a state of "homeostasis."

In this chapter we will outline only a handful of the new generation of healing agents that are quickly coming into prominence and that are producing dramatic and scientifically recorded results. This list will undoubtedly grow considerably larger with the passing of time and additional research and observation.

All of these particular "medicines," both drugs and nutritional supplements, have three main characteristics in common: (1) they are legal; (2) they are extremely effective (they work); (3) they have no negative side effects, although oftentimes the body will labor through *healing crises* as it gets well.

I have personally experimented with and been subject to the beneficial results of these new treatments and can personally recommend them. I am also extremely grateful and have a great deal of admiration for those pioneering physicians who have stepped away from the conventional mold and have dared to look in a different direction in order to help alleviate the suffering of mankind.

DHEA: "THE HORMONE THAT DOES IT ALL"

Pharmaceutical grade DHEA are available by calling
MYCA, Inc. at 713-774-8914.

According to Alan R. Gaby, M.D.: "DHEA, the hormone that does it all...may turn out to be the most important medical advance of the past decade." When I encountered Mild Silver Protein, I didn't realize the magnitude of the discovery until I had studied "The Dead Sea Scrolls of Modern Medicine" and the potential implications for humanity became apparent. And I became even more overwhelmed when I personally experienced the dramatic results of using the product. I came to the conclusion that something as impactful as this could only happen in one lifetime.

But then, while attending an Apitherapy convention in 1994 in Bethesda, Maryland, I was fortunate enough to meet Dr. Bradford S. Weeks, M.D., from Clinton, Washington. Dr. Weeks was instrumental in founding the American Apitherapy Society and served as its president for 4 years. In my discussions with him, I asked if there was any substance in addition to the Apitherapy that would be helpful with Multiple Sclerosis. His answer was *yes* and then he proceeded to tell me about the "master hormone" produced by the adrenal glands and which was available naturally from the *wild yam*. I then received a host of articles and research studies which truly amazed me. Like the Mild Silver Protein, it seemed at first almost too good to be true. But if it were true, it would mean a whole lot to me and to thousands of other people who would be initiated into the DHEA club.

After checking it out, it would appear that what Mild Silver Protein will become to the field of antibiotics, DHEA will be to the field of hormonal therapy. That seems incredible to me...two modern *miracle breakthroughs* in medicine:

MILD SILVER PROTEIN–Antibiotic Therapy
DHEA–Systemic Hormonal Therapy

But that's not all. As a researcher I feel compelled to also emphasize yet a third modern miracle breakthrough: it's called DEPRENYL and is now awaiting approval from the FDA. I will discuss this safe and effective drug in detail very shortly.

RESEARCH ON DHEA

From **University Medical Research Publishers:**
"In yet another double-blind experiment, Dr. Vincent P. Calabrese of the *Medical College of Virginia* shows a positive relationship between the use of DHEA and the relief of fatigue.

"One of the more amazing substances that may eventually become a potent weapon in the battle of the bulge is DHEA, a hormone that is produced by the adrenal glands of mammals that can also be derived from the Mexican yam, according to Dr. Arthur Schwartz at Temple University. A study at Temple's School of Medicine found that DHEA caused weight loss without a change in appetite. Weight loss occurred because calories were converted to heat rather than fat. Dr. Schwartz said, "DHEA is a very effective anti-obesity agent.

"DHEA seems to a have a stabilizing effect on all human body systems. It can help overweight people to lose, and underweight people to gain weight.

"It (DHEA) appears to block growth of carcinogens.

"In a recent study performed by Dr. Eugene Roberts of the Department of Neurobiochemistry for Beckman

Research Institute of the City of Hope, Duarte, California, DHEA has raised levels of energy, endurance, limb power, strength, and agility in patients suffering from Multiple Sclerosis, a disease affecting the central nervous system. DHEA enhances the immune system, prevents cancer, and has immeasurable influences throughout the human body.

"Elizabeth Barrett-Connor, M.D., at the University of California of Medicine in San Diego, tracked DHEA levels in 242 men aged 50 to 79 for twelve years. She found that a 100 microgram per deciliter increase in the DHEA sulfate level was connected with a 36% reduction in mortality from any cause and, in particular, a 48% reduction in cardiovascular disease. When DHEA levels fall, the enzyme system accelerates, increasing production of both fatty acids and cholesterol. This obviously could promote obesity and arteriosclerosis."

"In a study of 5000 women, the highest risk of breast cancer was linked with the lowest levels of DHEA.

"In patients infected with HIV, AIDS does not develop until DHEA levels begin to fall, or rather, the fall of DHEA levels portends the onset of AIDS.

"In the November 1991 issue of the *Journal of Infectious Diseases*, Dr. William Regelson demonstrated that people with HIV virus do not suffer from full-blown AIDS until their adrenal output of DHEA drops. Blood samples from HIV-positive patients at the University of California at San Francisco were tested for both DHEA and T-cell levels, the immune cells that are primarily affected with full-blown AIDS. Men with low levels of DHEA had double the risk of full-blown AIDS compared to men with normal DHEA levels."

From John Hopkins Department of Medicine:
"The (research) results show that high levels of plasma DHEA inhibit the development of

arteriosclerosis and they provide an important link to the epidemiologic studies correlating low DHEA-S plasma levels with an enhanced risk of cardiovascular mortality."

QUOTES

From Dr. Julian Whitaker's newsletter,
HEALTH AND HEALING:
"DHEA: the closest way we can get today, to a **fountain of youth**."

"Blood levels of DHEA...is one of the most reliable markers of aging. Most age researchers agree that to retard aging you must maintain the known markers of aging at a level comparable to what you had at age 20 or so. Declining blood levels of DHEA are also markers for disease."

"DHEA seems to protect against both diabetes and obesity."

"With higher levels of DHEA...many diseases just melt away...decreases heart attacks and strokes...lowers blood pressure in animals...helpful in cancer, Alzheimer's disease, Multiple Sclerosis, memory loss, chronic fatigue syndrome, and Parkinson's disease...increases estrogen in women and testosterone in men to levels found in younger men and women...lowers blood cholesterol level."

"DHEA is virtually non-toxic as the body seems to use what it needs."

"These are the facts. DHEA is extraordinarily safe. Your body tends to utilize the extra DHEA if it needs it, and ignores it if it doesn't."

"DHEA, an extremely safe steroid-like hormone, reverses the expression of both the obesity gene and the diabetes gene in experimental animals."

"In humans, DHEA has been shown to increase the

sensitivity of cells to insulin."

"Why isn't DHEA given to the millions that could benefit from it? Because the FDA is standing, gun in hand, protecting the interests of the drug companies."

"DHEA is the most powerful single therapy I have ever seen."

From Dr. Deepak Chora's best-selling book
AGELESS BODY, TIMELESS MIND

"...DHEA is a marker for the body's exposure to stress. On the other hand, high DHEA levels are associated with reduced incidence of coronary artery disease, breast cancer, and osteoporosis. Higher DHEA is also associated with longer survival and decreased death from all diseases in older men."

"...the DHEA reservoir was depleted from stress."

From Dr. Atkins' Newsletter, January 1994
HEALTH REVELATIONS

"I strongly believe that using DHEA will improve your health and extend your life."

"Long before anyone realized DHEA was going to prove so significant, a study on 5,000 apparently healthy women on the Isle of Guernsey found that those who were destined to get breast cancer had subnormal DHEA levels up to nine years before their cancer was diagnosed."

"There is a striking connection between DHEA and heart disease."

"(DHEA)...it shows every sign of becoming an important treatment for diabetes. It has been shown to improve memory and it may also be useful against arthritis, lupus, and Crohn's."

From Dr. Vincent Glampapa, April-May 1994
MUSCLE MAGAZINE

"DHEA has demonstrated to be beneficial in increasing muscle size while reducing fat."

ADDITIONAL INFORMATION FROM
DR. ATKINS' *HEALTH REVELATIONS*

TIRED OF AGING?
THE FDA IS BLOCKING YOUR
ACCESS TO ONE INHIBITOR

"What would you think of a substance that blocks cancer and cardiovascular disease as it retards aging? I thought so, and so let me tell you about one of your own hormones...DHEA (dehydroepiandrosterone). I strongly believe that using DHEA will improve your health and extend your life. Dr. William Regelson, the most noted of DHEA researchers, calls it the 'mother hormone' because it is the precursor of all other hormones, including our major sex hormones.

"DHEA is produced by your adrenal glands in larger quantities than any other adrenal hormone, and is abundant when you're 20. But when you reach 80, you're going to be making only 10-20 percent of your original high levels. The graph of this decline closely matches the increase of the killer illnesses of aging, cancer and heart disease.

"Coincidence? Hardly. Supplemental DHEA has been given to experimental animals, and the results are phenomenal. A 1988 study was done at John Hopkins in which rabbits with severe arteriosclerosis were treated with DHEA. They had an almost 50% reduction in plaque size. Dr. Arthur Schwartz at Temple University gave DHEA to mice bred to develop breast cancer, and they remained cancer free! The hormone also prevented lung tumors and bowel cancer in the mouse population. And it significantly extended their total life span.

"These very startling results have created considerable excitement in the scientific community. Hundreds of papers have been written on the hormone over the course of the last five years. And yet almost nothing has appeared in the media, for the Food and Drug Administration has made it very hard for anyone–even physicians–to get access to DHEA for the purpose of treating patients. I'll soon tell you what you can do about that."

Can DHEA protect my heart?

"There is a striking connection between DHEA and heart disease. For a long time, scientists have been trying to discover why the well-established link between consistently high insulin levels (hyperinsulinism) and heart disease exists. This area is of particular interest to me because hyperinsulinism explains why the low carbohydrate diet that I put so many of my patients on protects them from heart disease. Mainstream physicians think that a diet that doesn't restrict fat must be bad for the heart. Not so. It's when your diet is free of refined carbohydrates, sugar, and other junk foods that your heart receives the greatest benefit.

"One of the chief reasons for the heart protective effects of a low carbohydrate diet is that it keeps insulin levels low and stable. But why does a high insulin level promote arteriosclerosis? According to Drs. Nestler, Ciore, and Blackard at the Medical College of Virginia, the reason may be DHEA. They noted in a 1992 paper that not only does DHEA have anti-arteriosclerotic effects, but high insulin levels reduce your body's production of DHEA.

"There is a striking connection between DHEA and heart disease.

"Lest I be accused of underplaying the benefits of DHEA, let me add that it shows every sign of becoming an important treatment for diabetes. It has been shown to improve memory in aging mice and there is very active ongoing research on using DHEA against Alzheimer's. In his new book. *Preventing and Reversing Osteoporosis* (Prima Publishers), Dr. Alan Gaby cites the strong association between low DHEA levels and bone loss in post-menopausal women. It may also be useful against Arthritis, Lupus, and Crohn's. But with every year that passes after you leave your youthful prime, your supply of this vital hormone is declining steadily.

Is the loss reversible?

"Yes, and I think you should seriously consider supplementation with DHEA. In slowing the onset of age-related illness this may be the most important article I've ever addressed to you. Unfortunately, you'll almost certainly need the help of a physician to obtain DHEA for you and to decide on your proper dose.

"DHEA is quite safe if you use it with an antioxidant such as vitamin E, at a blood level normal for your gender. A typical corrective dose for women might be 50 to 100 mg per day (in three divided doses), and for men between 100 and 250 mg. Start at the low level and have your DHEA levels measured every few months until you reach the level of a healthy 30-year-old. Do not take DHEA if you are suspected to have prostate cancer. And since it promotes production of the male hormone testosterone, it may produce such masculine characteristics as facial hair if you take too high a dose.

(Reversible, if you lower the dose.)

"When it comes to DHEA, you have a powerful enemy in the FDA. This organization has made serious and successful efforts to limit access to it. It may eventually ban DHEA altogether. You see, drug companies are trying to manufacture a synthetic version of the natural hormone, and if the FDA can keep the natural, inexpensive hormone off the market, there will be enormous profits to be made someday when 'DHEA-analog- the miracle drug' appears. But at the rate at which drug development proceeds,that could be ten or fifteen years down the road, and it could never match the Real Thing." Now with our pharmaceutical grade DHEA men 225 mg a day and women 125 mg a day is sufficient.

APITHERAPY
(BEE SERUM THERAPY)

For information on Apitherapy,
Call MYCA, Inc. 713-774-8914.

After I was diagnosed with Multiple Sclerosis I quickly discovered that there was no cure for this disease and very few treatments were available to try to control it. I checked into *Interferon* but the potential side effects could possibly be worse than the disease itself.

Then I heard some interesting information from a doctor friend of mine, Dr. Joe Cardot, who directed me to the studies and documentation of Charles Mraz who had been active in the use of Bee Venom Therapy for over 60 years. To a person who was quite desperate (me), the new insight into this healing technique was both fascinating and exciting (see article in this section).

According to Mraz, Bee Venom Therapy is quite effective, with no adverse side effects and very low cost. There has been very little interest from the medical profession because it is a fairly difficult treatment to give or receive, coupled with the fear most people have of getting stung by a bee. In general, doctors feel that there are plenty of drugs available for use instead.

But, according to Mraz, interest is growing rapidly in the healing power of this treatment, especially with the substantial coverage the media is giving it.

I heard about and attended an Apitherapy convention which turned out to be well-attended and extremely beneficial. I met over 250 people that had either improved partially or completely from Multiple Sclerosis. I also met Charles Mraz, Pat Wagner, and Amber Rose, who wrote a very outstanding book *Bee In Balance*, outlining the Bee Venom therapy.

I volunteered as the "guinea pig" in an audience of hundreds to be administered the treatment (please see photo at end of book). It was an incredibly beneficial experience because after the first "live treatment," I experienced about a 75% improvement in mobility and the audience was amazed. So was I.

I later did considerable research and came to the realization that this was a highly therapeutic substance that was in the honeybee and that it was a natural cortical steroid and a natural anti-inflammatory and that it could help me recover from Multiple Sclerosis.

I now receive treatments two to three times per week and am approximately 90% improved from my condition. I believe it has tremendous potential in this country once people understand it and read up on the scientific data. Multiple Sclerosis can be brought *under control* but not *cured* because, like a diabetic must remain on insulin, the Bee Venom Therapy must be administered regularly for the rest of a person's life.

The following testimonial is excerpted with permission from *Bee in Balance* by Amber Rose:

"A LITTLE BIT OF BEES, A LITTLE BIT OF GOD, AND A WHOLE LOT OF ME!"
Lonny's Story–A Testament to the Miracle of Bee Venom Therapy

I got my first symptoms in 1983. My left eye

went blind but the doctors had no idea what was wrong. The doctors put me in the hospital. I will never forget this one day when I saw an old man crying because he couldn't see. I remember thinking, "I'm so lucky...at least I still have one good eye!" A month later, I began to have trouble with my right eye. On January 11, 1985, I was on my way out of the community center when I realized that I couldn't see anything at all. I was too scared to tell the receptionist that I was blind.

Some time later I began to have trouble walking. The doctors gave me steroids, which caused me to develop sugar diabetes. In June 1987, I had another flare up. I couldn't hold my fork, my hands and arms became weak, and I lost all the strength in my legs. I was afraid I would never walk again. I had my ups and downs after that. I was in and out of the hospital for years and eventually I went into a nursing home in August of 1992, at the age of 36.

In September of 1993, I had my first 6 bee stings. I have been feeling better ever since. It has been uphill for me all the way. I have had no bad days. I owe it all to Pat Wagner and Amber Rose. It used to take two nurses to help me transfer from the bed to the wheelchair. After the first few weeks of bee stings it only took one nurse to help me. Then I started wheeling myself around in the chair, because I had more strength in my arms.

My arms and hands have gotten so strong now that I can feed myself for the first time in years. I can hold my radio and change the stations on my own. This makes me feel good about myself. I like doing things for myself.

On March 20, 1994 I had my miracle. I started

to walk again. I have been using the parallel
bars and the walker. This is really something!
I'm gonna get out of here! People ask how I
did it and this is what I say, "A little bit of bees,
a little bit of God, and a whole lot of me!"

The following article appeared in the *American Bee
Journal*:

Bee Venom Therapy for Multiple Sclerosis
by Charles Mraz

I have been active in the use of Bee Venom
Therapy for some 60 years, since 1934. It has
been so successful, I have continued using it
to this day on an even larger scale. Though
B.V. Therapy is effective with no adverse side
effects and at a very low cost, there has been
no interest by the medical profession to use it.
This is understandable, since B.V. Therapy is
not an easy treatment to give or receive, as
well as the fear most people have of getting
stung by a bee. As some doctors have said to
me, "We do not need Bee Venom Therapy to
treat rheumatic diseases, we have many drugs
for this purpose."

For years I have wanted to treat M.S. with
B.V. Therapy, as it is considered to be a
rheumatic disease and I felt sure it would be
effective. M.S. is a serious and often fatal
disease. It is only natural that a victim will go
to the best neurologist for advice and
treatment. What makes M.S. such a sinister
disease is that the victims lose all their
muscular functions; walking, hand control,
vision, bladder control, hearing, etc.

Eventually it becomes impossible to swallow food to keep alive.

It was through an unusual chain of events that I had the first chance to treat two cases of M.S. with B.V. Therapy. About six years ago, much to my surprise, a lady came to see me and asked if I would treat her M.S. with B.V. Therapy. She then explained she first came to see me 5 years before to treat her arthritis, which I did. She said she was fine for 5 years. Then symptoms started coming back and she went back to her doctor who told her she did not have arthritis, but that she had M.S., and that she had had it for at least 6 to 10 years. Obviously, she had M.S. when I treated her 5 years before. "If it made me well then," she thought, "I will try again."

With my long experience treating all forms of rheumatic diseases with B.V. Therapy, it was not difficult for me to develop a program to treat her for M.S. Soon after we started, another lady about the same age (42), had similar symptoms. They usually both came for treatments at the same time three times a week for three months. Then twice a week for 2 months, with 10-15 stings for each treatment. Since M.S. usually involves nerve function, I treated the trigger points along the nerve meridians of the body. I have rarely seen the women since, but they appear to be normal in their functions so far, after six years.

Since then I have treated many more cases of M.S. Almost all of them have responded very well, some of them dramatically. Fatigue is the most common complaint from people with M.S., and with B.V. Therapy it seems to be the first symptom to be relieved. Improvement in other functions seem to follow, sometimes dramatically and with others, more slowly. There appears to be improvement in almost all cases.

After 60 years of struggle trying to create an interest in the healing power of Bee Venom Therapy, interest seems to be growing. More people are starting to inquire to beekeepers for a supply of bees to use to treat their various problems. I feel strongly that beekeepers should take an interest and help make bees available to those that want to relieve their suffering.

One of the simplest methods to make a supply of bees available for home use is to put about 50 to 100 bees in a glass jar with a supply of honey. A mayonnaise jar with a metal cover works well. Remove the liner from the inside of the cover, and then punch holes in the cover for the bees to get a supply of air in the jar. Be sure the holes are not too big, so that bees won't escape through them. Put a large tablespoon of honey, preferably crystallized, in the bottom of the jar. Cover with a single thickness of Kleenex to help prevent bees from drowning in the honey. A piece of comb honey is ideal. Be sure there is enough honey as they will quickly die if they run out of it.

Then place a piece of cardboard tubing, such as from a toilet paper roll, in the jar as a place for the bees to cluster. It is difficult for bees to cluster on slippery glass. Bees will live a week or more in such a jar, as long as they have a supply of honey.

To get bees into the jar from the hive, make an "upper entrance" in the back of the hive body, about a 7/8 inch hole just below the handholds. To get bees into the jar, simply place the open jar over this hole in the hive and rub it back and forth to disturb the bees. They will soon come out through the hold to investigate the disturbance and find themselves inside the jar with a free supply of honey. When there are enough bees in the jar, slide the jar slowly against the side of the hive body towards the edge. Then slide the jar off the hive body and quickly slap on the cover. The whole operation will take just a minute or two in warm weather when bees move freely. Having the hole in back of the hive keeps it away from the guard bees at the main entrance.

We get bees from our hives to use for B.V. Therapy every day of the year. Often in the winter, temperatures will drop on occasion to below zero. Bees do not come out of their hives readily below 30 degrees Fahrenheit.

For a supply of bees from a hive in the winter, this can easily be done by a method that does not disturb the bees and will not interfere with their wintering.

Secure a piece of 1-inch Styrofoam or "Blue Board." Cut it to the same dimension as your inner covers. Leave the center hole in the inner cover open. On top of the inner cover place the insulating board, or Styrofoam. This will make a space between the inner cover and the Styrofoam board about a half-inch thick. Replace the outside cover. This Styrofoam board makes excellent insulation for winter.

When some bees are needed, even if it is minus 30 degrees below zero, simply remove the outside cover. Then carefully lift up the Styrofoam board. You will find a layer of bees spread over the two inside surfaces, still with cold and hardly moving. It is a simple matter to take a spoon, scoop up some bees and knock them into a jar supplied with honey. Since the bees cannot fly, you can handle them just like so many beans. Cover up the hive again and the bees will hardly know you were there. There is no need to remove the inner cover or disturb the bees inside the hive in any way. As soon as you take the stiff bees into the warm house, they will revive in a mater of minutes, all ready for business. If it is a strong hive, it can supply bees almost every day, and still winter perfectly.

The following article is by Pat Wagner, a victim of Multiple Sclerosis:

GOT M.S.? USE B.V. THERAPY!
Yes. Bee Stings for Multiple Sclerosis! They Work!

Almost 24 years ago, I was diagnosed with Multiple Sclerosis. Through the years I experienced the medications, hospitalizations, hopes, letdowns, and tears, too. I fought not to succumb to a wheelchair. I thought that would be the worst of it. Little did I know that on February 24, 1992, my neurologist would say that the medications he was prescribing were no longer effective. My M.S. had taken it's course, and I should not look for improvement—little, if any. But I learned that a wheelchair was the least of my M.S. problems.

Years ago, when I could walk, my foot dragged. When I could see to write, my fingers could not grasp the pen. How could I feel whether or not my baby's diaper pin was through the cloth? I could burn myself and not even feel that! And lock my apartment door for safety?–No way. How could someone get in when I called for help to get off the floor? Oh well, that was years ago. Things change.

Now, back to that day, February 24, 1992. My condition? I was wheelchair bound. No chance of moving a toe–I had no feeling or movement in my legs at all. Hug my new grandaughter? Sure. If someone put her in my lap and "kept an eye on us" to make sure we didn't fall. Bowel and bladder control? Not me! But then, I couldn't see the people who could see me. So, why be embarrassed about it? I would never recognize them the next time we met. You see, I was all but blind. Did you say something? Sorry, but I was deaf in my right ear, too. Talk about exciting. I was too weak to lift a sandwich. I could wear myself out sitting up in bed. Hey, don't laugh. That took some real coordination and effort! After all, I had to push the button on my hospital bed and by the time I was basically upright, I had to go through it all again, in reverse. Why? Because I was *exhausted*. And you can just forget about me even attempting to roll over in bed. But, through it all, I could still breathe. So what's the big deal about being in a wheelchair? I was wrong in thinking that was the worst of it.

But there is another date. One month later, March 24, 1992. That was the day I started using Bee Venom Therapy to treat M.S.!

Yes, bee stings! I have yet to have one person not respond positively to BVT (Bee Venom Therapy). In fact, there are several who have obtained feeling back, when nothing else had worked. Many have begun getting their vision back–from double or even triple–to single, and then have the blurriness begin clearing too! Others were hospitalized, yet saw no improvement. But when BVT was used, the improvement came. Doctors are getting inquisitive, and some (including my own neurologist) are referring patients to me to look into this "bee sting thing." Though I am not a doctor, my bottom line to them is basically that when they give medicines (ACTH, steroids, antibiotics, etc.) they are giving the adrenal glands (your internal get well system) a day off for bad behavior. You see, those glands produce the very medicinal properties the doctors are using for treatment. However, bee stings tell your adrenal glands "Hey! Wake up! You are going to work overtime until this person is *well again!*"

Sick or not, we all have adrenal glands. Sometimes they just do not function properly. That is when we either let doctors do their thing, or we do it by using bee stings to cause our own system to do its thing. And, as we all know, the ultimate goal is for us to get well. Of course, there is no money in bee stings for doctors, so they may not suggest such a treatment. On the other hand, God's bees sure do make getting well quite cost effective for us, don't they!

What have you got to lose? A wheelchair? Numbness? Rigidity? Incontinence? Or could it simply be just your inability to see the person you wish you had the ability to hug? Whatever it is, go ahead and lose it! You have everything to gain.

As a victim of Multiple Sclerosis, I thank God for His honeybees and what they have done for me. They have given up their lives and given me life–again! There is nothing like the sweet (natural and healthy) sting of success!

Thank you for giving me the chance to once again share my experience with others. As a closing note, may I simply remind you that bees are good medicine, and you don't need a prescription!

THE COMPONENT PARTS IN HONEYBEE VENOM

There are 76 different components in bee venom, but not all of these components are consistently present in every bee's venom. There are six primary components which are thought to provide the major therapeutic benefits of BVT.

Hyaluronidase: Physiological properties–loosens the glue which connects cells, making the tissue more permeable. Healing substances have greater access to the cells; the elimination of toxic substances also becomes easier.

Phospholipase A1 & A2: Physiological properties– contained in all venoms, it is an emulsifier which acts to detoxify the cells.

Apamin: Physiological properties–assists damaged nerve receptors by specifically enhancing critical aspects of nerve transmission.

Melittin: Physiological properties–Melittin attacks cerain cell walls, creating the "sting." It has bacteriocidal and other healing properties. While it causes the histamine reaction which causes swelling and inflammation, it has strong anti-inflammatory effects.

Histamine: Physiological properties–produces signs of inflammation, well known to allergic sufferers who get relief from their symptoms using antihistamines.

Mast Cell Degranulating Peptide: Physiological properties–another agent which leads to the release of histamine. It has positive effects on neurochemistry. It may produce a feeling of mental alertness and improved concentration.

The following compounds also exist in some bee venom and are also known to have beneficial effects:

"Compound X": Physiological properties: appears to potentiate the effectiveness of other compounds in the venom.

Dopamine: Physiological properties–An effective neurotransmitter that increases motor activity.

Norepinephrine: Physiological properties–a strong neurotransmitter that mediates the "fight or flight" response.

Adolapin: Physiological properties–an anti-inflammatory agent which produces an analgesic effect.

APITHERAPY SOCIETY – 1-802-436-2708

PAT WAGNER, Apitherapist and recovered M.S. Victim

For information call: 1-301-843-8350

AQUA RESONANCE

For information on Aqua Resonance
Call MYCA, Inc. 713-774-8914.

"Bio-Water" has been found to be a specific form of water instrumental in key cellular functions. Research has shown that the lack of this specific form of water is responsible for cellular aging.

Studies done at the University of Pennsylvania by

Gilbert Ling, at the University of Texas by Ivan Carmen, at the University of California (Berkeley) by James Kleg: and researchers in Europe are all finding that water in the cytoplasm isn't merely in a random state in which reactions are taking place. There are actually four different primary forms of water found in every cell type, and these four different forms of water are the basic building blocks of how cell systems work.

Dr. Lee Lorenzen is the leading researcher in the understanding of Bio-Water. He holds a Ph.D. in Nutritional Biochemistry and is licensed in clinical nutrition with the American Licensing Board of Nutrition. Dr. Lorenzen is the discoverer of the template induction process and is a world-renowned expert in micro-cluster technology. He has lectured extensively on the life sciences in 42 states and 25 countries, and was recently awarded an honorary Doctorate Degree in Medicine from the International Oakland University for his pioneering work in this field.

Dr. Lorenzen has shown that the structure of the average cell in the human body has a skeleton much like our own system. This is called the <u>cytomatrix</u> or the matrix of proteins. There are thousands of proteins. These helical proteins stretch not only throughout the cell, but from the nucleus through the cell membrane and interconnect to other cells. *This is a highly complex conduit of water-protein structure that carries what is now shown to be very high frequency information.*

Like the layers of an onion, water surrounds protein. If you were to look down the long side of the protein you will notice that there are rings of bound water right on the protein itself. Beyond that there are secondary rings of water and tertiary rings that may be going out 7, 8 or 9 layers. Every one of those layers have a different function as to how they carry electrical information. The water inside these helical proteins has a density much lower than normal water. It also carries electrical information at a much higher rate than normal water because it is in a *structured* form: it's in little clusters. These little clusters help translate this protein from a random material into something that carries information very much like fibre optics. If you take a protein like this and you put structured water at the center of it, you find out that this matrix is carrying waves of information at a very high speed.

Herbert Froylic at the University of London discovered that these waves of information are moving somewhere around 1011.Hertz. These are frequencies far beyond radio or micro waves. That's how fast information is moving back and forth through the cells. Cell systems can't carry information unless the water has *specific structure.*

Research done by Dr. Kateyama in Japan has found that when we are first born, the water in the cells is highly structured and the water is very mobile. It's moving back and forth very rapidly. This obviously helps to carry oxygen and nutrients into the cell, and helps to remove carbon dioxide, toxins and other components out of the cell very rapidly so that the cell functions normally.

Researchers have discovered that the structure of Bio-Water changes as you grow older. Instead of free-flowing in small clusters, the water becomes bound to other cell material and is less able to deliver nutrients and remove waste. We are also discovering that the clustered water molecules communicate important biochemical information and the cell communication is also impaired as we grow older.

As we age, there is a gradual dehydration process that actually takes place. Dr. Kateyama's research says that by the time we are 60, almost three fourths of the water in the blood alone has actually disappeared! If water is not surrounding those proteins, then those proteins aren't carrying the cell information correctly. If the cell information isn't being carried correctly, then cell function is not there. Dr. Robin, recent Nobel Prize winner in Medicine, has shown that these cell proteins must carry these waves of information very effectively to make the cell system work. The only way to make the cell systems work efficiently is to make sure that the water turnover rate is rapid, and moving in and out of the cell system quickly.

Dr. Lorenzen has discovered a method that recreates the condition of the cell's water structure to be as it was when we were first born (Bio-Water). He calls this water

Aqua Resonance.

When added to distilled water it gives your system a solution that is already in a biologically active form to carry water and its information back and forth more rapidly.

Dr. Farber's Comments: The very concept of having the molecular structure of the water in one's body *clustered* and *organized,* as opposed to scattered and disassociated is a mark of genius which could someday win the Nobel Prize. Since our bodies are made up of about 70% water, it is only logical that if 70% of our body is in perfect communication on a cellular level, then we could be 70-100% healthier.

According to one of my patients: "I am 44 years old and am going through the "change of life" which accompanies that age bracket. My symptoms included profuse night sweats as well as hot flashes. Nothing helped me until I began taking Aqua Resonance A.M. and P.M. and then I immediately began improving and my night sweats and hot flashes began diminishing and then stopping. I want to thank Dr. Lorenzen for his biological creation which has brought me to a *whole new level of health* during menopause, which usually disrupts a woman's entire life. I also have much more energy and my entire system works better.

One of the diseases which I (Dr. Farber) have had to conquer is Multiple Sclerosis. Although I am 80-90% better as a result of Bee Venom Therapy, I was still having problems with *sleeping* at night. I would usually have to take either Nyquil or Benadryl to fall asleep When I began on the Aqua Resonance P.M. it was like a natural sleeping pill. I would fall asleep immediately and have a good night's sleep, with no side effects. The Aqua Resonance P.M. contains Melatonin which stimulates the pituitary gland and induces sleep. In addition, every function in my entire body is working more smoothly. The Aqua Resonance program also speeds up the action of the Mild Silver Protein, helping it move more rapidly through the system.

I strongly recommend that anyone utilizing Mild Silver Protein also make Aqua Resonance A.M. and P.M. part of their dietary program. This should take the individual and place him on a much higher level of health (the Aqua Resonance *eye drops* are much more effective than Visine, having cleared up an optic neuritis infection in just three days).

SHARK CARTILAGE
by Alex Duarte, O.D., Ph.D.

For information on Shark Cartilage,
Call Sharon, Dr. Duarte's seceretary, at 916-272-9697.

Scientific research has now demonstrated that cartilage, particularly shark cartilage, is producing dramatic results in the treatment of the most degenerative and life-threatening diseases, including cancer. Cartilage has proven to be safe and effective in psoriasis, eczema, colitis, enteritis, poison ivy/oak, acne, varicose ulcers, pruritus ani, fistulas, hemorrhoids, wound healing, phlebitis, ulcers, cold sores, shingles, lupus and cancer.

Cartilage is an acidic mucopolysaccharide/protein complex that does also contain collagen, glycosaminoglycans, including chonoritin sulfate A. B, and C. These compounds make shark cartilage (1) The most powerful anti-inflammatory agent and wound healing substance in the world; (2) Stimulate the cellular and humoral components of our immune system. This makes it effective against bacteria, virus and fungal infections; (3) Contain an anti-angiogenisis factor that shuts off blood vessel growth to tumors, which kills malignant or benign tumors.

MEDICAL LITERATURE REVIEW

Stronger and Accelerated Wound Healing: Dr. Prudden and Dr. Allen showed cartilage-treated wounds increased the overall wound tensile strength by 42% over the control group (1). Also, cartilage-treated wounds healed faster than their genetic potential with cartilage (2).

Osteoarthritis: Cartilage reduces the inflammation of osteoarthritis and the polysaccharide portion stimulates protein and chondroitin sulfate synthesis in the joint (it may restore joint integrity) (3). Seven hundred moderate to advanced osteoarthritic patients were treated with oral bovine cartilage at 9 grams per day. Fifty nine percent were totally cured, twenty six percent had a good response, eight percent had a fair response and only seven percent had a poor response (4).

Shark cartilage study: In five year double blind study on 147 patients at the Department of Internal Medicine and Rheumatology at Polyclinic of the Medical Faculty of Charles University in Czechoslovakia, Dr. Rejolec showed an 85 percent reduction in pain scores in the cartilage group compared to a 5 percent in the pain reduction group treated with standard drugs (NSAID–nonsteroidal antiinflammatory drugs). More significantly, there was 63 percent less joint degeneration in the cartilage treated group (5).

Rheumatoid Arthritis: Dr. John F. Prudden treated nine patients with severe rheumatoid arthritis with an average of 500 cc of subcutaneously injected bovine cartilage. Three had excellent results while six had good results. This shows there was a 100 percent effective response rate. Realize that no other medicine has ever produced these kinds of results. All of the patients in the study suffered severe pain and stiffness in multiple joints, primarily the knees, wrists, elbows, hips and fingers (6). Oral preparations of shark cartilage are currently producing similar results when patients take 9 grams (9,000 mgs) per day (7).

Cancer Research: In 1983 at the Massachusetts Institute of Technology, Dr. Ann Lee and Robert Langer, Ph.D. proved cartilage contains a protein that inhibits the formation of blood vessels to tumors (benign or malignant). They also showed that shark cartilage had 1000 times more of this protein than that of bovine (calf) cartilage (8). The substance is known as the antiangiogenesis factor. "Anti" means against, "angio" means blood and "genesis" means to create. Thus, it stops or inhibits the formation of blood vessels to tumors. Dr. Judah Folkman of Children's Hospital of Boston at Harvard University has shown that if a tumor cannot establish its own blood vessel network, it cannot grow beyond 1 or 2 cubic millimeters. If a tumor cannot get nourishment and removal of its waste, it will die.

Dr. Brian Durie, while at the university of Arizona Health Sciences Center, using in vitro (test tube) stem cell assays, showed that shark cartilage was highly effective at killing Myeloma 8226, WIDR (Colon) and MCF-7 (breast) cancer colonies.

G. Atassi, Ph.D., of the Jules Bordet Institute in Brussels, Belgium, the largest and one of the most prestigious cancer research centers in the world, showed oral administration of cartilage to be effective against cancer. Nude mice (mice without immune systems) were given human melanoma, and then 48 hours later the experimental group received shark cartilage powder. The shark cartilage group had a 60 percent reduction in tumor size at 21 days, while the untreated group experienced rapid tumor growth (10).

Human Cancer Studies: The landmark study of cartilage therapy for cancer began in 1974 when Dr. John Prudden was granted a study protocol by the Food and Drug Administration. All of the patients in the study had failed with chemotherapy, radiation and surgery. The following types of cancers were treated by Dr. Prudden: breast, cervix, ovary, prostate, lung, liver, bone, stomach, pancreas, brain, thyroid, Hodgkin's Disease (lymph) (11). In 1985, Dr. Prudden published his results in the "Journal of Biological Response Modifiers," a peer reviewed journal, which showed a 61 percent complete response (35 percent cured, 26 percent cured with some relapse after discontinuing cartilage therapy) (11). Ninety percent of the patients had a positive response and some of the cures were achieved the fastest when chemotherapy was combined with cartilage. In fact, cartilage protected the patients from the terrible side effects of chemotherapy (12). Thus cartilage may be taken and should be taken with standard forms of treatment.

Dr. Prudden's study was conducted with bovine (calf) cartilage. Let's now examine what shark cartilage has done for terminal cancer victims. This study was entitled, "The High Rate of BioActivity (reduction in gross tumor size) Observed in Advanced Cancer Patients Treated with Shark Cartilage Material" and was a cooperative study between I. W. Lane, Ph.D., and E. Contreras, Jr., M.D. The paper was published in *The Journal of Naturopathic Medicine,* 1992 Volume (3) 1:86-88.

Initially, 7 of the 8 terminal patients had a positive response. By the end of the 12 week study, 6 of 8 were recovered (75 percent cured). Dr. Contreras' study was conducted on colon, breast, pancreatic, cervical and prostatic cancers.

Let's examine a couple of case histories from this study. The first one is a forty-eight year old man who had been suffering with inoperable sarcoma covering the entire back side of his right thigh. The tumor had been mostly resistant to radiation and continued to grow. Even after seven weeks of cartilage therapy, there was no visible sign of relief. Dr. Ernesto Contreras, Jr. decided to surgically remove the tumor. During the operation, Dr. Francisco Contreras found that the tumor had gelatinized and had begun to decay. It appeared that the cartilage therapy did work and was slowly breaking down the tumor from the inside out. Happily, there was no metastasis to the lung which is common with this kind of cancer.

Another case involved a forty-eight year old woman with advanced uterine/cervical cancer that had invaded the bladder. Once again, radiation was not of any help and the woman was in a great deal of pain and had open ulcerations. After seven weeks of shark cartilage therapy, the pain was eliminated and the tumor was eighty percent reduced. After three months, the tumor was one hundred percent reduced with only a scar remaining. The pain was completely gone.

Safety: Oral, rectal, vaginal and topical administration of cartilage has proven to be totally non-toxic and non-mutagenic. Cartilage should not be taken by nursing mothers, pregnant women or by anyone who has had a heart attack within the last 30 days or anyone who will have surgery within a month or had surgery within a week.

REFERENCES

1. Prudden, J. and Allen J., "Clinical Acceleration of Wound Healing with a Cartilage Preparation: A Controlled Study, *"The Journal of the American Medical Association,* May, Volume 192, 1965.
2. Prudden, J., Balassa, L., Wolarsky, E., "The Acceleration of Healing, "Surgery, Gynecology and Obstetrics, Vol. 128, pp 1321-1326.
3. Bollet, A.J., "Stimulation of Protein-Chondroitin Sulfate Synthesis by Normal and Osteoarthritic Cartilage, "Arthritis and Rheumatism, 11:663, 1968.
4. This information is contained in Part II, "General Description of Catrix, Summary of Dosage Forms and Results of Catrix Therapy," *The Journey,* a professional publication distributed to Doctors by Dr. Prudden.
5. Rejholic, V., "Long Term Studies of The Antiosteoarthritic Drugs, *"Seminars in Arthritis and Rheumatism,* Vol. 17, No. 2, Supplement 1, Nov. 1987.
6. Prudden, John F., and Balassa, L., "The Biological Activity of Bovine Cartilage Preparations, *"Seminars in Arthritis and Rheumatism,* Vol. 3, No. 4, Summer, 1974, p. 298.

7. Duarte, A., "Jaws for Life, The story of Shark Cartilage," self published, Jan. 1993, p. 18. (Copies are available from Infor-Med at (916) 272-4247).

8. Langer, R., Lee, A., "Shark Cartilage Contains Inhibitors of Tumor Angiogenesis," *Science*, Sept. 16, 1983, Vol 221, pp 1185-1187.

9. Durie, Brian, M.D., Professor of Hematology and Oncology, University of Arizona Health Services Center, Reuters News Service, Worldwide Release, March 7, 1984.

10. Lane, I., William, PhD., and Comac, Linda, "Sharks Don't Get Cancer," New York: Avery Publishing Group, Inc. 1992.

11. Prudden, John F., "The Treatment of Human Cancer with Agents Prepared from Bovine Cartilage," *Journal of Biological Response Modifiers*, 4:551-558, 1985.

12. Ibid.

13. This information is contained in Part II, "General Description of Catrix, Summary of Dosage Forms and The Results of Catrix Therapy," of *The Journey*, a professional publication distributed to Doctors by Dr. Prudden. This information is more thoroughly covered in the book, "Jaws for Life, The Story of Shark Cartilage" by Alex Duarte, O.D., Ph.D.

MELALEUCA

Melaleuca (alternifolia oil) is becoming well known (rediscovered) and is widely used by myriad healthcare professionals including dentists, physicians, veterinarians, chiropractors and therapists.

Believed to have originated in Australia, the Melaleuca alternifolia tree grows wild in the swamps and in the low-lying flood prone areas (it is also called the "tea tree" and is grown on plantations today). The oil from this tree is an exceptionally potent antiseptic bactericide.

Australian medical literature as far back as 1930 reported that Melaleuca was radically effective against infections which had resisted treatments of various kinds for months...and were cured in less than a week. Sore throats were quickly healed. Foul odors from wounds or abscesses were quickly eradicated. Melaleuca dissolved pus and left infected wound surfaces clean.

Eventually Melaleuca alternifolia oil was introduced in the United States, where it is now reported as having been successfully used in treating acne, anaerobic vaginosis, insect bites, infected wounds, skin cuts and abrasions, and conditions of the mouth and throat (it is non-toxic).

DEPRENYL

Clinically Proven Facts

Our body produces dopamine, and without its effect, we cannot exist. The dopamine manufacturing process declines as we age and with that decline comes senility, loss of mobility and strength, depression, weakness in the immune system, loss of memory, loss of body hormone content, loss of sex drive and a battery of neurological diseases.

Longevity Implications

Indications are that Deprenyl will increase the life expectancy of people 40-60%. Fifty to one hundred years of monitoring would be the only way to prove or disprove the current longevity predictions. Considering the fact that 80% of what works on animals also works on people...and given the fact that the pharmaceutical actions noted with animals treated with Deprenyl have also been noted in humans...leads us to believe that the 40-60% increase in life span observed in rats will also be noted in the future for human beings taking Deprenyl.

Proven Effective

It works on depression, learning, cognitive and motor function, senile dementia, pain, energy deficiency, ulcer formation, hormone release, sex drive dysfunction, revival of dying brain cells, Parkinson's Disease, Alzheimer's Disease, Multiple Sclerosis, ALS (Lou Gehrig's Disease), blepharospasms, high blood pressure, stroke-induced paralysis, mental dysfunction.

More Facts About Deprenyl

It is an extremely safe product to take. It was developed thirty years ago as an anti-depressant. The side effects noted in three decades of usage are reported as negligible to none. Clinical trial studies in the past ten years have uncovered some absolutely amazing properties of Deprenyl, including the ability to stimulate the tissue in that part of the brain called the substantia nigra in order to naturally produce more dopamine. It has been recently ascertained that brain cells do not die immediately, and coupled with the fact that the administration of Deprenyl will revive dormant and malfunctioning brain cells... could reflect potential for dramatic help for many people. It has proven extremely helpful, not only for neurological diseases, but also for people that have suffered a stroke.

In summary, the proper administration of Deprenyl prevents the depletion of dopamine, therefore preventing much of the brain cell death which leads to age-related body deterioration and dysfunction.

RODAKEM

For information on Rodakem,
Call Sharon, Dr. Duarte's seceretary, at 916-272-9697.

Few diseases are feared and dreaded more than disorders of the connective tissues and of the nervous system. The reason: these diseases are mostly considered "incurable " by physicians in North America, including Multiple Sclerosis, Strokes, Alzheimer's Disease, Parkinson's Disease, Optic Neuritis, etc.

This conclusion is simply *not necessarily so.* Alternative Healthcare and Therapies are proving to be dramatically successful in more and more specific cases.

According to Dr. Alex Duarte, O.D., Ph. D.:"The primary purpose of Rodakem is to accelerate healing of the connective tissues. It has also been shown to substantially help nerve regeneration and therefore has been used with great success in brain and central nervous system disorders." The following is an excerpt from Dr. Duarte's book *How To Obtain Miracle Medicines Offshore Legally* (selectively quoted).

The following information was taken from a report produced by the late Charles Kaelin, previous District Manager for Rodakem Laboratories, Rodaquina, S.A., Mexico. Please note that most of this information is in the form of anecdotal evidence, and should not be considered to be scientifically proven, unless so stated.

The primary purpose of Rodakem is to accelerate the healing of connective tissue. It has also been shown to substantially help nerve regeneration, and has been used with great success in brain and central nervous system disorders. Conditions ameliorated by Rodakem include: Parkinsonism, Stroke and Paralysis, Diabetic Neuropathy, Autism in Children, Mental Retardation, heart Arrhythmias, Neuromas, Gliomas, Meningiomas, Neurofibromatosis, Phlebitis, Scar Tissue Reduction, Optic Neuritis, and Multiple Sclerosis.

PARKINSONISM

Parkinsonism has been treated very successfully with Rodakem, leaving the patient with much improved equilibrium, reduction in tremors and pain and, in some cases, a complete resolution of the disease within 5 weeks to 15 months. One young gentleman had Parkinson's Disease to the point that he perspired profusely, couldn't drive, couldn't sleep, and felt indescribably weak. In his own words, he was on the verge of suicide and felt his life was hopeless. After taking Rodakem for

120 days, his sweating, chattering teeth, shaking limbs and insomnia had all ceased. His own physician was astounded.

STROKE AND PARALYSIS VICTIMS

According to Mr. Kaelin, one of the Rodakem patients, a Mrs. Simpson, 67 years old, was taking Rodakem following a stroke. Before Rodakem, Mrs. Simpson woke up one morning to find that she could not pick up or hold any objects. She had a loss of equilibrium and tried to call her husband, but could not make a sound.

Later, at the hospital, she was discovered to have a clot on the brain. Ten days later she was discharged from the hospital with a dragging right leg and slurred speech. Nine months later, a large lump was removed from her left breast. Six months after that, with approval from her doctor, she began taking Rodakem. She went from being severely depressed, physically handicapped with very high blood pressure to a speaking, walking, happy individual in just six months time. Her blood pressure became normal without medication and she continued to do well.

DIABETES

The next case is that of Mr. Gonzales, who was suffering with diabetes, stroke and paralysis, high blood pressure, chest pain and difficulty breathing. Mr. Gonzales' doctor prescribed Rodakem and gave the man 4 oral ampules and 3-4 tablespoons of bran meal per day. Within a short time, Mr. Gonzales' facial paralysis was completely improved. In addition to this, amazingly, his doctor was able to take him off Diabenese for his diabetes, and his blood pressure became normal. Within a year and a half, Mr. Gonzales had no noticeable symptoms of the stroke or paralysis. The diabetes had completely normalized.

Another diabetic patient, a 67-year-old woman, had scratched her ankle on a sharp object resulting in a wound that would not heal. Later, a large ulcer developed and became secondarily infected. Several doctors and one year later, she was worse and not better. Her only hope now was to have amputation. A close friend recommended Rodakem and after the first week, she noticed a lessening in the size of the ulcer and no pain killers were needed. Five weeks later, her ulcer was completely healed. It appears that Rodakem has a profound effect on stimulating connective tissue to heal, as well as somehow improving circulatory function. It has also been used on nervousness, depression, asthma and low body temperature. All of these conditions have different causes, yet Rodakem seems to be supportive in a general way.

One particularly interesting case is that of a man that had suffered from failure to grow bone after an osteotomy. Even though his doctor took a piece of the bone from the man's hip and implanted it into the tibia, callus production was not efficient. However, after taking Rodakem for a few weeks, there was remarkable production of callus, and after one year the calcification was perfect.

In other cases, Rodakem has been shown to help palpitations and fibrillations of the heart. In yet others, aplastic anemia and fractured vertebrae appear to be resolved. One woman had a red blood cell count which was extremely low and dangerous. After taking Rodakem for 4 weeks, she found that her blood count began to rise. After several months, her blood was at a normal level, and her vertebrae were completely healed.

For children, Rodakem may prove to be a truly miracle medicine, having a profound effect on autism and mental retardation. Anya started taking Rodakem when she was eight years old. Almost immediately, her awareness and comprehension improved remarkably. She listened, began to carry out simple basic instructions for the first time, and began to respond to her name. There was a break of six weeks when she did not take Rodakem, which allowed her parents to see that the improvements were permanent. She did not appear to lose any of what she had gained.

When she began taking Rodakem again, she immediately improved more. She started playing with toys and developed an interest in other children. She carried out verbal instructions faster and more accurately than before. Her parents state that they will keep using the product as long as it helps their child.

One of the more exciting applications of Rodakem is on scar tissue. A 50-year-old woman, by the name of Becky, had scar tissue on her arm with puckering and lumping that changed to normal skin within a one year period on Rodakem. Her energy also multiplied ten fold, and she was able to walk distances she could have never contemplated before. Also, a severe arrhythmic beat of her heart completely resolved.

A scientific study was started on January 7, 1964 in the city of Mexicali, B.C., Mexico. Twenty-six patients of the Instituto Mexicano de Seguro Social were selected for the study. All had dermocollagen lesions of 6 months to 10 years duration. Some of these were caused by vaccinations, burns, surgery, trauma, and others of unknown origin.

The study took place over a period of three years, though some of the patients could not stay for the full length of the study. All false keloids (scar tissue) were eliminated from this study. Complete blood counts, urine analysis, liver function, and pathological studies were made, along with the measurements of the specific electrical potential of the scar tissue itself. Each patient was given 3 ampules per day orally, 1 ampule on an absolutely empty stomach 15 minutes before each meal. At the end of the study, 5 patients had no more scar tissue at all, 18 patients had improved up to 95%, and the remaining 3 patients experienced softening of the scar tissue without reduction in size. No side effects were observed in any of the cases.

Rodakem has also been shown to be helpful on neurofibromatosis, a hereditary disorder that produces pigmented spots and tumors of the skin, tumors of the peripheral optic nerve and acoustic nerves and subcutaneous and bony deformities. As the disease progresses, the tumors cause severe neurological problems in the spinal cord, cranial nerves, vision and hearing centers. Eventually all this leads to blindness and deafness.

The various deep tumors such as neuromas, gliomas, and meningiomas can be treated by the appropriate surgical removal. However, the underlying cellular disorder is unknown and no general medical treatment is available.

A young man that had been suffering from tumorous growths around his kidneys experienced remarkable and dramatic reduction in said tumors after taking Rodakem for 6 months. He had several large growths completely covering, and to some degree obstructing, his anal area, restricting urine flow, and affecting the size and shape of his reproductive organs. These tumors reduced considerably in size, allowing his reproductive organs to return to their normal size. His kidneys have seemed to heal and no dialysis has been necessary.

It seems that Rodakem may be able to help people recover from eye injury, providing the injury is not too extensive. In 1971, a young woman named Jill sustained an eye injury in which a sliver of glass lodged in her eye. Although the doctors removed the glass, the injury caused the vision in that eye to be sketchy and blurred. Her vision returned to normal by April of 1979 after having taken Rodakem. One explanation for this could be that by reducing the majority of the scar tissue, normal corneal and retinal morphology allowed more normal vision to prevail.

Another condition known as phlebitis

(inflammation of the veins) has also been shown to be resolved with Rodakem. Harold was told that his leg might have to be amputated due to phlebitis. After taking Rodakem for 6 months, Harold still had his leg and returned to all of the activities that he had participated in before his phlebitis episodes.

Rodakem has also been shown to be helpful with patients who suffer with respiratory ailments. Such was the case of an 80-year-old patient who was hospitalized in April of 1975 with pain in his upper right abdominal quadrant, including a cough and jaundice. The official diagnosis was pneumonitis, liver enlargement and fever. In July of 1975, liver and spleen scans showed a lesion in the right lobe of the liver. Medical treatment was to no avail, and biopsies were considered inadvisable. Rodakem treatment began at a rate of 4 ampules per day. Two months later, this man's bilirubin and alkaline phosphate levels were almost normal. Approximately one year later, his scans were completely normal, and the patient continues to take Rodakem at a rate of 2 ampules per day.

Rodakem has helped patients recover from progressive heart arrhythmias, heart murmurs and hypoglycemia. Rita was a 70-year-old woman who had suffered a stroke. She was partially paralyzed, had lost her speech and her memory and had elevated blood pressure. After 29 days of taking Rodakem, she could walk, talk, eat, and her memory had completely returned. Her blood pressure is now normal without blood pressure medication.

The next conditions that have been shown to be improved by Rodakem is rheumatoid arthritis and spondylitis. A 31-year-old man was suffering from a fever of 104 degrees, had acute pain in the peripheral joints as well as the hips and shoulders. He was bedridden for 3 months. The pain and stiffness in his spine and the thickening and tenderness of his left elbow resulted in limited motion and a reduction in the grip strength in his right hand to 28 pounds.

This man also suffered from fluid retention in his right knee. His spine was semi-rigid and tender to palpation. He had suffered with these conditions for over a year when he started Rodakem on December 19th, and by January (only 12 days later), his only complaint was moderate stiffness in his hands. There was no pain while resting or engaging in walking. His back pain had disappeared and his hands were only slightly limited in their motion with his grip strength now 115 pounds.

On February 2nd he increased his intake of Rodakem, and seven days later there was no spine tenderness whatsoever. His grip strength was now 240 pounds with his right hand. The patient was able to bend at the waist, putting his fingers within six inches of the floor. In order to determine if the Rodakem was the cause of the healing response, his physician took him off Rodakem and within several days the pain, stiffness and loss of range motion began to return. The patient began Rodakem once again and continued to make even greater improvement than he had. Soon the patient became objectively and subjectively free of pain and symptoms. His primary goal was to share his experience with Rodakem with those who suffer any kind of scar tissue buildup or back injuries, as he feels it is the most wonderful, non-toxic medication in the world.

Perhaps one of the most profound applications of Rodakem is with multiple sclerosis victims. Hector was a man of 40 years of age who started getting headaches and blurred vision in December. His symptoms increased, becoming more frequent, longer lasting, more painful and less responsive to pain killers. He also began to experience numbness and muscle spasms in the right arm, hand and leg. He became very hoarse and suffered edema in the right leg.

Full medication treatment was applied but to no avail. Hector began to use crutches and started taking morphine to relieve the intense pain. He experienced increased spasticity of the right limbs, including the loss of sensations of heat and cold. He developed optic neuritis and atrophy of the left optic nerve. Soon, paralysis set in the right limb and started to raise his blood pressure. It seemed that Hector was near the end.

Multiple vitamin as well as mineral supplements, along with Rodakem, were started immediately. Only mild analgesics were given because more powerful pain killers can block the action of Rodakem. Within two months of starting with the Rodakem, vitamins, minerals, and analgesics, the pain was gone. There was a disappearance of both the headaches and the eye pain. There was a lessening of the spasticity of the muscles, and during the fourth month the patient regained normal movement of limbs, and sensations of heat and cold. Most importantly, his eyesight returned and he no longer needed crutches to walk.

Rodakem can be used on cancer patients, and has shown to improve their health status and help in their recovery. It has also been used for many of the illnesses of animals, especially animals that have begun to lose their eyesight or motor control.

TECHNICAL ANALYSIS OF RODAKEM

Rodakem is comprised of three pairs of oxidation reduction compounds of simulated coenzymatic action which attempts to regenerate the connective tissues.

Formula–Each of the ampules contains: tetrahydroxyquinone, Rhodizonic acid, triquinoyl, polycarbon suboxide, polymer resulting from the action of sulphuric acid with acetaldehyde and ethyl alcohol (0.0166 mg). Each of these substances are combined in a 10 ml vehicle.

Characteristics–The composition of this product was formulated in the hopes of controlling the velocity of reactions of the enzymatic system of oxido-reductors which affects the electro-chemical metabolism of various tissues. Scientific testing *in vitro* and *in vivo* has shown this Redox support system is valid.

The action of the three pairs of oxido-reductors with reversible potentials is sufficiently stable and constant. The oxidations of dehydrogenation type are accelerated at the molecular level and inhibit the oxidation of the oxygen transference type and follow the conduits of energy of cellular respiration. This results in the production of an atomic reaction in a chain that protects the tissue oxidation and conserves the normal structure and functioning of the cells while restoring the potential of oxido-reduction. Interestingly enough, there have not been any traces of the metabolites of Rodakem in the blood, urine, or feces of patients having taken Rodakem.

Rodakem is indicated in the treatment of keloids (scar tissue), and any histopathological cause of hyalin degeneration. Rodakem is completely non-toxic and treatments may be taken for long periods of time without any risk to the patient. Patients that suffer vascular insufficiency and epidermal lesions should also take Rodakem.

Precautions–All toxic substances must be avoided when taking Rodakem. This means no alcoholic beverages, including wine or beer, no tobacco, and no other medications such as relaxants and sedatives which can block the action of Rodakem within the cellular system. Rodakem is a complete normalizer, and is more effective when used alone. Also, avoid exposure to or the ingestion of insecticides, etc. Insecticides block Rodakem's action.

After opening an ampule, its contents

should be consumed completely and immediately, otherwise oxygen in the air can interfere with the stability of the oxido-reduction reactions and diminish its effectiveness. Avoid exposing the product to direct sunlight.

Side Effects–No undesirable side effects have been so far observed.

Dosage–Drink Rodakem on an empty stomach, alone or with an equal amount of pure drinking water. Do not mix Rodakem with any other type of liquids. Patients that are between birth and 5 years old may take one-half to one ampule per day, children 5 -12 years of age should take 1 to 2 ampules daily, and adults should take 4 to 6 ampules per day. Note: if dosage is 6 ampules daily, distribute as follows: 2 ampules at bedtime on an empty stomach, or any time during the night. If the dosage is 4 ampules a day, take on an empty stomach 2 ampules before breakfast and 2 at bed time. Note: due to Rodakem's non-toxicity, in unusual cases as many as 8 to 10 ampules per day can be taken. Being completely non-toxic, Rodakem represents no risk whatsoever for children or adults unless the patient is allergic to the vehicle (the diluent). Rodakem is currently available to you as an outpatient at Hospital Contreras. This may change in the near future.

THE CENTURY CLINIC

While Rodakem is not yet available in the

United States, there is a homeopathic clinic in Reno, Nevada that has an outstanding success rate in treating connective tissue diseases. Over the years I have referred many seriously ill patients to this clinic and the majority of these patients have had remarkable recoveries. The doctors at this clinic concentrate on finding the cause of the disease and then work to find the cure. Take the following case of Jo Graham as an example. The doctors at the clinic found several viruses in Joy's spine. Once the culprits were found, a program of homeopathic anti-viral and connective tissue repair medicines were administered. What followed was a miracle: after 11 years in a wheel chair, Joy Graham walked. The name of this great facility is the Century Clinic, 390 Brinkby, Reno, Nevada 89509, telephone (702) 826-9500.

RODAKEM

By Dr. Francisco Contreras, M.D.

Rodakem is a very special formula which is a mixture of six oxidation-reduction compounds, to which we have added three herbal products that work synergistically and enhance the anti-oxidant effects.

1. Rodakem is 100% non-toxic and no contra-indication for its use has been found.

2. It is a very potent detoxifier and increases the circulation in damaged tissues, helping in the regeneration of cells.

3. Many years ago a similar compound was used by us in Mexico in a clinical trial to see the effects on young keloids. More than

60% of them reduced in size or disappeared completely.

It has been very useful against the following problems: aplastic anemia, chronic pulmonary disease, rheumatoid arthritis and osteo-arthritis, hepatitis and toxic liver damage, nephritis, acute or chronic, Parkinson's disease, Multiple Sclerosis, Alzheimer's...and helps in the recovery of central nervous system damaged by strokes or toxic conditions.

Rodakem usually works slowly and will require months of treatments in chronic degenerative diseases, but sometimes could show beneficial effects in a few weeks in acute conditions. The usual dose is 40 drops three to four times a day in distilled water or fresh juices. It should not be mixed with any other liquid or food.

The bottle should be put in a cool place, never exposed to strong light or to the air for long periods of time.

COENZYME Q10
By Morton Walker, DPM

For information on Coenzyme Q10
Call MYCA, Inc. 713-774-8914.

The scientist who is responsible for much of what we know about CoQ10 is a highly regarded biomedical researcher with many awards to his credit.

Born in Decatur, Illinois in 1906, Dr. Karl Folkers, Ph.D., Ashbel Smith Professor and director of the Institute for Biomedical Research at the University of Texas, is the 1986 recipient of the Priestley Medal for his contributions to chemistry.

The American Chemical Society's highest honor, the Priestley Medal is just one of a long list awards that Dr. Folkers has received during his distinguished career. His work, spanning almost six decades, has, in the words of a colleague, "contributed immensely to our basic knowledge of life processes."

Dr. Folkers believes that a gap exists between chemistry and medical nutrition. He has spent much of the past 35 years attempting to close that gap.

This distinguished nutritional chemist has devoted much time researching Coenzyme Q10, or ubiquinone (so named because it is ubiquitously present throughout the human body). In 1957, while employed by the pharmaceutical giant, Merck & Company, Dr. Folkers reisolated CoQ10 directly after it was first uncovered in pure form from beef heart muscle by scientists at the University of Wisconsin. He determined the compound's structure using the then new technique of nuclear magnetic resonance spectrometry. Then he synthesized it and produced it by fermentation.

PHYSIOLOGICAL EFFECTS

Nutritional chemists know of ten different coenzyme Qs, but only the tenth one has been found extensively in human physiology.

Dr. Folkers became convinced that CoQ10 ultimately would be used to treat heart disease because it is a component of the enzyme complexes involved in respiration and is necessary for human life. Indeed, nearly all of the scientific investigations involving CoQ10 relate to its ability to protect the heart. It acts as a catalyst in the chain of chemical reactions (respiratory chain) that creates cellular energy by real activation of the coenzyme adenosinetriphosphate or ATP.

The CoQ10 compound is found most abundantly in

organs that require a large supply of energy such as the stomach, intestines, heart, liver, uterus, testicles, and immune system.

CoQ10 is known to quench free radical pathology by its antioxidant effect. The compound strengthens cellular membranes. Although not itself classified as a vitamin, it behaves in a manner similar to vitamin E. Moreover, clinical studies show that it aids in lowering elevated blood pressure, benefits those with periodontal disease and reduces symptomology for people suffering diabetes, deafness and impaired immunity.

Lack of CoQ10 is noted to be a factor in the aging process, too, since levels of the compound in aging individuals decrease with the passage of time. Additional reports advise that CoQ10 is useful for treating muscular dystrophy and myopathy. And it has a place adjunctively to diet for counteracting obesity.

Very important for oncologists to know is that Coenzyme Q10 tends to protect human heart tissue from adriamycin, the cancer chemotherapeutic agent that is highly toxic for the heart. Unfortunately, the conventional medical community has ignored this food factor for offsetting cardiac side effects in the adriamycin treatment of cancer.

FOR HEART DISEASE

Coenzyme Q10 has been used since the mid-1970's in Japan to treat cardiac disease. Japanese clinical research shows that about 70 percent of patients with congestive heart failure benefit from administration of the compound. In 1982 alone, about seven million cardiac patients in Japan were prescribed CoQ10 and the number so treated has since been growing each year. Despite this record, American and European cardiologists have not accepted CoQ10 as an adjunctive treatment for heart disease. The problem–as with most nutritional therapies--has been the absence of a monitoring technique for proving the effectiveness of CoQ10 treatment to satisfy the U.S. Food and Drug Administration.

This problem is a general one in biomedical research. Dr. Karl Folkers points out, "Whatever the disease, you need something you can measure objectively and with reliability, and that is not always easy to identify. Sometimes, we don't study the disease we would like to study, but the one that we can follow."

With coworkers at the Scott and White Clinic in Temple, Texas and Methodist Hospital in Indianapolis, Dr. Folkers employed impedance cardiography to prove the beneficial effect of CoQ10 on normal subjects and on patients with advanced heart disease. The clinical response of those victims of severe cardiomyopathy to the oral administration of the compound is often spectacular and there are no side effects.

"Coenzyme Q10 has a lifesaving and life-extending activity for patients with severe cardiomyopathy," the 86-year-old scientist stated.

"I have worked on Coenzyme Q10 longer than on any other project in my life," Dr. Folkers added. "I never would have imagined 20 years ago that I would work on it so long. But once you develop a goal, to elucidate the medical uses of the compound, you just keep working."

A major Japanese heart study concluded that CoQ10 improved symptoms in cardiac patients who experienced no benefit from standard treatment with diuretics and digitalis. It decreases arrhythmia (irregular heartbeat) even in those patients showing arrhythmia as a side effect of receiving psychotropic drugs.

WHERE TO FIND

Adverse effects of supplementing with CoQ10 are minimal or nonexistent. Even with taking the compound in high doses it is difficult to bring on the potential of gastrointestinal upset, loss of appetite, nausea, and/or diarrhea.

CoQ10 may be found as a part of certain foods such as beef heart; salmon, mackerel, sardines and other cold-water fish; peanuts; and spinach. Most often it is available in supplemental tablets or capsules of 10 mg, 20 mg, and 30 mg. No optimal daily dosage is recorded, and a user must go by how he or she feels. Some clinical trials have used as much as 600 mg. a day to elicit a therapeutic effect, but most studies have reported on patients receiving 50 mg to 300 mg daily.

CLINICAL STUDIES ON HEART BENEFIT

*In an experimental double-blind study, 10 men and women with stable angina pectoris received in a random order 150 mg CoQ10 daily or placebo. After four weeks, subjects as compared to controls experienced a 53% reduction in the frequency of anginal episodes.

*Twenty seven patients with ventricular premature heartbeats and no clinical findings of organic cardiopathies received coenzyme Q10. Results were markedly beneficial in 22% and the rest received a slight reduction in their irregularities.

*In a double-blind study of 80 patients, daily

administration of CoQ10 for 12 weeks increased cardiac ejection fraction significantly, reduced shortness of breath, and increased muscle strength for 89% of them.

*Twelve patients with advanced congestive heart failure and an insufficient response to diuretics and digitalis received CoQ10 100 mg. daily and were followed for seven months. Subjectively they felt less tired, activity tolerance increased, shortness of breath at rest disappeared, heart rate fell, and heart volume decreased.

*Thirty four patients with severe congestive cardiomyopathy received 100 mg of CoQ10 daily. Eighty two percent improved as shown by increase stroke volume and cardiac index. Two year survival rate was 62% compared to 25% for a similar series of patients treated by conventional methods alone.

BALANCED HORMONAL THERAPY
By John Parks Trowbridge, M.D.

For information on Balanced Hormonal Therapy, Call Dr. John Parks Trowbridge's office at 713-540-2329.

"I haven't felt this good in 20 years," offers one 75-year-old man, with a cheerful twinkle in his eye. "All I do is take my supplements, follow my eating program, and get my shots. My joints no longer hurt, my legs are stronger, my mind is sharper...and I have a lot more energy."

Too good to be true? That's what too many people think, as they turn their back on one of the most revolutionary discoveries in modern medicine: **Balanced Hormonal Therapy** (or BHT for short) has made sweeping improvements in the health of patients for the last 20 years!

How can BHT help you? If you suffer with
- joint aches and pains
- muscle aches or cramps
- low back pains or sciatica leg pains
- limitation of motion
- loss of strength
- loss of energy
- osteoporosis (softening of bones)
- bursitis or injury-related discomforts
- loss of sexual drive
- loss of sexual function or performance
- bothersome menopausal symptoms
- depression or loss of interest in life
- emphysema, asthma, lung problems
- frequent infections
- other health problems that don't seem to get better despite the best efforts of your doctors.

BHT could be an important part of a treatment program that could help to restore better balance and function to your body. The reason that BHT has helped people with so many different problems is simple: hormones are the "controlling switches" that can "turn on" the healing processes inside you.

How does BHT work? In a nutshell, it works by restoring a natural "buildup and repair" balance to your hormone profile (Cortisone drugs, by contrast, are "tear-down" hormones). As you grow through teen and early adult years, your hormone levels are higher and balanced to keep you healthy and active. As you pass the age of 30 or 40, though, hormone levels decline as part of the aging process. You slow down. Your systems work less well. You repair broken down parts less rapidly. And you feel all these problems as aches and pains, loss of energy, loss of interest, and loss of performance. According to Harold Varon, M.D., of Dallas and formerly a Baylor professor of endocrinology who discovered this approach, BHT appears to be a natural and successful way to counter this degeneration trend.

No studies have been done to show whether BHT can add years to your life–but Dr. Varon's experience with severely ill patients over the past 20 years has certainly shown this: BHT can *add life to your years!*

Why aren't all the doctors excited about BHT? Dr. Varon developed the BHT program in the early 1970's, after observing that many women with rheumatoid arthritis felt considerably better when they were pregnant. He has reported his findings (along with Drs. Finney and Millwee at the 69th Annual Scientific Meeting of the Southern Medical Association in 1975 and at a Dallas workshop on "Hormones and Arthritis" in 1977). As with many new discoveries, this one hasn't sparked the interest of the physicians who are treating the patients. Until that time, Americans will continue to suffer and spend BILLIONS of dollars on aspirin, expensive arthritis drugs, laboratory tests, doctor visits, and physical therapy programs.

"I tell people about how good I feel–and they can see how much better I'm moving," says one of our patients, "but they just shake their head and change the subject. All they'd have to do is follow the program and they'd all get better."

Why can't people believe that new discoveries really might be the answer they've been hoping and praying for? In this modern culture, some of the best ideas are slowest to "catch on."

So what is the treatment program with BHT? BHT involves injections of hormones to produce the desired healthy "buildup and repair" balance--for women, progesterone with estrogen; for men, progesterone with testosterone and HCG. Most people do well on monthly injections after they've gotten expected relief. Until then, you take more injections if you have more discomfort—once weekly or every 2 weeks, then every 3 weeks, until you feel better. Most patients can expect to see improvements within the first 5 or 6 injections–many note changes within the first 2 weeks. Insurance companies usually pay for injected medications, within your policy guidelines. Medicare usually doesn't pay for any medications.

For The Woman...

"I was shocked that these injections have helped me feel so much better so quickly," shares one of our 83-year-old patients. "From the very first, my arthritis pains decreased and my energy and enthusiasm went way up."

How can BHT help you today? Many women know that their hormone cycles affect how they feel "all over." And many women know that they "feel the effects of aging" much more so after menopause. And many women claim that they felt "really good" when they were pregnant (after those first few weeks of turmoil!). What they don't know is that their balance of hormones can be safely and surely regulated by periodic injections, so that they can "feel better" most of the time for the rest of their lives.

Pregnancy is a special condition where a woman's body begins to "build up" to nurture and build a baby–all under the control of protective hormones, mostly progesterone. The balance of these hormones allows for rapid healing and better handling of stress. Women with the crippling disease, rheumatoid arthritis, often notice a marked improvement in their symptoms during this time of pregnancy hormone balance.

The BHT program is a series of hormone injections to give you this pregnancy balance–at a lower level, so you don't have pregnancy side effects–to help keep your body feeling and acting younger for years.

How do you get started on BHT? As in any important treatment program, start with a consultation with the doctor. Your age, your medical condition, other medications, your future plans–all of these factors affect the choice of proper treatment for you.

In general, you should be "current" with your pelvic and breast exams (including mammogram x-rays), even if you have had a hysterectomy. You should be "current" with tests that monitor your general health (blood count, chemistry panel, urinalysis) and with any other tests that monitor any illness conditions. When all is in order, you can start BHT injections. You can expect to come in more often at first, but very quickly you can start a "monthly booster" every 3 to 4 weeks.

What about your hormones and other medications? If you are already taking "menopause hormones" (premarin, Ogen, Estraderm, Provera, and so on), you can expect to discontinue these, since the BHT will set the balance for you.

If you are still in your child-bearing years, you need to remember (1) that the progesterone dose in BHT is used in Europe as a birth control method (though not approved as such here) and (2) that your periods likely will diminish or stop, although an altered bleeding pattern is possible. If you later decide to attempt pregnancy, you will need to be "graduated" back to having usual periods over about 6 months. You can start your injections at *any* time in your menstrual cycle, since the BHT balance will take over your hormonal controls.

If you are menopausal and have *not* had a hysterectomy, you need to know that most women do just fine but some do experience resumption of "period bleeding," This is controllable with special herbal drops (an old midwives' remedy) or with changes in the hormone injections. However, unexpected vaginal bleeding always requires proper medical evaluation.

With regard to other medications, including hormones such as thyroid, you should not expect any important interactions or changes in your program.

What about side effects to look for? Fluid-loading (edema, swelling in the legs) is the most common side effect–and one that is easily controlled with medications (diuretic or "water pill") or nutritional supplements (herbal diuretics or pyridoxine/B6). You can expect advice on which will be the best for you–and that might change later. Hair loss or hair growth is extremely rare and easily controlled. "Senior" women sometimes notice breast swelling and tenderness or even pains. This usually passes quickly and sometimes means a change in the hormones injected.

The risk of cancer, in Dr. Varon's experience, has been extremely low–certainly no higher than with oral hormones (which offer none of the other benefits) and probably far lower. The risk of worsening other medical conditions, such as The Yeast Syndrome, appears minimal. Women who have had cancer (especially of the breast or female organs) or who have a heart condition require special evaluation and monitoring.

How does BHT fit in with other treatment programs? Quite well, in fact. You start with getting your BHT injections once every week or two until your symptoms (joint pains, other problems) improve, then slide to every 3 or 4 weeks on a continuing basis. If you don't have serious symptoms, start out and continue on a 3 to 4 week schedule. Since BHT helps only with hormone balance, continue with proper evaluation and treatment of your underlying medical problems. Most people feel continually better over the next several months, starting within the first few weeks.

For The Men

"I can think more clearly and concentrate for hours now," assures one of our 75-year-old patients. "I feel stronger, can work longer, and feel better than I did when I was 50."

What about side effects to look for? Fluid-loading (edema, swelling in the legs) is the most common side effect–and one that is easily controlled with medications (diuretic or "water-pill") or nutritional supplements (herbal diuretics or pyridoxine/B6). You can expect advice on which will be the best for you–and that might change later.

Stirring up a hidden prostate infection is more likely the more you are beyond 50 years old. To reduce this likelihood, you can expect to be on antibiotics for 1 or 2 months when you start the BHT injections. Men with prostate enlargement problems often get improvement–but will require special management. Return of stronger erections, sexual desire, and sensitivity are common.

Hair loss or hair growth usually depends on your genetic tendency for "male pattern baldness." Men rarely notice swelling and tenderness of the breasts; this usually passes quickly.

Chelation Therapy
by John Parks Trowbridge, M.D., FACAM, FABCT

For information on Chelation Therapy,
Call Dr. John Parks Trowbridge's office at 713-540-2329.

"Chelation" comes from a Greek word meaning "claw" or "pincher," and that pretty much explains how it works, too.

A specially made molecule, like a protein building block but not the right shape for your body to use, can "grab hold" or "pinch" toxic metals and take them out of your body.

What do toxic metals have to do with getting healthier?

Toxic (or "heavy") metals are everywhere in our environment. When they get inside the body, they tend to stay. This can put a strain on every part of body function, blocking the critical chemical reactions called "metabolism" (how your body does the jobs of staying alive). If these toxic metals stay inside, they contribute to aging changes and illness.

Lead comes from gasoline, paint, batteries. Mercury sneaks in from so-called "silver" fillings (which are 50% mercury), contaminated fish, paint. Arsenic is found in old residues from spraying crops. Cadmium can build up over years from cigarettes, tires, plating on metals. Aluminum gets in from cookware, aluminum cans and foil, antacids, and many antiperspirants.

If no one suspects that toxic metals could be damaging YOUR health, no one checks for them–and they're NEVER found. You might be suffering needlessly for many, many years.

What is the "Chelation Treatment Program?"

For over 40 years, trained doctors around the world have been treating their patients with chelation therapy.

The medication is mixed with vitamins, minerals, and other nutrients and given through a vein in your arm ("IV") and treatments can last from 1 to 3 hours. A patient sits in a chair, relaxed and chatting, reading or watching TV. Every few treatments, blood and urine is collected to check on progress.

Where does the chelation medication go?

The special medication (called E-D-T-A) travels in the blood through your 60,000 miles of blood vessels. Within 24 hours, almost all of it is passed out through the kidneys. But as it passes through, it can cause many beneficial changes to occur in your body–basically a "body tune-up."

Worldwide experience has shown that chelation therapy works best for circulation problems and hardening of the arteries. Many times, it also helps people suffering with degenerative diseases such as diabetes and arthritis. All the while, it is pulling out harmful toxic metals from your body—and starting changes that move abnormal calcium OUT of soft tissues (hardened arteries, joints, skin and others) and back INTO bones.

How do you get started?

First, of course, you look for a specialist who is BOARD CERTIFIED in chelation therapy, one who has the training and experience to make the treatment work best (and safest) for you. Make an appointment for a consultation to discuss all your health concerns. If chelation seems "right" for you, your next appointment is for a "nose-to-toes" complete physical (except for a female exam) and specialized testing. As with any important medical treatment, side effects are possible, therefore tests have to be evaluated in order to plan a safe and effective treatment program.

You then begin your chelation treatments, which are usually scheduled once a week, though you can take them more often to feel better faster (especially if you're "at risk" for serious problems like heart attack, angina heart pains, stroke, or gangrene). Most people with serious illness start with a program of 30-40 treatments (sometimes more). They then graduate to a booster program of one treatment each month–for a period of years.

In addition to treatments, your program will include nutritional supplements (raw materials to help your body repair itself), wholesome dietary changes, and prudent exercise. Testing could show the need for additional medications, but most often chelation means FEWER medications, not more.

How much does chelation cost?

Nothing that is worthwhile is inexpensive, but chelation often costs about the amount of your *deductible* for major heart surgery. Many people often return to work (or play), making it all "worth it."

What Experts Are Saying About Chelation Therapy

"Experimentation and usage of EDTA chelation therapy has resulted in the development of techniques for the successful treatment of the catastrophic (disastrous) effects of arteriosclerosis (fatty hardening and blockage of blood vessels) involving coronary artery (heart) disease, stroke, senility, early gangrene (blockage of blood flow into toes or fingers, foot or hand, leg or arm), essential hypertension (high blood pressure), peripheral vascular occlusive (blockage of blood vessels into legs or arms) disease, osteoarthritis, and related disorders. ...

"Clinical studies...have consistently shown a definite improvement in the circulation of the patient as evidenced by improvement in skin color, improvement of arterial pulsation (blood flow) in the feet, return of normal temperature to the feet, regaining ability to walk long distances comfortably, elimination of anginal (heart) pain, improved brain function and improvement of muscle coordination.

"Chelation therapy generally results in a significant improvement in coronary (heart) circulation in most cases to the extent that the patient no longer requires the use of nitroglycerin or similar drugs. ...**In a large number of cases chelation therapy has been found to improve kidney function, decrease the amount of insulin required by diabetics, and produce significant improvement in arthritis and some cases of Parkinson's disease."**

> Halstead, The Scientific Basis of
> EDTA Chelation Therapy,
> 1979, page 14

"In the course of earlier tests, Dr. W. Blumer and Dr. T. Reich found that the cancer mortality (death) rate among 231 adult persons living adjacent to a heavily traveled highway was much higher than among persons living in a traffic-free section of the same town.

"The authors postulated (suggested) that the higher cancer mortality was due to automotive emissions as well as dust from "automobile roads," since they contain lead, cadmium, and other carcinogens (cancer-causing chemicals).

"During the 18 years of follow-up, (looking at patients treated with EDTA chelation therapy compared to others in the "traffic area" who were not so treated), **only one of the 59 chelated patients (1.7%) died of cancer; of the 172 persons not treated with EDTA, 30 (17%) died of cancer, or ten times more percentage wise.**

"Dr. Harry B. Demopoulos, associate professor of pathology at New York University Medical Center and an internationally known cancer researcher, has correlated heavy ("toxic") metal accumulation (such as lead, aluminum, cadmium, others), free radical (chemical "rusting") activity, and lipid peroxication (chemical injury to fats, including cholesterol) with the initiation (start) and promotion (continuation) of cancer."

> Cranton and Brechner, "First the Good News: Other Chelation Payoffs," Chapter 7 in Bypassing Bypass, 1984

"Patients with free radical-related diseases ("rusting" changes that cause degenerative diseases) other than arteriosclerosis (fatty hardening of blood vessels) were also treated, with **good to excellent results in 91% of patients.**

"Diseases treated included essential hypertension (high blood pressure), vascular and stasis ulcers of the lower extremities (legs), psoriasis, systemic lupus erythematosis, pulmonary emphysema, ulcerative colitis (inflammation disease in gut), ocular (eye) cataracts, diabetes mellitus, osteoarthritis, rheumatoid arthritis and hepatitis (inflammation of liver)."

> Deucher, Journal of Advancement in Medicine, Winter 1988

"It is predicted that when such a (longer, more desirable) life span is attained by man, it

will be by the application of at least two of the following three approaches:
(1) Chelation, to control (limit) and break down (reverse) metal cross-linked macromolecular aggregates (severe chemical changes that cause hardening of arteries and other soft tissues, due to "toxic" metal changes). ..."

Bjorksten, Rejuvenation, 1980

There exists extensive data concerning the use of chelation therapy on heart disorders, leg blood vessel diseases, brain blood vessel disorders, high cholesterol problems, and others.

Why, if "chelation" works so well, have most people not heard of it before? Why aren't more doctors in favor of it?

The answers are basically simple. Chelation therapy is not heard of extensively because the news media has not done its part to share this wonder-working treatment with the public. All too often, these "fact finders" and "truth seekers" simply call their favorite "medical expert" for his or her opinion on "this chelation thing." As you might imagine, most of these "experts" have had little or no contact with chelation therapy...and the official AMA position hasn't taken into account the half-million Americans who have received these treatments—many with dramatic benefits–in the past forty years.

Consequently, too many physicians "aren't in favor of it" because they don't know very much about it. There is an old addage that says "You're always *down* on what you're not *up* on." The simple truth is, many doctors are not aware of the complicated details about how chelation therapy helps restore better function in body organs. Physicians are trained for years in "illnesses" and medications and operations used to *treat* them. But learning about *clinical nutrition* and *cellular metabolism*—the real processes inside that allow your body to rebuild itself back to health–happens AFTER medical school and specialty training. If you didn't learn about it, you can't have much of an opinion on it.

So, the dilemma must be considered: On the one hand, there is a treatment program that works wonders for most of the folks who try it. On the other hand, the people who need it most haven't heard about it–or they shy away because "their doctor is worried that it isn't right for them."

The bottom line is that the only person who can give you an honest evaluation is a **board-certified chelation therapy specialist.**

---

4 KEYS FOR SUCCESS
PUSH – PRAY UNTIL SOMETHING HAPPENS
WITH THE 4P'S
PATIENCE
PERSISTENCE
PERSEVERANCE
AND
PRAYER

You have not accomplished your goal until you have made your last attempt. And you have not made your last attempt until you have accomplished your goal.

Dr. M. Paul Farber

MEDICINE OF THE 21ST CENTURY

GenesisWest Clinic

LIVE CELL THERAPY

(ORGANO THERAPY)

GenesisWest Research Institute for Biological Medicines is located in the small seaside town of Playas on the Baja coast, only 30 minutes drive from the San Diego airport.

My research attracted the attention of another well-known research scientist Jacob Swilling, Ph.D. Dr. Swilling has conducted his own research with earlier versions of colloidal silver. Dr. Swilling has the advantage of advanced darkfield microscopy system combining video and computer graphic storage and retrieval capability to study and record changes at cellular level. In particular, assisted by Dr. Sergio Amescua, he conducted research to determine the effect of colloidal silver to potentiate the effect of other therapies. The most dramatic study was in combination with the well-known vaccine 714X developed by the famous microbiologist Gaston Naessens. In a very well structured study with cancer patients at his clinic GenesisWest, he has recorded changes, in control studies, demonstrating how colloidal silver potentiates the effect of 714X in the control of the piermorphic cycle (a mutating cycle that becomes more pathological as the immune system is unable to control its development).

Following his invitation I decided to visit Dr. Swilling for a hands-on experience with advanced technology and experience used in GenesisWest. This clinic is regarded as one of the most advanced of its kind, using only natural biological medicine to treat cancer and degenerative diseases. Mild Silver Protein is used at this clinic, patients receiving as many as five tablespoons daily.

The approach at GenesisWest is very unique. The philosophy that drives GenesisWest is one which emphasizes that it is the body that heals itself. "There is nothing out there that heals the body," says Dr. Swilling. "We have to begin by revealing everything that is out of balance. Thereafter, we work to determine the cause of the imbalance. This approach presents a list of what I call multi-causal factors including bacteria, fungus, virus, parasites, chemical toxicity, toxic metals, pH, nutritional, biological, immune imbalanc and so on. Treatment programs are customized to correct imbalances by removing the cause. The objective is to bring about a balance the way our creator intended. The so-called miracles of healing are seen when this balance is achieved.

Dr. Swilling is excited about the potential of the new Mild Silver Protein to reduce bacteria, fungus and parasites. He discussed with me the possibility of administering Mild Silver Protein silver intravenously to volunteer patients and his plan to prepare a special study in this regard, using modified equipment. Dr. Swilling is also a consultant to a recently established HIV and AIDS clinic in downtown Tijuana, a unique model based on this research in Biological Medicine.

He believes the potential of intravenous administration of Mild Silver Protein is awesome! Whereas, this was not possible with previous colloidal silver, the small micron size of Mild Silver Protein makes this more feasible.

I agreed to be admitted as a patient. Having experienced the program beginning with the advanced technology, the scientific interpretations, the detox and customized therapy, administered by a well-trained medical staff, I departed with an overwhelming experience begging the question why our restrictive system opposes this approach to more natural healing Biological Medicine.

Readers may be interested to know about a unique Predictive Medicine one-day evaluation program offered at GenesisWest. Using the same advanced technology and approach, this program is described as an Early Warning Detection of trends towards disease. Dr. Swilling states that early detection followed by effective intervention can avoid a later crisis. For further information call (619) 424-9552.

CELL THERAPY

In many parts of the world and particularly in Europe there are over 50,000 physicians using Cell Therapy, not only for regeneration but also as a treatment of preference selected to MAXIMIZE SELECTED THERAPIES IN THE TREATMENT OF MANY DEGENERATIVE DISEASES.

SCIENTIFIC STUDIES

An increasing number of scientific studies are clearly emphasizing that most illnesses, diseases, and aging is the result of nutrient deficiencies and biochemical imbalances.

New research has identified biological substances that can be taken orally in the form of supplements that work synergistically with Cell Therapy to slow degenerative processes known to accelerate the aging process. These include carefully lyophilized glandular extracts of ovine (sheep) specially imported from New Zealand, potent antioxidant enzymes made from specially grown organic sprouted seeds, new combinations of pancreatic enzymes, RNA and DNA factors, and bio-active co-factors that improve circulation, remove inflammation, energize and supply oxygen to the cells. When combined in an individually planned diet with selected natural wholefoods the potential to regenerate the body's biological systems can be dramatic.

ORGANO-THERAPY
CELL THERAPY
AN EMERGING SCIENCE

Cell Therapy:

Everyone wants a long life. No one wishes to grow old.

Literature and folklore are replete with Dorian Grey and Faustlike characters, who have embraced demonology, some to the point of losing their immortal souls, to retain the passions and appearance of youth.

Today, in a modern age that has discovered and unlocked many of the secrets of physiology and metabolism, the possibility of separating chronological from biological age is finally becoming credible.

We are all aware of movie stars, contemporary with ourselves, for whom the aging clock appears to have stopped. They continue to win the beautiful girls or attract a myriad of male admirers. Plastic surgery? Yes, most likely, but besides just appearance, these stars continue to emanate a magnetism and body language that identifies them with an age group far their junior.

The news media report to us the activities of celebrities in sports, business and politics who maintain a jet set schedule of activities that defies their age. They miraculously sustain the virility of youth and retain a heartiness and vitality that enables them to travel, compete, and vigorously enjoy the fruits of life, success, and companionship well into their senior years.

Truer words have never been spoken: "We are as young as we feel." The most handsome looking man or beautiful woman will not enjoy and project the aura of youth and potency if, inside the body, there is an old man or woman struggling to take a nap.

Unquestionably, exercise, genetic inheritance, good nutrition, and personal habits play a major part in maintaining a youthful body. In addition to these obvious requisites many of our most visible celebrities sustain their buoyant physiques and confident appearances by occasional visits to one of the distinguished European spas or clinics that specialize in revitalization and, specifically, the medically respected technique of Cell Therapy.

Simply stated, Cell Therapy is the preparation of cells taken from specific organs of an unborn animal fetus which has been bred and maintained specifically for the purpose. These cells are then selected and injected into a human recipient where they travel to the similar organ from which they were taken to revitalize and stimulate that organ's function.

For many years in America, this prophylaxis has remained confined to the world-traveling rich and famous. Not only has the therapy been very expensive, but knowledge of its success and safety have been kept from the public at large, due to the failure of American medical education to include biological inter-relationships.

Physicians, however, regularly prescribe hormones and enzymes which are extracted from the organs of horses, cows and pigs. Surgeons routinely inject supplemental cellular collagen, derived from calf skin, to erase the wrinkles of facial aging, and replace worn heart valves with a porcine equivalent. The interrelationship of all mammalian physiology is well defined and, when properly understood, can be used for man's benefit.

Conventional American medicine continues to merely cover up, or camouflage, the symptoms of aging organs and declining mental abilities with chemically contrived pharmaceuticals which are not found in nature. These work only so long as they are not broken down by the metabolic process. Conversely, the physicians who practice biologically compatible Cell Therapy, as perfected in Europe, actively stimulate degenerated tissues to renewed vitality for a long term effect.

Doctors without personal experience or research, who dismiss Cell Therapy offhand, should inform themselves of the multitude of controlled laboratory and clinical experiments throughout the world that irrefutably prove the efficacy of this biological modality.

Presently, in European clinics, under government sanction, Cell Therapy has been proven with over 2,000,000 patients, to retard aging and achieve restoration of defective body systems, using the youthful cellular components found in nature.

CELL THERAPY
THE MECHANISM AND HISTORY

Cells are the elementary components of life. Scientists estimate that the human body contains over 100 trillion, which have all resulted from one cell through division. This process is continuous throughout life as old, injured, or weakened cells are gradually replaced.

In healthy young persons these cell divisions take place regularly. Spent cells are constantly being replaced by new vigorous cells. As we become older this process increasingly slows. Overfatigue, the stresses of modern civilization, drug interventions, inadequate nutrition, and improper detoxification are all contributing factors, along with nature's biological time clock, which disrupt cell division. The result is gradual dysfunction of organs and body systems, of which cells are the building blocks.

Additionally, our modern age contains countless influences which often uniquely affect individual organs, resulting in degenerative diseases. In many cases, the cells of our youth are capable of overcoming these maladies. As our systems age, and cell division slows, our bodies have less ability to repair and survive.

Medicine's quest to reduce the manifestations and infirmities of old age and degenerative diseases has been continual. Medical history is replete with efforts to renew body functions by treatment with a similar or like matter (homologous substances). In 1400 BC, the Indian physician, Susutra, recommended his patients eat the reproductive glands of young tigers to overcome impotence. The Roman, Nestrius, advised drinking the blood of fallen gladiators. The 16th century German doctor, Paracelsus, had his patients imbibe ground heart, for heart disease, kidney for kidney disease, etc. He coined the phrase "like heals like."

As primitive as these elixirs of youth sound today, they contain an element of logic that has led, in this century, to modern cell therapy which creates conditions through revitalization of cells and organs, whereby good health, freshness and vigor can be enjoyed well into advanced chronological age.

CELL THERAPY
ITS FOUNDER

In 1931, Professor Dr. Med. Paul Niehans, a greatly respected Swiss surgeon, while serving as head of staff at one of the renowned hospitals in Switzerland, became increasingly interested in endocrinology (the study of ductless glands). Specifically, he studied the work of colleagues who were experimenting with the implantation of animal glands into patients whose organs were not functioning properly. Dr. Niehans' research led to the conclusions that, while the functions of all corresponding mammalian organs (congeneric organs) are almost identical, there are certain subtle differentiations of cell content that make them, most often, not compatible or transferable between species. This was not true, he determined for the cells of organs still developing in the fetal stage.

Under the microscope, the cells of all fetal mammals, organ for organ, are almost indistinguishable. Step by step, the brilliant and versatile Niehans began developing the principles that have made cellular therapy possible.

One of Dr. Niehans' first discoveries was that cells derived from the organs of as yet unborn, fetal animals could be injected into the human body without triggering the natural defense mechanism that acts to reject foreign protein. It was not until two decades later that scientific studies proved his observations. It is now known that genetically determined tissue antigens (a toxin or substance from which the body attempts to defend itself) develop only right after birth. It is the absence of these antigen factors that enables the fetus to develop and not be rejected by the mother, and for a host to accept unrelated fetal cells without triggering the immune reactions that would ordinarily occur and cause the cells to be rejected and destroyed.

In medical crisis whole organ transplant operations, mature organs are used. To prevent their rejection, the host's immune system must be overridden by heavy use of suppressive drugs which opens the body to invasive diseases. Fetal cells used for cell therapy are not recognized by the recipient body as being foreign. They remain undetected and so, to a certain extent, can become new building blocks to restore specific worn or ailing organs.

Dr. Niehans' empirical observations indicated that cells from a specific fetal organ, when injected into a host, appeared to migrate through the body, and the function of the corresponding human organ almost invariably improved. This has been validated by scientifically controlled laboratory and clinical experiments, most recently by atomic technique. Drs. F. Schmid and H. Lettre at Heidelberg University conclusively demonstrated, by radio tagging and tracing specific organ cells from a fetal donor, that the host's bloodstream transported the vast majority of the cells to the counterpart organ of the host.

The mechanism of cellular recognition, whereby cells with the same function congregate and bind to each other, has been extensively researched by Nobel Laureate Roger W. Sperry at the California Institute of Technology. He theorizes that the surface of each cell is endowed, not only with an identification code, but with the means of interpreting the codes of other cells and, upon contact, to latch onto cells that fit their exact code – like a key fitting into a lock. An additional mechanism is proposed by Dr. Saul Roseman, a professor of biology at Johns Hopkins University, who suggests that when migrating cells pass over a tissue, they may, through cross talk, actually alter its propensity to latch onto passing cells.

In the 40 years following his first successful experiments, Professor Niehans applied his discoveries in

Cell Therapy over 50,000 times.

Included among his patients were such celebrities as Jan Paderewski, Gloria Swanson, Somerset Maughn, Charles Chaplin, Paulette Goddard, Konrad Adenauer, Joan Crawford, Charles de Gaulle, Dwight and Mamie Eisenhower, Dolores Del Rio, Winston Churchill, Charles Boyer, Bernard Baruch, the Duke and Duchess of Windsor, Joseph Kennedy, Noel Coward, and many others of equal fame. In 1953 Dr. Niehans was called to the bedside of ailing Pope Pius XII. In gratitude for the successful result of his own Cell Therapy, the Holy Father inducted Professor Niehans to membership in the Papal Academy of Sciences. The renown created by enthusiastically reported results on these celebrities reached other European physicians, who, subsequently, substantiated Dr. Nienans' results.

TECHNICAL EVOLUTION OF CELL THERAPY

Throughout the first years of Cell Therapy practice, it was necessary to dissect and prepare cells from a donor fetus and administer them all within a 20-minute period, after which the vital life qualities of the cells rapidly deteriorated.

This system has many obvious disadvantages, such as limiting the number of patients that can be treated, and making therapy extremely expensive. It can also, under certain circumstances, be dangerous. Too little time for an adequate check of sterility and zoonosis (the transfer of disease between animal and man) remained between removal of the cell material from donor and injection into patient. It was impossible to totally preclude the transmission of viruses and bacteria and to assure constant quantity and quality.

A partial solution to this problem was the development, in 1955, of lyophilization. In this process, the cells were frozen under vacuum and all of the water removed. The resultant dry powder could then be put up in uniform quantities which could be stored and then placed into saline solution just prior to use. This paved the way for thousands of doctors throughout the Federal Republic of Germany to include the science of cellular therapy in their armament against disease and degeneration.

During the ensuing 10 years, voluminous research using these dry cells in treating over 20 different syndromes was published, and the statistics confirmed their beneficial activity. As dramatic as these published reports were, Dr. Joseph Miller, Sr., personally collaborating with Dr. Niehans, recognized that while lyophilizing conserves all of the beneficial biological substance of the cells, it results in the formation of ice crystals, which tend to rupture the cell membranes, and removes all of the intracellular fluid. These factors eliminate the cell's ability to regenerate when returned to solution, so the vital life force is gone. They continued to seek a method that would maintain the cell organelles intact and provide true Cell Therapy.

CRYOGENICS, THE BREAKTHROUGH

The final step toward the general availability of true Cell Therapy was achieved by Dr. Miller after Dr. Niehans' death in 1971 when he applied the new science of cryogenics (the use of super low temperatures which has made possible the revolutionary long-term preservation of live sperm for artificial impregnation and the creation of banks of human bone and tissue available for transplant) to Cell Therapy.

Finally, it was possible to flash-freeze cells, at a -196 degrees centigrade, into a state of suspended animation. This process totally prevents the formation of ice crystals. It provides unlimited time for thorough bacteriological and serological tests, and preserves the ability of the cells to resume normal biological activity in their natural fluid state, when returned to body temperature.

Fetal cells extracted from specially procreated fetal calves and prepared by highly trained technical specialists, in specifically designed laboratories, can now be stored indefinitely deep frozen, and shipped by air in refrigerated containers. At their destination the cells can be maintained in super low temperature freezers. When warmed and injected into a recipient they contain the same vital life force as if the recipient was actually beside the fetal donor during the original cell procurement process.

SYMPTOMS INDICATIVE OF CELL THERAPY

Manifestations where appropriate Cell Therapy has proven beneficial over the last two decades include:

Subnormal Functioning of Glands:

This includes underdeveloped sex organs, menstrual disorders, sterility, premature menopause, obesity, impotence, emaciation.

Premature Aging:

Symptomatic, loss of skin tone, aching joints, general exhaustion – both mental and physical, lack of vitality and libido, failing eyesight and hearing.

Chronic Degenerative Disease:

Deficient blood supply to limbs, rheumatism, shortness of breath, edema, and osteoporosis.

Susceptibility to Infection and Disease:

Chronic indigestion, degeneration of heart, kidneys, lungs, inactive or impaired immune system, allergies.

Maldevelopment in infancy:

Downs syndrome, birth injuries, encephalitis, CP.

CELL THERAPY – FOR HEALTH MAINTENANCE AND REVITALIZATION

All Cell Therapy is based on the principle of treating a malfunctioning organ with vital cells from the corresponding organ of a fetal donor: heart cells for heart degeneration, liver cells for liver degeneration. Because it is most usual for organ systems to dysfunction as a whole, all of the associated organs should be treated with corresponding cells.

For general revitalization, multiple combinations of basic cellular infusions are recommended. These should cover the organ systems that metabolically degenerate with age, and include cells from the vascular, hormonal, urogenital, digestive, respiratory and skeletal systems. As the physiological deteriorations of old age begin with a decrease in secretions from the sex glands, particular emphasis is placed upon their stimulation and maintenance. Cell implants from organs with specific sexual functions are selected according the the sex of the recipient. Male recipients receive cells from male donors, and female recipients from female donors. In addition to the basic revitalizing combinations, specific cells are selected, by an experienced physician, depending upon the individual's needs. For instance, a diabetic would require additional pancreas. Excessive obesity might require additional thyroid.

Along with many other effective therapies which have been scientifically validated and government sanctioned in Europe and around the world, Cell Therapy is, at present, unaccepted by the American Food and Drug Administration. Consequently, this proven revitalizing therapy has been reserved for the few who could afford an expensive trip to Europe and the $6,000 to $8,000 fees charged by such specialized revitalization clinics as La Prarie, Brenner Park, Clinique Niehans, Biotonus, and Four Seasons. There you find such famous names on their registers as Elizabeth Taylor, Henry Kissinger, Barbara Streisand, Sly Stallone, Gen. Alexander Haig, Lee Iacocca, David Rockefeller, Billy Graham, and many other busy influential persons who desire to retain youthful vitality and vigor.

Although several clinics in the Bahamas and Mexico

claim to offer Cell Therapy, their use of lyophilized dry cells, or cell tissue obtained locally from slaughter houses at best reduces effectiveness, at worst can be dangerous. The inability of Mexican facilities, technicians, and the lack of strictly controlled (contaminant free) animal population to supply the necessary donors, have prevented authentic, totally effective and safe, Cell Therapy from becoming available in this hemisphere.

CELL THERAPY NOW ACCESSIBLE TO AMERICANS

The highly technical field of cryogenic cell preparation has been instrumental in establishing Instituto GenesisWest-Provida in Playas, Tijuana, Mexico, where true Cell Therapy by specialists is finally available on the American Circuit.

Cells are processed exclusively from specially selected fetal donors. This should be emphasized, as the technique of obtaining certain cellular substances from minute organ systems is so highly skilled and technical that other laboratories must obtain these unique cells from older, larger animals, where potency is reduced and antigen content increased.

Specialized staff select, process, and flash-freeze cells at -196 degrees centigrade into a state of suspended animation, all well within 20 minutes. Strict bacteriological and serological observations are maintained throughout the process.

Not only is the real Cell Therapy, previously available only in Europe, now accessible close to our own border, but at a much reduced cost. The enormous devaluation of the Mexican peso makes any procedure possible in that country a tremendous bargain. The entire cost of revitalization therapy, including a five-day detoxification and rest period at a world class facility, is far less than the rich and famous have had to pay the European spas and clinics for the same program.

Upon completion of examination and testing, the

appropriate cell combinations for revitalization of the individual beneficiary are selected and given into the posterior musculature. Usually four to eight separate cell combination infusions are administered. These incorporate all of the major organ systems that are age-effected. For unique individual degenerative problems, additional specific cells may be added.

Because these are natural biological suspensions, there are no side effects or rejection. The host body accepts the material and the cells commence the journey to their homologous organ systems. For the following three days, the recipient remains quiet and toxin free, while the cells are being assimilated. At the conclusion of a final medical conference, the recipient may return home to normal activity.

WHAT THE RECIPIENT CAN EXPECT

Initially you will experience a minimal reaction. However, most recipients report that beginning six to 12 weeks after the infusion of new cells greater vitality is noticeable, and the body begins to exhibit progressive positive changes. Joints and discs become more and more flexible and weight tends to stabilize at a normal level. A revitalized immune system increasingly resists many of the allergies and degenerative diseases of aging. Almost all clients experience a new willingness and desire for new and exciting endeavors. Most recipients talk here of regained energy as renewed sexual satisfaction and an enthusiastic appetite for life develops and healthy vigor is replacing former lethargy. A renewal of youthfulness seems to take place. Furthermore, during this time period the person usually begins to look more youthful and alive, as eyes appear brighter, and skin tone, skin texture and color improve.

Occasionally an organ experiencing unusual dysfunction might require an additional time schedule and a booster infusion to maximize cell regeneration.

Younger recipients receive a bonus benefit from Cell Therapy, as the new cells arrest and slow cellular degeneration before it has the opportunity to advance. A number of professional athletes receive Cell Therapy to extend their playing careers.

The effects are long lasting. Any future infusions are usually on the basis of the host's chronological age; 35 to 45 years, every five years; over 45, every three years. Normally, Cell Therapy should not be taken sooner than six months after a previous treatment.

While this information emphasizes health maintenance and the retardation of the physiological aspects of aging, the phenomenal ability of cells to repair the pathological degenerations of such chronic metabolic diseases as asthma, emphysema, Parkinsons, diabetes, arthritis, ulcers, heart, psoriasis, and certain mental disorders, far surpasses many orthodox and alternative therapies, and is an adjunctive for many more. Information on the application of Cell Therapy to a specific chronic disease should be discussed with a physician thoroughly familiar with its procedures and benefits.

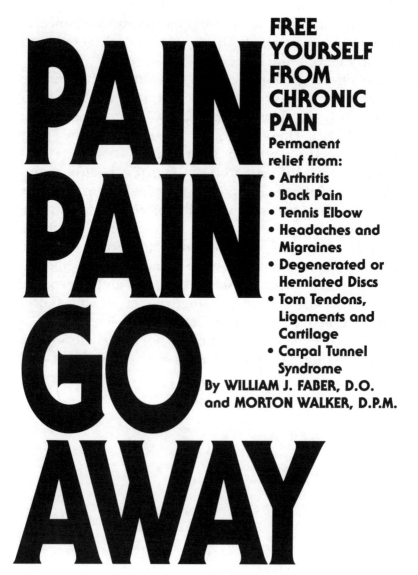

PAIN PAIN GO AWAY

FREE YOURSELF FROM CHRONIC PAIN

Permanent relief from:
- Arthritis
- Back Pain
- Tennis Elbow
- Headaches and Migraines
- Degenerated or Herniated Discs
- Torn Tendons, Ligaments and Cartilage
- Carpal Tunnel Syndrome

By WILLIAM J. FABER, D.O. and MORTON WALKER, D.P.M.

**"CONGRATULATIONS...FOR A COMPLETED
BOOK THAT IS EXTREMELY WELL DONE.
IT WILL EDUCATE MILLIONS
ABOUT CHRONIC JOINT PAIN RELIEF!"**
– George J. Goodheart, Jr., D.C.,
developer of Applied Kinesiology (from the Foreword)

RECONSTRUCTIVE THERAPY ELIMINATES CHRONIC JOINT PAIN!

Any day of the year, one American in five suffers from chronic joint pain. Reconstructive therapy – a simple biological technique that involves injection of fluid into the joint to stimulate the repair of tendons and ligaments – can eliminate their suffering. What is more, its cost is far lower than the less effective surgical or pharmaceutical remedies it replaces.

Although used for over 40 years, until now this remarkable technique has been known to only a small group of innovative physicians. In this book you will read about the many successes that have resulted from its use. Its effectiveness is well-documented, both in individual cases and in clinical studies. By using this holistic therapy, it is possible to correct the causes of musculoskeletal pain rather than merely masking it.

By presenting information about reconstructive therapy in terms a layman can understand, the authors expect the technique to become widely known and readily available for the millions of sufferers to whom it offers hope.

RECONSTRUCTIVE THERAPY

ARE YOU LOOKING FOR A WAY THAT MIGHT HELP YOU... GET OUT OF YOUR PAIN AND GET BACK INTO YOUR LIFE.

Maybe you've seen yourself lose out before; this new medication or that new exercise seems helpful, you feel a little better, but it doesn't really last. Maybe you have grown resentful – maybe fearful or anxious, even treated for depression. It's easy to feel fed up or stuck if you can't exercise like before. You might have even felt threatened with worsening neck, back, or joint pains coming suddenly, out of your control. Maybe you're bored with the hassles of hurting. You're understandably cautious about trying something else "new."

Take a closer look right now: Reconstructive Therapy (**"RT"** for short) deserves your attention. Maybe this way of thinking and treating could help you with a clear understanding of why your back, neck, or joints are hurting – and how you might get back into your life now.

FIND YOUR PROBLEM – THEN LOOK FOR WHAT MIGHT FIX IT NOW

Your diagnosis has to be crystal-clear – that's why doctors do exams and tests, to find a treatment that works. If aspirin, exercise, drugs, surgery, chiropractic adjustments, and other procedures haven't produced the results you wanted...maybe what is causing your pain still remains to be seen. You might discover other treatment options that could help now with your continuing pains and limitations.

Any injury – some sudden and obvious, but others gradual, repeated, and hardly noticed – can **stretch and tear** the rubbery ligament bands you need to **support** your neck, back, and other joints. **Instability** shows up first as a very slight **"wobble,"** with stiffness, soreness, muscle spasm, pain. Over time, unstable wobble can tear down the joint and disc structures; this can show on x-rays as degenerative **arthritis** changes and even **disk problems.**

You know what this might look like in your daily life: constant back discomfort, sore and stiff muscles, sometimes sharp pains (maybe even down your leg or arm), disabling headaches. You might be wakening not ready to face the day – even irritable and "stressed out." You watch every activity carefully, staying home instead of going out, avoiding things you'd like to do for fear of hurting. What would the years ahead mean if you found a way to live without your pain instead of continuing to live with it?

WE DON'T OFFER MORE OF
WHAT YOU GOT BEFORE

You're still looking for answers if you haven't gotten enough help with aspirin, ice-packs, heating pads. Or exercises "to make you stronger." Or prescription drugs for "arthritis" or pain or muscle spasm. Or a corset or cane. Or chiropractic adjustments and physical therapy. Or cortisone shots and stronger pain-killers. Or simple surgery – or maybe serious surgery. The end of this road can be frustrating...if you have gotten the very best that modern medicine has offered you, and you're still hurting and more limited as the days go by.

One alternative you might consider has been "on the sidelines" for over 40 years: Reconstructive Therapy. RT stimulates natural healing processes by placing fluid into support bands around injured joints. Your body responds by making stronger tissue. Makes sense. This healing response is the same kind your body makes when sealing the incision from an operation. In over four years of treating pateints with RT, we have seen many painful neck, back, and joint problems show improved function and reduced pain, without daily drugs or surgery.

Spine: State of the Art Reviews devoted the entire volume 9, issue 2, May 1995, to 15 articles on RT treatment of the lower back. Favorable reports on RT were made at the Second World Conference on the Sacroiliac Joint and Low Back Pain (San Diego, November 1995). Unfortunately no manufacturer has presented to the FDA the scientific studies that the government requires for RT solutions to be "approved" for labeling as safe and effective treatments for neck, back, and other joint injuries and arthritis, so the FDA has not reviewed RT for approval. This might explain why many physicians don't know about RT or wouldn't think of it as helpful for their patients.

MAYBE THIS ALTERNATIVE IS ONE
YOU WANT TO TRY

Certainly no physician can guarantee results for any particular person – and individual results do vary with any treatment, whether drugs, surgery, physical therapy, chiropractic, or RT. Reconstructive Therapy might offer you an alternative for which you've been looking, to treat the problem causing your problems, to get stronger again and regain a brighter outlook.

Low back pain, neck pains, and headaches are more common than you might think, some of the most frequent problems seen in medical offices. And the costs are staggering: Americans are estimated to spend some $25 billion each year on professional care for backaches alone. But God meant you to work, play, exercise, and live life with a strong, painfree neck, back and other joints. All you really want is a body that can keep you **happy and independent,** not one that looks like you have to struggle just to stay even, still not fixed, still frustrated.

IS IT TIME FOR YOU TO LOOK
INTO YOUR ALTERNATIVES

A skilled specialist personally trained by world-renowned Dr. William Faber, Dr. John Parks Trowbridge is certified in RT by the American Board of Biologic Reconstructive Therapy, sponsored by the American Academy of Neurological and Orthopaedic Surgery. He also serves as an Examiner of the Board. Dr. Trowbridge is an internationally-renowned bestselling author and leader in health matters, listed in two dozen separate editions of **WHO'S WHO.**

We help people who drive for hours or who fly in from many states and from four other continents. Our mission is straightforward: we work to get you out of your pain and back into your life. When what we do is what is the right choice for you, we've done our job just right. Call today for details on RT, so you can decide for yourself whether this might be an alternative you've been looking for: simply dial **1-800-FIX-PAIN** (349-7246).

DATE 1-16-95

"I HAVE A VISION"

I HAVE A VISION OF A WORLD WHERE MANKIND IS FREE FROM SLAVERY AND BONDAGE TO EXCESSIVE SICKNESS, DISEASE, DISABILITY, UNNECESSARY DEATH, EPIDEMICS OF MODERN DAY PLAGUES OF BIBLICAL PROPORTIONS, AS WELL AS THE SPECIAL INTEREST EXPLOITATION AND ECONOMIC DEVASTATION WHICH ACCOMPANIES THIS MODERN DAY SLAVERY DEVASTATING THE LIVES OF FAMILIES AND INDIVIDUALS. — Dr. M. Paul Farber

inspired and written on
Martin Luther King's birthday

COLLOIDAL GOLD

by Dr. Garry Smith, N.D., Ph.D.

HISTORY OF COLLOIDAL GOLD

"Michael Faraday, the English chemist, first produced COLLOIDAL GOLD in a pure state in 1857. It is believed that Alexandria, Egypt, was the original location where GOLD was first used for medical purposes, although it has been used for centuries by alchemist. During the middle ages alchemists developed an "elixir" liquid gold which purportedly has the ability to restore youth and perfect health. Paracelsus, the forerunner of modern pharmacology, was one of the greatest known alchemist/chemists, developed medicines from metallic minerals including GOLD to cure the sick. The Chinese have used GOLD coins for centuries in cooking rice to help maintain the body's GOLD levels.

DR. FARBER'S COMMENTS:

It has been said "THAT THERE IS NOTHING NEW UNDER THE SUN." Modern man in his Arrogance and Pride tends to think at times that all great Discoveries are a result of Modern Technology. Dr. Garry Smith states, "that it is believed that Alexandria, Egypt, was the original location where GOLD was first used for Medical Purposes. Who knows how much knowledge from Ancient Times has been lost. When Julius Caesar occupied Egypt during the reign of Cleopatra, the GREAT LIBRARY was destroyed by fire and perhaps centuries of knowledge, which may never be recovered was lost to man.

Since "it is recorded that Alchemists of the Middle Ages developed an "elixir" liquid GOLD which purportedly had the ability to restore youth and perfect health," there must have been some Reported Anecdotal events of this phenomena happening. This correlates with the Scriptures from Exodus which I reported earlier in which the Golden Calf was burned and turned into a Golden Liquid.

Modern Man puts all his Faith into Modern Pharmacology. It is interesting that it was the Pioneer and Forerunner of Modern Pharmacology, Paracelsus, who first used GOLD by developing it into Metallic Minerals. He recognized that GOLD could be a Nutritional Mineral Supplement centuries ago. His foresight and vision has been fulfilled as the F.D.A. now recognizes COLLOIDAL GOLD as a Nutritional Mineral Supplement. There are many anecdotal modern day reports of the sick recovering from a variety of diseases which I reported earlier in this chapter.

Just as early pioneers in the American West used Silver Coins to preserve milk because of its AntiMicrobial Qualities, so also did the Chinese use GOLD in the cooking of rice to get the Mineral Element GOLD into the body to maintain adequate levels of the Nutritional Mineral Supplement GOLD. It has been said for centuries "That Where There is Smoke There is Fire." Reports like this would have not been handed down and would have died on the vine if there had not been some Elements of Truth to them. Perhaps the Rediscovery of GOLD for its use in the Field of Health and Medicine will be haled as the Discovery of Another Cave of THE DEAD SEA SCROLLS OF MODERN MEDICINE. Further Scientific Studies need to be done with GOLD, just as I have done with SILVER. I am looking forward to pursuing this project. I as well as Bill Moyers who worked extensively with Chinese Medicine can both attest to the Wisdom and Value of many of their Ancient Remedies. I suggest adding 7 drops Mild Silver Protein to a 2 oz. Bottle of the Colloidal COLL/AU 30, The COLLOIDAL GOLD, to prevent the growth of bacteria which can accidentally occur by touching the dropper to the mouth. As I said earlier Gold does not have antimicrobial qualities.

WHAT DOES GOLD DO?

GOLD has strong unequaled effects on the physical body, in health and sickness. COLLOIDAL GOLD was commonly used in the treatment of disease in the United States before 1940 and as early as 1885 for the cure of alcoholism. Additional uses have been found to include treatment of arthritis, skin ulcers, burns and mental conditions.

GOLD does not have the germicidal/antibiotic action of colloidal silver, but it does act on degenerative conditions. It has a balancing and harmonizing effect on the emotional body particularly with regard to unstable mental and emotional states such as depression, melancholy, sorrow, fear, despair, anguish, frustration, suicidal tendencies, or maladies commonly referred to as the sickness of the heart. Aurum metallicum, a homeopathic remedy made from GOLD, is used to treat people in a suicidal state. GOLD has a direct effect on the rhythmic, balancing, healing activity of the heart and helps improve blood circulation. It is highly beneficial for rejuvenating sluggish organs, especially the brain. GOLD has been used in cases of glandular and nervous incoordination, helping to rejuvenate the glands, stimulate the nerves and release nervous pressure. GOLD is beneficial to the digestive system.

DR. FARBER'S COMMENTS:

No other element can equal the healing effects of GOLD, in certain areas of health. It is hard to believe that something which was commonly used in 1940 and as early as 1885 could have been lost and so easily forgotten. However, all one has to do is review The Dead Sea Scrolls of Modern Medicine on Silver to not only see that this is possible, but also inevitable when it comes to politics and economics. Gold was known as a Cure for Alcoholism as well as a Treatment for Arthritis, Skin Ulcers, Burns, and Mental Conditions. Obviously, these "so-called" difficult diseases would not have been recorded unless the Early Pioneers using Gold had not experienced Dynamic Results in their treatment.

Since according to Dr. Smith "GOLD" does not have the germicidal/antibiotic action of Colloidal Silver, one must handle it in a different manner. It is important not to contaminate it by touching its dispenser to one's mouth. Glass containers which hold the Gold for dispensing should also be boiled after usage. As said earlier add 7 drops of Mild Silver Protein to a 2 oz. Bottle of the GOLD.

The body's warmth mechanism is positively affected by GOLD, particularly in cases of chills, hot flashes and night sweats. GOLD has been used to treat alcoholism by diminishing the craving and desire.

DR. FARBER'S COMMENTS

Dr. Smith states that "the body's warmth mechanism is positively affected by gold." From a physiological point of view the warmth of the body is a direct result of circulation chilling effect and where circulation is increased we see increased warmth. Since GOLD is helpful in cases of chills we can only induce that it helps with increasing circulation. Since it helps with hot flashes and night sweats we can also deduce that GOLD has some controlling mechanisms over the circulation of fluids such as water of which blood is made up of. The recorded data that GOLD diminishes the craving and desire for alcohol shows that alcoholism is a direct result of a mineral deficiency and that Gold is one of the main minerals that one is deficient in. If this knowledge were implemented by society toward ALCOHOLISM, we could bring under control what has become a national Epidemic and Worldwide Scourge.

Used alternatively or in conjunction with silver, GOLD helps strong natural defenses against diseases and promotes renewed vitality and longevity. Silver calms inflammatory conditions while GOLD builds, regenerates and balances.

GOLD is used primarily with all types of mental, emotional and physical degenerative conditions. In homeopathic philosophy, it is believed that healing starts with the intellect, then the emotions and finally the physical. GOLD acts very positively on the brain and emotions indicating it is one of the first substances one should take when attempting to heal sickness.

DR. FARBER'S COMMENTS:

It is important to have the knowledge that GOLD can be used Alternatively or in Conjunction with Silver. In my opinion one should implement both of these Minerals in their Colloidal State into their Nutritional Programs. Since GOLD creates a Renewed Vitality and Longevity we can deduce that GOLD not only slows down the Aging Process but also increases Energy Output. SILVER – CALMS INFLAM-MATORY CONDITIONS; GOLD – BUILDS, REGEN-ERATES AND BALANCES. A simple method which I devised to remember this was to take a lesson from history. When the GOLD Strikes occurred there was increased wealth, excite-ment, as well as a Regeneration and Balancing of the economy. After this excitement settled down, people began craving luxury and beauty to calm their inflamed appetites. They craved Silver utensils, jewelry, and art forms. This helped to calm their Inflamed Appetites.

Since GOLD is used in all types of
MENTAL
EMOTIONAL
PHYSICAL DEGENERATIVE CONDITIONS

we can see how it would be helpful in a degenerative condition such as Cancer as well as calming the Mental and Emotional conditions that always accompany such Degenerative Diseases.

Acupuncturist and Veterinarians who use acupuncture dip their needles in GOLD to help make the acupuncture point work better. It helps increase the energy transfer from the needle to the acupuncture point and increases the effectiveness of the acupuncture treatment. They also use silver, which acts in much the same way. Veterinarians also give GOLD to animals for mental problems. (How they know they have a mental problem is beyond me.)

DR. FARBER'S COMMENTS:

According to Dr. Smith's comments about GOLD'S use by acupuncturist in veterinarian medicine it makes the acupuncture point work better by increasing the energy transfer from the needle to the acupuncture point. We can therefore deduce that one of the many properties of GOLD is to increase the electrical activity both intracellularly as well as within the cell itself. The health of the body is dependent on the communication level that takes place through the DNA of the cells. If this communication level is off and inhibited then the body moves towards a state of DISEASE. Dr. Lee Lorenzen, the scientist who developed Aqua Resonance which I talked about in my first book "THE MICRO SILVER BULLET" has proven this to be true. I believe this fact of Higher Conductivity is one of the most important factors as to why GOLD works in the improvement of one's HEALTH.

GOLD works on the mental first, then the emotions, and then the physical. Homeopathic remedies work much the same way. We give Aurum Metallicum (as a homeopathic remedy) for people who are suicidal. It works very well. Again proving GOLD works on the mental.

DR. FARBER'S COMMENTS:

Suicide has become a National Tragedy especially among our youth and especially our teens. GOLD has a proven history of working toward reversing people's tendency toward the desire to commit suicide. It has been used in the form of Aurum Metallicum which is a homeopathic remedy successfully for years. If we could introduce COLLOIDAL GOLD into the dietary regimens of these high risk groups, I feel that we could go a long way in the reduction of the Frequency and Rate of Suicide in this country and eventually the world. Nothing is more tragic than the loss of life through suicide. When we can eventually eliminate this problem from the planet Earth, it will be a blessing from HEAVEN. GOD accomplished this mental healing with Moses and the Children of Israel and there is no reason we cannot accomplish this again in Modern Day Times.

People who are sick mentally go through various stages of emotional degeneration as follow:

Frustration
Dissatisfaction
Irritability
Anguish
Anger
Rage
Sadness
Fear
Grief
Phobia
Indifference
Apathy
Suicidal
"GOLD helps in all cases."
Good Luck,
Dr. Garry Smith, N.D., Ph.D.

DR. FARBER'S COMMENTS:

I have been a Clinical Psychologist for the past 30 years. This list of mental problems encompasses the heart of Mental Disease. Since it has been proven historically possible since Ancient Times to balance out these Negative Emotions, we are sitting at what I would deem a BREAKTHROUGH IN MODERN "NATURAL" PSYCHIATRY. Since psychiatry traditionally utilizes medicinal substances to balance out mental disease, the use of GOLD would fit right in with one very positive exception. This exception is that COLLOIDAL GOLD has no side effects or toxicity. In my opinion and with the approval of your Physician, we can take a person on Prozac and get them off this drug in two to four weeks and free of all the symptoms they went on it for. In my opinion the biggest side effect of Prozac is suicide. I have personally witnessed this tragedy several times.

Also, in my opinion and with the approval of your Physician, we can get children off of Ritalin and free of all the symptoms they went on it for. According to NEWSWEEK MAGAZINE, March 18, 1996, Ritalin has a Side Effect of a 10% Attempted Suicide Rate on children who have been on it long term when they reach adulthood. In my opinion 95% of these children are suffering from a Systemic Candida Yeast Infection from the taking of Antibiotics without the replacement of the Good Acidophilus Bacterium which can be corrected with my Mild Silver Protein Protocol. These children also need to get off of sugar products, junk foods, fast foods, and caffeine and follow Dr. Feingold's Diet as outlined in his book covering this subject.

In my opinion this same Phenomena holds true for the use of PROZAC for Depression and Manic Depression. I will go into these two subjects in detail in my upcoming book, "THE MICRO GOLD BULLET, A NATURAL ANSWER TO ENDING MENTAL DISEASE." I have personally witnessed several suicides following the usage of Prozac.

WAKE UP PARENTS BEFORE WE UNCONSCIOUSLY SACRIFICE A WHOLE GENERATION OF OUR CHILDREN AS WELL AS OURSELVES!!!

ANATOMY AND PHYSIOLOGY SIMPLIFIED

In order to understand how and why Lyme Disease is so devastating to the human body, it is important to understand what ANATOMY and PHYSIOLOGY are and how they interact to make the body work and function as a whole unit.

**DON'T LET THESE BIG WORDS SCARE YOU.
THEY ARE SIMPLER
THAN YOU MAY THINK.**

The author as a Physician spent four years of formal study studying both Anatomy and Physiology in depth, as well as over 25 years preliminary and continuing education. These many hours and years of study are necessary for a doctor in order that he has a complete and full understanding of the human body and how it works. This course of study is often times very complex, intricate, and detailed. This is the right course of action if you are going to be a PHYSICIAN.

However, the author feels that this is not necessarily the best approach for the LAYMAN, for the sociologically average and yet very IMPORTANT PERSON who will be reading this book in his or her attempt to recover and get well from both Lyme Disease and Candida Yeast Infections. With this thought in mind the author will know through examples, comparisons, analogies, and parables explain ANATOMY and PHYSIOLOGY in a simplified form:

**ALL THE LAYMAN NEEDS TO KNOW
ABOUT
ANATOMY AND PHYSIOLOGY**

Let us now use our imagination to compare and picture the HUMAN BODY to a HOUSE in a CITY both structurally and in function.

STRUCTURAL = ANATOMY
FUNCTION = PHYSIOLOGY

The SECOND thing both the Human Body and a House need in order to be in existence is SUBSTANCE. Substance is the raw materials from which anything is made. For example, concrete from which a FOUNDATION of a house is made is composed of sand, water, and gravel.

SUBSTANCE = COMPONENT PARTS

The Human Body is made up of MATTER which according to Carl Sagan, astronomer-scientist, is "STAR DUST" which had its ORIGIN in the "BIG BANG" of GOD'S CREATION. This ORIGINAL MATTER then over millions of years was acted upon by all the LAWS and FORCES of NATURE. For example, a diamond is merely COSMIC START DUST that eventually became the CARBON ATOMS of COAL which when having been subjected to high pressure over a long period of time became so concentrated that it became a DIAMOND.

A house needs bricks, mortar, lumber, nails, shingles, hardware, and literally thousands of other COMPONENT PARTS in order to be constructed by its builder. In the same manner the human body needs protein for its building blocks along with fats, carbohydrates, vitamins, minerals, enzymes, amino acids and literally thousands of other substances in order for life to continue and grow. These are the same substances and materials which were used by the CREATOR when the FIRST MAN and WOMAN were CREATED. The author feels that it would be interesting to note here that recent SCIENTIFIC ARCHAEOLOGICAL DISCOVERIES in which the fossils of animals that should not have EXISTED during CERTAIN PERIODS OF TIME if the "Theory of Evolution" had been correct have in fact been found and documented as well as the hand of a man predating thousands of years the date that evolutionist say life began from a single microbe. In the light of this irrefutable evidence evolutionists are giving up this erroneous theory in favor of the "ASTRONOMICALLY CORRECT BIG BANG" which correlates with the "BIBLICAL STORY OF CREATION in the 'HOLY BIBLE.' "

The FIRST THING before a home is built one must first have the idea of what the house is to be like and then a design and a blueprint. In the same manner the FIRST THING GOD, the CREATOR of MAN first had an IDEA in HIS MIND and then also a PATTERN or BLUEPRINT which was his OWN IMAGE from which MAN was CREATED. This IMAGE is imprinted into our DNA which contains the BLUEPRINT of the Human Body.

BLUEPRINT = CREATIVE IDEA

GOD by his action spoke the WORD and the COSMOS and man were created. Man by his physical actions builds the home and the city where it dwells and both the city and the home are created.

Many modern day cities and homes have all of their basic functions controlled by a computer which through an electrical system of many wires and transformers goes to every part of the house that has function. The lights, the temperature, and even the physical security system of the home is controlled by a main computer and then perhaps smaller computers for each section. The human body has a brain which is connected to all its functional parts through the nervous system and acts as its main computer. Each cell has its own intelligence and acts as mini computers to give both direction and function to each cell.

MAIN COMPUTER = BRAIN
SMALLER COMPUTERS = NERVOUS SYSTEM

The Main Computer of a city or a home will contain all

of the knowledge that city or home needs in order to function completely and properly. Similarly, the Human Brain and the Nucleus of every cell contains within it all of the knowledge necessary to build, run and repair the human body.

ELECTRICAL SYSTEM = NERVOUS SYSTEM
WIRES = NERVES

Every main area of a house, powered by electricity including the lights and appliances of a home are connected by wires and switches for this current to pass through and be turned off and on. Similarly, every major area of the body is connected by nerves which pass through the spinal column to every cell, tissue, and organ of the body. The spinal column, as any Chiropractor will tell you is the SWITCHBREAKER system of the body. Just as a switchbreaker will shut off in a house or an engineer will hit a main breaker in a city to shut down a certain area in time of repair or trouble, so also does the vertebrae of the spinal column serve this same function between the nerves and the functioning parts. The computer of the home and the brain of the body also have control mechanisms for turning on and shutting off different areas of the body. These control mechanisms can also speed up or slow down the flow of current in a wire of a house or the flow of nerve supply and the biochemical reactions of the human body.

MOVEABLE VERTEBRAE = SWITCHBREAKERS

Copyright Material 3-29-94

Every home has a pantry where food is stored and a kitchen where food is prepared and a dining room where the food is eaten. In the same manner with the Human Body all of the foods and nutrients are produced by Nature which is the pantry of the human body.

These foods are then used in their raw form and or cooked by man using his intelligence and various tools for the harvesting in the fields and cooking in the kitchen. The human stomach, intestines, and digestive system are the dining room of the human body. The food and water which is taken in from this dining room are then digested and prepared for assimilation into the body. In the actual kitchen we use utensils such as knives and forks to chop, cut, and grate food. This is analogous to the digestive process which takes place in the stomach and intestines. At this point the digested food is ready for distribution into all of the cells of the body so that every organ, gland, and system may be nourished and sustained.

MOUTH AND TEETH = KITCHEN
STOMACH = DINING ROOM

At this point in a city both trucking systems and pipelines carry both the solid and liquid products to the stores and into the homes. These trucks and pipelines carry food to all of the grocery stores where they are then distributed to all of the individual people who shop in the stores. In a similar manner the BLOOD CARRIES both solid and liquid matter to the fatty storehouses of each of individual cells and into the cells themselves. Another example of the blood and circulatory system would be the highway and street system of the city or the hallways of a house. Also, as just mentioned the pipes which carry various substances and materials such as water lines and gas lines are a circulatory system similar to the blood system of the body. One pipeline may carry water and another gas into the house and throughout different parts of the house.

BLOOD SYSTEM = HIGHWAY AND STREET SYSTEM
CIRCULATORY SYSTEM = PIPELINE SYSTEM

The sewage system carries the WASTE PRODUCTS out of a home and dumps them into a sewage processing system. In addition to digesting the food substances put into the body, the stomach, colon or large intestines, and the small intestines carry the undigested waste of the body into the bowel where they are then processed and then dumped into the toilet and then the sewage system.

STOMACH AND INTESTINES = SEWAGE SYSTEM
BOWEL = TOILET

Every home has a foundation upon which it is built as well as beams and supporting structures. Similarly, the human body has a pelvis and a skeletal system which serves as the foundation and supporting structures for the body. The Human Spinal Column is the Main Supporting Beam of the body and the bones of the legs, arms and feet are part of the supporting structures which in this case are moveable like the wheels of a trailer of the stairs that unfold. The bones of the arms and hands can also be used to support the body and yet in the human body they are also moveable. Imagine in a city that there is a large crane being used to help build a highway. This crane will have moveable joints similar to the elbows and wrists of the body which are capable of performing actions and doing work. Just like a home has a whole host of hand tools such as broom and mops which are capable of doing work, so also does the human body have arms and hands which can move things and do work.

PELVIS AND SKELETAL SYSTEM = FOUNDATION
SPINAL COLUMN = MAIN SUPPORTING BEAM
ARMS AND HANDS = HOUSEHOLD TOOLS

This crane would also have a series of pulleys and siding for support and strength. This is like the ligaments and muscles of the body. A home has shingles on its roof just like we humans have hair on our heads as well as finger- and toenails for protection from the outside elements. A home could have a camera surveillance system hooked up to a television. The body has the human eye through which an image goes across the optic nerve and is displayed upon the retina.

LIGAMENTS AND MUSCLES = PULLEYS AND LEVERS
HAIR AND NAILS = SHINGLES AND SIDING
EYES = SURVEILLANCE SYSTEM

Copyright Material 5-3-94

A home has different rooms such as living rooms, dining rooms, and dens in which different functions are performed. In the same manner the human body has different organs in which different functions are performed.

ORGANS = SPECIALS ROOMS

This list could go on and on. However the author thinks that you the reader get the SIMPLE POINT. You might want to take out a paper and pen and see how many other comparisons you can think of. The point the author is wishing to make is that the ANATOMY of the human body is really no more difficult than understanding how a home or a city is constructed. PHYSIOLOGY is no more difficult than understanding how the different parts of this home or city interact to keep LIFE MOVING.

Perhaps the words MOVING or MOVEMENT are the KEY WORDS to PHYSIOLOGY. It is the movement and interaction of different substances which make LIFE possible. A home has windows and doors through which air and objects can pass through. Similarly, the human body has lungs with which to breathe and a mouth and anus for objects to pass in and out of.

BREATHING LUNGS = OPEN WINDOWS
MOUTH AND ANUS = DOORS AND WINDOWS
PHYSIOLOGY = MOVEMENT

Perhaps the most important word here is the word called

MOVEMENT

LIFE = MOVEMENT
DEATH = STAGNATION

If you the reader understand the principles of MOVEMENT and STAGNATION in relationship to all which has been discussed in this chapter you also understand two other seemingly difficult subjects.

PATHOLOGY
and
NEUROLOGY

Pathology is the condition of disease and illness which occurs to any part of the body where FREE MOVEMENT is blocked and STAGNATION sets in. NEUROLOGY is merely the study of the nervous system and the interconnection of the nerves which make it up. If you understand the ELECTRICAL SYSTEMS of a house and a city or the communication lines of a telephone system, then you now also understand the supposedly complex subject called NEUROLOGY. You the reader now have a simplified layman's understanding of four seemingly complex medical subject. Use it WISELY!!!

ANATOMY – PHYSIOLOGY –
PATHOLOGY – NEUROLOGY

When everything in the human body is in a state of movement and there are no blockages then life proceeds uninhibited and HEALTH is the GOOD RESULT. When the processes of LIFE become stagnant, disease and death are sure to follow. Therefore it is important for the reader to be very cautious and wise about what they put into their body and how they let it interact with the elements of the world. One must in WISDOM as is so pointed out by the PROVERBS of the BIBLE and of SOLOMON choose WISELY in every situation in LIFE.

The Author suggests that the reader take some time out to read and study PROVERBS for TIPS OF WISDOM as well as DEUTERONOMY which contains the MOSAIC DIETARY LAWS which still hold true in these modern times showing how TIMELESS and UNIVERSAL they are.

Do not think that LYME DISEASE and CANDIDA YEAST INFECTIONS are too difficult to understand or too impossible to CONQUER. They are not if they are but looked upon SIMPLY in the same manner which we just looked upon the supposedly difficult subjects of ANATOMY and PHYSIOLOGY.

In both of these diseases you have an infectious micro-organism which are the SPIROCHETES and the YEAST respectively. All we have to do is the same thing COLIN POWELL suggested to do during the GULF WAR.

Copyright Material 5-3-94

This was to seek out the enemy and kill till all are dead. Let us however not make the same mistake and leave some survivors behind like we left Saddam Hussein as well as part of his armies. He or it, the micro-organisms, will raise up its UGLY HEAD again and repopulate and seek to conquer and raise havoc again.

THANK GOD!!!
We Now Have A Proven Substance

MILD SILVER PROTEIN
To Accomplish This Task

Documented Research which the Author has obtained from the early 1900's to 1938 from some of the most established and respective Medical Labs, Universities, and Hospitals of the time show without a doubt that the COLLOIDAL SILVER kills completely over 650 DIFFERENT BACTERIAL AND VIRAL MICRO-ORGANISMS including SPIROCHETES and YEAST.

This is all a matter of PUBLIC RECORD and can be obtained by interested individuals just as the Author obtained it. The RESEARCH DOCUMENTS consist of $8^1/_2$ inch by 11 inch documents almost a half an inch thick. It is Mind Boggling how much GREAT RESEARCH was accomplished and then lost and forgotten by our generation.

Our GOOD NEWS is that the Author has been fortunate enough to REDISCOVER it and pass it on to his readers to be used as an answer for both the SPIROCHETES of LYME DISEASE and the YEAST cells of CANDIDA.

THUS, WITH FAITH IN GOD AND THE
PROPER TOOLS IN OUR HANDS, WE BEGIN
OUR JOURNEY BACK TO HEALTH AND RECOVERY
COUPLED WITH THE HOLISTIC METHODS
LISTED AND DISCUSSED IN THIS MOST
IMPORTANT BOOK WHICH CAN LEAD ONE
BACK TO LIFE AND HEALTH AND HAPPINESS.

Acknowledgements

To all my family, friends, physicians and health practitioners who helped me to overcome and conquer these diseases and who gave me the encouragement and support to write this book and see it through to publication...thank you.

*Abraham Farber–A special "thank you" to my grandfather for building within me a foundation for accepting the Messiah.

*Colonel Leonard Farber–Father of the author

*Jean Farber–Mother of the author

*To our new daughter, Mariah Paige–Welcome to our lives and may your life be free of all diseases based on the knowledge that we now know.

*Matthew R. Farber–Son of the author

*Jacob Farber–Scott and Rachel Farber's new son and Arnie and Manette's new grandson

*Michael A. Rodriguez–Godson of the author

*Cesar Rodriguez–Chiropractic assistant

*Chad, Todd and Scott Farber–Nephews

*Harvey Katz, R.N.–Author's brother-in-law

*Carolyn Katz–Author's sister (Houston) & nieces Michelle & Lisa

*Yvonne Schwartz–Author's sister (Los Angeles) and her husband Herb and daughter Rene

*Arnold Farber–Author's brother

*Manette Farber–Author's sister-in-law

*Mrs. Jeanette Goldner–Author's mother-in-law

*Les and Marty Simon–My next door neighbors

*Mr. and Mrs. Ayaz Merchant–My next door neighbors, and managers of "Chili's" where many meetings were held in developing this book

*Dr. Richard Dean & Michelle Golden, D.C.– Chiropractic Physician

*Dr. Mark Crawford, D.C., Dr. Robert T. Gross, D.C. and Chiropractic Assistant Terri Scott

*Dr. Michael Davis, D.C.–Chiropractic Physician

*Dr. Robert Sones, D.C.–Chiropractic Physician and Chiropractic Assistant Pam Jolly

*Dr. Bernard Jensen, D.C.–Thank you very much for your wonderful work, field of Iridology. You demonstrated and set the example that a doctor of chiropractic can expand horizons of the holistic healthcare field.

*Dr. John Parks Trowbridge, M.D.–Friend, colleague and writer of introduction to this book

*Dr. Joseph Vargas, Ph.D., N.D.–Certified Colonic/Therapist

*Mr. and Mrs. Richard Freeman–Spiritual leaders, Beth Messiah

*Dr. Thai–Chinese medicine and herbs

*Dr. Edward Morris, M.D.–General Practitioner

*Dr. Jan DeVries, Ph.D., N.D.–Holistic Doctor and author

*Mr. Alan Boxman–Certified Massage Therapist and receptionist Sharron Reiszren

*Viviana Rojas–Massage Therapist

*Linus Pauling–Dr. Farber is a student of Linus Pauling's works and is a friend and associate to a fellow doctor and scientist, Dr. Eric Vanderby, who studied and worked with Linus Pauling for many years as well as Mother Teresa

*Dr. Cornelius Matwijecky, M.D. and wife Jane–Neurosurgeon

*Dr. Lee Lorenzen–Scientist and developer of Aqua Resonance

*Dr. Francisco Carillo, M.D.–Hospital Español, Mexico

*Steven Levine, Ph.D. and Parris M. Kidd, Ph.D., for their contributions to the "Dead Sea Scrolls of Modern Medicine"

*Dr. Joe Cardot, N.D., Ph.D.–Pioneer and researcher into Mild Silver Protein

*Dr. Andrew Weill, M.D.–Holistic Doctor and author

*Dr. Edward Taub, M.D.–A National Spokesman for the A.M.A.

*Dr. Richard and Janette Keats–Dr. of Ophthamology

*Dr. Alex Duarte, O.D., Ph.D.–For his research contributions to this book

*Dr. Audrey Steingoldings, M.D.–For her medical care

*Dr. Robert H. Schuller–Minister, "Hour of Power"

*Dr. Robert Anthony Schuller–Minister, "Hour of Power"

*Dr. Willy Burgdorfer–Discoverer of causative agent of Lyme Disease

*Dr. Thomas Craig, Ph.D.–Head of Parasitology, Texas A&M University

*Conroe Veterinarian Clinic–Dr. Briers, D.V.M., Dr. Umlong, D.V.M.

*Dr. Janis Zinn–Dentist and victim of Lyme Disease

*Dr. Carl Cleveland, Jr., D.C.–President, Los Angeles College of Chiropractic

*Dr. Carl Cleveland III, D.C.–President, Cleveland College of Chiropractic (Kansas City, Mo.)

*Dr. Shelby Elliot, D.C.–President, Texas Chiropractic College

*Dr. Meynard M. Nussbaum, D.P.M.–A best friend of 40 years and his wife Jeanie

*Dr. David Wolf, D.P.M.–Friend and supporter who taught the author that it's O.K. to walk to the sound of a different drummer

*Allen Pauly and wife Barbara–A best friend of over 40 years, for his support and advice as well as his introduction to the works of Dr. Andrew Weill

*Dr. Robert Mendehlson, M.D.–Author and mentor–A posthumous "thank you" for the positive influence and impact this mentor had on the author's life…and the courage which he exemplified to bring about positive change in the medical profession.

*Dr. Paavo Airola, Ph.D., N.D.–A posthumous "thank you" for all which he taught the author about nutrition, herbs, naturopathy

*Dr. Gordon Ruesink, N.D., D.C.–A posthumous "thank you" to this mentor and father figure who put the author's foot on the path of knowledge and wisdom

*Dr. Tam Thai–Master Acupuncturist

*Theodore Cherbuliez, M.D.–President, The Apitherapy Society

*Harry J. Gayner, Ph.D.–National Burn Foundation

*Dr. Stephen Waller–Neurologist

*Patritcia Salvato, M.D.

*Charles Mraz–Author, and Inventor of Bee Venom Therapy

*Charlton Heston–For genuine inspiration through your movies, especially "The Ten Commandments" and "Ben Hur"...my favorite male actor

*Barbara Streisand–Thank you for your inspirational films such as "Yentle"–my favorite female entertainer

*Hal Lindsey–For the powerful influence of his books "The Late Great Planet Earth," and "2,000 A.D."

*Russel Holt and Brad Fishman–Attorney and friend

*Sue Guiterrez–Former secretary and Chiropractic assistant

*Minerva Cortez–Former Chiropractic assistant

*Daniel and Susan Lerner–Friends and Congregants of Beth Messiah

*Steve Steves–Friend and certified Nutritional Counselor

*David and Andrea Perkins–Friends and supporters

*Joe Burke–Friend, supporter and early pioneer of Lyme Support Groups and newsletters

*Linda Sutton–For keeping the retreat clean and beautiful

*Blair Traxler–Friend, horse trainer, builder

*Norris Hairstylers of Houston–For their continued support and encouragement: Benito, Norris Sr. and Jr., Eve, JoAnn, Claudine, Sarah, Maria, Lupe, Maye, and Bill

*Memories Unlimited (Bo Moss)–For great photography

*Alfred and Clarissa Torres–Margarita's Restaurant in Conroe, Texas

*Mahuash and Kami Thorouzan–Harvest House Village Inn

*Kit Lui and Ming Truoong–Hunan Village Restaurant

*Dorsey Moonen–Conroe Health Food Store

*Mike and Peggy Howeth–For patience and support

*Amy Lauro–Professional musician and piano and voice teacher

*Kwik-Kopy–Linda Vega and Jimmy Booth

*Ken and Betty Nicols–"I Can't Believe It's Yogurt"

*John and Adrian Godre–Friends and supporters

*Amber Rose–Author of "Bee In Balance"

*Pat Wagner–Proponent of Apitherapy

*Dr. Bradford S. Weeks, M.D.–Apitherapy physician

*Martin Seligman–Thanks for the input from your book "Learned Optimism"

*Pat Case–Hastings Bookstore

*Doctor's Hospital–formerly on staff in East Houston

*Richard Preston–Author of "Hot Zone," thanks for your great book that gave me inspiration

*Dustin Hoffman–A special thanks for your latest movie "Outbreak." I am living it in real life–hope to meet you in the future

*Elizabeth Taylor–My favorite female actress (thank you for Cleopatra), a special thanks for the wonderful work you have done with victims of AIDS.

*Stephen Spielburg–Thank you for "Schindler's List" and for inspiring me in having no fear of imagining the impossible

*Morgan Freeman–For demonstrating the many political obstacles that need to be overcome (through the movie "Outbreak")

*Dr. Hugh Ross, Ph.D.–Thanks for the conviction that religion and science need not be separate

*Billy Graham and his son Franklin–For planting the first seeds for Jesus in my heart

*Pastor Buddy and Caroline Hicks and daughters Shari, Angela and son Trey–Deerbrook Church

*Mark and Sherry Mears–Missionaries to Zambia

*Jerry and Gerald Davis–Evangelists, Missionaries

*Gus and Kathlene Elowitz–Spiritual leaders, Congregation Messiah Jesus

*Rabbi Marty Waldman–Congregation Baruch Hashem, Dallas

*Frank and Betty Longino–Liberty Seminary

*Dr. Oral and Evelyn Roberts–Oral Roberts University

*Pastor Chris Brock and wife Ann–Victory Christian Center, Humble, Texas

*Rabbi Eliezar Urbach and his wife Sarah–Holocaust survivors, for their contribution towards the under-standing of Yeshua HaMashiach and Messianic Judaism

*Pastor and Evangelist Benny Hinn–For his crusade in Dallas at which I became a born-again, spirit-filled Messianic Jew

*Tommy Conroe–"Book of Life" Christian Bookstore

*Octogenerian–Original colleague (82 years old) of Albert Einstein, who I had the opportunity to share with

*Ruth Bender–Original student of Albert Einstein, who I had the privilege to study with.

*Casey Wolters–Thank you for the technological support for my computers

*Coop Cooper–Best friend of over 40 years and wife Connie

*Amanda Ginns and son Brian–It was a pleasure helping Brian with the COLL/AG-40, The MICRO SILVER BULLET, thank you for getting my book and research into the hands of your cousin Mike Wallace with "60 Minutes."

*To "60 Minutes"–Mike Wallace, Morley Safer, Ed Bradley, Steve Kroft, Leslie Stahl, and Andy Rooney. I have been a Devoted Viewer for the past 28 years since the beginning of your broadcast. Your programs on AIDS and other Infectious Diseases inspired me Greatly in the Development of this book. I feel that we now have the ANSWER to all of these Epidemics with no Side Effects or Toxicity. A gift to Andy Rooney in response to one of your programs: The END to the COMMON COLD since the MILD SILVER PROTEIN kills all Staph, Strep, and other Microbial Agents of the COMMON COLD including all Mutations. See, Andy, there's HOPE FOR MANKIND after all.

*Larry King–I hope to share all the scientific findings on AIDS, Lyme Disease and Candida Yeast Infection with you and your listening audience in the near future. I have been a loyal fan of yours for many years.

*Oprah Winfrey–Looking forward to being on your show some day to share all the information on how to heal all these infectious diseases which are plaguing your listening audience.

*CNN–To Ted Turner and Jane Fonda whose Exercise Video my wife has been using for years. May the Knowledge in this book reach the CNN Audience in the Near Future.

*A SPECIAL THANK YOU TO PAUL AND JAN CROUCH.

*TBN has been an incredible inspiration.

*Dra Kaplan–long-time friend of Dr. Paul and Marie

*Richard and Mari Lee–Noah's Ark Christian Bookstore – thank you for your support and help with our new book

*Micki Jones–Iridologist, Herbalist and author of "A PRACTICAL GUIDE TO HERBAL EXTRACTS"

*Steven Levine–Thank you very much for your input in the researching of *The Dead Sea Scrolls of Modern Medicine.*

*Brent Spiner, LIEUTENANT COMMANDER DATA, "STAR TREK THE NEXT GENERATION"–Little did our mothers know during our Grade School Carpool that our future work would have International Significance; you, Brent, as an actor and me as an Author, Scientist, and Researcher

*Carl Sagan–To my Posthumous Mentor. May the knowledge which we now have in the Field Of Complementary Medicine prevent other people from dying unnecessarily from Cancer and the Side Effects of Conventional Treatments.

*Ronnie Mintz–May my Breakthroughs in Diabetes and Multiple Sclerosis be dedicated to your memory so that others need not perish from these diseases.

*Dr. Bill Robins, M.D. and Dr. Bill Williams, M.D.–next door neighbors who as a youngster inspired me to become a physician.

*Mr. and Mrs. Victor Kracer–friends in Mexico

*Rabbi Marty and Arlene Waldman–Messianic Rabbi in Dallas

*Martin Luther King–who gave his life to free his people

*During the early 1960's Dr. Farber saw President John Fitzgerald Kennedy while attending a speaking engagement in Houston, Texas. As a result of his example, Dr. Farber, out of LOVE for his Black Brothers and Sisters, made the First Attempt to integrate a Fraternity at the University of Texas during the Civil Rights Movement of the 1960's.

ACTORS

*Ben Kingsley–Congratulations and Thank You for both "GANDHI" and "MOSES." Both movies inspired me tremendously in my work. Your acting was Superb and I hope to meet you someday in the Near Future.

*Sean Connery–Thank you for the movie "MEDICINE MAN." Yes, it was possible to Lose The Cure for Many Diseases. However, it is also possible to rediscover it.

*Israel and Miriam Levy–Thank you for helping to ground me in the Torah of the God of Abraham, Isaac, and Jacob. I hope to visit you someday in Israel.

*Paul Levy–In prayer for your recovery from Multiple Sclerosis

*Marvin Lynn Brown–To my fellow Bar Mitzvah partner and friend of over 40 years. I pray that when you recover from Multiple Sclerosis through Bee Venom Therapy, it will be a shining example and inspiration to many others who are afflicted. To Bob and Zelda Brown, Mazol Tov for sticking by your afflicted son during his 20-year affliction with Multiple Sclerosis. Marie and I are praying for his Complete Recovery (Rafuach Schlelama).

*Ron Charlton–Congratulations on Bryan's complete Recovery from AIDS through Mild Silver Protein.

AUTHORS

*Alex Haley–who through "ROOTS" gave his people a heritage and foundation

*Isaac Asinov–whose prolific imagination changed our image of Science and its possibilities

*A Special Thanks to TRINITY BROADCASTING NETWORK

* Magic Johnson–May the information in this book which will be given to you and the Mild Silver Protein bring about a complete healing of your AIDS situation. We have scientifcally documented that the Mild Silver Protein not only inhibits replication of HIV, any latent formation, and also kills the AIDS virus with no side effects and no toxicity.

*Kwik-Kopy Printing, Kingwood, TX, Debi Center, Brenda Themis–Thank you for all your help for organizing the manuscript for this book.

*Kaye's Printing, Fargo, ND, Lee Allen, Carol Leach, Gary Bendewald–Thank you very much for all your efforts in the publishing of this book. It could not have been done without you.

*Diana Rutherford–A special thank you for your wonderful work in the typesetting of portions of this book.

*Mr. Reginald Martin, Unit Director District D, KROGER Grocery Stores & Mr. Tim Halfin, Regional Director of the Pharmaceutical Division of KROGERS–I both Salute and Congratulate you both on your Wisdom, Courage, and Vision at this Dawn of the 21st Century in bringing the *"Micro Silver Bullet"* book and the People's Doctor Product Line including COLL/AG-40, MILD SILVER PROTEIN into the reach of the Common People of this Great Country of ours, the United States of America. May the KROGER CHAIN be blessed for bringing the relief of so many illnesses into the reach of the average man and woman, both old and young.

*Gene Egidio, author of *WHOSE HANDS ARE THESE?* and Internationally Renowned Healer–A special thank you for your wonderful healing work and also for getting an autographed copy of my book to one of my favorite actresses–Linda Gray, actress on Dallas and Models, Inc.

*Princess Diana–I was deeply moved along with the rest of the world on this Saturday, September 6, 1997, by your funeral service at Westminster Abbey. The world will long Remember and Honor you for your Selfless Devotion to many of the challenges and causes facing Mankind including the AIDS Epidemic, Leprosy, as well as your Devotion to the Common People. I dedicate what the Lord Jesus Christ referred to in my Near Death Experience as the Cure for AIDS and every other infectious Disease to your Memory. In the Name of the Lord GOD the FATHER in Heaven, His Son Jesus Christ, and the Holy Spirit MAY YOU REST IN PEACE.

*Mother Teresa–You were truly a Devoted Servant of Our Father in Heaven and our Lord and Savior Jesus Christ, and the Holy Spirit. Your Selfless Devotion to Mankind and Dedication to the Poor and Downtrodden and Saintly Example will be Forever Remembered by the Entire World. But mostly you will be Remembered by your UNDYING AND ENDLESS LOVE. I have No Doubt that you are reaping your Eternal Reward and you are sitting at the Right Hand of Our Lord Jesus Christ in the Kingdom Of Heaven. May your Example serve as an inspiration to all of us for Generations to come. I Hope and Pray that I will get to meet both you and Princess Diana in the Kingdom of Heaven when my time comes for the Second Time to be with HIM.

*Leonardo da Vinci–A thank you to my Posthumous Mentor for giving me the example that a man can be a Master of Many Arts and Sciences.

A SPECIAL THANK YOU TO

Trinity Broadcasting Network

AND

PAUL AND JAN CROUCH

TBN has been an incredible inspiration and support to me during my time of illness and during my time of searching for a reason to go on. Hope to meet all of you someday. Without you, writing this book would have been doubly difficult...and perhaps not possible at all. I want to thank you Paul and Jan...many of those people and ministries on TBN that quite literally made my day...every day...every week...every month...etc.:

JOHN OSTEEN

DR. RICHARD EBY, D.O.

DR. E. V. HILL

JEFF AND RENE FENHOLT

DR. WHITTAKER, M.D.

JAY SEKULOW

EFRIM ZIMBALIST, JR.

MARILYN HICKEY

ROY ROGERS AND DALE EVANS

PAT AND SHIRLEY BOONE

JESSE DUPLANTIS

DEAN AND MARY BROWN

ZOLA LEVITT

JACK AND REXELLA VAN IMPE

PETER AND PAUL LALONDE

ALVIN SLAUGHTER

STEVE BROCK

JACK HAYFORD

KEN AND GLORIA COPELAND

REINHARD BONKE

DR. JESS MOODY

JOHN AVANZINI

GREG LAURIE

DWIGHT THOMPSON

JERRY SAVELLE

DINO KARTSANAKIS

BENNY HINN

MARIO MURILLO

HAL LINDSEY

DAN AND BONNIE SCHAEFFER

DAVE ROEVER

DR. HUGH ROSS, PH.D.

JOHN HAGEE

DR. REGINALD B. CHERRY, M.D. and wife LINDA   DR. ED YOUNG

"The Micro Silver Bullet"™
A preliminary Scientifically Documented Answer to the Three Largest Epidemics in the World

LYME DISEASE
AIDS VIRUS
YEAST INFECTION

Dr. Willy Burgdorfer, scientist who discovered the Spirochete as the causative agent of Lyme Disease and the author, Dr. M. Paul Farber.

Famous Medical Doctor, Teacher, Lecturer, and Author, Dr. Andrew Weill, M.D., with Dr. Farber in Montana.

Dr. Paul and Marie Farber with Dr. and Mrs. Robert Mendehlson at their Holistic Health Retreat located in the Little Switzerland of America, Ouray, Colorado. *John Mendelsohn, M.D.*

Dr. Carl Cleveland III and Dr. Carl Cleveland Jr., father and son, Presidents of Cleveland Chiropractic Colleges, in Los Angeles, CA, and Kansas City, MO, with Dr. Paul Farber.

Allen Pauly, 40-year friend of Dr. Farber who supported his struggle with Lyme Disease and with the publishing of this book.

Dr. John Parks Trowbridge, M.D., Author of "The Yeast Syndrome" which has sold over 3 million copies as well as Dr. Farber's personal physician, friend and colleague.

Pat Wagner demonstrating Dr. Farber's recovered left arm and hand following "Bee Venom Therapy." The condition was medically diagnosed as "permanently disabled"... Multiple Sclerosis.

Pat's Book
"How Well Are You Willing To Bee" – $27.00
For Information on Multiple Sclerosis
301-843-8350
5431 Lucy Drive
Waldorf, Maryland 20601

Charles Mraz, Pat Wagner and Amber Rose at the Apitherapy Conference in September 1994 in Bethesda, Maryland.

Amber's Book
BEE IN BALANCE – A Guide to Healing the Whole Person with Honey Bees, Oriental Medicines, & Common Sense. To obtain book, contact Arnie Farber at 713-774-8914.
In summer of 1997, Bee Venom Therapy was approved by the FDA.

Dr. Farber, who is a student of Einstein's Works, including Theory of Relativity and Atomic Energy, discussing Einstein and his theories with Ruth Bender, one of Albert Einstein's still living original students while in Vienna, Austria.

Adolph, The Mountain Man, who studied herbs with the Ute Indians with the Farbers.

Master Artist Werner Henze with the Farbers in Ouray, Colorado.

327

Dr. Tam Thai is Dr. Farber's friend and associate in the field of acupuncture.

Hanna Kroeger
Her accomplishments in the field of natural health care were astounding. She discovered many amazing ways to restore health using herbs, special diets, baths, massage, etc.

Paul and Marie Farber receiving a blessing and a charge from Dr. Paavo Airola, World famous Author and Nutritionist to go forward with his work and add to it our own works and books.

328

A special posthumous thank you to Albert Einstein whose incredible works provided inspiration and a challenge.

Dr. Farber prays that the understanding of $E=MC^2$ become easily understood to all the readers of this book so that the average layperson can understand the depth of Einstein's understandings. Linus Pauling, being a close friend and fellow scientist of Albert Einstein, would have given Einstein a deep understanding of Holistic Health Care.

TEXAS A&M

A special thank you to my posthumous mentor, Linus Pauling.

Linus Pauling

Thomas M. Craig D.V.M., Ph.D., Department of Veterinary Microbiology and Parasitology, Texas A&M University, with Dr. Farber.

Dr. Robert Schuller & Dr. E.A. Taub, M.D., a national spokesman for the American Medical Association on "The Hour of Power" worldwide television broadcast.

Dr. Farber and his Godson Michael Rodriquez at San Juan Capistrano on a trip to visit with Dr. Robert Anthony Schuller.

Dr. Richard Dean & wife Michelle Golden—4th generation chiropractor. Dr. Farber expresses his gratitude for their support and great professional chiropractic care.

A special thanks to Dr. Edward Morris, M.D., who, in Dr. Farber's opinion represents everything good about what a general practitioner should be.

The Farber's with Messianic Jewish Rabbinical Scholar, Teacher, Author, and Holocaust survivor, Eliezar Urbach.

Dr. Paul Farber with his grandparents & parents at his Bar Mitzvah at age 13.

Colonel Leonard and Jean Farber, Dr. Farber's Parents.

332

Col. Leonard Farber.

Four generations of the Farber family; Abraham, Leonard, Paul and Matthew.

A special thank you to my grandfather, Abraham Farber, who first introduced me to the Biblical concept of the Messiah and for a deep love for the Father, God of Israel.

J. Marie Farber with Matthew Farber and granddaughter Madison Suzanne at the Holistic Health Retreat in Conroe, Texas.

Dr. Farber and son Matthew Farber with granddaughter Madison Suzanne.

334

On Dr. Paul's left is son, Matthew and granddaughter Madison Suzanne and nephew, Chad. On Dr. Paul's right is wife, Marie, mother, Jean and sister, Carolyn.

Dr. Paul and Maire Farber at their 20 acre Healthtouch Total Health Care Retreat and Treatment Center, and Lecture Center in the Beautiful Pine Woods of Conroe, Texas.

David and Andrea Perkins, a constant source of support and inspiration.

A special thanks to Dorsey Moonen, Conroe Health Food Store, for her nutritional contribution to elimination of Herxheimer Reaction.

A special thanks to Ed Arnstein, Nutrition Consultant of "A Moveable Feast," for giving Dr. Farber his first introduction to Mild Silver Protein.

Dr. Meynard M. Nussbaum, D.P.M., 40-year friend and his wife Jeanie with the Farbers.

336

Dr. Paul at the Little Switzerland of America Holistic Health Retreat and Hot Water Springs in Ouray, Colorado.

Colonel Leonard Farber at Dr. Paul and Marie's Holistic Health Retreat in Ouray, Colorado.

Paul Farber, receiving intravenous antibiotic treatment before the discovery of Mild Silver Protein.

Dr. Cornelius and Jane Matwijecky, M.D.

Conchita Yao delivering chelation therapy at the offices of John Parks Trowbridge, M.D.

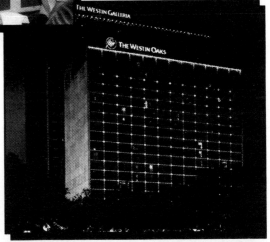

The Westin Oaks and Westin Galleria in Southwest Houston, Texas will serve as Dr. Paul Farber's Houston offices and for personal group consultation and lecture hall and hotel facilities.

Ixodes Scapularis tick which carries the Spirochete, the causative agent of Lyme Disease.

Kathryn Krenzke, Dr. Trowbridge, Misty Faulk, Cathy Guion, Tammula Palmer, Nanda Ziemer, Conchita Yao, René Parker (not shown Karen McNeely, Diana Marshall, Kelly Uren and Wendy Mosley). Pain Relief Center for Arthritis and Sports Injuries. 1-800-FIX-PAIN—1-800-349-7246.

Arnie & Manette Farber, Dr. Farber's brother and sister-in-law.

Yvonne Schwartz, Dr. Farber's sister.

Dr. Joe J. Cardot, N.D., Ph.D. & wife Carmen.

340

This book is dedicated to Yeshua HaMashiach, Jesus Christ The Messiah, and "His Father Who Art In Heaven, Hallowed Be Thy Name."

Designed by Dr. Paul Farber

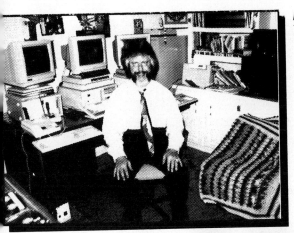

Dr. Farber at his Conroe,
Texas retreat.

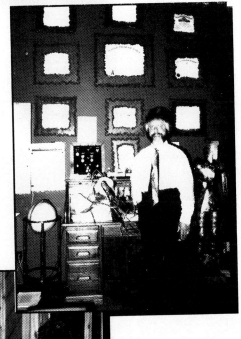

With his faithful
companion "Sheba."

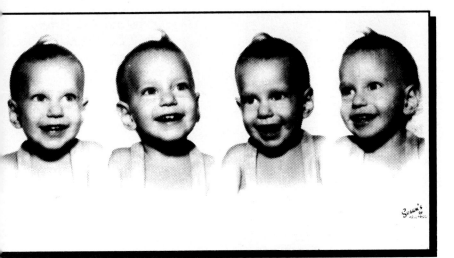

Scotty

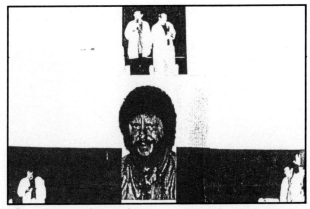

Star Trek's William Shatner and Leonard Nimoy, Captain Kirk and Spock being thanked by Dr. Farber for Star Trek's positive influence on his Scientific Endeavors and Research.

Dr. Paul and Marie Farber with Dr. Earl Rice, M.D., close friend of Elizabeth Taylor.

Dr. Paul and Marie Farber with Dr. James A. Kholos, cable television interview in Hollywood, California

Prophecy of Second Coming of Jesus Christ.

"And He shall give His angels charge over thee to guard thee in all thy ways."

Genesis 1:26 And God said, Let us make man in our image, after our likeness.
Genesis 1:27 So God created man in his own image, in the image of God created he him; male and female created he them.
Daniel 7:9 As I looked, thrones were set in place, and the Ancient of Days took his seat. His clothing was white as snow, the hair of his head was white as wool. His throne was flaming with fire, and its wheels were all ablaze.
Daniel 7:10 A river of fire was flowing, coming out from before him. Thousands upon thousands attended him, ten thousand times ten thousand stood before him. The court was seated, and the books were opened."

God creating man by Michaelangelo, Sistine Chapel, Rome, the picture of the Father is very near to the vision seen by Dr. Farber in his near death experience.

Dr. Paul Farber with Dr. Alan Lazar. Dr. Lazar is the chiropractic physician for many actors and actresses in Hollywood.

Dr. Jacob Swilling of GenesisWest Cancer Clinic in Tijuana, Mexico.

Dr. Garry Smith with wife Wanna and Dr. Farber. Dr. Smith is a pioneer researcher in the field of Colloidal Silver, Colloidal Gold, and Mild Silver Protein.

Dr. William J. Faber, Author of "Pain, Pain, Go Away" on Reconstructive Therapy with Dr. Paul Farber and Dr. John Trowbridge.

Dr. Paul and Marie
Farber with Dr. Alex
Duarte's secretary,
Kristi Kelly.

For information on
Offshore Medicine call,
916-272-9697.

Colonel Leonard Farber once contended with the actor Jimmy Stewart for the rank and position of General.

THE COLONEL LEONARD FARBER COLLOIDAL SILVER MEMORIAL FUND

Marie Farber with Ruth Bender, one of Albert Einstein's original students.

A special thank you to Dr. Alex Duarte for his continuing support and vision in seeing the scientific importance of my findings even at the beginning stages of my research.

Scientist and researcher Dr. Lee Lorenzen, Ph.D, (developer of Aqua Resonance) with Dr. Farber.

Dr. Earl Rice, M.D., Dr. Robert E. Cater, M.D., Dr. Bob L. Owen, Ph.D, D.Sc., at Natural Health Federation Conference.

Dr. M. Paul Farber with Dr. Johan Kotze from South Africa with Dr. Paul Farber and Mr. Welcome Masoni, Right Hand Man to President NELSON MANDELA.

Dr. Farber with Dr. Kotze's cousin Willie Matthee who is working with getting the use of Mild Silver Protein in the CITRUS INDUSTRY.

350

THE COLL/AG KIDS OF SOUTH AFRICA
The First Generation of SOUTH AFRICAN
Children to have the Potential of a Life com-
pletely free of Infectious Diseases including
THE COMMON COLD and FLUES.
The Coll/Ag kids in the picture with Dr.
Farber are left to right Taryn MacMurray,
daughter of Greg and Agnes MacMurray;
Ruané Kotze, daughter of Dr. John and
Rustelle Kotze and Brendon MacMurray,
son of Greg and Agnes MacMurray.

Dr. M. Paul Farber with Mr. Greg MacMurray who is Supervising the bringing in of MILD SILVER
PROTEIN to SOUTH AFRICA and eventually ALL OF AFRICA.

A SPECIAL THANK YOU TO
CORNERSTONE CHRISTIAN TELEVISION
Dr. M. Paul and Marie have enjoyed
appearing on CHRISTIAN TV with you and we
appreciate your support.

Colonel Leonard Farber once contended with
the actor Jimmy Stewart for the rank and
position of General.
THE COLONEL LEONARD FARBER
COLLOIDAL SILVER MEMORIAL FUND

Charles Mraz, Founder and Developer of
APITHERAPY

Rash from Lyme Disease Bite. This gentleman
received Mild Silver Protein three days after
being bit, the rash disappeared and he never
had any symptoms.

Vice President Tom Scott; President Oleen
Eagle; Evelyn Kean, Director of Optimum
Health; R. Russell Bixler, CEO
CORNERSTONE TELEVISION

Norma Bixler, Russ Bixler, and Ruth Fisher who was extremely active in the Kathryn Kuhlman Ministry and now has her own Healing Ministry.

Evelyn Kean, Marie Farber, Dr. M. Paul Farber, and Russ and Norma Bixler in Pittsburgh at CORNERSTONE TELEVISION.

Marie and Dr. Paul with Russ and Norma Bixler

Dr. Farber with Sylvia Provenze, President Pittsburgh Chapter of the National Health Federation, NHF.

354

Jeff and Doug Lioon, fellow researchers with Dr. Farber, Evelyn Kean, Dr. Paul and Marie Farber.

Dr. M. Paul Farber touring the Nutritional Laboratories' Plant where many of "The People's Doctor Product Line" are produced.

Dr. Jan DeVries   Dr. M. Paul Farber

ULTIPLE SCLEROSIS is recognised as a growing problem. In some Scandinavian countries, Holland, Britain and North America, the figures are rising by the day. In the UK alone it is estimated that between 50,000 and 60,000 people suffer from this debilitating disease; in the USA figures of 350,000 are quoted. What are the causes of the problem? And what can be done about it? Could it be possible to prevent MS? When we look at the countries where there is no occurrence of MS whatsoever, the immediate answer is YES.

Jan de Vries has studied — and treated — Multiple Sclerosis for over twenty-five years. He has learned that every MS patient is different and that their problems must be treated individually. He emphasises the importance of diet and environment: sufferers must build up their immune system. Even the smallest interference with that delicate mechanism, the human body, can trigger off problems out of all proportion to the cause. For example, silver mercury amalgam fillings in teeth can affect your health.

This book draws attention to a variety of factors and how they can be dealt with to improve the quality of life for all MS sufferers. It is a relevant and important alternative approach to the problem.

Dr. Jan DeVries and Dr. M. Paul Farber are in correspondence regarding the works in this book.

Maureen K. Salaman, President Emeritus, National Health Federation with Dr. M. Paul Farber and Dr. Martin Gallagher, D.C.

Maureen K. Salaman with Dr. Francisco Contreras, M.D.

Dr. M. Paul Farber and Dr. Martin Gallagher, radio talk show host.

Dr. Francisco Contreras and
Dr. M. Paul Farber.

Dr. Garry Smith with Dr. M. Paul
Farber, fellow Colloidal Silver and
Mild Silver Protein research
scientist.

Cesar Rodriguez, Dr. Farber's
godson and Bee Venom therapist.
409-441-1247

Dr. M. Paul Farber with brother,
Arnie Farber.

1996 International Tesla Symposium

𝒜 Word
from the President

Featuring Dr. M. Paul Farber and
J.W. McGinnis, President, TESLA
Society.

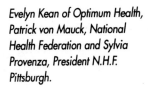

Evelyn Kean of Optimum Health,
Patrick von Mauck, National
Health Federation and Sylvia
Provenza, President N.H.F.
Pittsburgh.

LETTERS...

To: Dr. Willy Burgdorfer
    Laboratory of Pathology
    Rocky Mountain Laboratories
    Hamilton, MT 59840

From: Dr. M. Paul Farber
    11811 I-10 East, Suite 300
    Houston, Texas 77029

Dear Dr. Burgdorfer:

It was an honor and a pleasure to meet you at the recent 1993 LYME Conference in Atlantic City which was held in your honor. Your discovery of Borrelia burgdorferi as the causative agent of Lyme Disease will certainly be recorded by history as one of the most important medical discoveries of the century. However, more important than this recognition is the hope and dignity restored to those thousands of individuals who have been suffering from the "Complex of Symptoms" which define Lyme Disease and have been misdiagnosed into over 25 disease processes which are incorrect. This incorrectness was and still is in many cases due to the fact that Borrelia burgdorferi was overlooked as the causative agent of Lyme Disease.

As a Holistic Physician of over 25 years experience I can testify to the fact that when patients are given the wrong diagnoses or no diagnoses other than to be told by an authority figure that it is all in their head and imagination, the results can be devastating both psychologically and physically to that individual. Not only is their a loss of dignity but also proper treatment can be many times not administered, which can lead to further complications and even death. Therefore, your discovery of the spirochete Borrelia burgdorferi is a humanitarian breakthrough, as well as a scientific one.

I have also been conducting scientific research in the filed of Holistic Medicine for the entire 25 years of my professional career. My special field of interest has been in both identifying and documenting the use of "natural remedies" in the cure of many of the major diseases which plague mankind.

I am of the belief and conviction that within the wonderful Realm of God's Nature there exist natural herbal type substances as well as natural mineral substances or combinations of these substances which can balance out the effects of any disease and in essence cure it, when correctly chosen and administered. I am also of the belief that certain modern technological scientific processes can be applied to natural mineral or vegetable substances without destroying the essence of that substance which can then then be used to cure many of mankind's diseases.

This process of curing disease by understanding nature through an understanding of the LAWS which govern nature actually goes one step deeper. If one can understand the intricate laws and balances which govern Nature and have governed it without change since the beginning of time, then one can understand from the interactions of the different elements of nature what it takes for "life," whether microscopic or macroscopic, to live, thrive, or die.

It is well understood and accepted by the scientific community that every living thing has certain physical parameters in which they can exist. For example, without food, water, gravity and oxygen, not to mention many other factors, man could not exist. As you well know, microscopic organisms have to have specific environmental needs met within certain fixed parameters, many times including a host to live in and feed upon in order for them to exist. For example, if the Ph or acid/alkaline balance as well as factors such as temperature, aerobic or anaerobic qualities of living organisms in relationship to oxygen, or the presence or absence of light are not within certain parameters within the "environment" of the body , a microorganism cannot live. This principle holds true of the body also.

Within the same realm of these natural laws, if a substance could be found which had no side effects and could disable the enzyme that one-cell bacteria, fungus and viruses use for their oxygen metabolism, then it would cause them to suffocate in six minutes or less upon contact, as was recently tested at the UCLA medical labs. It was found that pleomorphic or mutant forms of organisms are just as vulnerable.

At the LYME Conference in Atlantic City it was announced that recent research has shown evidence that even after extensive antibiotic treatment, spirochetes can still be found hiding in the fibroblast of the muscle cells. If this is the case, then conventional antibiotic treatment can control Lyme Disease but cannot cure it. This is the reason for reoccurrence of symptoms as these surviving spirochetes begin to multiply.

The reason that there are second and third generation antibiotics is because pleomorphic or mutant forms of these microorganisms develop which are resistant to the first generation of antibiotics. I believe that this is possibly the case for the recurrence of the "Symptom Complex" of Lyme

Disease, as well as the spirochete's powerful ability to hide itself in the specific parts of the body such as the fibroblast. My own personal experience has shown me that they also tend to hide in the deep muscles surrounding the joints in the extremities of the hands and feet, where the blood flow is not as intense...as for example, in the internal organs of the body. The temperature is usually slightly cooler.

I have personally been going through and simultaneously, out of the need for my own personal survival, been intensely researching and developing Holistic as well as medical type treatments to treat both the cause and the symptoms of Lyme Disease. It is amazing how much an individual bent on scientific investigation and documentation as well as discovering the truth, can learn when he, as a doctor, is thrown without privilege of free will or warning into the situation of being a Lyme victim himself. This most physically intense as well as psychologically taxing and time-consuming year began on June 14, 1992 when I woke up paralyzed from the waist down after being bitten by an adult female Xodius Scapularis engourged tick, which was found to be attached to my occipital lobe beneath my scalp for over two weeks before it was discovered.

The tick was analyzed and identified by Dr. Thomas Craig, Ph.D., head of the Paracytology Department at Texas A & M University in Bryan, Texas. The tick had been sent to him within two days after I discovered it on my scalp. It was mostly in tact, as I had surgically removed it by digging the sharpened nails of my right hand into my own scalp, reaching under the tick and removing both tick as well as tissue and blood.

I immediately enclosed the tick in a jar and took it to my veterinarian, who had it expressed up to Texas A & M to the experts in the field of parasite identification.

Even after extensive intravenous antibiotic treatment with both penicillin and the cephalosporin Rocephin totalling 57 days within a three month period, I am still not totally free of Lyme Disease and have reoccurences and portions of the Lyme Disease Symptom Complex. At different times I suffered blindness in my left eye to the degree of being legally blind due to inflammation of the cranial nerves causing suborbital optic neuritis, loss of feeling and movement in my upper extremities, as well as significant gastrointestinal shutdown and heart distress and chronic fatigue, in addition to reoccurences in my lower extremities as well as the discomfort of full body edema.

Fortunately, through various Holistic Methods which will be outlined in my upcoming book, I have been able to control about 75%-95% of the symptoms and live virtually free of pain and symptoms both during and between, I was unable to find a substance that could kill the spirochetes. I feel that the antibiotic treatment was about 70% successful. However, there were many unpleasant side effects from conventional intravenous antibiotic treatment.

After the conference I became discouraged at the possibility of having to live with Lyme Disease for the rest of my life, especially after having been made aware of the recent research on the survival of the spirochetes in the fibroblast, even after extensive antibiotic treatment. Being a researcher and a scientist who is unwilling to quit, I jumped back into my research in search of a substance or set of internal environmental conditions that could kill the spirochetes or any pleomorphic mutant forms of the original spirochete as well as spirochetes hiding in the fibroblast of the muscles.

I am cautiously excited to say, Dr. Burgdorfer, that I believe it is possible, God willing, that I have rediscovered that substance and its application to Lyme Disease. The name of this powerful wide spectrum antibiotic is Mild Silver Protein.

I will now take the liberty to further quote from a pamphlet on Mild Silver Protein which I have enclosed for your perusal. I think that you will find this information both fascinating and exciting. I am also including a four-ounce vial of the substance so that it can be tested in the laboratory at the Rocky Mountain Institute on spirochetes in vitro. God willing, when this is successful, I propose a Double Blind Study on a human population with confirmed laboratory-diagnosed Lyme Disease that can be rechecked after administration of the Mild Silver Protein. I would be more than happy to help design this experiment with you, Dr. Burgdorfer. I gained a great deal of experience at the University of Texas in Austin when I worked and taught as an Associate to a professor in Experimental Psychology in designing Double Blind Studies and other experimental methodologies. This would be very inexpensive to do as I feel we will have no lack of volunteers when the time comes, especially since there are no known side effects from the almost forgotten and lost "Medical Nutritional Mineral Mild Silver Protein" which have ever been documented. It reminds me of the actor Sean Connery's statement in the movie "Medicine Man" when he, as a scientist, said to another scientist: "Haven't you ever discovered something and then lost it and been unable to find it, hoping you can find it again in the future?" I believe that there could be no better description of Mild Silver Protein.

If we are successful, then WE WILL HAVE DISCOVERED A COMPLETE ANSWER for Lyme

Disease which also takes into account the pleomorphic or mutant forms of spirochetes which eliminates the reinfection factor which can be caused from those mutations as well as the hiding of spirochetes in the fibroblast, through the rediscovery and application of an already proven wide spectrum antibiotic which was originally advertised and labeled for use in 1938, and is still protected for use under the guidelines of those same laws. In order to not underestimate the proven importance of pre-1938 drugs, it should be noted that both morphine sulfate and thyroid tablets, two of the most successful and widely used drugs of this century, fall into this category.

In order to have what could be defined as a complete answer we must not only kill all the spirochetes, but we must also have a method which creates no new symptoms such as the Herxheimer Reaction in which patients encounter a variety of symptoms such as fever, chills, rash, and increased symptomatology and exacerbation of symptoms. I will now quote Dr. Charlene DeMarco from "The Lyme Threat" newsletter, Winter/Spring 1993: "It is thought that it is caused by an allergic response to antigens or foreign substances released by the organisms when it is killed and that these substances may have endotoxic properties. Usually this reaction is seen with intravenous antibiotic therapy, but it can occur during oral antibiotic therapy as well. Herxheimer reactions are very common during treatment of Lyme Disease. It usually consists of fever, chills, sweats, joint and muscle pain, and exacerbation of symptoms. This reaction is also encountered with penicillin, Lysomal (digestive enzymes are released which cause tissue damage with the destructive inflammation of small blood vessels). This reaction is also elicited in response to spirochete demise. Dorland's Medical Dictionary has the term "spirochetolysis."

Keeping the above Herxheimer reaction in mind, I would like to establish a THREE PART DEFINITION of what could be considered a complete answer for Lyme Disease if all three parts of this definition are satisfied.

1. The Causative Agent of Lyme Disease which are the spirochetes Borrelia Burgdorferi are killed along with any mutant or pleomorphic forms, also Candida Yeast microorganisms. 2. No iatrogenic side effects such as the Herxheimer Reaction are created by the method of treatment which can overshadow the disease itself and would mask the progress being made by the demise of the spirochetes.

3. All symptoms as well as damage caused to the cells, tissues, organs, and systems of the body are healed and restored back to normal.

Number 1 and Number 2 of this three-part definition could be accomplished through the use of Mild Silver Protein . Number 3 can be accomplished through the use of Specific Proven Holistic Methods (which will be outlined in detail in my upcoming book) which can restore and rebuild these cells, tissues, organs, and systems of the body back to a point of homeostasis and normality.

Dr. Burgdorfer, if we can demonstrate the effectiveness of Mild Silver Protein, both in the laboratory as well as a Double Blind human study, then we will have found a cure to the second largest disease to devastate this nation through the rediscovery of what may be considered one of the greatest discoveries made by the Medical Profession, along with time-proven methods of Holistic Medicine. In essence we have a marriage of two complimentary methods in order to get a complete answer as defined above. Mild Silver Protein also falls within the parameters of Holistic Medicine since silver is a natural inorganic substance found in the earth and created by nature.

MILD SILVER PROTEIN RESEARCH

I will now quote some information from a paper on Mild Silver Protein Research. Then following the quotation, I will comment on it in relationship to our goal of finding an answer for Lyme Disease.

"This substance which was in wide usage 70 years ago priced itself out of the market due to the high cost of manufacturing. It sold at about $400 and ounce back in the 1930's.

Mild Silver Protein:

1. Is non-toxic
2. Has no known side effects
3. Has no reaction with other medications you may be taking
4. Is a powerful antibiotic against viruses, bacteria, parasites and fungus
5. Has anti-inflammatory properties
6. Is a natural prophylactic
7. Was used for years safely by the Medical Profession around the world
8. Has been successfully used on over 650 different diseases
9. Is available in high-concentrate form
10. Costs 95% less than in the 1930's

As you can see, this wonderful, almost forgotten medical miracle could have worldwide implications not only in Lyme Diseases but in any disease involving viruses, bacteria, parasites, or fungus of

which 650 have already been proven. It is amazing
how economics plays such a large part in scientific
discovery.

A substance with such great applications and
potential has literally been forgotten simply because
at one point in history (in this case the 1930's) it was
priced out of the market by less expensive drugs.
Now that the cost has gone down due to
technological advances in the manufacturing of Mild
Silver Protein substances, a $1600, 4-ounce vial now
costs only $55.

If we can reprove its effectiveness in the
laboratory, as well as in the field, then perhaps we
could be instrumental in not only finding an answer
for Lyme Disease, but also for restoring Mild Silver
Protein's application to the other 650 diseases which
it was proven in the early research of the 1930's to
affect. These can be reproved in modern
laboratories and then the wide use application of
this substance could take place.

WHAT EXCITING TIMES IN WHICH WE ARE
LIVING AND HELPING TO SHAPE

"Mild Silver Protein: What Is it? It is electrically
charged particles of silver that are extremely small,
usually ranging from about 0.01 to about 0.001
microns in diameter and suspended in distilled
water.

The highest quality of Mild Silver Protein is
actually gold in color, according to medical
literature. Previously manufactured at about 200
parts per million (ppm), it is highly concentrated at
about 5000 ppm, is gold in color and has the quality
for injection use."

Since Mild Silver Protein has the quality for
injection use by qualified health professionals, it can

then become the preferred method of treatment by the Medical Profession in serious cases and administered orally in less serious cases. It is available in 100cc bottles for injection usage. According to the 245th edition of Dorland's Medical Dictionary, viruses range from 200-300 mu to 15 mu in size. This means that the Mild Silver Protein is smaller in size than a virus and thus has the ability to penetrate it.

What is the therapeutic value of Mild Silver Protein? According to medical journals from around the world, it is a powerful wide spectrum antibiotic that disables the enzyme that all one-celled bacteria, fungus, and viruses use for their oxygen metabolism, causing them to suffocate in six minutes or less upon contact...as it was recently tested at UCLA Medical Labs. Pleomorphic or mutant forms of the organisms are just as vulnerable. Most prescription antibiotics kill only a few different disease-causing organisms, but Mild Silver Protein is known to be successful against 650 diseases.

Veterinarians also find it useful against canine parvovirus as well as other diseases of small and large animals. Trace amounts of silver are prophylactic or protective in nature as it strengthens the immune system. The British Medical Journal also reports that it rapidly subdues inflammation and promotes healing.

Due to the fact that Mild Silver Protein "disables the enzyme that all one-celled bacteria, fungus and viruses use for their oxygen metabolism, causing them to suffocate in six minutes or less upon contact, it is not limited to killing just a few microorganisms like modern antibiotics do, but instead encompasses a wide spectrum of disease-causing microorganisms. Since silver is an inorganic metal that cannot be absorbed by a cell, I believe that it functions by interfering and blocking the functions of the enzyme which governs oxygen metabolism. For example, if you were to paint the gills of a fish with silver paint and then put that same fish back in the water, it would die from oxygen starvation. In a sense, using layman's terms, the silver would "clog up the works."

Since in Lyme Disease we need to strengthen the immune system because of all the damage which has been done before treatment by the spirochetes, the Mild Silver Protein takes on the additional function of strengthening the immune system since "trace amounts of silver are protective or prophylactic in nature." Also, since it "rapidly subdues inflammation and promotes healing" it will also be effective in Lyme Disease as the great amount of inflammation caused by the spirochetes needs to be subdued.

How is Mild Silver Protein used? Application is dependent on the problem. It is tasteless and can be taken orally for such conditions as parasites, candida, herpes, chronic fatigue, staph and strep conditions, shingles, and over 650 viral and bacterial diseases. It has been successfully used in septic conditions of the mouth including pyorrhea and tonsillitis. Applied to the skin it can help in acne, warts, open sores, athletes foot, just to name a few. In the eye it can help conjunctivitis as well as other forms of inflammations and infections of the eyes with no stinging or irritation. It can additionally be used vaginally, anally, or atomized into nose or lungs. An injectable form is also available in 100cc bottles for qualified health professionals.

Since it is tasteless and can be taken orally it is both easy to use as well as non-abrasive to the pallet, making it more desirable to the patient. Since Mild Silver Protein has been previously proven effective in both Candida and chronic fatigue, it has additional applications for Lyme Disease. Since Candida has been shown to manifest many times due to the triggering effect of antibiotic treatment, its effects can be eliminated by the non-use of conventional antibiotics. In this situation this side effect called Candida, which is a yeast type infection, can also be eliminated by the Mild Silver Protein. Conventional antibiotics are not the cause of Candida, but rather they act as a catalyst to trigger this yeast infectious growth by killing the acidophilus, the friendly bacteria. Since the eyes are affected in Lyme Disease in the forms of pink eye, inflammations as well as irritations, pain and discomfort both suborbital and supraorbital, and suborbital optic neuritis due to inflammation of the cranial nerves, Mild Silver Protein should help in all these conditions, especially since it causes no stinging or irritation. Since the lungs are affected in Lyme Disease and Mild Silver Protein can be atomized into the nose and lungs, this would have additional benefits to the respiratory system.

Since an injectable form is available in 100cc bottles for qualified health professionals, this will give to the Medical Profession a new and powerful tool to treat their patients who have Lyme Disease without complications from the Herxheimer Raction. I personally went through the Herxheimer Reaction the first time after having 10 days of intravenous penicillin, a second time following a 14-day course of 2 grams of the cephalosporin Rocephin, and a third time following a 31- day intravenous treatment of 2 grams a day of the cephalosporin Rocephin. The reason I chose to do these conventional antibiotics was because at the time I had no knowledge of Mild Silver Protein or the possibility of a Herxheimer Reaction. Had I known about Mild Silver Protein as well as the possibility of a Herxheimer Reaction from conventional antibiotics, I would have chosen the Mild Silver Protein treatment.

After the conventional antibiotic treatment I personally experienced increased pain in my hands and feet as a result of extreme edema and vascularitis, itching and burning over the entire body and more specifically the chest area, burning in the eyes, sleep disturbances, nervous system irritability, as well as increased parathesias in the hands, arms, legs and feet. At the time, because I felt so bad, I concerned myself as to whether the antibiotics had actually killed the spirochetes, because I did not discover the information about the Herxheimer Reaction until I read Dr. Charlene DeMarco's article in the Lyme Threat newsletter. In many ways I am grateful that I did not know about the Herxheimer Reaction. Had I known, I would not have had the personal experience which will allow me to make the readers of my book aware that there is a better and safer route to kill the spirochetes.

Also, a patient will be able to avoid the same mistake I made of taking more antibiotics because they still have symptoms when in fact the symptoms are the side effects of the antibiotic treatment rather than the spirochetes, as the majority of the spirochetes have been killed by the antibiotics. The danger is overtreatment due to the perpetual symptomatology caused by the treatment which is misdiagnosed as persistent Lyme Disease.

I did the Mild Silver Protein for a 10-day period once I had rediscovered it to make sure that I had killed any mutant or hiding spirochetes. I experienced absolutely no side effects from the Mild Silver Protein, as predicted in its literature. After the treatment I began throwing off the effects of the Herxheimer Reaction and began slowly improving, also using Holistic Methods to speed up my recovery and detoxify my body from the heavy dosages of antibiotics which were intravenously put into my body over a 3-month period.

I recently had a patient, a young lady who was diagnosed and treated by seven different medical doctors for Epstein-Barr Virus, Chronic Fatigue Syndrome, and Irritable Bowel Syndrome. She received gamma-globulin antibiotic treatment for the first two and Maalox for the bowel. She not only did not improve, but began losing weight to below 95 lbs. for a 5'7" girl of 23, which is about 25-30 lbs. low. She was told that nothing else could be done and her bowel syndrome continued to worsen. I, as her attending Holistic Physician, put her on one teaspoon of Mild Silver Protein a day, along with a cup a day of pure aloe vera juice for the bowel three times a day. Within a week she gained 5 lbs., her bowel began clearing up, she had more energy than she has had in seven years and she continued to improve so dramatically that within a month she should be fully recovered and back up to her normal weight of 125 lbs. She experienced absolutely no side effects from the the treatment and her mood and attitude is now happy and positive. All of this because a long forgotten medical answer was able to kill the Epstein Barr Virus, and a simple herb was able to clear up her bowel.

What a compliment this would be to some of the Founding Fathers and Early Researchers in the Medical Profession who first discovered the concept as well as the methodology of creating Mild Silver Protein, only to be priced out of the market in the post 1938 era. Thank God that due to modern scientific technology, it is practical again for widespread usage.

"WHAT ARE THE SIDE EFFECTS OF MILD

SILVER PROTEIN? There are no known side effects that have ever been recorded from the use of high quality MILD SILVER PROTEIN, according to the medical literature. Additionally, there has never been a recorded case of a drug interaction with any other drug. It is non-addicting, the body does not build up a tolerance to it and studies show that MILD SILVER PROTEIN is not deposited under the skin like other silver compounds with causes grey skin. It is tasteless, odorless, non-toxic non-stinging to the eyes, safe for pregnant and lactating women."

Since there are no known side effects, the clinical monitoring of a patient's progress and eventual recovery will not be masked by the Herxheimer Reaction. If the symptoms from the Herxheimer Reaction or Candida Yeast Infection are mistaken for the symptoms of Lyme Disease, a physician's wrong decision to continue more conventional antibiotic treatment will be made, when in fact the spirochetes have already been killed and it is the reactions to the antibiotic which are now causing the problems. If this is the case, the continuous perpetuation of the Lyme Disease Syndrome will seem to never end. Perhaps this is one of the errors being made in making Lyme Disease appear to be more long term than it actually is.

If the spirochetes can be killed by the antibiotic Mild Silver Protein and no additional symptoms are created, then the toxic reaction from the demise of the spirochetes will be the only phenomena that the physician and patients will have to wait out together. At that point, the disease will have truly ended, since the pleomorphic and mutant forms of the spirochetes will also have been killed. At that point, the physician could then implement additional Holistic Methods to help rebuild the nervous system and the immune system. Then the patient can begin to have health restored to all the cells, organs, glands, and systems of the body, which can be accomplished through a properly prescribed nutritional program.

Since there has never been a known case of a drug interaction with any other drug, we do not have to concern ourselves with symptoms that could be created by such an interaction which could also mask recovery. Since it is non-addicting and the body does not build up a tolerance to it, a patient will not be prohibited from future use. Since the silver molecules are too small to be deposited under the skin, no cosmetic problems will result from its usage.

Since it is tasteless, odorless and non-toxic, patients will have no fear, discomfort or revulsion at using it. Since it is non-stinging to the eyes, it can be used to relieve pink eye and other eye irritations and inflammations. Since it is safe for pregnant and lactating women, those females who are infected by Lyme Disease can be treated without concern of harm to the fetus by the side effects and interaction of drugs. If the spirochetes can be killed early enough by the Mild silver Protein and no further harm is created, then the fetus has a better chance for survival as well as not being harmed.

"HOW COME I HAVE NEVER HEARD OF MILD SILVER PROTEIN?" Seventy years ago, it was widely used. It subsequently priced itself out of the market due to the high cost of manufacturing it at that time. Numerous articles in medical journals on Mild silver Protein can be found, usually dating before 1910. New articles and data will soon be appearing as more doctors rediscover this safe but effective mineral solution.

It is not unusual for the power of economics to have a great effect not only on medical research but also medical drugs. Competitiveness rather than quality is many times the prevailing situation. Since Mild Silver Protein has retained its quality for the last 50 years and now due to new methods of chemical engineering has actually improved the quality, the cost is down to a point where it can compete in the modern marketplace.

Since no other antibiotic in the market can accomplish all that Mild Silver Protein can without side effects and also kill mutant forms without having to create another drug, Mild Silver Protein wins the competition. I am currently researching to obtain more of the numerous articles printed before 1940, which I have named the Dead Sea Scrolls of Modern Medicine.

WHAT DOES THE F.D.A. SAY ABOUT MILD SILVER PROTEIN ? It is considered to be a pre-1938 drug and may be continued to be marketed without submitted evidence of safety and effectiveness, which is required of all prescription drugs marketed after 1938, as long as it is advertised and labeled for the same use as 1938.

The post World War II generations have a tendency to believe that all the great discoveries in medicine are a result of modern technology. This short-sided thinking is a result of both ignorance as well as a media and marketing brainwashing due to a constant bombardment of advertising which has taken place since that time. In fact, men of genius have existed since the beginning of time. Daily parts of our lives like the electric light bulb discovered by Thomas Edison, the concept of the wheel discovered by Pre-Historic Man, the first airplane built by the Wright brothers, the first Trans-Atlantic flight by Lindberg...as well as the greatest compositions of music in the world by Mozart, Beethoven and Bach were pre-World War II. Thousands of discoveries came from Greek and Roman cultures. Books could be and have been written on tens of thousands of discoveries that have been made. Perhaps it is true that "there is nothing new under the sun" except the rediscovery of the Laws of Nature which have been with us since the beginning of time. Why should modern man get so arrogant when we can't even cure the common cold and despite our advance in science, we as a nation are extremely unhealthy. Now with Mild Silver Protein, we can cure the common cold.

It should also be noted that on the other side of the coin the new relevance that spirochetes have on the lives of men as discovered by yourself is marvelous. Yet the microorganism called the spirochete has also been around since the beginning of time, probably before the first man ever stepped foot upon the earth. Perhaps at one time we lived in harmony with them until something upset the built-in balance of nature. Perhaps it is time to give up our arrogance, prejudices, and ignorance and embrace truth when it stares us in the face.

WHAT ABOUT MILD SILVER PROTEIN FOR AIDS? Since in active AIDS the suppressed immune system of the body is open to all kinds of disease, Mild Silver Protein is the perfect non-toxic drug to use with the wide spectrum antibiotic effect. A researcher at Brigham Young University sent Mild Silver Protein to two different labs, including U.C.L.A. Medical Center. The center then replied that "it killed not only the HIV virus but every virus that was tested in the lab." According to the F.D.A. rules, Mild Silver Protein cannot be used for treating the HIV virus but could be used as an antibiotic for all the acquired diseases of active AIDS.

At the Lyme Conference in Atlantic City, the attending doctors got a good taste of the attitude with which the F.D.A. functions in reference to its greater concern for special interest groups and almost total lack of concern for the welfare of Lyme victims. This was also pointed out at this convention when the representative of the F.D.A. was challenged by a doctor who treats Lyme Disease for ignoring the TRUTH about the outbreak of Lyme Disease in Missouri in favor of the special interests of the Insurance Companies. This is the old story of politics, special interest groups, economics, greed and possible corruption which will always have to be fought. It is a story of good, hard-working people's lives being sacrificed for the economic gain of the few with total disregard for the truth or the welfare of the doctor's patients.

Just as the researchers at Brigham Young University sent samples of Mild Silver Protein to researchers at two different labs at U.C.L.A., I am also sending a vial of it to you at the Rocky Mountain Institute in Montana for testing on spirochetes. I have strong feelings that you and your colleagues will be just as successful as the U.C.L.A. medical labs. I pray that you are and when you are I will be available to help you take the next step on a human population. Good Luck!

WHAT ABOUT THE DOSAGE OF MILD SILVER PROTEIN ? Most adults will take one tablespoonful twice a day sublingually for one month...and then one tablespoon for two months...and then one teaspoon a day for maintenance and prevention. Children or babies would take a proportionally smaller dose. Another way to determine dose is kinesiology or muscle testing. Optimum dose may require more or less Mild Silver Protein.

As can be seen, the dosage used is not very heavy. This gives strong indications that Mild Silver Protein is a very potent substance. Kinesiology is a science of muscle testing which I know quite well and would be able to teach to other Medical Doctors. Manipulation and specific adjusting of the vertebrae of the spinal column as well as the extremities are also sciences I would be willing to teach and share with a population of Medical Doctors such as the group which I met at the Lyme Conference. These techniques could be utilized for pain control during the course of Lyme Disease while the spirochetes are being killed by the Mild Silver Protein as well as before and after the spirochetes are killed.

WHAT ABOUT MILD SILVER PROTEIN FOR PETS? Yes! The amount you use is dependent on the size, whether it be a cat or as large as a dog or horse. Use a dropper to put it down their throat or just put it on their food or in their water. My wife Marie killed the worms in one of our cats with Mild Silver Protein, showing that it can also work on multi-celled organisms.

Since household pets such as dogs and cats are one of the vectors through which the ticks of Lyme Disease come into contact with the human population, it is important that these animals be protected. It would be an interesting Research Project to see if an infected Xodius Tick that was attached to a dog or cat would have its ability to produce spirochetes disrupted and perhaps destroyed if the animal were treated with Mild Silver Protein . If this proved to be true, then it could also be used as a preventative and prophylactic for the spread of Lyme Disease. It should have a similar effect on fleas.

DOES MILD SILVER PROTEIN CUT OUT THE NEED TO SEE A DOCTOR? It is a great product, but a person's health is important. When the situation warrants it, a person should see a holistic physician.

It is important that either the Medical Doctor or Chiropractor which a suspected Lyme patient chooses as their treating physician be knowledgeable of Lyme Disease and open to the use of Mild Silver Protein as an antibiotic with no side effects, as well as Holistic Methods of pain control and rebuilding the body from the effects of Lyme Disease.

WHAT ABOUT OTHER FORMS OF COLLOIDAL SILVER ? We are starting to see crude forms of it coming onto the market, claiming to be a better product. These other products are usually very dark and grey to black in color. You must remember how microscopically small a virus or bacteria is. Only Mild Silver Protein that is 0.01 to about 0.001 microns in diameter will work. The best quality of Mild Silver Protein will be clear and gold in color. Ours is prepared in a multi-million dollar facility using the most sophisticated high-tech equipment to both ionize the silver and electromagnetically charge it.

It is extremely important if not vital that the quality of the Mild Silver Protein be such that it is 0.01 to 0.001 microns in diameter in order for it to be effective. If we utilize a good lab such as the one who produced the vial I sent to you, it will be safe. It is important to remember that these particles of Mild Silver Protein are both ionized and electromagnetically charged.

WHAT ABOUT THE FRIENDLY BACTERIA IN THE BODY? Mild Silver Protein does not discriminate between friendly and disease-causing bacteria in the body. It will be important to replace the lactobacillus Acidophilus by eating a good fresh yogurt or taking acidophilus supplements. I prefer Danon Yogurt about three times a week. If the patient takes about 1/3 cup of pure Aloe Vera Juice 1/2 hour before eating the yogurt, then the yogurt will not form mucus.

DOES MILD SILVER PROTEIN HAVE TO BE REFRIGERATED? Keep it in a clear, dark cupboard, never on a sunny window ledge or a refrigerator. The shelf life is 5 years. You will notice small particles forming the longer you have it. This is small amounts of silver that are clumping together. This is not harmful and usually shaking the bottles will make the particles disappear...or you can filter the Mild Silver Protein using a cheesecloth or a coffee filter if you desire to.

Mild Silver Protein is very easy to store and its quality is very easy to detect. If all of these parameters are followed, then there is very little chance of getting a bad batch of it.

WHAT AN EXCITING TIME FOR A RESEARCHER TO BE ALIVE! We have before us the opportunity to stop the second largest epidemic taking place in the United States as well as the world. We not only have the opportunity to stop it, but we also have the opportunity of stopping it without creating any iatrogenic diseases or severe side effects such as the Herxheimer Reaction which I have painfully had to live through three different times in the course of my treatment for Lyme Disease.

I also feel that because of your position of respect in the Medical and Research communities, as well as your discovery of the spirochetes as the causative agent of Lyme Disease...coupled with my knowledge of Holistic Health Care, that we can get this knowledge of the curative power of Mild Silver Protein to the general public as well as their treating physicians in good time.

In addition to the humanitarian aspect of helping mankind, we have the opportunity of making medical history in the treatment of Lyme Disease, the second largest epidemic in the world. Also, God willing, when we are successful further research could literally change the face of antibiotic therapy and have applications toward the answer of literally thousands of infectious diseases without fear. Also, since Mild Silver Protein is now so inexpensive, it would become the method of treatment in third world countries.

I, as a physician, researcher and author, look forward to working with a man of your character and calibre. I will anticipate much further communication with you both by mail and telephone in our continuance of this research. Once you receive this letter and have a chance to review it, please write to me with your comments. I pray that the researchers at the Rocky Mountain Institute, which is approved by the U.S. Government through the National Institute of Health, can begin testing the vial of Mild Silver Protein immediately on live spirochetes. I am sending copies of this letter to the below mentioned people who I met at the Lyme Conference. I feel that they could all have positive input in both the research as well as the ability to spread the results of this research when the time is right.

Again, I am very pleased and happy that you enjoyed the POEM which I wrote for you. It was an extreme honor to share the head table with you and also to address the group of Medical Doctors . I look forward to both long and healthy lives for both of us so that we can continue our research and get on with the most important business in the world, THE BUSINESS OF MANKIND.

I wish all those concerned who are receiving this research document the best of luck and God speed. With patience, perseverance and persistence, we will achieve our mutually desired goal and be successful.

With great respect I remain respectfully yours,

Dr. M. Paul Farber

cc: Tom B. Schwan, Ph.D., Research Scientist,
Rocky Mountain Laboratories

Scott Samuels, Ph.D., Research Scientist,
Rocky Mountain Laboratories

Joe Burke, President, American Lyme
Disease Alliance

Dr. Jan DeVries, Ph.D., N.D., International
Author and Lecturer and Researcher and
European Adviser on Natural Healthcare to the
President of the United States

To: Mr. John Broadcaster (actual name deleted)
    Action 35 News
    P. O. Box 13
    Houston, Texas 77001

My name is Dr. M. Paul Farber and I have been a practicing physician in the Houston area since 1975. I have also been a fan of yours for more years than I can remember, since my family represents four generations of Houstonians. I have had a great deal of respect for the work which you have done for the "common man" and I applaud you for your years of effort as well as your accomplishments.

Included in this letter is a copy of my credentials and as you can see, I have been in the Natural Healthcare field for over 25 years. Recently, while pondering the information available on the AIDS epidemic and also doing an objective analysis of the situation of there being no effective cure for this virulent virus, I came upon an interesting hypothesis and extrapolated what I feel could be a potential cure for this disease which has taken tens of thousands of lives and threatens to take even more throughout the world.

One of my fields of interest has been microbiology, as well as how to ecologically balance various aspects of Nature. After reviewing all literature available to me, I have found that most research in the field of AIDS has been to find a vaccine which could neutralize or cure this virus. Since this has not been accomplished I feel that perhaps we are missing the "forest for the trees" and the answer could lie in something much simpler, such as understanding certain balances and relationships in Nature in which the certain variables involved can be calculated.

Since it has been proven that the AIDS virus is an ANAEROBIC VIRUS, which loses all virulence when outside the body and is therefore transferred only by avenues such as sexual transmission or use of hypodermic needles, it seems logical that this virus could not live in an aerobic atmosphere. We as humans breathe the air and therefore live in an aerobic environment and are exposed to the element Oxygen as well as Nitrogen. When this air is breathed it enters the body and from the alveoli of the lungs is then transferred by osmosis to the blood in the circulatory system where the hemoglobin of the blood then gathers the Oxygen to take to every organ, tissue, and cell of the body.

However, this oxygen is not 100% pure and arrives in combination with other gases and therefore lacks the properties and concentrations of pure manufactured oxygen which is the element which kills the anaerobic substances, which are substances that cannot live in the presence of Oxygen.

It is my hypothesis that if the AIDS Virus was exposed to high concentrations of Oxygen on a cellular level, then the virus would have no choice by the Laws of Nature but to die, since it is an anaerobic substance and cannot live in the presence of pure Oxygen, any more than a fish could live out of the water in the presence of an aerobic environment. Since Oxygen is a non-toxic as well as non life-threatening element, this could be accomplished by putting an AIDS victim who has been medically diagnosed through the AIDS

BLOOD TEST in a highly monitored environment such as a hospital where all vital signs and life functions could be medically monitored with the same type of equipment found in an intensive care unit.

A double blind study could be set up where a population of confirmed AIDS victims could be monitored using pure Oxygen with an AIDS blood test being administered every 24 hours to check for the presence of the virus and at the same time not over-stressing the body with too much extraneous activity. At the same time and under the same conditions, a CONTROL GROUP of AIDS victims could be monitored in the same manner while breathing the normal air from the environment, while the first group was receiving pure Oxygen administered through an Oxygen mask or in an Oxygen tent or in a hyperbaric atmosphere tank. Whether it took 1 hour, 24 hours, 72 hours or even up to 3 weeks to achieve the result of killing the virus...the time would almost become insignificant as long as the goal was achieved.

Over a period of hours utilizing the above procedure, every organ, tissue, and cell of the body should be saturated with pure oxygen and yet the patient would be unharmed. Pilots have flown for many hours on Oxygen for many years with no harm coming to them. If, God willing, this hypothesis is correct, then the AIDS virus would be destroyed upon this concentrated exposure to pure Oxygen. The control group should show no changes while the group treated with pure oxygen should eventually show no trace of the AIDS virus. All other factors in this Double Blind study would be controlled and complete adherence to the Scientific Method would be employed, followed, and monitored. The amount of time that it takes each person to achieve this would be affected by body constitution, individual differences, as well as the degree of infection with the AIDS virus.

Many times in history we have been shown that oftentimes the answer to a complex problem is very simple. Examples are how the dreaded disease "scurvy," which killed many thousands and had terrible symptoms, just like the AIDS Virus, turned out be no more than a Vitamin C deficiency and was cured with limes and oranges. Malaria became controlled by annihilating the mosquitoes that carried the disease. Beri Beri turned out to be a B1 Vitamin deficiency. Penicillin, which has saved thousands of lives, was discovered by accident when a piece of rotting bread grew the substance we now call Penicillin, a very powerful antibiotic. Each of these, with the exception of the latter, was a plague in their own time in history, just as the AIDS epidemic is now. If this hypothesis is correct, then the amount of death, suffering and wasted resources affecting the Human population in our civilization at the present time would be nothing less than a blessing from God, showing his infinite mercy toward mankind. If it proves to not be correct, then nothing will be lost and "no harm" will have been done as the Father of Medicine, Hippocrates, requested and we as physicians have all agreed to live by.

Becoming more attuned to this hypothesis through many hours of deep scientific contemplation was not enough, as I realized that if indeed it turned out to be valid upon utilizing the scientific method to test it, then I would still have the problem of getting this information into the proper hands to be tested, and then made available to the population. I think that you could be instrumental in helping me to achieve that end.

On February 8th in the Houston Chronicle, I ran across an article about the AIDS CONFERENCE being held on March 20 and 21 at the Westin Oaks Hotel in the Galleria. I saw many doctors at the Baylor College of Medicine who specialize in this field. I would like to enlist your help in getting this letter and this information into the correct hands for Testing and Verification. I would be willing to act as a consultant with the medical profession, having always had a great deal of respect for the folks at Baylor.

If indeed this treatment proved successful, then the next step would be to create a Nutritional and Herbal program to help rebuild the body as well as a program of Chiropractic, Acupuncture and Therapeutic Massage, to relieve the body of pain and restore normal nerve function, circulation, and metabolic balance. This would involve a Total Healthcare Program to balance the Immune System in order to bring it back to a pre-disease standard and return to Health. This Total Health Care Program could be specifically designed to strengthen and rebuild the Immune System from all of the devastation which it has suffered from the disease. As you may have noticed in my resume, this has been my area of specialty for many years. If we are successful, the rewards to mankind would be overwhelming. Not only would tens of thousands of lives be saved, but the economic savings to these individuals and to society as a whole would be immeasurable by moral, ethical, and humanitarian standards.

This would prove to be a fairly inexpensive form of treatment, so it is extremely important that it not be halted by individual political or economic concerns. One who is wise should also be cautiously aware that there are those who seek an expensive and profitable remedy to this situation, and who would not like to see this hypothesis succeed. When it comes to finding a cure to one of the plagues of the 20th century, profit and greed should not be a motive, from both a humanitarian as well as a moral viewpoint.

Albert Einstein once stated that if you cannot solve a problem at one level of thinking, then it is necessary to change one's level of thinking in order to find a solution to the problem.

I look forward to meeting you soon. Please feel free to contact me at your earliest possible convenience so that we may discuss any proposed plan of action on this vital matter.

> Sincerely Yours and in hopes of
> a better future for all Mankind

Dr. M. Paul Farber

Note from Dr. Farber: This letter was written before the discovery of Mild Silver Protein. We have now scientifically proven that our special formulation not only inhibits growth and any latent formation of the HIV AIDS virus, but also KILLS the HIV virus. It is non-toxic and has no known side effects.

Recent studies, pointed out by Dr. Alex Duarte, have shown that oxygen in the form of Ozone has actually killed the AIDS virus. This both proves and gives validity to my original hypothesis. Although the oxygen method works, the use of Mild Silver Protein is much easier to implement on a worldwide scale.

DATE: 08-01-93

FROM: Dr. Paul Farber
       11811 I-10 East, Suite 300
       Houston, Texas 77029

TO: Dr. Carl Cleveland
    Cleveland Chiropractic College
    6401 Rockhill Rd.
    Kansas City, Missouri 64131

Dear Carl,

I hope that all has gone well for you, your dad, your lovely wife and the Cleveland Chiropractic Colleges since we were last together on the Carribean cruise. The cruise and seminar was a marvelous, enjoyable, as well as educational experience. We had a wonderful time and it was fantastic to renew old friendships as well as to make new ones. I also enjoyed the seminar and I gathered a lot of new knowledge and information as well as my credit hours for that year.

I wanted to bring you up to date on the research which I was doing concerning a cure for the AIDS virus as well as to inform you about a book which, God willing, will be published within the next 12 months entitled Mild Silver Protein, A Scientifically Documented Answer To Lyme Disease, AIDS Virus and Yeast Infection."

Less than a month after the cruise I discovered that I had been bitten by the Ixodes Scapularis, a white-tail deer tick which causes Lyme Disease. I became deathly ill and almost died. However, the good Lord and His Son Jesus Christ pulled me through, which allowed me to document all which took place during my illness and near death experience, as well as both treatment and answer.

Rather than repeat the details of that experience in this letter, I have included a copy of the letter which I recently wrote to Dr. Willy Burgdorfer, Ph.D., the scientist who discovered the causative agent of Lyme Disease, the Spirochete...as well as an updated letter to Dr. Robert Schuller from "The Hour Of Power." When the book is published next year, you will then get the whole story, which is quite a phenomenal drama.

An additional interesting event occurred several months ago when I attended the Lyme Conference in Atlantic City, New Jersey. The conference was made up of over 500 medical doctors who are treating Lyme Disease around the country and one lonely Chiropractor with Holistic credentials. I had written Dr. Burgdorfer a poem (writing poetry is one of my hobbies) and I have included a copy for you and your dad. I gave the poem to Dr. Burgdorfer in whose honor the banquet was given at the conference.

Much to my surprise, during the banquet I heard my name called out. Dr. Burgdorfer then had me come up to the head table and read the poem and then address the 500 medical doctors and their wives. I was received in a wonderful manner. I suppose that you cannot underestimate what can happen to a Cleveland graduate. I even received a certificate from a Medical College in New Jersey, as well as the A.M.A. Can you imagine a medical certificate with a D.C.'s name on it? It seems as if

"The Times They Are a Changin" as Bob Dylan so beautifully stated in his song.

Perhaps when the book is completed in the near future, I will come to a homecoming and address the future doctors of Cleveland Chiropractic College, if you ever so desired. I have formed my own publishing company and much activity is happening. There is not one book written by a doctor who has personally gone through Lyme Disease who is also a Holistic physician and Chiropractor. The epidemic is in every state in the nation and has been documented in over 30 foreign countries. Therefore, the book has a potential international readership as well as international implications because of my rediscovery of Mild Silver Protein, which I have dubbed the "Silver Micro Bullet." I am sharing research with and working with the people at the Rocky Mountain Institute in Montana.

I hope that you enjoy the materials which I have included as well as a book which changed the direction of my focus, entitled "The Great Aids Hoax." I have included a copy of this letter as well as the additional materials to your dad in Los Angeles for his information and review.

Again, I truly enjoyed the cruise as well as the fellowship. I hope that the materials which I have sent to you will be helpful in your educational endeavors. I am writing my book on Lyme Disease in such a way that it can be utilized as a textbook for Chiropractic colleges, as well as medical schools to cover the field of Lyme Disease. I pray that it will be extremely comprehensive as well as informative and enlightening.

Best of everything and good fortune in all your

endeavors.

I remain your friend and fellow graduate,

Paul

TO: Mr. or Ms. Manic Depression
  (actual name deleted)

RE: RESEARCH
  Began December 21, 1993
  Findings for Applicable Answer
  Completed January 21, 1994

Dear Ms. Manic Depression,

It was a pleasure talking with you just prior to the Christmas Holidays. I pray that they were rewarding for you and for your family. Let us pray and hope that upon the understanding and application of the information from the books on manic-depression which I have researched and forwarded to you, that 1994 will be the happiest and healthiest year of your life since you became afflicted by this very debilitating disease called Manic Depression. I apologize that it took so long for me to get this information to you but I had to dig deeply in order to research out and uncover what would provide you with the best possible answers. I am happy to say that I am very pleased with the outcome of this research and my own understanding of what causes this unwanted disease as well as providing a NON-INVASIVE answer, which should if followed correctly and with the right frame of mind and spirit, bring about the desired results. Once you begin the FULL PROGRAM which I have outlined for you, I feel as your Physician that you could be experiencing some positive changes within two weeks to six weeks. You are going to be rebuilding all the systems in your body which cause this disease when they malfunction and act below normal levels as well as the NEUROTRANSMITTERS in your brain, as well as the brain itself. God willing, if you are religious about the program and do not deviate from it we should look for a 50-75% improvement within a year by January of 1995. As you do the program, this mental goal should be foremost on your mind. Repeat this phrase daily:

"EVERY DAY AND EVERY WAY, THANK GOD I AM GETTING BETTER AND BETTER."

Write these goals and WISE saying in large letters on posterboards and place them on the front of your refrigerator, in your bathroom, and near your bed and read them at least three times a day in the morning when you awake, in the midday, and at night before you retire.

This positive reinforcement as well as your FAITH will provide the track for this CURE to run upon. Quit looking for a magic medicine or a simple answer for this disease. Unlike Lyme Disease, which is caused by one infectious organism, this disease is systemic and the result of many things which I will summarize and which will be outlined in the books which my wife Marie and myself have given to you for your recovery.

Again, do not concern yourself about paying me for my services. I prayed deeply on this matter and I will help you in every way possible so that your future recovery can pave the way for many others who are afflicted just like yourself...to finally have a non- invasive cure which WORKS. It will be paid for 10,000 fold by scientifically documenting the Mild Silver Protein answer which I have rediscovered for Lyme Disease, thus putting an end to the roller coaster ride of this plague called Lyme Disease, complicated by the Candida Yeast Infections caused by the incorrect usage of the present day antibiotics with no regard for restoring the normal friendly acidophilus bacteria of the body. Again, there are no charges between people whose business is MANKIND. Someday I hope to see you on Oprah Winfrey, Sally Jesse Raphael, or Whoopi Goldberg telling your story with your spouse and I by your side so that tens of thousands of other women and men like yourself can have new understandings for their own recoveries and answers. Also, someday we will do the same thing once we document and prove the Mild Silver Protein answer for killing the spirochetes of Lyme Disease... and my book is published to broadcast this and my other findings concerning Candida Yeast Infections to the World.

An additional bonus was the good fortune of my being directed to Dr. Moses. This is the Physician who was also afflicted with Manic-Depression and through the same type of efforts outlined in the information which I have sent to you, has almost fully recovered and now has it under control. Although he did not do the electric shock therapies, he tried the current medical drugs and methods now in use with no results and with great discouragement. He decided not to quit and began researching for a cure, like I have done for you. I am happy to say that he was very successful. I have talked with him personally and informed him about you and about your condition. He was very sympathetic and more than willing to be of help and service to you. Since he has personally been through Manic Depression and has almost fully recovered, I STRONGLY SUGGEST that you both call him and then correspond with him by mail. In addition to what I am sending to you, his personal experience, discoveries, and consultation should prove to be invaluable.

I suggest reaching him at his office and setting up

a time when you can talk to him at length at his home. Then set up methods by both phone and mail to keep in touch with him as you have more questions and progress on your road to recovery. Perhaps someday, if Dr. Moses so chooses, I will offer my services to co-author a book on MANIC DEPRESSION with him since I have the Naturopathic and Nutritional credentials and he is a Doctor who has personally experienced Manic Depression, just as I have personally experienced Lyme Disease as well as a Candida Yeast infection.

Also, if you have been on any antibiotics and have not been replacing the natural acidophilus flora, then it is possible and probable that your condition is also being complicated by a Yeast infection. I have also included an autographed book by Dr. John Parks Trowbridge, entitled the "Yeast Syndrome." He is my physician for the yeast problem which I got as a result of the intravenous antibiotics for the Lyme Disease, without being advised to replace the natural acidophilus flora. He is also a friend and colleague and his book can prove very valuable for you.

The good news is that the grain-free diet which I have outlined for you for Manic Depression is very similar to the diet for yeast-related problems. If after you read this book and upon further consultation I confirm yeast, I may add Mild Silver Protein which can help to alleviate a yeast infection and its related mood swings.

Do not be discouraged that the methods of the past did not work nor about your age. The human body is a remarkable creation. Once you begin giving it all of the proper nutritional elements and herbal catalysts from NATURE which it needs and requires...and discontinue all harmful foods and habit patterns, nature has a way of accomplishing remarkable things, sometimes bordering on the miraculous. Either advise your present doctors or decide on your own about discontinuing all Invasive Therapies such as the Medical Drugs which did not work as well as any shock therapies. I am not a medical doctor so I neither prescribe prescription drugs or take people off of them. However, I do advise reading the available prescription drug books available in health food stores that outline all of the side effects of different drugs. It is my opinion, based on anecdotal experiences and observations, that they could only prove harmful and destructive to you at this stage. You will get quicker and better results from the programs which I have outlined for you.

NOW LET US BEGIN THE HEALING PROCESS

My wife Marie, who is a tremendous health practitioner in her own right, and I have included two additional books for you to read: "Your Family Tree Connection," by Chris M. Reading, M.D. and Ross S. Meillon; and "Nutritional healing," by James F. Balch, M.D. and Phyllis A. Balch, C.N.C. I have underlined the most important parts in the sections on both depression and manic-depression as well as some additional information. It may take you a while to assimilate the information and get all of the substances and materials which you need to begin the program. You should be able to find most of what you need at your local health food store. What they do not have they can probably order for you. If you cannot find an item, call me and I will give you other sources.

Do not begin until you have all of the materials arranged and in a proper and accessible order.

ONCE YOU BEGIN DON'T EVER STOP OR GO BACK TO OLD HABIT PATTERNS

From my research it seems that the central issues involved with Manic-Depression revolve around these basis concepts.

SUMMARY

Please read from the remarkable book "Your Family Tree Connection" by Dr. Chris M. Reading ,M.D. and Ross S. Meillon. In this most revealing book on orthomolecular medicine, hereditary factors and food allergies are linked to your problems with Manic-Depression. I will now summarize some of the basic concepts for you and your spouse to look for in understanding and conquering this disease. I truly believe that despite the past failures, you will soon be on the road to recovery and renewed happiness. The failures in treatment thus far only mean that you and your doctor's understanding of what the cause of your illness was and how to treat it were WRONG. So what's new? All that matters is that now you will have the correct answer, and you must apply it RELIGIOUSLY.

BASIC CONCEPT

1. Manic-Depression, contrary to the narrow belief of orthodox psychiatry is not just the result of strains, stresses, pressures and conflicts in one's environment or upbringing. Although all of these factors including one's situation in life affect or aggravate the problem, the core issue lies in the not so obvious.

2. Once the Manic Depressive patient realizes that all of the age-old stigmas that cling to this "so called" mental disorder are not all their own fault but due to underlying hereditary and dietary factors and food allergies, then one's humanity can be restored instead of being ripped and stripped away because no known cause is apparent.

3. One of the factors that is a strong possibility is a WHEAT ALLERGY. The gluten in wheat which is a gelatinous, sticky gray, protein substance and which gives dough its consistency, can trigger the Manic Depressive symptoms which you have been experiencing by interfering with certain brain functions. Recent research has shown that, for example, Multiple Sclerosis, certain arthritis problems, as well as SLE, lupus erythematomous can also be triggered by an allergy to the gluten in wheat.

4. You need to prepare a "FAMILY TREE" which will indicate as to whether you are predisposed to autoimmune disease. Read the story of Ellen and Pat in this book, who received tranquilizers, antidepressants, drugs, shock treatment, and sleep therapy, but only found relief when their food allergies were uncovered by their "family tree." Also the story of Coralie whose severe depression "melted away quite obediently" once her family tree altered her SLE. Read the sections listed in the index on page 270.

5. Dr. Reading states that "in the light of the cases reviewed in this book on *Your Family Tree Connection,*" and perhaps 1500 others like he treated, he is convinced that psychiatric problems almost always have physical causes–and the most common of these is gluten sensitivity, or in plain words GRAIN ALLERGIES.

6. Dr. Reading further states the difference between *Organic Psychoses* – which stem from organic or physical causes and...*Affective Psychoses* – which come entirely from stress factors in the patient's environment or upbringing.

He believes, based on his experience, that Organic Psychoses are the only kind that there are and that Grain allergies are the most common cause.

He further states that psychosis victims are no more to blame for their condition than flu victims. So any basis for attaching a stigma to mental illness is instantly and permanently destroyed. These conditions can be prevented and if already occurred, treated by means of the 'family tree.'"

This is much more humane and pleasant than battering people with shock treatment, psychosurgery, and massive doses of antidepressants.

7. Grain allergies cause a malabsorption of essential vitamins and minerals. See page 175 in the next to the last paragraph for a list of possible symptoms which indicate that psychoses can be caused by grain allergies.

START REJOICING AND CELEBRATING

You and any mentally affected relatives can be cured swiftly and easily on a strict grain-free diet and HEFTY DOSES of relevant VITAMINS & MINERALS. So don't waste a day. You can be tested for grain allergies as well as vitamin and mineral deficiencies.

8. It is important to realize as to whether you may be allergic to other foods such as milk and legumes. Read pgs. 176-182 about the diseases called Pyroluria and Porphyria and also how even schizophrenia may be an allergic reaction. Manic Depressive psychosis is X-linked in many families, and if yours is one, your family tree is your surest path to prediction, prevention and cure.

You are now armed with all of the information which you need to conquer this most unwelcome condition. Begin implementing the entire program after you have read the material and gotten all the supplies. I will be available by phone to help guide you and answer any pertinent questions. Keep a *positive attitude* and a strong faith in GOD. Whatever religion you practice, read supportive literature from the Bible and other sources about Faith and Hope. We are physical, mental and spiritual beings and in order to get a complete healing all three parts must be addressed.

GOD BLESS. You are about to embark on a great adventure and in addition to my physical efforts Marie and I will be praying to God, Jesus Christ, and the Holy Spirit for your complete and full recovery.

Dr. M. Paul Farber

DATE: 7-16-93

FROM: Dr. M. Paul Farber
B.A., B.S., M.A., M.S., N.D., Ph. D., D.C.

11811 I-10 East, Suite 300
Houston, Texas 77029

TO: Dr. Jan DeVries.
Southwoods Road
Troon, Scotland

Dear Dr. DeVries,

It was an honor and a pleasure to meet with you several months ago when your world tour brought you to Houston, Texas. Our meeting and encounter in Conroe was also very significant and meaningful to me. It was as if I was able to meet an ELDER BROTHER involved in the same work and mission here on earth. I deeply appreciate your offer to write comments for the back cover of my upcoming book "Mild Silver Protein...A Scientifically Documented Answer To The Three Largest Epidemics In The World..." I will be honored to include it on my book as well as your picture and contributions in my book. My wife, my son Matthew and I fully accept your gracious invitation after the book is published to come to England and Scotland so that you can help to promote it in Europe. It is wonderful how small the world is and the fact that we had a common friend in my Mentor Dr. Robert Mendehlson, M.D. Dr. Mendehlson and I lectured together in Colorado and he became a wonderful close and personal friend as well as an inspiration to me. You remind me so much of my other friend and Mentor Dr. Paavo Airola, Ph.D., N.D. who inspired me to put my thoughts and ideas down in books when the time became ripe. I am looking forward to meeting your friend Dr. Vogel when I am able to come to Europe. We are as you pointed out to me in Texas, truly BROTHERS in the same work and our unselfish sharing is very important.

I hope that your meeting with President Bill Clinton and his wife Hilary went well and was successful. I would be interested to hear the results of this meeting as well as their reaction to the book which I shared with you entitled "THE GREAT AIDS HOAX," by Mr. T. G. Fry, as well as my comments to the President that I wrote in the beginning of the book. I hope that you enjoyed this very enlightening book and that you utilize the information in your work. This book points out some of the early falsehoods perpetuated about AIDS.

Since our meeting I was fortunate enough to REDISCOVER a substance called Mild Silver Protein which I will be expounding as an answer to LYME DISEASE as well as the opportunistic diseases that accompany AIDS. If indeed there is one specific AIDS virus to kill, the Mild Silver Protein will do it. There are certainly many other opportunistic viruses that can be eliminated that actually infect people with IMMUNE DEFICIENCES that could save many lives if eliminated.

I have included in this correspondence to you a copy of the letter which I wrote to Dr. Willy Burgdorfer of the Rocky Mountain Institute in Montana, who is the discoverer of the causative agent of Lyme disease, the spirochetes. I have also included a vial of Mild Silver Protein so that you will be able to conduct some of your own research as well as to know the address for obtaining more. I feel that my research has led me to come across a long lost medical miracle which has international implications. If you were not aware of it I hope that I have done you a service in making you aware of this most incredible substance that can kill all infectious viruses and bacteria with no side effects as well as the fact that there are no mutant or pleomorphic strains created. It is also important to realize the fact that it is both economical and available to the poor as well as the wealthy. Mild Silver Protein has great possibilities for use in Third World Countries and could relieve much suffering. When you are able to obtain more Mild Silver Protein I would appreciate your testing it on SPIROCHETES as we are going to do at the ROCKY MOUNTAIN INSTITUTE as well as individuals infected with LYME DISEASE. Your results would have more impact in the European Continents because of your reputation there. I wish you the best of luck and much success.

I have also included copies of my original "AIDS LETTERS" and my research on the use of supersaturating the body with oxygen to kill anaerobic micro-organisms. Hopefully, this information will prove useful to you also.

When I complete my manuscript I will send to you a copy for your review and comments which I can utilize for the back cover. I would appreciate if you would gear some of your comments toward that purpose. I hope that you enjoy it and that the book will prove helpful not only to your patients with

LYME DISEASE but to all patients all over Europe.

I have begun reading your books and I began with "VIRUSES, ALLERGIES & THE IMMUNE SYSTEM. They are simply fantastic works and I compliment you. The information is proving very helpful to me. I will be looking forward to receiving a reply and a letter from you. I feel that there is much to be gained from our correspondence and I appreciate your offer while in Conroe to do so. Thank you very much for all that you have already shared with me and all of the help with my book that you have offered to me. As I stated, since this is the first of my works which I have decided to have published, I have much to learn and need all of the help which you can offer which you have learned from your experiences.

May God bless you and your work.

In the name of all those wishing to help MANKIND...

I remain sincerely yours.

Dr. M. Paul Farber

PRELIMINARY SCIENTIFIC STUDIES

(UNEDITED)

FOX CHASE

January 24, 1995

Dr. Paul Farber
Route 13
Box 1923
Highway 105E
Conroe, TX 77303

Dear Dr. Farber:

As requested, we are sending you our recent data on silver protein mediated Borrelia burgdorferi growth inhibition.

Preliminary laboratory studies on Borrelia burgdorferi spirochetes revealed that COLL/AG-30 (mild silver protein) solutions reduce the growth rate of these cells significantly and eventually lead to cell death. It has to be pointed out, however, that the spirochetes tested belong to a laboratory ATCC strain which is widely used in cell and tissue cultures and does not represent recent isolates from Lyme disease patients. In these tests, various concentrations of COLL/AG-30 solutions were added to the culture of Borrellia spirochetes. Low concentrations of this solution (ranging from 2 to 10 parts per million) slowed the growth rate of the spirochetes over a time span of 1 to 3 days. Higher concentrations (between 15 to 75 parts per million) had a much faster deleterious effect on cell replication leading to cell death. The growth inhibition depended on the concentration of the silver protein and on the duration of treatment.

More studies are definitely necessary to obtain a clearer picture of the interaction between silver protein and Borrelia burgdorferi. As these preliminary studies suggest, growth and replication of Lyme spirochetes are measurably inhibited by COLL/AG-30 in the in vitro setting.

We hope that you will find this information helpful for the publication of your book on novel bactericidal methods.

Sincerely,

Margret Bayer

Margret Bayer, Ph.D.

MB/rd

TEMPLE UNIVERSITY
A Commonwealth University

School of Medicine
Department of Microbiology
and Immunology

Philadelphia, Pennsylvania 19140
(215) 707-3203
Fax: (215) 707-7788

February 2, 1995

Dr. Paul Farber
Route 13
Box 1923
Highway 105 East
Conroe, Texas 77303

Dear Dr. Farber:

Preliminary studies on your silver micro-bullet preparation (1500 ppm) show it to be effective in inhibiting and killing strains of *Candida albicans* and *Cryptococcus neoformans in vitro*.

Four strains of *C. neoformans* were tested and they were killed by the preparation at 150-300 ppm. The growth of these strains were inhibited at a concentration as low as 0.3 ppm.

Three strains of *C. albicans* were tested and they were killed by the preparation at between 46 and 93 ppm. Growth was inhibited at between 0.7 and 1.4 ppm.

Additional studies should be done to evaluate *in vivo* effectivity.

Sincerely,

Helen R. Buckley, Ph.D.
Professor

HRB/mm

DEPARTMENT OF HEALTH & HUMAN SERVICES   Public Health Service

National Institutes of Health
Rocky Mountain Laboratories
Hamilton, Montana 59840
(406) 363–3211
FTS (700) 322–8400

January 13, 1995

Dr. Paul Farber
Route 13
Box 1923
Highway 105E
Conroe, TX 77303

Dear Dr. Farber:

This is to inform you that we have received from Mr. Kimball a sample (12 ml) of your colloidal silver (1,500 ppm) preparation and have evaluated its effectiveness in a preliminary pilot study against the Lyme disease spirochete, *Borrelia burgdorferi* (B31) and against the relapsing fever agent, *B. hermsii* (HS-1).

In both tests, BSK cultured spirochetes were treated with 150 and 15 ppm of colloidal silver. When examined 24 hours later, none of the treated cultures contained live spirochetes. Few spirochetes, all dead, were observed at 48 hours.

Additional *in vitro* and *in vivo* studies are in progress and will be reported as soon as results become available.

Sincerely yours,

Willy Burgdorfer, Ph.D.
Scientist Emeritus
Rocky Mountain Laboratories
Microscopy Branch

Tom G. Schwan, Ph.D.
Senior Staff Fellow
Laboratory of Microbial Structure
  and Function

WB/TGS:bk

Toxicity of Mild Silver Protein, Jan 27, 1995

Product: Mild Silver Protein provided by Discovery Experimental & Development, Inc., 29949 State Road 54 West, Wesley Chapel, Florida

Testing Facility: All tests were performed under the direction of Dr. R.C. Renlund, DVM, by staff of the Division of Comparative Medicine (DCM), Medical Sciences Building, Faculty of Medicine, University of Toronto. All experimental procedures were performed according to ethical guidelines, approved by the appropriate committee on animal experimentation.

This report is a summary of reports prepared by Dr. R.C. Renlund.

Summary: The aim of this study was to examine the health effects in rats exposed to either acute or chronic administration of Mild Silver Protein solutions at various concentrations either by intravenous injection or by presentation in drinking water. An initial (dose finding) study where rats received injections, via tail vein, of either 0.015, 0.075 or 0.15 mg in 1 ml of physiological saline solution, showed no observable ill effects either immediately or 8 days after injection. In a follow up study, 4 rats in each of 2 groups that had received intravenously, daily either 0.015 or 0.15 mg Mild Silver Protein in 1 ml of physiological saline after 12 days of treatment showed no abnormal, clinical or behavioral signs. In a further follow up study, applying high dose injections of 1500 ppm Mild Silver Protein to 3 animals, 3 times per week for 4 weeks no clinical signs or gross pathological changes were observed. The weight gain of the treated and 3 control animals showed no significant difference. Alternatively, 15 rats fed with Mild Silver Protein solution in their drinking water, 1.5 ppm for 40 days, which 18 mg total/350 gram rat, also showed no clinical signs of gross pathological changes at the end of the 40 day treatment period.

Protein stabilized mild silver solutions are said to possess antiseptic properties. These solutions seem to provide means of controlling infections which may not be responsive to currently available antibiotics. If these preparations are to be applied *in vivo*, it is necessary first to obtain measures of tolerance or toxic reactions. The following studies profile the toxic response in the rat model were performed.

Materials, animals and methods: The material tested was a specially formulated protein-stabilized silver solution called Mild Silver Protein. It was supplied by Discovery Experimental and Development Incorporated, Wesley Chapel, Florida, USA 33543. Standard Wistar rats were obtained from Harlan Sprague Dawley, housed in plastic cages with automatic watering system and were fed Ralston Purina Lab Chow 5001. To obtain a sensitivity or a toxicity profile, using a minimal number of animals, a staged experimental approach was used. Dose finding experiments employed increasing doses covering low to high exposures. The animals were either injected via tail vein or exposed by addition of the silver preparation in the drinking water. The animals were weighed daily and examined for gross pathological features.

Toxicity tests: The experimental conditions and results are given in the reports from Dr. Renlund and reiterated here in brief.

Test 1: (DCM report, 26, July 1994)

Ten rats ranging in weight 176 - 200 grams were divided into 3 treatment groups, A, B and C, with 3 animals each and one served as an optional control. A single dose, 1 ml of 0.15, 0.075 and 0.015 mg/ml Mild Silver Protein Solution was administered using the tail vein.

The animals were observed for an 8 day period and neither clinical nor behavioral signs were seen.

Test 2: (DCM report, September 2, 1994)

Ten rats ranging in weight 176 - 200 grams were obtained from the supplier noted above and divided into groups A, B and C with 4, 4 and 2 animals in those groups. Individuals were marked and received 1 ml of 0.15, 0.015 mg/ml Mild Silver Protein solution in group A and B respectively, daily for 12 days, by injection via tail vein. The 2 animals in the control group, C were sham injected with 1 ml of normal physiological saline.

There were no observable clinical or behavioral signs after the 12 day exposure period.

Test 3: (DCM report, December 15, 1994)

Eighteen rats were divided into a treatment group comprising 15 individually marked animals that were fed with Mild Silver Protein solution in drinking water (1.5 ppm) over a 40 day period. Three animals were fed regular drinking water and served as controls. All animals received normal rat chow (see above) and were weighed daily.

After the 40 day period none of the animals showed clinical signs, abnormal behavior or gross pathological features.

Test 4: (DCM report, January 2, 1995)

In a high dose study 6 rats were divided into 2 groups of 3 animals each, groups A and B respectively. Animals in group A received 1ml of 1.5 mg/ml Mild Silver Protein solution by injection into a tail vein, 3 times a week for 4 weeks, which is 18mg total for rats weighing about 300 grams. The control group B, received sham injections at the same time schedule. The animals were weighed at regular intervals.

Over the treatment period there were no clinical signs and no gross pathological changes associated with the chronic intravenous injections were observed.

This report is based entirely upon the data provided by Dr. Renlund, Director of the DCM (For details see data provided by Dr. Renlund).

N.B.: At the highest dose (18 mg / 300 gram rat) there were no observed adverse effects within the treatment period; the data does not permit us to make a statement regarding the metabolic fate of the silver. If these data can be extrapolated to the human scale, then a 60 kilogram individual would have to be given 3,600 mg (3.6 gram) to receive an amount equivalent to the test animals (rats). This corresponds to the injection of 1 ml of a solution containing 300,000 ppm of Mild Silver Protein.

John Barltrop

M.A., D.Phil, D.Sc.

* 1-ml containing 300,000 ppm is equivalent to injecting 84.5 bottles of Ag-CIDAL in an individual weighing 132 pounds.

** Dr. Barltrop formulated Ag-CIDAL. He was a professor of Biochemistry at OXFORD UNIVERSITY until his retirement.

TEMPLE UNIVERSITY
A Commonwealth University

School of Medicine
Department of Microbiology
and Immunology

Philadelphia, Pennsylvania 19140
(215) 707-5203
Fax: (215) 707-7788

March 20, 1995

James T Kimball
Discovery Experimental and Development, Inc.
29949 S. R. 54 West
Wesley Chapel, FL 33543

Dear Mr. Kimball:

My laboratory has studied the effects of Special Formulation of Mild Silver Protein on human immunodeficiency virus type 1 (HIV-1) survival and on latency reactivation of HIV-1 in the human lymphoblastoid B cell line, M57 3 The results of our preliminary experiments are presented in the two tables below. Table 1 shows the viricidal properties of Special Formulation of Mild Silver Protein while Table 2 shows the ability of Special Formulation of Mild Silver Protein to inhibit latency reactivation of HIV-1 from M57 3

TABLE 1 In vitro viricidal properties of Special Formulation of Mild Silver Protein on HIV 1 III B strain after one hour treatment with Special Formulation of Mild Silver Protein at 37°C as measured by syncytia formation on SupT1 cells.

Concentration of Special Formulation of Mild Silver Protein in parts per million (PPM)	Dilution of HIV-1 which Induced Synoytia Formulation on SupT1 cells			
	10^{-1}	10^{-2}	10^{-3}	10^{-4}
None	+++	+++	++	+
1000 ppm	0	0	0	0
100 ppm	+	0	0	0
10 ppm	+	0	0	0
1 0 ppm	++	++	+	
0.10 ppm	+++	+++	++	

The results the above experiment show that exposure of HIV 1 to 1000 ppm of Special Formulation of Mild Silver Protein for one hour at 37°C completely eliminates infectious HIV 1 as measured by syncytia formation on SupT 1 cells. Exposure to between 100 ppm and 10 ppm for one hour at 37°C significantly reduces HIV-1 infectivity as measured by syncytia formation on SupT1 cells.

TABLE 2 In vitro effect of Special Formulation of Mild Silver Protein on Recovery of HIV-1 from latently infected Lymphoblastoid B cell line MS7-3.

Concentration of Special Formulation of Mild Silver Protein in parts per million (PPM)	Number of Lymphoblastoid Cells required to induce Syncytia Formation when cocultured with SupT1 cells			
	10^5	10^4	10^3	10^2
None	+·+	+++	+-	+
1000 ppm	0	0	0	0
100 ppm	0	0	0	0
10 ppm	0	0	0	0
1.0 ppm	++	+-	+	+
0.10 ppm	++±	+++	+¬	+

These experiments above show that exposure of Human Lymphoblastoid B cells latently infected with HIV-1 strain IIIB to special formulation of mild silver protein at 1000 and 100 ppm eliminates latently infected HIV-1 as measured by the ability of the Lymphoblastoid cell to form syncytia when cocultured with SupT1 cells. Exposure of Lymphoblastoid cells to 10 ppm of special formulation of Mild Silver protein significantly reduces their ability to form syncytia when cocultured with SupT1 cells.

Take together these new in vitro results on the viricidal (anti-HIV-1) properties of Special Formulation of Mild Silver Protein and the ability of Special Formulation of Mild Silver Protein to inhibit latency reactivation in a human lymphoblastoid cell together with our previous results on inhibition of HIV-1 replication in vitro demonstrate some of at the invitro bioactive properties of Special Formulation of Mild Silver Protein. A possible future avenue of research could be to determine whether Special Formulation of Mild Silver Protein has synergistic or additive effects against HIV-1 in vitro when combined with approved therapeutic AIDS drugs such as Azid deoxythymidine (AZT) or Interleukin 2 (IL-2)

Sincerely,

Earl E. Henderson, Ph.D.
Professor

416

TEMPLE UNIVERSITY
A Commonwealth University

School of Medicine
Department of Microbiology
and Immunology

Philadelphia, Pennsylvania 19140
(215) 707-3203
Fax: (215) 707-7788

February 2. 1995

Dr. Paul Farber
Route 13
Box 1923
Highway 105 East
Conroe. Texas 77303

We are sending you our recent result on mild silver protein received from Mr. Kimball.

We tested the ability of mild silver protein to inhibit human immunodeficiency virus type 1 (HIV-1) replication in the human T cell line. SupT 1. as measured by syncytia formation. We found that mild silver protein inhibited HIV-1 replication in SupT 1 cells as measured by a reduction in the appearance of syncytia in cell culture. There appeared to be little if any acute toxicity associated with the dose of mild silver protein which inhibited HIV-1 replication (See Table 1 below).

Table 1

INHIBITION OF HIV-1 (IIIB)

Replication by mild silver protein as measured by syncytia formation in SupT 1 cell cultures.

TREATMENT	SYNCYTIA	TOXICITY
NONE	+++	-
Mild Silver Protein 1.500 ppm		
1/10 dilution	None	Toxic
1/100 dilution	None	Toxic
1/1000 dilution	0	None
1/10000 dilution	12	None
1/100,000 dilution	++	-

Mild Silver Protein
10,000 ppm

1/10,000 dilution	None	None
1/100,000 dilution	+	None

As you can see mild silver protein inhibited HIV-1 replication in SupT 1 cells at about 1.5 ppm without significant toxicity towards the cells. These results are very encouraging and suggest additional experiments that could be done. Please let me know if you would like additional tests done and whether I can be of any help to you in your plans to develop these compounds.

Sincerely,

Earl E. Henderson
Professor

PERSONAL TESTIMONIALS

JDV/FL

27 February 1995

Dear Dr. Farber,

It is with the greatest pleasure that I think back to when I met you after one of my lectures in Texas. We had a wonderful talk together. You asked my about Lyme Disease and told me a little about your research work.

Now I am excited to see what you have done since we met two years ago and to see the success that you have had with your findings. I am very happy that you have kept me informed and I am sure that your research will take you further and help others in more ways than one.

Please keep me informed and I shall do my very best at this end to do what I can for you.

Meanwhile, I wish you all the best.

Kind regards.

Jan DeFries
(Dictated by JdV - signed by secretary)

December 27, 1995

To: Dr. Paul Farber

Dear Dr. Farber:

Jack has had medical problems for close to two years. Although we do not know what caused them, he was in Kuwait after Desert Storm, working for a private company in construction. He was there for nine months, many times coming across bunkers with dead Iraqis in them, as well as breathing the oil smoke.

Shortly after coming back to the United States, he started developing fevers, aching, trouble sleeping, loss of balance, fainting, and total lack of energy. These symptoms increased to the point of Jack's being unable to work at all for the last two years. On four separate occasions, he reached a fever of 105+ and was hospitalized for one week each time. The fevers were coming on anywhere from 12 to 15 times a day. He was in bed most of the time. He went through Mayo Clinic for six weeks and they were unable to diagnose his symptoms. He found a doctor who gave him many dollars worth of vitamins and put him on an I.V. vitamin cocktail. This worked for two to four days at a time but not consistently.

Through referrals, one being with Dr. Dwarte, we were able to find you, Dr. Paul Farber. Jack has been on Mild Silver Protein for approximately eight weeks. Jack is now working 10 hours a day, six days a week. His feeling of well being has returned, although he is still somewhat tired (which we attribute to his lack of exercise the last two years).

We are, of course, extremely happy and have high hopes that the previous condition or symptoms will never return. We can only attribute this to Mild Silver Protein.

Sincerely,
DeAnna

April 22, 1996

To Whom It May Concern:

I am going to share a short story about some trauma my husband, Jack, and I have experienced in hopes it may help some of you out there.

Right after Desert Storm, Jack spent about nine months in Kuwait, returning December of 1990. In May of 1991 he lost a kidney due to cancer. Shortly after, he started developing short lasting fevers several times a month. He then developed benign masses in his chest which had to be removed. The fevers persisted in 1992, increasing to several times a week. During the next few years, Jack had several angioplasties. We were wrong in thinking this would stop the fevers. They increased to the point of his being hospitalized on four separate occasions, for a week each time, with temperatures of up to 105°. The hospitalization, along with heavy antibiotics, managed to lower the temperatures but the fevers persisted ranging from 101° to 103°, sending him into uncontrollable shaking, sweating and shivering. They would last one to four hours and were so frequent, for two and a half years, Jack was lucky to spend one hour a day out of bed. The fevers would leave him in a totally exhausted state and I could tell it was getting to him mentally. He also had periods of loss of balance and began fainting. We were spending thousands and thousands of dollars trying to find out what was wrong with him. We tried heart, cancer, diabetes (Jack is diabetic), contagious disease and every other specialist we could find. They took out his gall bladder, not it. They took out his spleen, not it. He tried holistic doctors and chelation. Didn't work. He spent six weeks in Mayo and ended up with a huge bill and a letter stating, "We are unable to diagnose Jack's medical condition."

In October of 1995, during my desperate researching of everything I could find, I was referred to Dr. Paul

Farber in Kingwood, Texas. He was kind enough to spend several hours on the phone with us, listening patiently to all Jack had been through. He then explained what he thought was Jack's problem and we purchased $700.00 worth of silver protein, "The Micro Silver Bullet." I have to admit, we were very apprehensive, having been through so many failures, but we were ready to try anything. Last October Jack started the silver protein, taking it religiously twice a day. The fevers started to subside. He had another angioplasty on October 20, 1995, and left immediately to work out of state on a temporary assignment. He encountered some tough days, but the fevers were subsiding more all the time. In February of 1996 Jack was offered a good position overseas. The fevers were all but gone, having one occasionally. He came home to pack. One more setback! The angioplasty had failed and Jack had a quadruple heart bypass on February 12. He came through with flying colors and three weeks to the day, March 4, Jack left for an overseas job.

He is so happy to be able to work and he has had no fevers for the last month.

We are both so thankful for Dr. Farber and the Micro Silver Bullet. Jack now has his life back and I have a healthier, happier husband whom I love very much and whom, for awhile, I thought I might lose.

Sincerely,
Deanna Frazier

TO WHOM IT MAY CONCERN:

I had been exercising in the morning to rehabilitate a muscle I had pulled earlier in the year and walked in the wind from my car to the fitness center. When I got home I took a nap after lunch and when I awoke I began sneezing. I figured it was an early spring allergy after watching the news and seeing the pollen count for Cedar and Elm was up. I sneezed almost uncontrollably that evening and all day Saturday using a full box of Kleenex and my left eye was nearly swollen shut – both eyes were red and itchy. I decided Friday evening to take a teaspoon of Mild Silver Protein – holding it under my tongue, swishing around my mouth and swallowing. On Saturday morning I used eye lotion made with clustered water formula and took another teaspoon of Mild Silver Protein, and repeated this Saturday evening. I was afraid I would be unable to attend church on Sunday, but after using the eye lotion again Sunday morning and taking another teaspoon of Mild Silver Protein, my eye looked presentable and my sneezing had ceased. I was able to sit through the service without a sneeze for which I and my sore back muscle were very grateful. By Monday I had no sign of allergy.

I have allergy and "Hay Fever" every spring – sometimes lasting a week or two. This is the fastest I have every had it stop and the itching around my eyes is completely gone.

Sincerely,

Bernice R. Launius

To Whom It May Concern:

I am so happy that I was introduced to Mild Silver Protein July 1995. I was suffering from an eye infection in my right eye.

I went to the ophthalmologist and he gave me some antibiotic eye drops to put in my right eye. I followed the directions and put the drops in my eye. The infection seemed to have gone away, but about ten (10) days later, the infection reoccurred in my left eye. Then about every ten (10) days my eyes would flare up again. Then someone introduced me to Mild Silver Protein.

I talked to Dr. Farber and asked him if I could put Mild Silver Protein in my eyes. Dr. Farber said yes, because they use a form of this in newborn babies' eyes.

My husband put a drop of Mild Silver Protein in my eye right before I went to sleep. The next morning my eye lids were crusted together and I needed to use a washcloth to cleanse the area around my eye. **After that my eye infection went away and has never reoccurred!**

Again I am so happy that I know about and have used Mild Silver Protein.

Sincerely,

Yvonne Schnitzer
Houston, Texas

Dr. Paul M. Farber,

I've had problems with my complexion since I was 11 or 12 years old. By the age of 14 my minor acne problem had left me with many physical scars on my face and back. I was diagnosed by this time as having cystic acne by one of my many dermatologists. My acne was not the typical teenager's acne. I had a number of painful sores on my back and face that would not heal for months. I was prescribed many different prescription medications including three cycles of *Accutane* (one of the strongest known acne medicines). Nothing, including a number of topical lotions, helped my situation. I even tried holistic medicine that worked only for a short time.

I had almost given up by the age of 24 until I tried Mild Silver Protein. I was to be married and wanted to have a reasonably clear face on my wedding day. I started using the silver about a month before my wedding and within two weeks I saw a great improvement. My face and back had cleared up and the onset of new problems had ceased. I do still have a small blemish every now and then, but not the painful sores that I remember from before. I continue using the silver product in small amounts every day to continue my success with my acne and to help with any other bacterial obstacles I may encounter.

Thank you for introducing me to your product and I wish you continued success with The Micro-Silver Bullet.

Sincerely,

Linda K. Anderson

Dear Dr. Farber,

I want to thank you for your BLESSED Nutritional Advice. As a DIABETIC now for more than 10 years, I have heard of how I should be taking Chromium Picolinate to help reverse my condition. My problem was that it hurt too much to take the Chromium Supplement. I mean sharp biting pains in my feet, each and every time I attempted to do the right thing. Consequently, I had given up on my best option. I didn't Want to; I just didn't like the pain!

I want to tell you Dr. Farber, that I had my doubts as to whether your recommendation would be beneficial. Now, I just Praise GOD; you were Right On! You prescribed the Chromium Picolinate in a tablet that ALSO contained THE TRACE Mineral Vanadium. You commented to me that these are the TWO MINERALs that All Diabetics are severely deficient in, and which are Absolutely Necessary for the Proper Functioning of the PANCREAS which is the organ which is responsible for regulating the BLOOD SUGAR of the Body and which when functioning properly produces INSULIN Naturally through the Islets of Langerham. Also when it is not functioning properly the result is first HYPOGLYCEMIA (Low Blood Sugar) which can then lead into DIABETES (Hyperglycemia). By taking the Chromium along with the Vanadium, I was able to digest the Chromium with NO PAIN; but that's only half the story. After four or five months of taking this mineral combination, I decided to test the waters again, and try the Chromium Picolinate by itself. To my satisfaction, I was able to make a painless transfer, which at the time saved two-thirds of the cost because you had not yet combined them into one formula.

Also Doc, I want to thank you for recommending DHEA to me. I had been consuming eight or nine Tylenols a day for foot nerve pain until you told me about DHEA. From day one of being on DHEA until now (approximately one year) DHEA has solved my problem, and has proved to be a wonderful Natural Pain Killer for me, PRAISE GOD. Now from further information you have given to me, I realize that DHEA is the Master Adrenal Hormone that is produced by the cortex of the Adrenal Gland. From my new understanding, I realize that it balances out the entire Hormonal System which is why it helps Diabetes so profoundly. Although it was not necessary for me to be on insulin, I now understand from your research that a person who is insulin dependent is able to produce their own insulin because their pancreas is now working properly as a result of the vanadium. From what you have explained to me, this formula should also help JUVENILE DIABETES since that is a form of DIABETES in which the Islets Of Langerham of the pancreas no longer produce insulin. You made the comment to me that I was perhaps the FIRST PERSON IN THE WORLD to be HEALED from DIABETES. I know that you cannot say it because of certain FDA Legal Restrictions, but I as a Spirit Filled Born Again Messianic Rabbi can. I feel that the LORD GOD IN HEAVEN and HIS SON JESUS CHRIST has used me as A WITNESS TO ALL OF THE OTHER DIABETICS IN THE WORLD, AND THAT IS WHY THE LORD ALLOWED ME TO BECOME THE first human being to be _CURED_ FROM THIS Devilish Scourge called DIABETES. What a Marvelous, Wonderful GOD and SAVIOR we have, full of COMPASSION, GRACE, FORGIVENESS, and MERCY. That is why I feel that he healed a Messianic Jewish Rabbi because in his wisdom he knew that I would become a WITNESS UNTO THE WORLD, and I will. I pray that you will put this letter into your new book, "THE MICRO BULLET." I have read your other book, "THE MICRO SILVER BULLET," and I understand that THE FATHER IN HEAVEN and HIS SON JESUS CHRIST has fulfilled their Promise and Prophecy to you which was made when you Died and went to Heaven for a five-minute period and met the LORD, and that literally thousands of HIS CHILDREN have recovered from Lyme Disease and Candida Yeast Infection, and that you have documented 15 recoveries from the AIDS VIRUS, *PRAISE GOD.* What a Wonderful Testimony that the LORD is showering HIS GRACE and MERCY upon the WORLD in these LATTER DAYS before YESHUAH HAMASSHIACH'S *SECOND COMING. How Grateful I am to be a part of this WITNESS and TESTIMONY.*

I understand that now due to the Fantastic Results which I received through our experimentation that you have gotten together with Jeff Lioon from a 30-year-old World Recognized Nutritional Laboratory and have Engineered and Developed a New Formula called GLUCOBAL which is short for GLUCOSE BALANCER which is a Premium Glucose Balancer, from you INITIAL INVENTION of a Formula which combined the DHEA (Dehydoespiandrosterone), the Chromium Picolinate and the Vanadium. I also understand that you are coming out with a GLUCOBAL PLUS which will contain all the other Nutritional Vitamins and Minerals that DIABETIC needs to be completely HEALTHY and also a NUTRITIONAL DIET PROTOCOL for DIABETICS to follow. *PRAISE GOD,* THERE IS NO DOUBT IN MY rabbinical mind THAT the LORD is not only using your KNOWLEDGE as a Researcher, Scientist, and Physician, but also your DEEP BELIEF in JESUS CHRIST not only as your LORD and SAVIOR but at the MESSIAH which he promised the Jewish People, and which your Namesake PAUL and his Physician Companion, LUKE, also brought to the Gentiles.

With Praise To God

Rabbi Gus Elowitz

Rabbi Gus Elowitz

Susan Diehl
736 Indiana Ave.
Glassport, PA 15045

Dear Dr. Farber,

In 1988 I was diagnosed with severe psoriasis. As a result of this disease I also have arthritis and fibromyalgia. I have been on everything from antibiotics to high doses of premisone to methltreate (a form of chemo) and nothing has worked. Most of these treatments made matters worse. In July of this year I started taking Mild Silver Protein and 7 Strain Multiple Probiotic Acidophilus. After only two weeks I started noticing changes in my skin. Prior to taking this regimen I was in constant pain. Now, after three months of using these products, my psoriasis is 90% cleared and I am pain-free.

Sincerely,

Susan Diehl

Susan Diehl

Silver Testimony

Patrice Winowich
1744 Timothy Drive
West Mifflin, PA 15122

Dear Dr. Farber

My husband and I have been taking the Mild Silver Protein for two months and it has helped me with my yeast infection as well as my allergies and asthma. My asthma was so bad that I had enrolled in a program at the University of Pittsburgh for an asthma study. After two weeks of being on the Silver, my asthma symptoms were so reduced that I canceled out of the Pitt study. When I called to cancel, they asked my why and I told them about the silver and they couldn't get me off the phone fast enough! I guess they are afraid to find a cure because they would have to cancel their research program. My husband also found improvement for throat congestion by using the silver. Thank you, Dr. Farber, praise God.

Patrice Winowich
Attended seminar at Monroeville Raddison
July 13, 1996

CURRICULUA VITAE

Dr. Willy Burgdorfer
Scientist Emeritus, NIAID, RML

Ph.D., University of Basel, Switzerland
Tropical Institute, Basel Switzerland
(Parasitology, Helminthology, Tropical Bacteriology)

<u>Honorary M.D. Degree</u> (Doctor medicina honoris causa),
University of Bern, Switzerland, 1986
<u>Honorary Life Membership</u>, American Society of Rickettsiology, 1986
<u>Honorary Life Membership</u>, International Northwest Conference on Diseases in Nature Communicable to Man, 1987

—Received Janggen-Poehn Fellowship, 1951
—Postdoctorate Research Fellowship, USPHS, 1952-1953
—Guggenheim Fellowship, 1964-1965
—DHEW Superior Service Award, 1974
—President, American Society of Rickettsiology, 1982
—Recipient of the Schaudinn-Hoffmann Plaque, 1985
—Received the 1988 Robert Koch Gold Medal (November 1988)...in recognition of the discovery of the pathogen (Borrelia burgdorferi) causing Lyme Disease
—Received the 1989 Bristol Award from The Infectious Diseases Society of America, recognizing his career reflected in major accomplishments and contributions to the acquisition of knowledge and its dissemination through teaching in an area of infectious diseases
—Awarded an honorary Doctor of Science degree by Montana State University in recognition of a long career of scientific achievement (1989)
—Received the Walter Reed Medal for outstanding contributions to tropical medicine (1990)

—Awarded an honorary medical degree (Doctor honoris causa) by the Medical Faculty of the University of Marseille in recognition of his scientific contributions to the epidemiology and ecology of arthropod-borne rickettsial diseases, and for his discovery of the causative agent of Lyme disease and related spirochetal disorders.

Member: Royal Society of Tropical Medicine/Hygiene
American Society of Tropical Medicine/Hygiene
American Society of Parasitologists
American Society of Microbiologists
American Society of Rickettsiology

Margret H. Bayer, Ph.D.
Senior Research Associate
Fox Chase Cancer Center

M.S. honors in biology, University of Hamburg
Plant Biology, Microbiology–Post graduate studies in Plant Physiology and Microbiology
Dr. rer. nat., Biology, University of Hamburg
Dr. rer. nat. habil., Dept. Biology, University of Hamburg–Field of Specialization: Plant Physiology

—Fellow, American Academy of Microbiology
—Member, Editorial Board, J. Bacteriology
—Fellow, Royal Entomological Society of London
—NSF and NIH Outside Reviewer
—Habilitation, University of Hamburg
—Damon Runyon Fellow

—American Society for Microbiology
—American Society of Plant Physiologists
—Royal Entomological Society of London
—International Soc. Study of Comparative Oncology
—Scandinavian Soc. for Plant Physiology

—Published more than 80 research papers, chapters and
articles in peer-reviewed journals and books

—Biographies cited in: Who's Who in America
Who's Who of American Women
Who's Who in Science and Eng.
American Men and Women of Science
Who's Who in the East

Helen R. Buckley, Ph.D.
Professor, Temple University
School of Medicine

University of London, Faculty of Medicine, Ph.D.,
Medical Mycology

—Fellow, American Academy of Microbiology
—Sigma Xi
—Fellow, Infectious Disease Society of America
—Editorial Board, *Clinical Microbiology and Infectious Diseases*
—Chair, Microbiol. Test Committee, Natl. Board of
Podiatry Examiners
—George A. Sowell Award for Excellence in Basic
Science Teaching, Temple University School of Medicine
—Lindback Award for Distinguished Teaching
—President, Medical Mycological Society of the Americas
—Published in over 65 publications

Lee H. Lorenzen, Ph.D.
Resonant Cluster Technology

Dr. Lee Lorenzen is the inventor and developer of a
variety of nutritional products created with resonant
cluster technology. He is the discoverer of the cluster
template induction process. He has a Ph.D. in

nutritional biochemistry and is licensed in clinical nutrition with the American Licensing Board of Nutrition. In February 1991, he became a founding member and Vice Chairman of the Japanese American Resonance Research Society, Tokyo, Japan.

Dr. Lorenzen is a member of the German American Society for the Advancement of Biological and Oxygen Therapies, Bad Fussing, Germany. He is also a member of the Price Pottinger Nutrition Foundation, San Diego, California. He has written and narrated twelve 30-minute videos on nutrition and prevention for the general public and has lectured extensively on the life sciences in 42 states and 25 countries. He is a sought-after speaker on stage, video and television.

Dr. Lorenzen has published articles on resonant field theory and the Russian culture in *Proceedings of the Western Pharmacology Society, Life Sciences* (London), *Food Technology–Japan, Up-To-Date Food Processing*, and *La Vie Japan.*

Dr. Lorenzen's work is widely known in Asia and he is widely recognized in Europe and around the world for his work in cluster resonant water technology. He was recently honored at the University Of Paris and also the University of Oslo, Norway. In Norway, he was awarded an Honorary Doctorate Degree in Medicine for developing alternative therapies in the healing arts.

Dr. Lorenzen received his M.A. in biology from California State University, Fullerton and his Doctorate in nutritional biochemistry at the Metropolitan Collegiate Institute, London, England. He has written numerous articles that have received worldwide recognition.

PERSONAL HOLISTIC DIARY

The Herxheimer Reaction:
A Small Price...A Big Reward!

What is our primary goal with respect to the use of Mild Silver Protein? It's simple: to kill the spirochetes that cause Lyme Disease and to also destroy the microorganisms associated with Candida Yeast Infection. Unless all (100%) of these microorganisms are completely eradicated, they will most likely regenerate and recreate these two diseases. This is the problem with conventional antibiotics: they don't kill **all** of the spirochetes and bacteria, due to *mutations* that have occurred. It has been proven that a remnant of these microorganisms hide in the deep fibroblast of the muscle tissues and in the organs such as the heart and liver. Mild Silver Protein, however (as opposed to conventional antibiotics), destroys them all.

That's the good news. The not-so-good-news is that when a spirochete or yeast cell is killed it emits waste products which are highly toxic and can make one feel nauseous, irritable, itchy, headachy, and generally uncomfortable. This process is called a *Herxheimer Reaction,* named after its discoverer. This reaction is part and parcel of the use of conventional antibiotics. However, the good point about Mild Silver Protein is that it generally *does not* cause a severe Herxheimer Reaction. The reason for that is that the microorganisms "suffocate" and pass out of the body very quickly, before they dissolve and contaminate the blood stream. An additional bonus is that Candida Yeast cells are also destroyed in the process.

After ridding the body of harmful spirochetes and bacteria through the use of Mild Silver Protein, it is imperative to replace the "good bacteria" (acidophilus) by eating yogurt or taking acidophilus tablets or both. In the meantime, if a Herxheimer Reaction does occur, there are methods that can lesson the severity and extent of the reaction.

Thanks to Dorsey Moonen at the Conroe, Texas Health Food Store, I was made aware of the neutralizing effect which the element Molybdenum has upon the typical Herxheimer Reaction. All a person has to do is take a mineral product containing Molybdenum. This really can be a great help! Thank God for health food stores, where one can find a storehouse of invaluable and helpful information.

I have also observed another event that is notable of mention. When an individual takes Mild Silver Protein for other reasons...such as the common cold, the flu, or one of the other 650 uses...they can have a mild Herxheimer Reaction, which could very well be attributed to the destruction of Candida Yeast Infection which they didn't even know they had. This phenomenon could also occur to a person who is infected with the spirochetes that cause Lyme Disease and don't even know they have the disease.

Note from Dr. Farber:

The great news to all of this is that if a Herxheimer Reaction does occur, it is a *positive diagnosis* that the harmful organisms that have invaded the body are being destroyed!

It is also important to remember to take "grapefruit seed extract" along with the Mild Silver Protein because it absorbs so quickly that although it kills all the yeast cells in the body, it could bypass some in those in the gastrointestinal areas.

An additional side bonus – many patients that are taking Mild Silver Protein for various diseases are reporting that if they have an acne problem, it is clearing up. We also found that even long standing cases clean up even more quickly when applied 3 times a day externally in addition to the internal dose. If all of the side effects of medicines in the world were this great, this would be a "Heaven sent Gift."

A MIGHTY VISION
MOSES AND JESUS CHRIST
MOSHE RABBINU AND YESHUA HAMASHIACH

A *VISION* in many ways is like a *NEAR DEATH EXPERIENCE* in that one does not choose to have one. It chooses to have him. I in no way chose to *DIE FOR A 5-MINUTE PERIOD AND BE ESCORTED BY GABRIEL AND TWO OF HIS ANGELS INTO THE KINGDOM OF HEAVEN* nor did I choose to be *SLAIN IN THE SPIRIT* and have a *HEAVENLY VISION OF MOSES AND JESUS* appear in the HEAVENS while I was driving my automobile down the highway. Perhaps the television series *HIGHWAY TO HEAVEN* starring Michael Landon before his passing was ready to take on a Whole New Significance in my life. Truly I was on the HIGHWAY and I was through MY VISION being escorted to a *HEAVENLY VISION* of two *SPIRITUAL BEINGS* who are playing a Tremendous Significance in My Life and my Life's Work for the Lord.

I was traveling on a freeway not far from my home listening to Praise Music on my stereo and praying to MY FATHER IN HEAVEN, HIS SON JESUS CHRIST, and the HOLY SPIRIT when in a Flash of a Moment I felt and experienced my SPIRIT and MY SPIRITUAL EYES being elevated into the Heavens. I had no trouble continuing to drive my automobile as the Holy Spirit guided me to be able to function on two Planes Of Consciousness at the same time, the Physical Plane and the Heavenly Spiritual Plane. Through the Beautiful White Clouds there appeared before me a *MIGHTY VISION OF MOSES AND JESUS* approaching me together in order to *DELIVER A MESSAGE OF GUIDANCE* in answer to a Prayer for Guidance which I was Deeply In Need Of.

Moses's Right Arm was wrapped around Jesus's Shoulders and I had a flash of Jesus for a moment appearing like *A DIVINE LIGHTNING ROD* in Moses's

Hand. What did all this mean? Why was I having this Mighty Vision and why were Moses and Jesus appearing together right before my Spiritual Eyes?

Then Moses began to speak to me saying the following words: "When you died and were escorted to Heaven My Brother and Lord and Savior Jesus made you aware that HE and HIS FATHER'S Children were in a state of MODERN DAY SLAVERY and that HE would use you as HE once used me in a different situation in Egypt to help free its Children from this MODERN DAY SLAVERY. The FATHER GOD gave to me a ROD through which flowed all His Divine Powers and it was through His Power and not Mine that all of the Miracles which took place Freed The Children Of Israel from Pharaoh's Ruthless Grip. In the same manner, it will be through *OUR FATHER GOD'S POWER*, not your own that he will free HIS CHILDREN of the LATTER 20th and EARLY 21st Century from the Modern Day Pharaohs. Do not worry or concern yourself as to how this will be accomplished despite the Goliath Size of the Enemy. Just as MY FATHER fave me a ROD to channel HIS POWER to free the Children Of Israel which HE did, HE has given to you MY BROTHER PAUL a ROD. This ROD is not made of wood. This ROD is the *POWER OF OUR LORD AND SAVIOR JESUS CHRIST AND ALL OF HIS ANGELIC HOST.* All the POWERS AND PRINCIPALITIES which your NAMESAKE PAUL spoke of in Ephesians as well as their Earthly Counterparts who are men and women who have chosen Satan's Ways instead of THE WAYS OF OUR FATHER AND SAVIOR shall be defeated just as Pharaoh and His Armies were defeated in MY DAYS. There will be Many Miraculous Events of Modern Day Plagues just like the "10 PLAGUES" in Egypt laid upon the POWERS AND PRINCIPALITIES working through the Evil Men of these MODERN DAY SPECIAL INTEREST GROUPS.

On Mount Moriah The FATHER GOD *TESTED* His Servant Abraham's Faith and Obedience by requesting him to sacrifice his Only Son Isaac. Moses was also **TESTED** like Metal in a Fire when Pharaoh exiled him from Egypt into a desert with no supplies that he may perish. After Jesus received The Holy Spirit through His Baptism with John The Baptist He was **TESTED** by Satan. These were just the beginning of Many **TESTS** WHICH The LORD GOD put before these men who wished to SERVE HIM.

Your author, Paul, is by no means in the category of these Great Men of the Bible, except for one area. He too is being constantly tested.

A PRAYER PSALM FROM PAUL

Heavenly Father, My Lord and Savior Jesus Christ, and Beloved Holy Spirit. Thou does test me Oh Lord as Thou does test metal in a furnace. Let my Faith be Strong and My Devotion to Thee without end that I may prove worthy of the Charge which Thou does put before me. Whether it be Finances, a Misdirected Government, a Special Interest Group, Powers and Principalities, or Satan Himself Grant unto me Strength, Courage, Singleness of Purpose, and Devotion to Thy Will that I might Serve Thee Perfectly with all of my Heart and Soul and Mind. Through the Words of Moses I can hear you say, LET MY CHILDREN GO FROM THIS MODERN DAY SLAVERY that they may have the Freedom to partake of "EVERY HERB BEARING SEED, that they can be Holistically Healthy with a Sound Mind, Body, and Spirit that they may accept the Messiah in these End Times.

"GREAT VISIONS OFTEN HAVE THEIR BEGINNINGS IN SMALL DREAMS."

PUBLISHED ARTICLES
BY
DR. M. PAUL FARBER

SUFFERING LYME VICTIMS...IT IS
TIME FOR ENCOURAGEMENT!

Before it hit me, I thought Lyme Disease was something miners got because they were around *lime* all the time. Can you believe it? But that's how much I knew about this plague when I was victimized around two and a half years ago, even though I have been in the healthcare profession for over a quarter of a century.

And then Lyme disease *struck me down,* causing 85 percent paralysis, joint inflammation, intestinal blockage, muscle disfunction...and a whole lot of pain that was hard for even a healthy 47-year-old to take. I was having trouble breathing, and I almost died, but through the grace of God, determination, and a lot of research, I was fortunate enough to discover **Mild Silver Protein, "The Micro Silver Bullet,"** and I am convinced that I am now totally healed of Lyme disease and that *it isn't coming back.*

If I sound a little excited, it's because I am. I personally *lived* this nightmare. I wasn't on the outside looking in, dispassionately observing and recording the ordeal. I was on the inside looking out...and most of the time the outlook was bleak.

When I first experienced the symptoms, I had no clue as to what had attacked my body (it was Lyme disease). After having tried everything I personally knew to resolve the situation, I went to a neurologist for a complete neurological and orthopedic exam, including a Magnetic Resonance Scan. He concluded that either I had Guillan-Bare Syndrome or multiple sclerosis, or I had suffered a stroke. Bad news is bad news, whether it's multiple choice or not.

In my opinion, Lyme Disease is the great medical imposter and impersonator...too often being diagnosed as something else, which allows it time to strengthen and proliferate in the body.

But, then, one day as I was listlessly bathing, I noticed a lump on my head, underneath my dark and white, thick, hair. On closer examination, I discovered that it was a tick embedded deeply in my scalp. I carefully extracted it, making sure that the head did not remain. I took the tick to a local veterinarian, who advised me to have it analyzed for disease. It was at this point that the puzzle began to come together.

I sent it to Dr. Thomas Craig, D.V.M., Ph.D., professor of the Department of Veterinary Microbiology at Texas A&M University. Sure enough, the verdict was that the tick was *Ixodes scapularis* which carries the spirochete, the causative agent of Lyme disease. I was convinced that I had Lyme Disease. But now what?

Still tolerating vicious symptoms and in excruciating pain, I went to a doctor who prescribed intravenous antibiotics, specifically penicillin and rocephin. This helped, but not a whole lot. My overall improvement was minimal, but, worst of all, I developed chronic side effects, including systemic Candida Yeast Infection, caused by the destruction of "good bacteria" in my body by the antibiotics.

I found myself between the proverbial "rock and a hard place." The more antibiotics I took, the worse the yeast infection got. It was the trap that many Lyme victims find themselves in today. And even when I felt better, I knew the Lyme Disease would re-emerge because the antibiotics kill only about 80 percent of the spirochetes, the remainder of which either hide in the fibroblast of deep muscle tissue or mutate and become resistant to antibiotics.

This was a roller coaster ride going back and forth between Lyme Disease and Candida Yeast Infection, but with one-way ticket: once you get on, you can't get off. I didn't want any part of it–no way! And neither do the thousands of others in this country and around the world!

I had to find something better. Being a physician, scientist, and researcher, I began a meticulous search for a cure for this great imposter and impersonator: Lyme Disease. Through a series of events I was led to what I call "the *Dead Sea Scrolls of Modern Medicine,*" the "lost" Mild Silver Protein publications of the early twentieth century, which include all microbiological research done between 1900 and 1938 by the top medical doctors, university scientists, and pharmaceutical companies of that time.

I felt privileged to be able to rediscover Mild Silver Protein (now formulated as **Mild Silver Protein**), an extremely potent, broad spectrum natural antibiotic that I believe kills spirochetes, bacteria, viruses, and fungi responsible for over 650 diseases. It was discovered and used by the medical profession over 90 years ago, but it was eventually "shelved" due to the inordinately high cost of producing it (over $400 an ounce), coupled with its extremely short shelf life for week or less. Today through advanced technology, **Mild Silver Protein** can be produced at a reasonable cost ($40 for a 4-ounce bottle, with five-year shelf life), making it accessible to the multitudes who are hurting.

When I think about it, I find it amazing that while everyone seemed to be struggling on the confusing treadmill of synthetic antibiotics, the answer (Mild SIlver Protein) was there "in front of our face" all the time. Sometimes it's hard to see the tree for the forest of confusion that surrounds it. I view this natural antibiotic as the answer that *works!* And fortunately, since it is a pre-1938 antibiotic, it has had FDA approval for almost a century and does not require a medical prescription.

There are absolutely no reported side effects from

Mild Silver Protein (none recorded in decades of use). Recent studies at the University of Toronto concluded that no toxicity, even in high dosages, results from using **Mild Silver Protein.** This antibiotic is attenuated silver that has been broken down, electrically charged, and suspended in mild silver protein solution, having been reduced in microscopic silver particles smaller than 0.001 microns in diameter (smaller than a virus or bacteria). Mild Silver Protein interferes with metabolism of oxygen by microorganisms, causing them to suffocate. Recent testing at the Fox Chase Cancer Center in Philadelphia revealed that "mild silver protein solutions reduce the growth of spirochetal cells significantly and eventually lead to cell death."

I began taking specific dosages of **Mild Silver Protein** as soon as I could, and the results were dramatic. In fact, I am totally free of Lyme Disease symptoms. I underwent a spinal tap at the neurological department of Parkland Hospital in Dallas, and no spirochetes that cause Lyme were found. I believe that it kills them all, including the spirochetal mutations (they can run, but they can't hide).

I have done considerable additional research on this natural antibiotic, conferring frequently with knowledgeable people in the field, including two years of interaction with Dr. Willy Burgdorfer,the doctor and scientist who discovered and pinpointed the spirochete as the causative agent of Lyme Disease. Dr. Burgdorfer encouraged me to get this information to the population as soon as was feasible, and he is optimistic about the program. He is contemplating conducting additional research at the Rocky Mountain Institute in Montana on the effect of **Mild Silver Protein,** on spirochetes in animal populations.

I am extremely anxious to get this information to as many Lyme disease victims as possible, because I believe it will bring a revolutionary, long-awaited solution to pain and suffering, both here and around the world. *It certainly worked for me,* and now that I know the answers detailed in my book *"The Micro Silver Bullet,"* I don't want anyone to go through the pain and suffering I went through. If I would have had my book, which is just being published, I would have been well in two to three months, rather than two or three years. But I must be careful in this communication process, basing it on providing responsible, quality information and on encouraging natural, non-invasive holistic healthcare procedures.

It is important that Lyme Disease patients be totally informed in order to make an intelligent decision on the intake of a medicine or other healing agent. My book provides additional information about this remarkable discovery, including a detailed account of all Natural Holistic Methods which I used to keep me functioning and free of pain during my illness. The book explains Mild Silver Protein and its unique critical formulation. Mild Silver Protein in any lesser and inferior form may not work effectively.

I will be writing an article every month for the L.D.U. and I welcome questions from Lyme sufferers and physicians. One of the topics John Park Trowbridge, M.D., and I plan to address is the use of Mild Silver Protein intravenously.

I look forward to keeping in touch with readers interested in Mild Silver Protein and to help Lyme victims move out of their present nightmare.

BEYOND COLLOIDAL SILVER

After rediscovering "THE DEAD SEA SCROLLS OF MODERN MEDICINE," I came to the conclusion that since the conventional antibiotics consisting of both Penicillin and the Cephalosporin, Rocephin were unsuccessful in helping me to recover from both Lyme Disease and Candida Yeast Infection, I needed to pursue a different route. Since in the early 1900's, Colloidal Silver was the treatment of the day for Gonorrhea and Syphilis and since Syphilis was caused by a Spirochete just as Lyme Disease was, I deduced that if it worked for the Spirochete that caused Syphilis it should also work for the Spirochete that caused Lyme Disease. The Spirochete that caused Syphilis is called Trepodema Pallidum and the Spirochete that causes Lyme Disease is called Borrelia Burgdoferi, so it was just a different Spirochete.

I tried about half a dozen different Colloidal Silvers which were out on the market. I did get better results than the conventional antibiotics but not complete and conclusive results as I still had symptomatology. I came to the conclusion that I was on the right track, but there were some important elements still missing. Being a scientist and researcher I began working with several laboratories to re-engineer the Colloidal Silver into a Mild Silver Protein that was technologically more advanced than any Colloidal Silver which had been previously manufactured. Before I could re-engineer the Colloidal Silver, I had to first determine why the Silver Formulas which I had previously tried were ineffective. I then worked with fellow scientists who were biochemists, and we analyzed these different formulas in the laboratory.

For liability purposes I will not discuss any particular brand name. Instead I will discuss in general the properties which separate a highly effective Mild Silver

Protein such as Mild Silver Protein which I was instrumental in engineering. Below I will list the problems which I uncovered in my research on Colloidal Silver Formulas.

1. Many of the formulas had too many Parts Per Million (PPM) such as 100, 300, 400 and 500. Some had too few PPM such as 3-5 PPM which are too weak and are ineffective.

2. Many of the formulas had too large a Micron Size per particle. Some had micron sizes ranging from 0.5 up to 1.0 and greater. Mild Silver Protein is .001 Microns.

3. Most all of the formulas contained Nitrites and Nitrates which are toxic and slow down the effectiveness of the Silver just like a pebble or a slight degree of curvature will slow down one of those Japanese Super Trains that usually go a thousand miles per hour when nothing interferes.

4. Most all of the formulas had an excess of sodium causing them to have an unbalanced ph, which was much too basic.

5. Many of the formulas were not suspended properly and had a tendency to come out of the solution and settle at the bottom of their containers.

6. Many had an extremely dark or gray color which indicated improper formulation due to Micron sizes which were too large and too many PPM.

7. Due to personal interactions and experiences with some of the companies that produces Colloidal Silver, questions were raised in my mind concerning moral integrity and ethics as well as their purpose for being involved in the field. Was their purpose merely profit oriented or were they humanitarian in their intentions. In my opinion the consumer must separate greed from good.

8. Many are made through a chemical process which is too harsh.

LYME DISEASE AND CANDIDA YEAST INFECTION: TRADING ONE DISEASE FOR ANOTHER

It's a roller coaster ride with a one-way ticket: once you get on, you can't get off.

That's generally the way it is when Lyme Disease is treated with conventional antibiotics, which kill about 80% of the spirochetes causing this plague, but which also destroy the "friendly bacteria" in the body. This naturally occurring "friendly bacteria" keeps the yeast microorganisms (which also occur naturally in the body) in check, not allowing them to over-populate the system.

When I was struck down with Lyme, I went through the standard antibiotic regimen (penicillin and rocephin). They helped, but not much. I knew that the disease was still there as I went through continuing relapses and more excruciating pain. I was perplexed and getting desperate.

But then, through God's marvelous grace and a lot of research, I was privileged to "discover" Mild Silver Protein. I took this natural antibiotic with dramatic results, and in time I believed that Lyme disease was history in my body.

Eventually, through additional research and a meticulous diagnosis by my friend John Parks Trowbridge, M.D. (author of *The Yeast Syndrome*), I learned that I had succumbed to a full-blown *Candida albicans* yeast infection after taking the antibiotic for Lyme Disease. Up to that point, my only experience with yeast (which is a living microorganism from the vegetable kingdom) was athlete's foot and vaginal infections in female patients.

I also learned what had caused the *Candida*–oral and intravenous antibiotics which had been prescribed for the Lyme disease. (Yeast infections can also be caused by birth control pills and sulfa drugs). The bottom line was that the "cure" was worse than the disease. Who could have predicted that an accepted, prescribed medical treatment of antibiotics would open the door for another disease that was quite possibly more devastating than the first?

This is no way an indictment of modern medicine which has saved countless lives. What I am saying is that you cannot disturb the balance of nature without suffering the consequences.

The major problem is that most physicians today do not recognize the symptoms of and correctly diagnose *Candida* yeast infections, and they assume that the continuing, persistent symptoms are still being produced by Lyme Disease. Then they will probably prescribe even stronger doses of conventional antibiotics, which will destroy even more of the "friendly bacteria" and allow the *Candida* yeast cells to multiply even more rapidly and further intensify the symptoms. It's a dead-end ride that never reaches a conclusion.

Although chronic yeast infection is generally not fatal, it will (like Lyme) make a person extremely sick. Also, the yeast microorganisms attack the brain and nervous system and can affect a person mentally as well as disrupt normal production of endomorphins (hormones that keep you feeling good when they are in abundance). I believe that the vast majority of people who have suffered and been treated for Lyme Disease will also have contracted a *Candida albicans* yeast infections.

But in the final analysis, there is new hope for victims of Lyme disease and *Candida albicans* yeast infections: Mild Silver Protein. When initially taken at the onset of Lyme Disease, this broad-spectrum natural antibiotic will not affect the "friendly bacteria" as drastically, thus making it easier to overcome *Borrelia burgdorferi*. If, however, synthetic antibiotics have been used. Mild Silver Protein can be taken to eradicate the yeast microorganisms that are the culprits in *Candida*. In the event that there is a mild "Herxheimer reaction," which may accompany the death of the yeast cells, there exists a holistic formula for neutralizing this effect. This is explained in my book, *Mild Silver Protein*.

It is most critical that a non-invasive, holistic dietary program of replacing the "friendly bacteria" in the body be undertaken immediately. This is also described in my book. The body and its immune system must be restored to a high state of health in order for it to function properly.

Please read the following lab report concerning the *in vitro* testing of the Mild Silver Protein on *Candida albicans* and *Cryptococcus neoformans*. (The Cryptococcus microorganism is what causes spinal meningitis in AIDS patients and is responsible for approximately 50% of all AIDS deaths).

PERSONAL HOLISTIC DIARY

What's The Essential Ingredient That is Causing such a Stir Both Inside and Outside the Medical Community?

What we have unfolding before our very eyes is a totally different approach to solving the dilemma of Lyme Disease and Candida Yeast Infection, the second and third largest epidemics in the world, respectively. It's called NATURAL MEDICINE, which is holistic healthcare in its purest and unadulterated form. It accomplishes its goals of alleviating suffering in the world in *perfect order* , through the application of God's own laws of balance.

But Natural Medicine, for the most part, has gotten a "bad rap" through the years. Supposed "esoteric truths" and emotional hype, along with Disney-like fantasies, have clothed it and given to it a superficial personality that many find objectionable. If you don't believe me, just walk into any health food store (as I have been doing for the past 30 years), and observe with a discriminating eye the unscientific philosophical claptrap, suggestive packaging and numerous books which may take you on a trip through "Alladin's Magic Kingdom"...but in the end will leave you just as sick and not much better off than when you began the journey.

The key then is to not "throw out the baby with the bathwater" when attempting to understand Natural Medicine and to appreciate it for what it is: the application of existing natural laws to achieve a balanced program of health through the use of organic and inorganic substances of Nature for the purpose of healing the body, mind and spirit. That's not so hard to understand.

As for my part in the approach to freeing people from the symptoms of Lyme Disease and Candida Yeast Infection, I can only explain it the way it was explained to me by Dr. Robert Mendehlson, my close friend and mentor: "I do not treat infectious diseases. I treat people. I use my scientific knowledge and training to help my patients achieve "homeostasis" a natural balance in the healthy body." One of the factors involved in this process is the use of Mild Silver Protein, a dietary mineral supplement. If during a treatment sequence with Mild Silver Protein (which is a dietary mineral supplement) a particular virus, bacteria, yeast, fungus or spirochete is eradicated, it helps the recovery process immensely. Such is the case with Lyme Disease and Candida Yeast Infection. I have helped "balance" many people over the years to a finely tuned point, but I have never *healed anyone.*

Only God can heal, and He does that through His natural laws and substances, which when followed and utilized bring health, happiness, prosperity and long life. When they are broken, they bring sickness, disease, death and destruction.

Physician Leads "National Healing Experience" On "Hour of Power" Program

(reprinted with permission from Dr. E .A. Taub)

Note from Dr. Farber:

For the past three years, I have had the privilege of following the Hour of Power ministry. On November 6, 1994 I saw Dr. E.A. Taub on the show and was very impressed with his presentation, especially in light of the fact that he is a national spokesman for the American Medical Association. He was presenting, via his book *The Wellness Rx*, many of the holistic methods which I have advocated for over 30 years. I contacted Dr. Taub and asked that he become a part of this book...and he was very open, very cordial and quite knowledgeable.

I would encourage those who read this book also purchase and read a copy of *The Wellness Rx*, available at most bookstores.

Edward A. Taub, M.D., a pioneer in the American Medical Association's effort at "Telemedicine" and Medical Advisor of the Feeling Fit...FOR LIFE! Centers, administered a wellness prescription to the nation on the Rev. Dr. Robert H. Schuller's "Hour of Power" television ministry on November 6.

The Wellness Rx is the title of Dr. Taub's new book now in its third printing by Prentice Hall. This family physician and board-certified pediatrician led an "Hour of Power" television audience estimated at up to 20 million viewers in a "Wellness Vaccination." Dr. Taub says the 7-day self-treatment program he initially developed to help smokers quit, will also work for stress management, backache relief, overcoming insomnia, defeating depression and losing weight.

Following the production of the program, Dr. Schuller praised Dr. Taub "for sharing with so much forthright simplicity, sincerity and eloquence."

"I know that our millions of viewers will be very deeply moved when they hear more about your new book *The Wellness Rx*," he added.

The "national healing experience" administered by Dr. Taub as he appeared with Dr. Schuller, isn't the first national telemedicine prescription administered by physician-author Taub. He is the National Spokesperson for the American Medical Association's 1994 "How to Quit" National Wellness Stop Smoking Campaign–the first national stop smoking program to be reviewed and approved by the AMA.

Dr. Taub is now conducting the largest physician's "housecall" in history to show smokers how to quit–via the powerful medium of telemedicine–on CNBC and on videotape. "How to Quit" represents the first use of television to deliver proven stop-smoking programs directly to smokers' homes.

The November 6 "Hour of Power" featured Dr. Taub conducting the actual 90-second emergency stress and healing meditation approved by the AMA for nicotine de-addiction.

Dr. Taub explains that beloved physician Dr. Jonas Salk, who developed the first polio vaccine in 1954, suggested the original concept of a "wellness vaccination" to him. Dr. Salk reviewed clinical results presented by Dr. Taub at the National Academy of Sciences in 1984, demonstrating how the mindsets of 2,000 children and their parents in his medical practice had shifted from illness to wellness "by promoting personal responsibility, self value and reverence for life."

"My Rx has no shots, no pills and the side effects are all positive!" Dr. Taub says. "This Rx is for people who are well and for people who are sick and tired of being sick and tired."

THE 31 NEEDS OF LIFE

Dr. E. A. Taub

1. Good Air.

2. Pure Water.

3. Comfortable Temperature.

4. Internal and External Cleanliness.

Unhealthy food taken into the body will foul it up and lead to sicknesses, diseases and degeneration.

5. Adequate Sleep.

Precious nerve energy is generated by the brain under the condition of sleep as well as the recuperation of other energies and faculties.

6. Love and Appreciation.

Loveless and unappreciated individuals are unhappy, usually lonely, often bored, and thus sink into a mire of depression, despondency and despair. Lack of love usually arises from poor health practices that make the individual vitiated and unhealthy, hence less than appreciable and lovable.

7. Foods of our Natural Disposition

Our natural biological diet predominately consists of raw fruits and vegetables with some nuts and seeds. Realistically that is very difficult. We encourage a striving towards this ideal and advise against cooked foods predominating one's diet.

8. Vigorous Activity or Exercise.

The rewards of exercise are enormous, especially mental acuity. No one can achieve health without being fit and capable.

9. Sunshine and Natural Light.

If you want a sunny disposition, work and play in sunlight and natural light as much as possible.

10. Play and Recreation.

Mental and physical games do indeed, re-create and tone up all faculties.

11. Rest and Relaxation.

The body recuperates much of its expenditures while resting and relaxing

12. Emotional Poise and Stability

Your feelings are begotten by your practices and life circumstances. Make your physical and mental conditions right--cultivate a positive, helpful, sharing and loving disposition--and your feelings will be happy, and, in fact, euphoric.

13. Pleasant Environment.

That which is good for us is pleasant, serene and harmonious. That which is bad for us is usually ugly, upsetting and repulsive.

14. Gregariousness.

15. Security of Life and Its Means

Unless we are secure in our persons and are reasonably assured of the needs of life for ourselves and family at the very least, insecurity results which stresses us, robs us of well-being and contributes to vitality-sapping concerns.

16. Creative, Useful work.

Humans feel good about themselves when they can fend for themselves and supply their needs by their own creative efforts.

17. Self-Mastery or Self-Control

If you understand what makes you and the world tick--If you have knowledge of causes and their effects--if you sense where people are coming from, this awareness will liberate your mind and put you in control of yourself. You'll be rationally directed rather than emotionally and impulsively tugged hither and thither, most often to your great detriment.

18. Self-determination or Personal Freedom or Individual Sovereignty.

Humans do not thrive if oppressed. They must be free in their persons from all unnatural compulsions and inhibitions.

19. Inspiration, Motivation, Purpose and Commitment.

Aimlessness gives rise to hopelessness and dissipation. We need goals in life to achieve our highest potential.

20. Expression of the Reproductive Instincts & Drives

21. Satisfaction of the Aesthetic Senses.

This is above and beyond a pleasant environment. We require extraordinary beauty in our artistic and cultural objects.

22. Self-reliance or Self-confidence.

We must feel ourselves adequate to cope with life situations.

23. A Good Self-Image or having a Sense of Self-Worth.

Having a feeling of importance in the order of things contributes mightily to our sense of well-being.

24. Humor, Mirth and Merriment.

Laughter, hilarity, humor and good fun contribute to good health. Those who does not have a sense of humor have a strike against them in the game of life. Research and studies have established the great value of humor to human well-being and happiness.

25. Music.

While this is within the realm of the aesthetic senses, the power of music which we appreciate, which arouses and inspires us, and which elicits fountains of hope and optimism, transcends the aura conjured up by aesthetic considerations.

26. Peace, Harmony and Tranquility.

States of war, strife, turmoil, conflict and fighting disturb, distress and destroy our sense of well-being. Hence, harmony and serenity must pervade our lives.

27. Thought, Cogitation and Meditation.

Though we have well-developed brains, precious few of us engage in profound thought or reflection. Too many of us are given to superficial rote invocations, instead of carefully and logically considered thoughts. Too many of us operate on energy-draining emotions rather than thoroughgoing reflection which gives rise to reassuring insights, understanding and self-mastery.

28. Smiling.

Perhaps the most contagious influence in the world is a smile! Smiling normally reflects a sense of inner contentment, happiness and wonderful well-being. A smile not only evidences your attitude of friendliness and caring, but communicates a message that warms those who observe it, engendering in them much the same feelings.

29. Friendship and Companionship

Really, these needs are implicit within the frame work of gregariousness, and love and appreciation which have been previously touched upon. This is meant to reinforce the need for close friends and at least one best friend whom we can confide and interact with.

30. Amusement and Entertainment.

While this need is implied and impinged upon in other needs considered, it is, nevertheless, helpful to spell it out. The word amusement means without thought. The average Americans spends hours daily before a TV set, at the movies and as a spectator to amusing events. This can be both beneficial and demeaning. While amusement does set aside our fears, worries and adverse concerns, most of it is superficial and dissipating. Little of it inspires, motivates, exalts or involves involvement. Involving yourself in amusing and entertaining others is perhaps more wholesome than being amused. We should go for participation rather than mere spectatorship. A creative hobby in which you take pride, like musical performances, music appreciation, games, competitive sports, and many other engrossing pursuits develop us into giant personalties. Interesting pursuits absorb us as nothing else can. They develop us so that we are more appreciated, admired and loved.

31. Fasting.

In view of today's exigencies which stress and depress us, insufficient elimination of our own wastes arises. Fasting is a beneficent measure that enables the body to catch up on its cleansing and homework. The body is a virtual panacea under the condition of the fast. Among the many benefits begotten by the body while fasting are detoxification, restoration, resolution of almost all diseases, even if pronounced "incurable," remarkable rejuvenation and extension of a perpetually younger appearance. Fasting should only be undertaken with the knowledge of your health practitioner of choice and under supervision.

POEMS

A TRIBUTE TO DR. WILLY BURGDORFER
GRANDMASTER OF LYME
The Discoverer of Borrelia Burgdorferi
The Causative Agent of Lyme Disease

"In the Battle Lines"
The Battle Field of the Body

Oh spiral Borrelia burgdorferi
An unwelcomed guest are thee
In the tick of nature you tarry
Like an ambush hiding in a tree

Warm blood of life you seek free
Unwilling host attached like feed
Spiralling like a turbulent galaxy sea
Hungry to consume bore and breed

Comes like an invader an unwelcomed guest
To invade–to ravage–to digest–and to eat
Human life so precious–God at His best
Unwilling to sacrifice my own human meat

Live your life in the balance of nature
All life is free to grow and to breed
But invade not God's created human creature
Destroy not in His image and human seed

Oh invading spirochetes Borrelia burgdorferi
A Ten Commandment–"Thou shalt not kill"
The human being–a Divine Holy sanctuary
No mercy–capital punishment– your bill.

Army of Mild Silver Protein the blood in my veins
Antibiotics join forces with white blood cells
To destroy the invader and stop all its gains
Bring life back to normal–restore and make well

To balance and neutralize with holistic ease
All systems all organs all glands and all cells
To restore to normal to cajole and appease
Bring back the ring of health a crisp clear bell

Oh spirochetes with power I slay thee today
A new body holistically free healthy and strong
New cells regenerate to create life inside
I pray no more crying–suffering–sorrow only joy and song

AN ODE TO DR. PAAVO AIROLA

Eight and sixty years ago in Europe we're told
In Kareia Finland a small place here on earth
A prodigy child forth and life did unfold
Seeds of young Paavo's roots were given their birth

Within this child a young genius did grow
A thinking mind of philosophy, music and art
Little premonition did young Paavo's parents know
That he would be honored and distinctly set apart

Emerging from World War Two's destructiveness
Tired mentally, unhealthy, and physically in pain
To Sweden he was led to Are Waerland the nutritionist
To learn the laws of nature that makes man's life sane

As a student and disciple Paavo's life did change
No drinking or smoking or unhealthy animal meats
Vegetarianism, fasting, and natural foods increase his range
As he developed a Health System to accomplish his feat

Science is important if man's knowledge is to expand
Biochemistry and nutrition this man Paavo did know
He worked and studied and developed concepts in his hands
From which the art and science of Biological Medicine did grow

A journey of travel would lead to intellectual wealth
Central America, Russia, Mexico, Australia, and Japan
A study of the centenarians and exceptional people of health
To learn the common factors of long living in man

Airola believed that man has a purpose on Planet Earth
To be spiritually, emotionally, and psychologically whole
Through Holistic Philosophy his research gave birth
To the Airola Optimum Diet that restores body, mind, and soul

Paavo said exercise, have proper attitude and peace of mind
Seek a life free of stress, unhappiness, worry and fear
If man would remove doubt and tension he would find
That life will become precious, healthy and dear

More important to him than material success and professional wins
Greater than the rewards of fame in the world or glory
Paavo fathered five children and seventeen grandchildren
Knowing that the wealth of family was man's most precious story

Fifteen widely read books on nutrition he did write
International best-sellers in seven languages abound
For the humanitarium health and welfare he did fight
Never shy or afraid top speak the truth through his sound

An artist, musician, and author as strong as the wind
Lecturing to layman and doctors with minds yearning to learn
Founding the International Academy of Biological Medicine
Teaching his pupils to think, evaluate, and discern

Paavo you said the world was still a jungle nutritionally
That even with all your efforts man was still blind
No one man can change the world but you taught thousands to see
And their hearts and minds lies your legacy's sign

On the deep ocean a last sharing aboard a beautiful ship
You said your work had been completed and done
Speaking with premonition about no fear of death in man's last trip
You with love bowed your head to the Father and
                        ASCENDED TO THE SUN...

                    With love and respect from
                    your student and friend,

                    Dr. Paul Farber with inspiration
                    and love from his wife
                    J. Marie Farber

All I have seen teaches me
to trust the Creator for all
I have not seen...

– Ralph Waldo Emerson

Let nothing disturb thee
  Let nothing dismay thee
    All things pass
      God never changes

Patience attains all that it strives for
  He who has God
    Finds he lacks nothing
      God alone suffices

Lord

make me an instrument of Your peace.
Where there is hatred, let me sow love,
where there is injury, pardon; where
there is doubt, faith; where there is
despair, hope; where there is darkness,
light; and where there is sadness, joy.

O, Divine Master, grant that I may
not so much seek to be consoled as to
console; to be understood as to understand; to be loved as to love; for it is in
giving that we receive; it is in pardon-
ing that we are pardoned; and it is in
dying that we are born to eternal life.

– Saint Francis Of Assisi

References
(Not Otherwise Noted)

Louis Reik, Jr., M.D. *Lyme Disease and the Nervous System*

John Parks Trowbridge, M.D., Dr. Morton Walker, D.P.M., co-authors of *The Yeast Syndrome,* Bantam Books, 1986

T.H. Anderson Wells, *Lancet,* 1918

Sir Malcom Morris, *British Medical Journal,* 1947

J. Mark Howell, *British Medical Journal,* 1947

Science Digest "Silver, Our Mightiest Germ Fighter," 1978

Stephen A. Levine, Paris M. Kidd, Allergy Research Group

Time Magazine, "Revenge of the Killer Microbes! Are we losing the war against Infectious Diseases?", 1994

Newsweek Magazine, "Antibiotics, The End of Miracle Drugs, 1994

Rocky Mountain News, "Bacteria Becoming Untreatable," 1994

Houston Chronicle, "Medical Disaster Seen," 1994

Houston Chronicle, "Disease Causing Bacteria Becoming More Violent." 1993

Houston Post, "AIDS Survey Reduces Estimate of Infection," 1993

Cleve and Campbell, "Diabetes, Coronary Thrombosis, and Saccharin Disease, 1966

Dr. Robert Schuller, *Power Thoughts*

Hal Lindsey, *Planet Earth–2000 A.D.–Will Mankind Survive?,*Western Front, LTD, 1994

468

Alan R. Gaby, M.D., "The Hormone That Does it All," Holistic Medicine, Spring 1993

Julian Whitaker, M.D., *Health and Healing,* February 1994

Deepak Chora, M.D., *Ageless Body, Timeless Mind,* Pgs. 165-167

Dr. Charles Atkins, *Health Revelations,* January 1994

Dr. Vincent Glanpapa, *Muscle Magazine,* April-May 1994

Amber Rose, L.A.C., L.C.S.W., *Bee In Backache,* December 1993

Charles Mraz, "Bee Venom for Multiple Sclerosis," American Bee Journal, 1993

Pat Wagner Waldorf, "Got M.S. use B.V. Therapy," American Bee Journal, 1993

Alex Duarte, O.D., Ph.D., *How To Obtain Miracle Medicines Off-Shore Legally,* 1993

Alex Duarte, O.D., Ph.D., *Jaws For Life, The Story of Shark Cartilage,* 1994

Health Food Businesses, "Coenzyme Q-10 (Co-Q-10), 1987

POEM
unknown author

GOD GRANT ME
THE SERENITY TO
ACCEPT THE THINGS
I CANNOT CHANGE, THE
COURAGE TO CHANGE
THE THINGS I CAN,
AND THE WISDOM
TO KNOW THE
DIFFERENCE.
AMEN

Live today as if you're
going to die tomorrow;
Learn today as if you were
going to live forever.

Dr. Paul

In Conclusion...

Berkley Bedell was appointed by the President of the United States to serve on the NIH, National Institute Of Health, Special Committee to find Alternative Natural Holistic Methods that could bring the cost of Health Care down dramatically in this country.

In Berkley Bedell, the American people have a real fighter and advocate for rights to the healing tools of Holistic Health Care and Natural Medicine. Having been a former victim of Lyme Disease who found relief through holistic methodologies, he is quick to champion the cause...and very quick to point out that Natural Medicine is not only extremely effective, but could save the country millions (if not billions) of dollars.

During the question and answer period at the end of the lecture, I stood up and told Congressman Bedell who I was, what I had been through and the effectiveness of Mild Silver Protein. I then asked him how to get this vital information into the right hands at the higher echelons in Washington, including the President. He surprised me by stopping his presentation, walking down from the podium, pulling out his wallet...and then handing me his personal calling card. He then said: "When your book is complete and you have all the proper documentation that you speak of, call me and I will take it from there." I intend to do just that.

It's one thing to have something in your possession that can quite literally change the face of healthcare in this country and around the world. It's another thing altogether to *make it happen*. Opposition is everywhere, especially from the entrenched governmental bureaucracy and the medical and pharmaceutical establishment who are profiting greatly from the status quo (things as they are). This opposition to the introduction and acceptance of anything new and innovative (and inexpensive) in healthcare is oftentimes reflected in Washington through proposed legislation to stymie meaningful change and to further restrict new products and methodology.

Bringing about substantial change in the *mindset* of the medical profession, as well as the powerful political establishment...is a monumental task. And after you've accomplished that, the word has to filter down to the man and woman on the street who should be on the receiving end of the benefits of Natural Medicine. It's a real challenge.

If the American people could just become knowledgeable of all the wonderful and often miraculous natural healing substances presently available through numerous Health Food establishments (as well as new innovations) and learned to apply them properly, then many of the ailments of mankind could be substantially alleviated or brought under control in a reasonably short period of time.

Let's make it so. Get involved in order to protect your constitutional rights to the availability of new, safe and proven products that could drastically change your health and your life.

The Micro Gold Bullet Conquering Mental Illness and Arthritis and also Certain Inoperable Cancers according to Dr. Edward H. Ochsner, M.D., B.S., F.A.C.S., Utilizing Colloidal Gold and Natural Holistic Methods

The Micro Gold Bullet
Conquering Mental Illness Utilizing
Colloidal Gold & Natural Holistic Methods

Exodus 32:15-20 NIV

When Moses approached the camp and saw the calf and the dancing, his anger burned and he threw the tablets out of his hands, breaking them to pieces at the foot of the mountain. And he took the calf they had made and burned it in the fire; then he ground it to a powder, scattered it on the water and made the Israelites drink it.

Dr. Farber's Commentary

At this point in Biblical History the Children of Israel had just been delivered by God through Moses's hand from four hundred years of slavery in Egypt, truly enough to make any human being mentally ill. Instead of showing patience and gratitude to God for their deliverance, in their depleted mental state they rebelled and disobeyed the Lord by creating an idol, the Golden Calf. God had just given the Children of Israel the Ten Commandments which were written by the Hand of God on two tablets of stone.

When Moses saw how the Children of Israel had sinned in their depleted mental state his anger burned and as stated in Exodus 32:15-20 NIV, "And he took the calf they had made and burned it in the fire; then he ground it to a powder, scattered it on the water and made the Israelites drink it." The question could then be raised; why did he make the Israelites drink this Liquid Solution of Gold. I believe that God in His Divine Wisdom knew the Calming Healing Effects which GOLD had upon the human mind. If he could get their minds more mentally clear, then perhaps they would see the wisdom in Repentance, which many of them did come to. Perhaps this Biblical Event was a foreshadow of the Beneficial

Healing Effects of Gold on the human mind. As a result of the lightning in the electrical storms which surely were present and the fact that the gold of which the calf was burned, this gold could have been in a Colloidal State and reduced to microscopic particles and suspended in a solution of pure water. By the Israelites drinking it, this solution would have gone immediately to work on their minds and thus their mental state.

Colloidal Gold, What Is It?

"Colloidal GOLD is simply the pure element GOLD and pure water. The GOLD is in ionic form. Those ions are about one billionth of a meter in diameter, which is so small that for them to move one quarter inch would be equal to going about eleven hundred miles. No physical machine or any other means could grind the GOLD so small. In the natural world only plants can produce GOLD in such small particles as colloidal GOLD. They do it the same as when they produce iron. They take the metallic iron from the soil which our bodies cannot use and change it into the ionic or colloidal form which we can use. (Eat your spinach!) The particles are so small they will stay in suspension in pure water indefinitely.

Just as you would never chew nails to get your iron, you should never take GOLD in metallic form...it can be toxic, causing problems in digestion, kidneys, and more. While metallic GOLD in foil form is used all over the world to help arthritis sufferers externally, no doctor would ever use it internally in metallic form.

Colloidal GOLD is made by a very technical electro-colloidal or electrolysis method that passes pure (triple deionized) water over .999 fine GOLD that is charged with frequency/high voltage electricity. GOLD ions are driven off the GOLD into suspension in the water which is then treated with Ozone (oxygen) and passed through a powerful magnetic field. The result is simply pure GOLD in pure water.

Another form of GOLD that is indeed used internally is GOLD cyanide salts which is created by dissolving GOLD using two very powerful acids. The resulting salts have produced some spectacular results, especially with arthritis sufferers, but is used only as a last resort because of the possible toxic side effects of the salts. Results of GOLD salt injections typically went as follows: Of every six patients, one would have to stop the injections because of side effects. Of the five that continued, one had no effects whatever, three were benefitted, and one was completely healed. (The arthritis was not reversed, but all pain and other evidence of active disease was stopped.)

This is indeed the same kind of GOLD that everyone thinks of when you say GOLD. It's chemical symbol is Au. It's atomic number is 47; it's atomic weight is 197. It is one of the heaviest metals with a specific gravity of 19.3, meaning it is 19.3 times as heavy as water. It is the most ductile and malleable of all metals. It can be beaten into sheets so thin it would take 300,000 sheets to make a pile an inch high. A single ounce can be drawn into a wire so thin it would be over 50 miles long. Ninety to ninety-five percent of the world's production is used for reserves to stabilize the world's currency. About half of the balance is used for jewelry, one fourth in the electrical industry, and about ten percent in the dental industry. Out of the tiny amount left over we get our GOLD for medical purposes but the tiny amount has had tremendous benefits for those who will use it in colloidal form.

History

GOLD has had more to do with the development, direction, and quality of human civilization through the millennia than any other element. It has caused nations to rise and nations to fall. It caused the rapid expansion to the west in America because of the GOLD rush frenzy such as the California, Yukon, and Black Hills GOLD rushes.

The effect of GOLD on individuals has been just as dramatic as it's effect on civilizations. Medieval alchemists spent many personal fortunes trying to turn base metals such as lead into GOLD. While out of their work sprang modern chemistry, the main goal of creating GOLD was never achieved...at least no one has admitted to it. The legends and stories of lost treasures and lost GOLD mines still fire our imaginations.

The use of GOLD for healing and control of pain has long been told in folklore and legends but the earliest documented use in modern medicine was in 1890 when Dr. Robert Koch discovered that the Tubercle bacillus could not live in the presence of GOLD. GOLD was then quickly found to be of benefit in all the conditions listed below. The use of GOLD to treat arthritis has been continuous since 1927. The ancient alchemists equated GOLD with the essence of sun, warmth, life in the earth, life force, ego, blood, etc. When we see the benefits of using Colloidal GOLD we can believe that perhaps those ancient scientists knew more than we have ever suspected until now.

How Can It Be Used?

All of the uses of Colloidal GOLD have not been found. As colloidal technology advances, it will revolutionize the way we have been using mineral supplements in the past. Medical science has proven beyond any doubt that the body can absorb essential minerals in the colloidal form far more rapidly than in the pill, powder or any other form. No one seems to know exactly how GOLD does what it does, but the problem is not whether or not the GOLD ion can help – it can! The problem is getting the little ion to where the problem is. Remember, for a quarter of an inch through flesh is like a person having to walk about eleven hundred miles and do so through a very dense, wet, dark and scary jungle. The solution is to take the recommended dosage topically, internally, or both as your health professional directs until the GOLD arrives at the problem area and has time to do the job.

Already the new, high tech, colloidal technology has put colloidal mineral and trace mineral products into the market that have caused remarkable, even revolutionary results. Colloidal GOLD has taken the place of metallic GOLD and GOLD salts and many believe it is a far better remedy for chronic inflammation, depression, drug and alcohol addiction and obesity. People use it topically for many different skin conditions as well as for problems deep inside muscles, tendons, and joints such as arthritis, bursitis, and Rheumatism. Taken internally at about one half to one teaspoon per day, it can circulate to all parts of the body.

COLLOIDAL GOLD IS NON-TOXIC
Promotes a general euphoric feeling of well being
Stimulates the body's restorative functions
Enhances the body's natural defenses against illness
Promotes vitality and longevity

This is a partial listing of conditions where colloidal GOLD has been used successfully.

- Brain functions
- Depression
- Despair
- Fear
- Frustration
- Drug addiction
- Alcohol addiction
- Melancholy
- Arthritis
- Burns
- Chills
- Circulatory problems
- Digestive disorder
- Gland function
- Heat flashes
- Night sweats

- Sorrow
- Anguish
- Seasonal attitude
  disorder
- Obesity
- Puncture wounds
- Cancer

"While we do not make medical claims, we still want to give this information to be used for educational purposes. We recommend that you consult your health care professional before using COLLOIDAL GOLD either topically or orally." This information was quoted from a leaflet prepared by the WATEROZ company for educational purposes only.

Colloidal Gold
by Dr. Garry Smith, N.D., H.M.D.

History of Colloidal Gold

"Michael Faraday, the English chemist, first produced COLLOIDAL GOLD in a pure state in 1857. It is believed that Alexandria Egypt was the original location where GOLD was first used for medical purposes, although it has been used for centuries by alchemist. During the middle ages alchemists developed an "elixir" liquid gold which purportedly has the ability to restore youth and perfect health. Paracelsus, the forerunner of modern pharmacology was one of the greatest known alchemist/chemists, developed medicines from metallic minerals including GOLD to cure the sick. The Chinese have used GOLD coins for centuries in cooking rice to help maintain the bodies GOLD levels.

What Does Gold Do?

GOLD has strong unequaled effects on the physical body, in health and sickness. COLLOIDAL GOLD was commonly used in the treatment of disease in the United States before 1940 and as early as 1885 for the cure of alcoholism. Additional uses have been found to include treatment of arthritis, skin ulcers, burns and mental conditions.

GOLD does not have the germicidal/antibiotic action of colloidal silver, but it does act on degenerative conditions. It has a balancing and harmonizing effect on the emotional body particularly with regard to unstable mental and emotional states such as depression, melancholy, sorrow, fear, despair, anguish, frustration, suicidal tendencies, or maladies commonly referred to as the sickness of the heart. Aurum metallicum, a homeopathic remedy made from GOLD, is used to treat people in a suicidal state. GOLD has a direct effect on the rhythmic, balancing, healing activity of the heart and helps improve blood circulation. It is highly beneficial for rejuvenating sluggish organs, especially the brain. GOLD has been used in cases of glandular and nervous incoordination, helping to rejuvenate the glands, stimulate the nerves and release nervous pressure. GOLD is beneficial to the digestive system.

The body's warmth mechanism is positively affected by GOLD, particularly in cases of chills, hot flashes and night sweats. GOLD has been used to treat alcoholism by diminishing the craving and desire.

Used alternatively or in conjunction with silver, GOLD helps strong natural defenses against diseases and promotes renewed vitality and longevity. Silver calms inflammatory conditions while GOLD builds, regenerates and balances. GOLD is used primarily with all types of mental, emotional and physical degenerative conditions. In homeopathic philosophy, it is believed that healing starts with the intellect, then the emotions and finally the physical. GOLD acts very positively on the brain and emotions indicating it is one of the first substances one should take when attempting to heal sickness.

Acupuncturist and Veterinarians who use acupuncture dip their needles in GOLD to help make the acupuncture point work better. It helps increase the energy transfer from the needle to the acupuncture point and increases the effectiveness of the acupuncture treatment. They also use silver, which acts in much the same way. Veterinarians also give GOLD to animals for mental problems. (How they know they have a mental problem is beyond me.)

GOLD works on the mental first, then the emotions, and then the physical. Homeopathic remedies work much the same way. We give Aurum Metallicum (as a homeopathic remedy) for people who are suicidal. It works very well. Again proving GOLD works on the mental.

People who are sick mentally go through various stages of emotional degeneration as follows:

Frustration
Dissatisfaction
Irritability
Anguish
Anger
Rage
Sadness
Fear
Grief
Phobia
Indifference
Apathy
Suicidal

"GOLD helps in all cases."

Good Luck,
Dr. Garry Smith, N.D., H.M.D.

COLLOIDAL GOLD IN INOPERABLE CANCER

by Edward H. Ochsner, M.D., B.S., F.A.C.S., Chicago
Consulting Surgeon, Augustena Hospital

When a patient with inoperable cancer seeks medical aid, there are three main problems which confront his medical adviser:

1. What, if anything, can be done to cure this patient?

2. If cure is impossible, what can be done to prolong the life, strength, and vitality of the patient, so as to make it possible for him to continue his ordinary vocation for a time, at least?

3. If neither cure nor prolongation of life can be accomplished, how can the remaining days of the unfortunate victim of this dread disease be made as comfortable as possible?

During 1924 and 1928 I read three papers on the use of colloidal gold in inoperable cancer, before three medical societies. In all of these articles I stressed the following points. That, in all cases, where the tumor is accessible to the knife or cautery, it should be removed surgically; that, when the condition is hopeless, colloidal gold helps to prolong life and make life much more bearable, both to the patient and to those about him, because it shortens the period of terminal cachexia and greatly reduces pain and discomfort and the need of opiates, in a majority of instances.

In all of my articles I further took the precaution to state, in unmistakable terms, that the remedy was not a cure-all that in my opinion it exerted a selective action upon the cancer tissue and that it would occasionally save the life of a patient who was suffering from cancer and who was otherwise doomed.

Since 1926, my experience with a considerable number of patients suffering from inoperable carcinoma convinces me that the statements made in these articles are very conservative and all well within the facts. This opinion is fully substantiated by scores of unsolicited letters from physicians from every section of this country and Canada, who have written me personal letters at various times stating their experiences with Colloidal Gold in such cases. In making a careful analysis of 50 of these letters, the following interesting facts are disclosed: Twenty (20) letters stated that there was a reduction in the size of the tumor or its disappearance; 30 reported reduction of pain and a considerable number stated that at no time were opiates necessary; 18 stated that the appetite and digestion improved under treatment; 20 reported a gain in weight and strength; 15 believed that it had definitely prolonged the life of the patient; and 6 said that the remedy had apparently resulted in a cure of the condition.

In this connection it is to be specifically noted that the foregoing facts and figures were not taken from answers to a questionnaire, but from general letters written to me by physicians, asking for suggestions regarding patients then under treatment, and incidentally reporting on patients previously treated. In a questionnaire that had been sent out, it is evident that a larger number of answers reporting general improvements would probably have been sent in, as is evidenced by the following short abstracts and quotations from various other letters:

CASE REPORTS

Dr. P.J.M. reports the following: "The patient is doing well, eating well, gaining weight and strength. The blood pressure is much better – white corpuscles increased and hemoglobin higher. Without question his life has been prolonged."

Here is a report from Dr. C.F.S., from far-off Guatemala, Central America: "The patient had in-operable carcinoma of the throat, with excruciating head pains, complete anorexia and insomnia. Shortly after beginning treatment with colloid gold the headache ceased; the appetite returned; sleep became normal; hemorrhages, which had been severe, ceased; the foul odor disappeared and the progress of the disease in the throat was suspended. The patient subsequently died from a hemorrhage."

Dr. C.L.W. makes the following comment: "I have had the opportunity of using colloidal gold in two cases. One has cancer involving the right side of the face. Both are about eighty years of age. In both the destruction of the tissue has continued, yet I am sure that it has been retarded. The special benefit received by these old patients has been their freedom from pain. In all such cases that I have treated before, morphine had to play an important part. No morphine has been used at any time with either of these patients. This has greatly relieved the anxiety of the family, as well as being great comfort to the patients."

Dr. L.H.N. reported a case of papillary adcno-carcinoma of the ovary in the Wisconsin Medical Journal of March 1988; operated upon February 18, 1925. From his published report I take the following: "Surgical treatment consisted in loosening of surrounding adhesions and removal of every part of the tumor mass that it was safe to remove. Fifty-one days after the operation he states that anorexia and constipation were still present, requiring two or three enemas and $1/4$ to $1/2$ gram (16 to 32 mg) of morphine daily. The patient was very much emaciated and cachectic and a tumor mass about the size of a grapefruit was again palpable to the right of the median line. The weight of the patient was less than 100 pounds at the time he started using colloidal gold, which was continued for two years.

One year ago, or nine years after the operation, I received the following letter from the doctor: "Mrs. H. is apparently cured. She weighs 180 pounds and works for others, besides doing her own housework."

Dr. K.F.S. reports the following: "I operated upon a patient for carcinoma of the stomach, doing a gastroenterostomy merely as a palliative, the growth having become too large and with too much involvement in the mesenteric glands to make it possible to do a resection of the stomach. This growth was not only macroscopically a carcinoma of the pylorus, extending over the lesser curvature and into the gastrocolic ligaments, but a microscopic examination proved it to be glandular carcinoma of a rapidly proliferating type. This finding was extremely interesting to me, as the stomach was so badly involved that there was barely room to do a gastroenterostomy, and a resection was entirely out of the question. About a year later the patient died from an intercurrent affection. The postmortem examination of the abdomen showed the gastroenterostomy functioning perfectly and complete disappearance of the cancerous growth."

Such evidence, of which the foregoing is only a small portion of the letters received, simply cannot be disposed of with a leer and smirk, or a "smart-alecky" remark. Can there be any question whose opinion is more trustworthy in such a matter, that of scores of practicing physicians with large clinical experience, or that of one whose clinical knowledge of cancer seems to have been very largely, if not exclusively, acquired by absorption while sitting in a well-cushioned office chair?

AND NOW I WISH TO REPORT A FEW OF MY OWN CASES

Mrs. E.M., age 50, was first seen in October 1927, and operated upon six days later – low median laparotomy.

Both ovaries were nodular, the size of a large grapefruit, and were removed. Several surgically inaccessible carcinoatous nodules were found in the parietal peritoneum. Microscopic diagnosis; papillocarcinoma of the ovaries. She was given colloidal gold for two years. When last examined, seven years after operation, she was found to be in excellent health. No recurrence has appeared.

Every practicing physician knows that whenever there are inaccessible carcinomatous retroperitoncal lymph glands, surgery alone is practically hopeless.

Mrs. M.L.M was first seen in August 1922, at the age of 58 years, when she gave the following history: Nine years previously she had a complete right mammectomy, which was followed by radium and deep x-ray therapy; one year later the entire area was covered with nodules, which were excised; six years ago the nodules reappeared. I started using colloidal gold and the nodules gradually disappeared and remained absent until two years ago, when they again reappeared and were again removed. All three operations were performed by prominent, capable, nationally known surgeons. In each case the diagnoses was confirmed by microscopic examination.

When I first examined the patient on this latest occasion, numerous nodules had appeared again. Colloidal gold treatment was started again, and the past 18 months the nodules have remained stationary. From a letter dated February 11, 1935, I quote the following: "The nodules are about the same. I feel well and my friends say I look extremely well." Dr. C.E.S., the physician who referred this patient to me, makes this observation: "My personal feeling is that Mrs. M. owes her life and present good condition to colloidal gold.

In addition to this case, I have at least four others in whom recurrent carcinomatous nodules disappeared, either temporarily or permanently, under colloidal gold treatment. Every surgeon of large experience knows how fatal recurrent carcinoma of the breast is. Under my form of treatment, the absorption of these carcinomatous nodules in such a considerable number of patients is, I believe, positive proof that colloidal gold has selective inhibitory action upon cancer cells.

Mrs. R. C., age 31 years, appeared for examination in May 1929, and the following history was supplied by the patient: "My mother had bronchitis six weeks before I was born. At birth I was 'choked up' and was ill much of the first three years of my life. At one month of age I had scarlet fever or measles – doctors disagreed as to the diagnosis – chicken pox as a baby; measles at 13. I was vaccinated at 14 and was very ill for three days; had German measles at 16; mumps at 37; and was subject to colds repeatedly, coughing for from four to eight weeks each time. At 20, a suitcase fell on my head from a rack in a railway train, and I have had pains ever since.

"At age 21, I began to have glandular trouble; at 23, removal of glands of the left side of the neck, and an operation on the left scapula, for tuberculosis, were done. At 26 there was an injury to my little finger, which became markedly swollen. At the same time a pimple appeared on the end of my nose and on the chin. At 27 I was referred by my local physician to the then probably most prominent internist in Chicago, for diagnosis and advice. He diagnosed the tuberculosis of the left lung and ordered open windows; tuberculosis of the left little finger, and ordered amputation; and tuberculosis of the skin of my nose and chin. He said that a few x-ray treatment should cure that, and also advised tuberculosis serum once a week.

"During the following three months I had 13 x-ray treatments without lead covers for my eyes or face. Several months later, I had the little finger amputated and an area of my left shoulder excised. A few months later I was sent to a prominent Chicago dermatologist, who diagnosed lupus vulgaria, and I was treated with Alpine light, x-rays, carbonic acid snow, etc. The pain was excruciating and the skin was much worse after these applications, until my whole face, cheeks and chin were raw. During these years, my weight varied between 120 and 180 pounds. One year before seeing you, an ulcer developed on my left cheek, and I again consulted a dermatologist, who diagnosed the condition as malignant."

When I first saw this patient there was an irregular indurated ulcer, about five centimeters in each diameter, involving the left cheek and extending up the left side of the nose, complicated by lupus vulgaria of the whole face, a small area in the lumbar region, one on the gluteal region and one on the left chest. Her whole face was markedly swollen and livid, with fissures about the nose and lips, her weight was about $158^1/_2$ pounds.

I started colloidal gold treatment at once. There has been no recurrence of the carcinoma, and the lupus is apparently checked. The fuarefaction of the skin and face has practically disappeared, although the skin is very strophic and scaling. Her general health and condition are greatly improved, her present weight being 173 pounds. The present condition of the patient can scarcely give an idea of the deplorable state she was in when I saw her for the first time. In this instance, colloidal gold seems certainly to have greatly improved the lupus and possibly to have prevented a recurrence of the carcinoma.

CONCLUSION

One of the purposes of this paper is to repeat the statement previously made that colloidal gold has an inhibitory effect upon cancer growths; and even if our diagnostic methods may, in the course of time, be greatly perfected, there will probably always be hundreds of patients who will delay consulting their physicians until surgical intervention is no longer possible.

In order to secure maximum results with colloidal gold in the treatment of inoperable carcinoma, the following conditions must be fulfilled: The preparation used must be stable, of definitely known strength and the particles of gold must be small and of fairly uniform size; the gold must not be held in suspension by the use of a stabilizer, such as gum arabic, or soluble gold salts, such as chloride of gold. Stabilizers seem to coat the particles of gold and this renders colloidal gold less active; moreover, the soluble gold salts are toxic, while pure colloidal gold is non-toxic, in suitable doses.

In all the cases reported in this article, a colloidal gold preparation which fulfilled the foregoing requirements and which contained 1/500 grain of metallic gold to ten drops was employed. The initial dose was 30 drops in a wine glassful of water one-half hour before each meal, three times a day. This was increased one drop daily to 60 drops at each dose. Nearly all patients tolerated this amount without gastric disturbances. If the tongue became beefy or if the patient complained of burning in the stomach, the dose was reduced 10 drops. This reduction in doses was continued as long as the patient needed colloidal gold. In some cases it has seemed desirable to use the remedy intravenously, in addition to the oral administration. The intravenous dose is 1 to 5 cc, twice a week.

I wish again to emphasize the fact that colloidal gold is not a cure-all, and never was the claim put forward that it was a cure-all, or even a thoroughly satisfactory specific. However, when all other remedies have failed, it will occasionally save a life; if not, it will often prolong life and, still more often, make the last days bearable and quite comfortable for the patient, without the use of narcotics. I maintain that these things are quite worthwhile.

The Lost
Micro Silver Bullet
Chapters

This chapter is dedicated to
Michael Landon "Little Joe Cartwright"

May the knowledge in this book help many
people from dying unnecessarily.

May the Lost Micro Silver Bullet Chapters
be like
the Lost Bonanza Episodes.

SPECIAL NEWS BREAK JUNE 1997

An individual in Canada with Pancreatic Cancer which is
caused by a Virus was given by his doctors only three days to
live. All Medical Attempts to save his life were unsuccessful. A
friend through this book *"The Micro Silver Bullet"* made him
aware of Mild Silver Protein, 2 Tablespoons 3 Times A Day.
After three days the doctors could find no more trace of the
virus in his body. After seven days he was released and the
cancer was gone.

This Book is Being Started During the
Christmas Season 1993 with
A CHRISTMAS PRAYER
FROM THE AUTHOR

As I begin this most important book this December of the Christmas of 1993 with but two fingers as my hands are crippled with but one aspect of the third stage of Lyme Disease, rheumatoid arthritis, and my entire body is being racked by constant debilitating and excruciating pain and I am still partially blind in my left eye, after being totally blind in my left eye, for two months, I dedicate this book as well as all which I have learned to heal myself and accomplish my complete recovery which will be a reality by the time this book is finished to all of the people who have died, been crippled or blinded, or who have suffered the indignity and torment of constant, debilitating, and excruciating pain in addition to the despair of hopelessness and fear of being confronted by a disease, a modern day plague, which seems impossible to diagnose, survive or cure.

I dedicate this book as well as my own life as a physician and doctor to the most important business of all businesses, the business which is exemplified by Christmas as well as Christ himself, the business called humanity and mankind.

There are tens of thousands of individuals throughout the continental United States, Europe, Asia and the world who will be stricken with Lyme Disease as well as thousands of individuals who will die whose families will never know what killed them that this book is designed to help and it will help them. If only one human being's life is spared and returned to him or her then all of the pain and suffering which the author had to learn to endure and overcome so that he might use this first-hand knowledge and wisdom which God has granted to him as a highly trained doctor, scientist, and researcher then this author feels that this life will have granted him the greatest opportunity a man could receive which is to lay down a part of his own life if not all of his life for a brother or sister that they may have life and have it more abundantly.

Introduction

In my own experiences I was unable to find a complete book on the market for the average layperson as well as the many dedicated doctors who would successfully treat Lyme Disease if they just but possessed the knowledge of how to recognize and diagnose it, treat it successfully, and teach future generations as well as this one how to prevent it as well as which health treatment methods can be utilized in order to survive its bizarre and diverse symptomatology. It is my fervent prayer that this survival guide based upon my own personal experiences of how to recognize, survive, overcome and cure this great imposter and imitator of over 25 major medical diseases will restore tens of thousands of people back to a normal, healthy and productive life as well as to prevent literally thousands of unnecessary deaths due to wrong diagnoses and lack of proper treatment just because up until the publishing of this book there was no one text which provided the knowledge and information on this subject available to the average layman as well as their physicians that could be easily understood and implemented.

It is the goal of this book to show those individuals who become infected with Lyme Disease as well as their doctors how to see through this great medical imposter and imitator so that it may be correctly diagnosed in order that the most successful methods of treatment as researched, uncovered, and organized into a complete treatment program by the author in his own quest to save his own life and to heal himself may be begun without delay so that you can avoid the pain, suffering, and

492

possible loss of life and crippling which accompanies this most unwelcome guest. The author, even though he is a physician with over 25 years of experience in the healthcare field, had to blindly search, research, and seek out the answers to this disease from a dense and dark forest of lack of understanding and knowledge on the subject as well as lack of information, incorrect information, misconceptions, and improper attitudes held by uninformed victims of the disease as well as their untrained and uneducated doctors whose hearts and intentions are pure but who lack due to no fault of their own but because of the newness of this discovery of Lyme Disease, the knowledge and methods necessary to both correctly diagnose and successfully treat this great medical deceiver. It is the goal of this author to fill this void and bridge the gap from not having to having the knowledge, understanding, wisdom, and skills necessary to both defend oneself from and defeat this most aggressive and merciless invader.

WHAT IS LYME DISEASE?
The Great Medical Imposter and Impersonator
What Lyme Disease is and What it is Not

When there has been no knowledge of a tick bite or severe exposure to fleas before the onset of neurological symptoms causing an individual to seek out medical care, the following wrong diagnoses are the most common diseases an individual could be labeled with, possibly for life, causing that individual to have a completely incorrect treatment program or perhaps no treatment program at all in the event it is a so-called medically incurable disease.

The results of such a misdiagnose could be any one of a combination of the following tragic scenarios:

1. The creation of iatrogenic diseases (doctor induced diseases) commonly called side effects in the "Physician's Desk Reference" the P.D.R. because of unnecessary drug therapy wrongly prescribed.
2. The unintentional withholding and/or delay of proper treatment for Lyme Disease as outlined in this book resulting in permanent neurological and organ system damage or possibly death.
3. A complete psychological nervous breakdown and unnecessary lifestyle change including dropping out of a normal healthy working lifestyle due to the minds accepting that an individual has a "so-called" incurable disease due to an authority figure physician's unintentional wrong diagnoses.

An incorrect diagnosis may include one of a combination of the following physical and mental diseases. One may also be blinded and experience the indignity and torment of constant, debilitating pain in addition to the despair of hopelessness and fear of being confronted by a disease, a modern day plague, which seems impossible to diagnose, survive or cure.

ORGANIC, STRUCTURAL, and PSYCHOLOGICAL
CONDITIONS AND DISEASES WHICH LYME DISEASE
and
SYSTEMIC CANDIDA YEAST INFECTIONS
IMPERSONATE AS AN IMPOSTER
Misleading All Reputable Diagnosticians
Which Gives Cause
To The Earlier Title Of This Book

"THE TWO GREAT MEDICAL IMPOSTERS
AND IMPERSONATORS"
A Doctor's Personal Experience
and
VICTORY OVER LYME DISEASE
and
CANDIDA YEAST INFECTION

The author wishes to state that MISDIAGNOSES is an EXTREMELY SERIOUS MATTER which can lead to Prolonged Suffering, Increased Pain and Discomfort, Debilitation, and even DEATH.

This book is about to go into great detail not only about how this phenomena comes about and the disasters it brings, but also how to PREVENT it from happening, and HEAL and CURE it after it has unwantingly occurred.

The author wishes also to state that you the reader are in for an EXCITING JOURNEY from the SLAVERY and BONDAGE of the PAIN and SUFFERING of Sickness, Disease, Epidemic, Pestilence, and Unnecessary Death.

To the HEALTH, HAPPINESS, and WELL BEING which can accompany a society who has Power and Victory over all Disease-Causing Micro-organisms as well as ALL THE NATURAL HOLISTIC TOOLS and TREATMENTS which can control or alleviate DIS-EASE CONDITIONS when they do occur due to accident or trauma.

The author is now going to quote from a book entitled "PROTECT YOURSELF FROM LYME DISEASE" by Diana Benzaia who was sponsored by The New York Medical College Guide To Prevention, Diagnoses, and Treatment. The author suggest that the reader purchase this very helpful and documented book for additional reading and information on Lyme Disease.

Diana Benzaia presents several different categories which include body areas involved as well as generalized conditions. It should be noted that each of these will fall into one of the authors three categories which are:

ORGANIC – O
STRUCTURAL – S
PSYCHOLOGIC – P

The author will place an "O," an "S," or a "P" in front of each body part or condition so the reader will have easy access to know whether this is a medical problem or a NATUROPATHIC problem as in the cases of ORGANIC DISEASE, a Chiropractic Problem as in the case of STRUCTURAL DISORDERS, or a PSYCHIATRIC PROBLEM as in the cases of PSYCHOLOGICAL ILLNESS:

NATUROPATHIC or MEDICAL = ORGANIC = O
CHIROPRACTIC = STRUCTURAL = S
PSYCHIATRIC = PSYCHOLOGICAL = P
ORGANIC (and/or) STRUCTURAL = O & S

Commonly MISDIAGNOSED Diseases are lettered in CAPITALS.

The reader can easily see that qualified and sincere professionals which work in all three areas are necessary. If it is possible to find a HOLISTIC NATURALLY MINDED PHYSICIAN who has credentials and understanding in all three areas who can work with you, THIS IS IDEAL. Regardless who you the patient choose to work with you, this BOOK should be read by the Physician and he or she should be willing to work with you and help and guide you through the methodologies expounded upon in this book.

"The Three Stages of Disease"
Diana Benzaia

Many medical scientists find it useful to classify the symptoms of Lyme Disease, like its sister disease syphilis into three stages.

First, syphilis starts with a skin or mucous membrane lesion that soon disappears. Second, the individual may be without symptoms for years; depending upon the latency period bacteria remains alive in the body but cause no clinical symptoms. Finally, new symptoms erupt causing problems in some of the same body systems that are affected by Lyme Disease, such as the brain and heart.

When Lyme Disease symptoms are classified, the rash and flu-like illness are called Stage 1; neurological and cardiac problems are called Stage 2, finally arthritic problems are called Stage 3.

However, many physicians do not consider each classification useful for a variety of reasons. The three stages can overlap and occur in inverse order. For example heart irregularities may be the first symptom noticed. Or once symptoms occur, they may continue unrelentingly.

Further, an extraordinary wide range of symptoms that are not covered by these stages can occur.

SKIN

O – ERYTHEMA MIGRANS – the classic bull's eye rash

O – Lymphocytoma – a rash that can resemble a form of cancer

O – Acrodermatitis chronica atrophicans – a spreading red rash that gives the skin a tissue paper appearance

O – Malar rash – a rash on the cheeks resembling lupus

O – Uticaria – hives usually caused by allergies

O – Septal panniculitis – inflammation of fatty tissue on the abdominal wall

O – Cellulitis – rash caused by a bacterial infection

HEART

O – Heart block – slowed heart rhythm caused by improper conduction of electrical signals in and to the heart

O – MYOCARDITIS – inflammation of the heart muscle

O – Pericarditis – inflammation of the membrane surrounding the heart

O – Arrhythmia – irregular heartbeats

O – Cardiomegaly – enlarged heart

O&S – Syncope – fainting

O&S – Dizziness

O&S – Shortness of breath

O&S – Chest pains – pain might feel like a heart attack

O&S – Palpitations – rapid heartbeat or skipped beats

O – Gallops – a triple cadence in heart sounds, caused by an abnormal third or fourth beat

NEUROLOGICAL

O&S – Bell's palsy – paralysis of a facial nerve

O&S – Radiculopathy – disease of the spinal nerve roots

O – MENINGITIS – inflammation of the membrane surrounding the brain

O – ENCEPHALITIS – inflammation of the brain

O – Peripheral neuropathy – disease of the peripheral nerves

O – Plexopathy – disease of the nerve networks

O – Chores – spasmotic movements of the limbs of facial muscles

O – Multineuritis multiplex – inflammation of multiple nerves

O – Transverse myelitis – inflammation of the spinal cord

O – Cerebellar ataxia – loss of muscle coordination caused by disease in the cerebellum of the brain

O –   Pseudotumor cerebri – a type of abnormal increased pressure in the brain

O –   Guillain-Barre – like syndrome

O –   MULTIPLE SCLEROSIS – like illness

O –   Seizures

O –   Cranial Arteritis – inflammation of arteries of the brain

O&S – Headache – ranging from mild to excruciating

O&S – STIFF NECK

O –   Dysesthiasis – impairment of normal sensation

O&S – Paresthesias – abnormal sensation such as burning, pricking, or tingling

O –   SLEEP DISTURBANCE

O –   Hearing loss

O&S – Hemiparesis – partial paralysis of one side

O&S – Paraparesis – partial paralysis of the lower extremities

ARTHRITIC

O&S – Arthralgias – painful joints

O&S – ARTHRITIS – inflamed swollen joints

O&S – Myalgias – aching muscles

O&S – Myositis – inflammation of muscles

O&S – Tendonitis – inflammation of tendons

O&S – Enthesopathy – disease located at the insertion of muscles

O –   Baker's cyst – a collection of synovial fluid that has escaped from a knee joint or a bursa and formed a new synovial lined sac in an adjacent area

NEUROPSYCHIATRIC

P –   Mood swings

P –   Irritability

P –   Poor concentration

P – DEPRESSION
P – Forgetfulness/memory loss
P – Dementia – general mental deterioration
P – PSYCHOSIS
P – Anorexia nervosa – like illness – loss of appetite

EYE OR VISION
O – Conjunctivitis – inflammation of the membranes lining the eyelids
O – Panophtalmitis – inflammation of the eye
O – Argyll Robertson pupil – loss of normal pupillary reflexes to respond to light
O – Optic neuritis – inflammation of the optic nerve
O – Photophobia – abnormal sensitivity to light
O – Diplopia – double vision when a single object is perceived as two
O – Iritis – inflammation of the iris

PREGNANCY RELATED
O – Miscarriage
O – Stillbirth
O – Fetal infection
O – Birth defect

MISCELLANEOUS
O – Fever
O – Fatigue
O – Sore throat
O – HEPATITIS – inflammation of the liver
O – Lymphadenopathy – disease of the lymph nodes

O – Splenomegaly – enlarged spleen
O – Hematomegaly – enlarged liver
O – Testicular swelling
O – Nausea

O –   Vomiting
O –   Cough
O –   Hoarseness
O –   Gastrointestinal disorders, including diarrhea and abdominal cramps

As noted earlier, the severity of the symptoms of Lyme Disease vary markedly from person to person, and within any individual patient. Some people may get off virtually scot-free with only the rash, others develop recurrent crippling arthritis, still others are bedridden with fatigue for months. Symptoms can wax and wane for years, flaring up and then calming down, seeming to disappear.

The diversity of experiences is endless, but because the striking similarity to syphilis can't be missed, doctors worry about what might yet be down the road for victims of Lyme Disease in the years ahead.

Dr. Farber's Comments

Therefore, the reader can clearly see what great difficulty both Licensed Physicians as well as Laypersons have in correctly determining what ones TRUE AND CORRECT DIAGNOSES is. The DISEASES and CONDITIONS which are most commonly MISDIAGNOSED for LYME DISEASE are in CAPITAL LETTERS.

Quotation: "Protect Yourself from Lyme Disease" pages 47-51 by Diana Benzaia

Copyright Material 7-14-94

The SECOND GREAT MEDICAL IMPOSTER is SYSTEMIC CANDIDA YEAST INFECTION. It becomes extremely confusing in that many of the DISEASES and SYMPTOMS which Candida Yeast Infections imitate OVERLAP with the same conditions and diseases which Lyme Disease imitate.

The author will also indicate with an O for Organic, a P for Psychological or Psychiatric, and an S for Structural as was done for Lyme Disease.

Some of the diseases which Candida Yeast Infections imitate according to Dr. William G. Crook, M.D. and Dr. John Parks Trowbridge are considered incurable by present medical standards.

These diseases include:
O –   Psoriasis
O –   MULTIPLE SCLEROSIS
O –   Chronic Hives
O –   Autism
O –   Arthritis
Some Symptoms and Conditions include:
O&S – Muscle Pain
O&S – Stiff Neck
O&S – Headache
P –   Fatigue
P –   Irritability
P –   Memory Loss
P –   DEPRESSION
P –   HYPOGLYCEMIA
P –   Learning and Memory Disorders
P –   Short Attention Span
P –   HYPERACTIVITY
P –   PARANOID PSYCHOSIS
P –   Delirium
P –   Hallucinations
O&P – Loss of sex drive
O&P – Impotence
O&P – Premenstrual Syndrome

O –   MULTIPLE SCLEROSIS
O –   PARKINSONIAN SYMPTOMS

O – Kidney and Bladder Urinary Infections
O – Pulmonary – lung problems
O – Neuritis
O – HEART DISORDERS
O – Respiratory Disorders
O – STROKE
O – Optic Neuritis
O – Digestive Disorders
O – Vaginitis
O – Skin Problems

As the reader can see the list is almost endless and very overlapping. The BOTTOM LINE is that both LYME DISEASE and SYSTEMIC CANDIDA YEAST INFECTIONS can literally produce all of these symptoms, diseases, and even more. This is because BOTH CONDITIONS interfere with all the MAJOR SYSTEMS of the body and therefore create a Multitude of Problems.

It is one of the GOALS of this book to get to the BOTTOM LINE of these multiple problems by seeing the connection between Lyme Disease, Systemic Candida Yeast Infections and their interrelationships. This will enable the Professional Physician as well as the Layperson to come to a

CORRECT DIAGNOSES
and a
CORRECT TREATMENT PROGRAM

The author is behind you the reader 100%
and wishes you God's Speed and much Good
Fortune in this GREAT ADVENTURE of finding
A PERMANENT CURE
for
YOUR PRESENT PROBLEMS

MYELIN BASIC PROTEIN
A NEW TREATMENT FOR
MULTIPLE SCLEROSIS

Multiple Sclerosis and related demyelinating diseases remain one of the unsolved neurological mysteries of our time. This common neurologic disorder primarily affects young adults and is more prevalent in persons of Western European lineage living in temperate zones. The disease still remains a puzzle to scientists exploring its causes. Pathologically, the disease in characterized by demyelination with reactive gliosis scattered in the white matter of the brain, spinal cord and optic nerve.

The common initial presentation includes weakness, numbness, tingling, spastic paraparesis or sphincter disturbances. The disease is characterized by frequent relapses and remissions which lead to increasing disability, weakness, spasticity, impaired vision and urinary incontinence. Approximately 20% of patients with multiple sclerosis have aggressive debilitating symptoms while the remainder may live a normal life.

Most treatments for multiple sclerosis (MS) have focused on the use of potentially toxic and immunosuppressive drugs such as steroids and cyclophosphamides. However, even the A.M.A. Book of Drug Evaluations provides no specific long-term benefit of these drugs, in recognition of the fact that they do not prevent further relapses.

Two major theories of pathogenesis of MS have been proposed; one, that MS is a viral disease of the CNS, the inflammatory response in the brain being anti-viral immune response, and two, that MS is an autoimmune disease in which infiltrating T cells recognize self-antigens and attack normal tissue. These two possibilities are not mutually exclusive: the autoimmune response may be triggered by environmental factors such as viral infections. However, the inability to transfer the disease to primates or to isolate virus from CNS tissue of MS patients, despite tremendous efforts, lends indirect support to the theory that the inflammatory process may be autoimmune in nature.

Physical Characteristics of Myelin

Myelin is a very important constituent of the white matter of the brain and the myelin sheath forms 50% of the total dry weight. Myelin is mainly responsible for the gross chemical differences between white and grey matter and accounts for the glistening white appearance and high lipid content of the white matter.

The myelin sheath is a greatly extended and modified plasma membrane that is wrapped around the nerve axon in a spiral fashion. Myelin acts as an electrical insulator surrounding the axon, the "wire" carrying the current. Myelin also facilitates nerve conduction. This lipid-rich material contains high concentrations of cholesterol, phospholipids and plasmalogens.

The basic proteins in myelin sheath are immunologically active and may cause an antibody response. Although early experiments used injections of MBP, recent studies suggest that the protein is active while taken orally.

Immunologists have not elucidated the cellular mechanisms which justify the use of myelin sheath extract in clinical practice. The Peyer's patches in the intestine contain the immunological receptor sites which recognize myelin basic protein. When a glandular extract of myelin sheath is taken orally in a patient with multiple sclerosis, the protein appears in ephithelial cells that line the lower small intestine. As a person's T cells circulate through the intestinal wall, complement cells that recognize MBP bind to these epithelial cells and are somehow inactivated. Receptors in the gut may signal the body to stop attacking its own myelin sheath. This basic premise forms the scientific justification for the use of this glandular extract.

Immunological Correlates – Mechanism of Action

Immunologic tolerance is defined as a state of specific immunologic unresponsiveness to an agent after exposure to the agent. An effective and long-recognized method of inducing immunologic tolerance is the oral administration of antigen, which was first demonstrated by Wells for hen's egg proteins in 1911.

Orally induced tolerance is a normal immune response that is considered to function in the prevention of allergic and autoimmune reactions to food antigens. Although the oral administration of antigen has been widely studied as a means of suppressing the immune response for a number of different cellular, protein and nonprotein (e.g. contact-sensitizing) antigens, it has not been applied in the suppression of autoimmune disease to a defined antigen until recently.

Adoptive transfer studies with animals fed other antigens have often shown that antigen-specific suppressor T cells are generated by feeding and are involved in actively suppressing the immune response. One of the primary goals for the treatment of cell-mediated autoimmune diseases is to specifically suppress autoreactive T cells. Other mechanisms, such as the production of soluble factors in the serum and the formation of antigen-antibody complexes have also been proposed and may represent additional or alternative mechanisms.

Oral induction of tolerance to autoantigens may provide a nontoxic, immunologically specific therapy for suppressing ongoing autoimmune processes in a variety of clinical conditions in which candidate autoantigens have been identified.

EAE – A Definitive Experimental Model

Recently, Howard Weiner and coworkers at Harvard Medical School have demonstrated that the potent suppressive effects of oral tolerance can be extended to the autoimmune disease, experimental autoimmune encephalomyelitis (EAE).

EAE has been frequently studied as a model for the human demyelinating diseases, particularly multiple sclerosis.

Suppression of both the acute and relapsing EAE disease episodes has been one of the major goals of research in multiple sclerosis. Therapeutic strategies used to suppress EAE include treatment with immunosuppressive drugs such as cyclophosphamide and cyclosporin, or injection of monoclonal antibodies directed against T cell subsets.

Oral administration of myelin basic protein (MBP) prior to EAE induction results in a profound suppression of clinical signs, a significant decrease in EAE histo-pathologic changes and virtually absent lymphocyte-proliferative responses to MBP. It is clear that myelin basic protein also elicits production of antibody which has been implicated as a participating factor in demyelination events.

MBP-induced oral tolerance in EAE profoundly suppresses the clinical neurologic signs, delays the onset of symptoms and significantly reduces the extent of mononuclear cell infiltration into the central nervous system. The oral introduction of antigen is known to readily induce tolerance and result in the systemic suppression of both antibody and cell-mediated immune responses.

Carol Whitacre and coworkers at Ohio State Medical School have provided evidence for the potent effects of orally introduced antigen in the autoimmune disease

EAE. Not only were *in vitro* lymphocyte proliferative responses significantly decreased in an antigen-specific manner following the oral administration of MBP, but the incidence and severity of both the clinical and the histopathological manifestations of EAE were markedly diminished.

The specificity or the orally induced tolerance to MBP has been found to be strikingly species-dependent with regard to the induction of clinical EAE. For example, tolerance resulting from oral guinea pig MBP is only effective in protecting rats against a MBP challenge and the same degree of specificity was observed for human MBP. However, attempting to orally tolerize rats against the self-antigen RMBP is unsuccessful.

It has been shown that following ingestion of protein antigens, minute amounts of these antigens are absorbed and circulate either in native protein form or in immune complexes. With continued exposure, a state of mucosal immunity develops concomitantly with active suppression of the systemic immune response. It is possible that the mechanisms in place to maintain tolerance to self-antigens in the rat either prevent the absorption of MBP from the gastrointestinal tract or, more likely, prevent the local mucosal immune response.

The application of oral tolerance to other models of autoimmune disease has recently received attention, including the suppression of type II collagen-induced arthritis, systemic lupus erythematosus and unveitis. A variety of mechanisms have been described for the maintenance of self-tolerance in the host. One major focus of study is the antigen-driven active suppression after oral administration antigens as a tolerance mechanism and as a method to downregulate autoimmune diseases.

Oral tolerance to autoantigens is both disease and antigen specific. Feeding MBP suppresses EAE but does not affect experimental autoimmune unveitis or rheumatoid arthritis. Similarly, feeding type II collagen suppresses arthritis models but not EAE. Thus, the secretion and action of antigen-nonspecific factors by regulatory cells induced by oral tolerance must occur in the local microenvironment of the lymphoid tissue where the immune response is generated, along migratory pathways of the effector cells and/or at the inflamed site on the target organ where the autoantigen is present. Studies are currently in progress to further elucidate the temporal sequence and location of these interactions ʳbetween regulatory and effector cells.

Use of Purified Glandular Extracts in Other Autoimmune Diseases

The model for the efficacy in using oral extracts of type II collagen in rheumatoid arthritis has recently been elucidated. The mechanism for such suppression relates to the generation of collagen-specific suppressor cells that are generated by feeding and that migrate to the joint where they are triggered by collagen to release antigen-nonspecific suppressor cytokines. Similar results have been found found in the suppression of diabetes by feeding oral insulin from pancreatic tissue. Thus, the treatment of an organ-specific autoimmune disease by oral tolerization may not require knowledge of the inciting autoantigen, only the oral administration of an autoantigen from the target organ.

MBP comprises 30% of the polypeptides of CNS myelin. Detection of MBP peptides in cerebrospinal fluid may indicate ongoing CNS demyelination. How MBP leaves its intracellular location to become accessible to autoaggressive lymphocytes within the CNS is a long-standing question.

In summary, resting autoreactive T cells may be activated in the periphery by molecular mimicry or by superantigens, cross the blood-brain barrier in an activated state and initiate an inflammatory response after exposure to self-antigen in the CNS white matter.

The final criterion requires that the autoimmune disease is effectively treated by tolerance induction to the autoantigen or by specific elimination of autoreactive T cells. Although this goal has not yet been accomplished in MS, therapeutic studies in EAE have demonstrated the potential feasibility of a variety of approaches.

The ongoing molecular definition of autoimmune processes in MS may make it possible to design a specific approach for the treatment of the disease. In this regard, researchers at Harvard Medical School have recently completed a phase one investigation in patients with early relapsing-remitting MS where they have attempted to induce tolerance to myelin antigens by oral administration of bovine myelin. The treatment protocol attempts to induce tolerance to myelin antigens by oral administration of bovine myelin.

REFERENCES

Wucherpfennig, K.W. et al. T-cell recognition of myelin basic protein. **Immunology Today 12**(8):277-82, 1991.

Brod, S.A. et al. Suppression of experimental autoimmune encephalomyelitis by oral administration of myelin antigens. **Ann. Neurol. 29**:615-22, 1991.

Higgins, P.J. and Weiner, H.L. Suppression of experimental autoimmune encephalomyelitis by oral administration of myelin basic protein and its fragments. **J. Immunol.140**(2): 440-45, 1988.

Whitacre, C.C. et al. Oral tolerance in experimental autoimmune encephalomyelitis. **J. Immunol.147**(7):2155-63, 1991.

Myelin Basic Protein can be ordered from Family Farm 281-351-4372

Fuller, K.A. et al. Oral tolerance in experimental encephalomyelitis and salivary antibody responses. **J. Neuroimmunol.28**:15-26, 1990.

Bitar, D.N. and Whitacre, C.C. Suppression of experimental autoimmune encephalomyelitis by oral administration of myelin basic protein. **Cellular Imunol.112**:364-70, 1988.

Miller, A. et al. Antigen-driven bystander suppression after oral administration of antigens. **J. Exp. Med.174**:791-98, 1991.

Berlet, H. et al. Soluble and bound acid protease activity of myelin from bovine cerebral white matter and spinal cord. **Neurochem. Res. 13**(5):409-16, 1988.

MAGNETIC FIELDS INFLUENCE HEALTH

Andreas Marx

Today's western medicine no longer fights against epidemics such as small pox, cholera, and tuberculosis. Instead, medicine today is confronted with symptoms such as tiredness, headaches, sleeplessness, and allergies, only to name a few of the daily complaints.

The many clinics today that are confronted with these daily complaints like nervousness, circulation problems, and so on, have little or no success in treating these symptoms with orthodox therapeutic methods.

After a patient complaining of sleeplessness has been examined and is pronounced organically healthy, many times the patient simply receives a prescription and often it ends up being just some type of narcotic sleeping tablets. Logically, this can't be the answer, especially after hearing reports from many doctors who treated such cases, that the sleeplessness disappeared completely during a vacation trip or a change of normal sleeping place. Knowing this, one should take another viewpoint and finally realize that many of these symptoms just could not come from one organic health problem.

Worldwide, many medical doctors and physicists have recently discovered and recognized a complete new problem of our civilized world and named it "geopathic disturbance." It is also sometimes referred to as "electric smog."

For example, the case history of the following patient could represent thousands of people with a similar problem. It goes like this: The patient says, "Since we moved into our new house, I suffer from sleeplessness. A good solid, sound sleep like I had in the old house I've never had here. Most of the time I wake up around three o'clock in the morning and can't sleep anymore. My wife can't sleep."

A geopathic disturbance expert examined the patient's bedroom and discovered that the head of the bed was exactly at the side of the wall where the power supply and all the electrical wiring of the house was located. With a magnetometer, the expert measured an extremely high electro-magnetic field that radiated over the head of the bed.

It was recommended to the patient that he move his bed into another position, away from the wall. Two days later, the patient and his wife had no more complaints about their sleeplessness. Many clinics in the United States and in Europe have made similar reports.

Other examples are by avoiding the use of electric blankets, waterbeds, telephones and electric quartz clocks that are too near the bed. Even removing televisions from the bedroom has caused patients to lose their pathological symptoms. Geopathic disturbances can often be found at one's working place. Some people suffer from electro-magnetic radiation when working near neon light tubes, electronic equipment, TV screens, and microwaves (microwave radiation leakage has been widely discussed as a possible health hazard).

Scientists from the University of Colorado reported that the death rate through cancer, such as leukemia, is more than average high in people who live within a 50-yard radius of outdoor power lines.

In Russia and Europe it's been proven through hundreds of experiments that electro-magnetic field disturbances cause many different harmful health problems such as high blood pressure, heart attacks, headaches, sexual disturbances, dizziness, nervousness, and blood diseases. The U.S.S.R. has very strict rules and exact instructions as to how much microwave radiation from radio stations and radar centers can be used so as to not harm the people.

If one stands under a 50-foot high-voltage power line, one is exposed to a field strength of 10,000 volts per meter. (Just a little over three feet.) The radiation is so strong that the leaf tips of plants grown under such mains are burned.

In 1973, W. Ross Adey, at the brain research institute of the University of California in Los Angeles, exposed monkeys to electrical radiation with frequencies comparable to what we are exposed to in our daily lives and he documented abnormal behavior by the monkeys. The disturbances in the animals affected their sense of timing, among other things. There are many such reports from scientists all over the country that would fill many written pages.

The earth's natural magnetic field has a strength measured at only about 3/4 gauge (the measurement of magnetic field strength). This magnetic field is one of the most important basics for all life on earth. In some areas in big cities, especially in high concrete buildings, one is isolated from this natural life force. On top of this, these natural fields are blanketed by much stronger electromagnetic radiation such as high-voltage power lines which can create an imbalance in the biorhythm.

Going back to the patient who suffered from sleeplessness, one can easily imagine what could have happened if this problem hadn't been recognized in time. Normally, such patients will be provided with sleeping tablets and tranquilizers, and later the dose will be increased because of the lack of results. This will eventually slowly toxicate the body and weaken the resistance system. Depending on the constitution, it starts negatively affecting the stomach and liver. Then the medical allopathic drugs have side effects with long-term use. Through long-term therapy of this kind, the kidneys could become damaged, which also could affect the heart and the circulatory system. The whole thing becomes a vicious cycle and the helpless patient runs from one medical specialist to another. He becomes slowly treated to death.

Of course, this is only the clinical outlook. One should not forget to look at the psychic and social aspect. A human being who has to live under such geopathic stress and runs into this vicious cycle also becomes disturbed in his emotional balance. This could have negative effects on his family life and work. Then if worse comes to worse, it may lead to alcoholism and drug addiction.

If we believe international experts, disturbances from electrical equipment based on today's standard of technology, are absolutely harmless. But these experts postulate their opinions as "state-of-the-art" and with that they leave themselves a back door open.

Today one understands science as being the opinion of the majority of experts that are officially acknowledged. The past has showed again and again that the research of outsiders can overthrow the collective opinions and help extend the knowledge of experts. For example, at around the year 1900, X-ray experts agreed on the harmlessness of X-ray radiation and in those days the strength of the radiation was 15,000 times stronger than what is accepted today. Also, many chemical substances that were taken off the market were accepted by experts and declared to be completely harmless until the last minute.

Even though a toxic substance can be deadly poisonous, at the same time it can cure when diluted correctly for therapeutic medical use. With this in mind, the physicist, W. Ludwig, at the University of Tubingen in West Germany developed a method of imitating the earth's natural magnetic field. It took about 20 years of research for Ludwig. Then he and an electronic engineer, E. Rasche, built an instrument that is able to effectively treat different diseases. Right now, some physicists and medical doctors are reported as having good results in treating patients by using the limited earth electro-magnetic field.

The Occidental Institute Alumni Association (O.I.A.A.) in San Francisco collects, translates, and publishes reports from all over the world pertaining to this research.

One important part of geopathic disturbance fields is the polarization. (Right and left spin in plane-polarized light.) The natural electro-magnetic environment in areas where there is a lot of alternating current (AC) has been turned from its natural clockwise orientation to a counterclockwise orientation. Nobel Prize winner Sir Lawrence Bragg (physics-optics 1915) stated that all healthy life on this planet can be described as oriented to the right. The German physicist and researcher, Dr. Mersmann, discovered that people suffering under electro-magnetic pollution have left spinning blood. The blood of cancer patients also shows a left spin. Healthy blood always spins to the right. Mersmann developed an electro-magnetic spin tester especially for this test. With this instrument and method, one is able to test almost every substance on its spin (orientation-polarization). It was learned that most healthy, organically grown foods spin to the right. The famous Dr. Morell of West Germany and E. Rasche developed a method and an instrument capable of changing a patient's left spinning blood back to its normal right spin by using electro-magnetic therapy. Some American clinics already use this new method and have started series of tests.

What can be done in the meantime until these tests are approved and finally recognized? We can't stop use of all of our electro-magnetic energy for power and communications. Experts in this field suggest that one should make sure that the electrical board in the house is properly grounded and that means not just grounded onto the water pipes like some telephone companies do, but to provide a separate grounding system for the electrical circuits.

Also, it helps to use shielded and grounded cables for all electrical equipment. Some electronics companies are already trying to develop geopathic balance devices which hopefully help to clean the electro-magnetics.

America's most highly respected physicists, doctors and engineers such as W. Ross Adey, Professor Robert Beck, Robert O. Becker, Pete Peterson, Ed Skilling, and others are researching these fields and have discovered possibilities and new ways of using these electro-magnetic fields successfully in medicine and for the benefit of human kind.

In West Germany, scientists have succeeded in transforming new theories in physics into useful medicine devices. Physicists, medical doctors, and engineers like W. Ludwig, F.A. Pop, F. Morell, Mersmann, E. Rasche, and Burghard Heim are well known in this field in Europe.

Dr. Ludwig discovered, for example, under electro-magnetic field therapy, a bone fracture heals in half the normal healing time.

When questioning medical doctors in America who are working in this field why these methods are still not approved and accepted in this country, one hears answers such as: "In West Germany more medical doctors are fed up with the poor results of allopathic medical treatments, so a wider majority is actively involved in the new field of energetic therapies. In America we are able to shoot a man up to the moon and build the most sophisticated computer system, but then at the same time we still think of therapeutic, medical equipment in the bio-electric ultra fine field as being 'spooky, radionic devices.' At the same time we also try to fight the civilization diseases with chemical pills and when all else fails, the last answer is always surgery."

Around 1920, medical doctors and physicists in this country developed electrical medical equipment. Some of these fine scientists were ending up in prisons, charged with being "quacks and dangerous." Of course there were many charlatans and fakers attracted to this field and it did cause justifiable investigation. Nevertheless, the FDA banned all so-called "radionic devices." America could have been the leader in this field today.

Well, we've made some progress. Acupuncture, the 5,000-year-old Chinese medicine, is still used intensively in Red China and is strongly supported by the government. Finally, acupuncture is being taught and used in some states of the U.S. If a treatment can survive for more than 5,000 years, then there must be something special about it because something that doesn't work could never stay alive through all these centuries.

In 1982, Dr. David J. Nickel, an acupuncturist himself, became the first in the medical history of the U.S. who requested major surgery performed with acupuncture anesthesia. In full consciousness he had a kidney stone removed and felt no pain. This gives hope to many patients with heart and circulation problems who need surgeries because it eliminates the risk of circulation breakdown caused by common anesthesia.

According to Chinese theory, acupuncture works with the body's own energy and many scientists believe that through this there is a point of contact between our western analytical thinking and the Asian empiric knowledge.

The philosopher, Schoppenhauer, made the following statement: "Every new realization goes through three stages. The first stage, one laughs at a new realization. The second stage, establishment will fight against it. The third stage everybody wonders why didn't we have this a long time ago. Right now, we are hopefully at the end of the second stage and for the benefit of all people in this country, let's hope that the third stage is only a few steps ahead of us."

Reprint from: The American Health Times

COMMENT:

We have two testimonials from competent independent sources that when a person with left-spinning blood holds the polarizer, his or her blood is turned to a clockwise spin. One of the researchers tested seriously ill persons. He reported that the blood returned to its counterclockwise spin when the polarizer was removed. The other researcher did not have that experience. He had the subjects hold the polarizer over the heart. This raises the interesting speculation as to what would happen if one wore the personal polarizer over his or her heart constantly. Would this keep the blood spinning clockwise, and would this be therapeutic?

There is also significant evidence based upon kinesiological and dowsing tests that our polarizers reverse geopathic disturbances. Observation of this phenomenon is what prompted us to offer the Life Field Polarizer as a research tool.

HOW DANGEROUS IS ELECTROMAGNETIC RADIATION?

What characteristic is shared by an electric blanket, a power line and a broadcast tower? All three emit electromagnetic radiation. These invisible electro-magnetic fields (EMFs), generated by currents running through electric wires, are not powerful and destructive like nuclear or X-ray radiation, and thus were once thought to be harmless. However, studies have suggested that people exposed to them run a higher risk of certain health problems, including miscarriages, learning disabilities and cancer.

No clear cause-and-effect relationship has been established between EMFs and illnesses, but the mounting evidence makes EMFs appear extremely suspicious. And because EMFs are generated by many sources – including microwave ovens, televisions and radios, military radar systems, and ironically, some treatments for cancerous tumors — many of us could be at risk.

Studies over the last 15 years have hinted at a connection between EMFs and health problems. EMFs have been implicated in behavioral changes, birth defects, memory loss and Alzheimer's disease. In 1976, two doctors at the Veterans Administration Hospital in Syracuse, N.Y., showed that the offspring of mice exposed to extremely low frequency EMFs from power lines were born stunted.

Other studies have focused specifically on the suspected connection between EMF exposure and cancer. In 1979, two University of Colorado researchers, physician Nancy Wertheimer and physicist Ed Leeper, pored through childhood mortality records in the

Denver area and correlated long-term exposure to weak EMFs with a higher incidence of cancer. Seven years later, Dr. Lennart Tomenius, a Swedish researcher, found the same relationship between EMF exposure and cancer rates among children in Stockholm. And in 1982, Samuel Milham, an occupational health physician in the Washington State Department of Social and Health Services, noted in the *New England Journal of Medicine* that he found more leukemia-related deaths in men whose work brought them in contact with electrical and magnetic fields, such as employees of utility companies.

Furthermore, EMFs have been implicated in pregnancy problems. <u>In 1986, Wertheimer and Leeper reported that women who used heated waterbeds or electric blankets, both of which emit EMFs, had longer pregnancies and a higher miscarriage rate.</u> And in 1987, Kurt Salzinger, a psychology professor at the Brooklyn-based Polytechnic Institute of New York, found that rats exposed to EMFs for 30 days had more problems than unexposed rats in learning to press a bar on command. Their offspring, exposed in the womb and for nine days after birth, developed permanent learning disabilities.

In their attempts to establish a cause-and-effect connection between EMF exposure and health problems, scientists have been trying to uncover just what effect EMFs have on the body. One theory says that EMFs of certain frequencies disrupt the normal role of calcium in the brain. Another theory says that EMFs affect how cells grow and reproduce. A third belief holds that EMFs make cells manufacture proteins they normally would not reproduce.

Researchers who believe in the EMF-illnesses connection have their critics. These skeptics emphasize that there is no proven cause-and-effect link between EMF exposure and cancer. At a Florida state government hearing on power line emission standards, Philip Cole, M.D., an epidemiologist (who studies the occurrence and control of a disease) at the University of Alabama, Birmingham, emphasized this absence of proof. Without a proven connection, Cole asserted, "There is no relationship between EMFs and cancer in human beings, or if there is an effect it must be of very low magnitude even among people who are moderately to heavily exposed."

Indeed, studies on diseases occasionally have the difficulty of trying to prove a causal link when researchers must rely on past records and events instead of controlled experiments. However, this lack of proof has not stopped lawyers from introducing available studies as evidence in EMF-related lawsuits. The judgments in several such suits were based on research showing a possible connection and *not* a definite link. In late 1985, a Texas jury ordered the Houston Lighting and Power Co. to pay a local school district $25 million in punitive damages after the utility built a transmission line through school property without the district's permission. In Florida, juries have awarded more than $1 million to owners of land next to high-voltage lines.

Another suit illustrates the potential effects of transmission lines and the EMFs they create on home owners trying to sell their homes. About 60 landowners in New York state filed a $60 million suit against the New York Power Authority, alleging that a half-completed power line from Canada into the state could produce a "cancerphobia corridor" where property values would tumble.

This fear of diminished property values brings up the question of what the general public can do to protect itself from this potential threat. EMFs are not like other harmful agents. They have not been proven dangerous, as has the outlawed, cancer-causing food coloring red dye #2, for example. In addition, unlike red dye #2 and other proven carcinogens, EMFs are almost unavoidable. The magnetic fields easily penetrate walls and bodies, and as of now, no protective shield is available.

With such a pervasive yet mysterious force around us, there's not much we can do to totally eliminate EMF exposure. There are ways, though, of minimizing our potential risks:

- Unplug and do not use electric blankets.
- Don't sit less than five feet from televisions.
- Don't allow children to peer through the doors of microwave ovens when they are on.
- If you're pregnant, cut down on, if not avoid, using video-displaying terminals (VDTs).
- Avoid taking jobs or living in areas where EMF exposure could be high. People at greatest risk are utility workers and those near transmission lines (No study has established a "safe minimum distance" from power lines.)
- Though EMFs have not been proven dangerous, the evidence clearly points to an association between them and health problems, and individuals have reason to be concerned.

June Bryon Emu

Electric currents emit electromagnetic radiation, which may be linked to health problems such as cancer.

With such a pervasive yet mysterious force around us, there's not much we can do to toally eliminate electromagnetic field exposure.

Concluding our series on electromagnetic fields and their effect on human biology, Simon Best surveys the growing concern and search for more information about the phenomenon of harmful earth rays or "geopathic stress." It is a phenomenon widely and officially accepted in parts of Europe, particularly Germany, but, largely because of the language barrier, almost completely unrecognized in Britain.

Examples of conditions giving rise to geopathic stress according to the Austrian dowser Käthe Bachler and published in her 1984 book "Der gute Platz." The best places to sleep are in areas clear of radiation from both underground streams and the Curry grid. In areas covered by both, illness – even severe illness like cancer – is likely in susceptible individuals.

WHAT WE DON'T KNOW ABOUT EARTH RADIATION

On first hearing, the idea of harmful earth rays sounds more like something out of a Star Wars scenario than a serious medical hypothesis.

But the view that harmful earth radiations – that is, ionising and non-ionising electromagnetic radiation emanating naturally from the planet's geophysiology – can cause or exacerbate many types of disease is one of a growing number of dowsers, doctors and alternative practitioners, especially in Germany, have come to accept over the past 50 years.

It is an ideal commonly now summed up in the term "geopathic stress."

So seriously is the notion these rays can be harmful taken in Germany that in1987 the West German government began to fund a DM 300,000 (£130,000) project to investigate the claim that cancer and other major diseases can be encouraged by living in places through which ran lines of geopathic stress.

The research is being undertaken by Professor Hildebert Wagner at the University of Munich's Institute of Pharm.

Other German research has been carried out on the location of accident "black spots" in relation to earth radiation. Engineer Robert Engros and Professor Karl-Ernst Lotz, now retired, have studied the high number of accidents and head-on collisions on certain stretches of road occurring for no apparent reasons.

In all cases drivers who survived reported having a complete blackout. In many instances Lotz has found underground water crossing the path of the road just before the "black spot" in question, which he proposed causes a form of radiation giving rise to geopathic stress (i).

Professor Jerry Mazurczak, at Warsaw's Academy of Agriculture, has developed apparatus to measure the photon emission of minerals from biological organisms when exposed to such stress. He is comparing such emissions from healthy and ill patients under various conditions.

But Germany is where the majority of work in this area is being carried out and where studies began. Some of the first research was undertaken by the German scientist and dowser, Gustav Freiherr von Pohl, and is presented in his seminal book recently translated into English (ii) (*see review in J.*) (*M May*).

In 1929 he mapped danger in houses in Vilsburg, south Germany, which were then investigated by the German Central Committee for Cancer Research in Berlin.

After checking the local hospital records it was found that all 54 patients who had died of cancer since records had been kept had slept in beds above points marked on von Pohl's map.

Further research, carried out by von Pohl and other doctors, added <u>asthma, depression, rheumatism, arthritis, MS, heart problems</u> and a host of other disorders to the list of illnesses that harmful earth radiation seemed to help initiate or exacerbate.

One of the most extensive and recent research projects was started by an Austrian school teacher, Käthe Bachler, in the 1970's. She dowsed 3,000 flats in 14 countries and interviewed 11,000 people.

She concluded <u>95 percent of the problem with children she investigated slept in beds or worked at desks placed at harmful sites.</u> She also checked a sample of 500 cancer cases: every one was found to be sleeping over harmful earth radiation.

Her findings were published in Austria in 1978 in a best-selling book which has just been published in Britain.

Included in the book is an impressive list of doctors all of whom confirm Bachler's findings and consider such radiation when treating their patients, as well as many examples from her 12,000-odd cases histories.

According to a talk she gave in June 1987 to the British Society of Dowsers, her research has been thoroughly analyzed and evaluated by a Dr. Karl Fischer of Salzberg, for this Ph.D. on "Radiesthesia and Geobiology," giving "highly significant" results, especially where underground water was involved (iv).

In Britain a London businessman, Rolf Gordon, has founded the Dulwich Health Society to spread the word about geopathic stress and has written and published a book about it, "Are You Sleeping in a Safe Place?" (iv).

He is certain his 26-year-old son would not have died of cancer had he been aware of the effect of geopathic stress.

Gordon lists some of the <u>main symptoms</u> of exposure to harmful earth radiation as feeling "run down" and <u>exhausted, depression, nervous tension, inexplicable mood changes, lack of appetite, pallor</u> and a <u>resistance to appropriate treatment.</u>

<u>Symptoms while in bed include insomnia,</u> disturbed sleep, nightmares, sleepwalking, crying out, <u>cramps, cold feet, tingling in arms and legs, grinding of teeth, excessive sweating, shivering,</u> and fatigue and lethargy in the morning giving a feeling of not having had enough sleep. Of course, many of these symptoms may be due to other physical or psychological disorders, but, excluding such causes. Gordon claims suffering from one or more of them chronically usually indicates being effected by earth "rays."

<u>In children excessive bedwetting or sleeping in strange positions in the bed often sideways or at the bottom (or the sides of a cot can) warn of such exposure.</u>

According to Gordon, the geopathic stress lines themselves are about 40 cm (1.5 ft) in width but some can be much wider. They can run in one direction or criss-cross a building.

Gordon claims the lines are haphazard and random. But in Germany and Austria they are more commonly believed to be manifestations of two regular and ordered geomagnetic forces – the Hartmann net and the Curry grid, both named after their 20th century German discoverers.

In his book Gordon shows how to locate harmful earth rays, or "stress lines," by dowsing (the usual method used) and, once carefully mapped, strongly recommends moving beds if these are found to be situated over them. He cites many examples of people whose health problems improved or cleared completely when such action was taken.

He estimates in Austria and West Germany more than 3,000 medical doctors use dowsers to assist them with their most severe cancer cases.

Rolf Gordon has also developed a device, called a Radi-Tech (vi) which, by plugging into an electrical socket, "frees the area within the building of harmful earth radiation without altering the course of the rays in any way."

Gordon, however, has his critics – one of whom, dowser Richard Pope, took him to task in a recent issue of the British dowser's journal for (viii) causing "undue fear and concern."

According to Pope, who wrote an examination of different types of geopathic stress and their possible cures from around the world, fear about the problem is almost more damaging than the problem itself and therefore counselling should form part of any treatment of the issue.

More established in Britain than Gordon, but having created less impact, is acupuncturist Anthony Scott-Morley who is based in Poole, Dorset. He has been researching geopathic stress for several years (viii).

Scott-Morley points out there are certain characteristics in geopathically disturbed zones. "Cold spots," active gamma radiation, changes in the degree of ionisation, AC charge, electrical resistance, acoustic levels, radio reception and geomagnetic fields have all been observed within buildings by physicists and engineers.

He divides the harmful rays into discharging fields (yin) and charging (yang). The discharging forces come from underground water, especially where streams cross, or rock cavities. The sources of charging disturbances are varied and include mineral deposits.

In addition, there are global energy grids notably the 2m by 2.5m Hartmann net and the 22m by 22m Curry grid. Rays above the grid intersections may be discharging or charging, he points out.

Scott-Morley <u>uses a Geomagnetometer, made in Germany, to detect very small changes in the geomagnetic field of the order of 10,000 nanatesla.</u>

He believes the gradient of the rate of change of the field is more important than the maximum reading for indicating geopathic areas.

He also considers that standing wave formations, produced by various broadcast signals, usually coincide when a person is reacting to such stress, and agrees that little progress in treatment will occur in these cases until the geopathic stress is shielded or removed.

Another British researcher with an international reputation in electromagnetic fields, Dr. Cyril Smith of Salford University, holds much the same view. He theorizes that a number of possibilities could explain the geopathetic phenomena:

- strong local magnetic fields
- geomagnetic field gradients
- slow neutrons emanating from rock fissures filled with water
- microwaves
- ionising gamma radiation, including radon
- high air ionisation
- radiative emanations from structured underground water

All or any of the above phenomena, he believes, could so seriously disrupt the homeostatic mechanism of an individual as to cause ill-health.

Only careful research will determine how much of geopathic stress can be explained by currently accepted environmental hazards.

But judging by reports of most of those doctors and scientists who have studied the phenomenon, the potential benefits for understanding the epidemiology and aetiology of many illnesses seems enormous.

The hope must be that it will not be too long before a major research project, like that currently in progress in Germany, will be funded in Britain.

REFERENCES

Gordon R., "Are You Sleeping in a Safe Place," Dulwich Health Society, 3rd cd 1988. (available from 130 Gipsy Hill, London, SE19 1Pl).

Geopathic stress...or seismicity?

SCOTTISH researcher Andrew Davie and American scientist Dr. Andrija Puharich have developed a theory based on geophysical phenomena to which they apply the word "seismicity."

According to Dr. Puharich, seismic events produce extremely low frequency scaler fields (ELF) which originated in magnetic monopoles at the core of the proton.

These fields, he believes, are the "fields of information *per se* of the universe."

His claim is their generation in humans results in a variety of effects from metal bending and levitation to those associated with geopathic stress.

He has now developed a new unified field theory out of the seismic effect or seismicity, which, he claims, explains the fundamental causes of health (and disease).

Puharich and Davie, who runs Geo-Rheological Surveys in Alloa, are hoping to air their theories at a conference next month at the University of Georgia organized by the International Association for Psychotranic Research.

We hope to present a report of their ideas in a forthcoming issue.

Examples of geopathological stress conditions arising from earth radiation according to the British dowser Rolf Gordon and published in his 1986 book "Are You Sleeping in a Safe Place?" (Dulwich Health Society). Unlike Bachler, Gordon appears not to acknowledge the Curry grid as a source however and his diagrams do not show the influence of underground streams ("black water").

ELECTRICITY CAUSES
HEALTH PROBLEMS OTA SAYS

According to Congressional experts, even weak electric and magnetic fields – such as those generated by common electric power systems, including household wiring and household appliances – may be a health hazard because in preliminary studies, including test-tube experiments, the electromagnetic fields they generate produced "substantial" changes in living cells.

The studies, which also suggested that women who sleep under electric blankets experience "dramatic" changes in their menstrual cycle, and linked an increased risk of childhood cancer to the use of heating pads, waterbed heaters and electric heaters during pregnancy, were published by the Congressional Office of Technology Assessment (OTA).

They represent the first comprehensive survey of the scientific evidence in a 20-year public health controversy over the safety of electric power transmission.

Several studies over the past 10 years have suggested that the high electric fields generated by power lines might be linked to illness, but many experts disputed the quality of the studies. Although the findings are fragmentary and inconclusive, they contradict a widely held belief that low-level electromagnetic fields (of 60 Hz or lower) are harmless.

According to the OTA study, the potential effects of electromagnetic fields range from slight changes in stress levels and memory lapses to cancer, miscarriages and problems in fetal development.

The paper was prepared by researchers Indira Nair, M. Granger Morgan and H. Keith Florig from the Department of Engineering and Public Policy at Carnegie Mellon University.

The researchers recommended further studies about whether electromagnetic fields affect the brain and central nervous system, which normally use low-frequency electric fields for cell-to-cell "communication."

The researchers did not find that low-frequency fields cause any damage to genetic material, which could precipitate cancer. They said some experiments indicated the fields altered the cell membrane, which could promote cancer if the alteration permitted toxic chemicals to enter cells.

According to the report, sources of electric fields such as wall wiring, appliances and lighting fixtures "could play a far greater role than transmission lines in any public health problem.

"Prudent risk-reduction strategies proposed by the Congressional analysts include putting new power lines in unpopulated areas, widening rights-of-way for existing transmission lines to prevent housing development in the area, developing new ways of wiring homes and offices and redesigning appliances to minimize the electromagnetic fields they generate.

STUDY LINKS POWER LINES, CHILDHOOD LEUKEMIA RISK

Children who live near ordinary overhead power lines are twice as likely to develop leukemia as children raised away from the magnetic fields associated with the lines, a state scientific panel reported yesterday.

The panel also estimated that 10% to 15% of all childhood cancer cases may be due to the magnetic fields generated by such power lines.

State health officials say the panel's report is the first time an impartial group of scientists has concluded that magnetic fields may be a danger to human health.

The director of the project, Dr. David Carpenter, dean of the State University of New York's Albany School of Public Health called the finding "disturbing" and urged immediate follow-up studies.

However, Carpenter said, children whose parents smoke face a far greater cancer risk.

The connection was reported in a 154-page study by the New York Power Lines Project. The project had commissioned 16 scientists from universities throughout the nation to study a range of possible effects on humans and laboratory animals caused by both high-intensity and low-intensity power lines.

One of the studies conducted in the Denver area between 1978 and 1983 found that children with leukemia and brain cancer are more likely to live in homes close to typical neighborhood power lines.

A team of researchers led by David Savitz, an epidemiologist at the University of North Carolina, coded all the homes in a surburban community according to their proximity to overhead lines, transformers and substations.

The cancer risk to children living closest to the power lines was 1.7 times higher than for children who lived away from the lines. The risk of developing leukemia in children was 2.1 times higher.

STUDY INDICATES LINK BETWEEN ELECTRIC AND MAGNETIC FIELDS, LEUKEMIA

A survey of deaths among workers who are exposed to high doses of electricity suggests that electrical and magnetic fields may cause leukemia, a doctor says.

In a letter published in the New England Journal of Medicine, Dr. Samuel Milham, Jr., of the Washington State Department of Social and Health Services, said he discovered the apparent link while updating a study of occupational mortality.

He found that in 11 categories of people who work with electricity and magnetism, the leukemia rate was 37% higher than expected. A total 136 workers died of leukemia between 1950 and 1979.

"These findings suggest that electrical and magnetic fields may cause leukemia," he wrote.

The highest excess of leukemia deaths was among power-station operators. Eight of them died, while the expected number was 3.1. Death from leukemia was also at least 50% higher than expected among linemen; television repairmen, aluminum workers, movie projectionists and subway motormen.

MICROWAVE RADIATION EFFECTS ON HUMANS

Stephen F. Cleary

After more than two decades of research, there are still many uncertainties concerning the effects of microwave exposure. Animal experiments have revealed apparent sensitivities at exposure levels below those commonly associated with the only know effect of microwave absorption: tissue heating. the effects fall into three categories: gross thermal damage due to high-intensity exposure, microwave-specific thermal effects at intermediate intensities, and apparently nonthermal effects at low intensities. Whereas the first category of effects are reasonably well understood, the second and third categories are not. Consideration of the unique way microwaves are absorbed in living systems provides some clues for resolving uncertainties in this area. (Accepted for publication 1 December 1982)

EXPOSURE SOURCES

Public concern about the deleterious effects of microwave and radiofrequency (RF) radiation on humans in increasing as microwave sources proliferate and exposure levels increase. There is a general awareness that "radiation" can induce damage and that exposure levels in homes, workplaces, and the environment are increasing. Recently there has been organized public opposition to the siting of microwave and RF sources such as microwave relay towers for long distance tele-communications and satellite earth stations for worldwide television transmission. A spate of legal actions have been initiated for purported radiation-induced morbidity, such as cancer and cataracts, due to occupational exposure.

The microwave and RF industries as well as federal agencies are concerned, since they bear the brunt of the responsibility and monetary burdens for microwave exposure problems. In a technological society such as ours that depends on rapid communications, it is not feasible to avoid exposure by eliminating microwave and RF sources. Instead, the effects of exposure of humans and other life forms must be determined and used to set realistic permissible exposure limits. The biological effects of microwave and RF are difficult to quantify, but one method, which involves the determination of the relationship between the body mass-averaged energy absorption and wavelength, can be used. It is limited, however, by the extrapolation of data from animal studies to humans.

BASIC MECHANISMS

Laymen often do not know the difference between nonionizing radiation (such as microwaves) and ionizing radiation, which has resulted in confusion and unwarranted concern. The differences in the biological effects of ionizing and nonionizing radiation are in the nature of the energy exchange between the electromagnetic field and atoms or molecules. The frequencies (v) of electromagnetic radiation in the ionizing region of the spectrum extend from 10^{15} to 10^{17} Hz. The corresponding quantum energies (E) per photon, according to Planck's relationship $E = hv$ (where h is Planck's constant = 9.54×10^{-14} kcal sec/mole) are 95-9500 kcal/mole. The quantized energy of photons of microwave radiation in the frequency range of 3×10^7 to 3×10^{11} Hz (30-MHz to 300-GHz) range from 2.86×1^{-6} to 2.86×10^{-2} kcal/mole.

Interactions of ionizing radiation photons involve sufficient exchange of energy to eject orbital electrons from atoms or molecules in so-called "single photon" events. Similar effects of microwave or RF radiation photons would require nearly simultaneous absorption of multiple photons. Effects such as the denaturation of biomolecules can be induced only at microwave or RF intensities that are so high that the temperature of the absorber is significantly raised. Thus the absorption of microwave intensities on the order of 100 milliwatts per square centimeter (MW/cm²) results in rapid tissue heating, and, if the exposure is long enough, irreversible tissue damage. (In certain applications, such as the microwave oven, this type of "damage" is known as "cooking.")

The major unanswered question is whether there are other mechanisms of interaction of microwave and RF radiation that cause reversible or irreversible alterations at intensities that do not result in delectable tissue heating. Such low-intensity effects would depend upon characteristics of the electromagnetic field other than the intensity, such as the wavelength or the instantaneous electric or magnetic field strength of amplitudeor pulse-modulated radiation.

To identify possible mechanisms of low-intensity microwave effects Cleary (1973) compared the activation energies for various biochemical effects and interactions (ranging from ionization to hydrogen bond disruption) with a photon energy of 10^4 cV, the photon energy of the radiation used in a microwave oven operated at 2.45-GHz. Since this microwave energy is so much less than the activation energies of the known molecular effects, there is no way to explain how biomolecules could be altered by low-intensity microwave or RF fields. This conclusion is consistent with data obtained from studies of the effects of low-intensity radiation on experimental animals and on cell and tissue preparations in vitro.

BIOLOGICAL EFFECTS

Most animal studies have suggested that reversible functional alterations are associated with small but detectable, field-induced temperature elevations (Cleary 1970, 1977). Examples include transient alterations in the number of circulating blood cells (lympocytes, leukocytes, and erythrocytes) (e.g., Baranski (1971). Deichmann et al, 1964), changes in nuclear structure and mitotic activity of crythroblasts and bone marrow cells in lymph nodes and spleen (Baranski 1971), increased numbers of lymphoblasts and lymphoblastoid transformations (Czerski 1975), alterations in immunocompetency (Liburdy 1977), Szmigielski et al. 1975), neuroendocrine changes (Baranski et al, 1972, Lu et al, 1980, Parker 1973), and teratogenic effects (Berman et al, 1978, Dietzel 1975). Irreversible effects, such as teratogenesis, involve higher exposure intensities than reversible alterations.

Although the majority of the reported effects of microwave and RF-radiation appear to be related to tissue heating, problems have been encountered in using animal data to predict effects on humans. First, nearly all of the studies have involved short exposure times relative to the lifespan of the animal. Effects that were not detected in acute or short-term studies have been found in the few long-term studies conducted to date. There are indications, for example, that protracted low-intensity microwave exposure may affect the animals' immune systems, increasing risk of infectious diseases (Mayers and Habeshaw 1973), Szmigielski et al, 1975) and neoplasms (Szmigielski et al, 1982). Such effects may be due to altered immunocompetents, but it has not been determined if this is an indirect effect of microwave-induced, nonspecific stress or a direct effect of the radiation on immunocompetent cells in vivo. Answers to specific questions such as this, as well as answers to more general questions concerning the effects of chronic, low-intensity exposure of experimental animals, will be forthcoming when sufficient resources are committed to the task. The solution of the second major problem – how to use such date for the assessment of affects on humans – is significantly more complex, however, due to the way microwave and RF radiation is absorbed in animals or man.

ABSORPTION EFFICIENCY

The amount and internal distribution of microwave or RF energy absorption in an experimental animal or a human depends on the size and shape of the body and its electrical properties, primarily the dielectric constant or permittivity (e) and the conductivity (σ). The body of an animal is like an antenna, the efficiency of which varies with the wavelength of the radiation. Gandhi (1975) has shown, for instance, that, as a consequence of the "antenna" effect of the body, the radiation absorption efficiency attains a maximum value of 0.022 W/kg per W/m? at a RF-wavelength of 4 m (frequency of 77 MHz) for a 1.75-m tall human weighing 70 kg. The amount of absorption also depends upon the polarization: the maximum occurs when the electric field vector ($\bar{E}$) is parallel to the long axis (height) of the body: the width of the body: the width of the body or weight also affects absorption, but to a lesser extent than the length.

The mass-averaged rate of energy absorption, which is referred to as the specific absorption rate (SAR), is shown as a function of frequency in Figure 1 for human and mouse models. These data were calculated by Durney et. al. (1978) by using homogeneous prolate spheroids of appropriate sizes and average dielectric properties for species modeling. The maximum SAR for a 5-cm long model of a mouse occurs at a frequency of about 2500 MHz (or a wavelength of 12 cm.). In general, absorption is maximum when the body length is parallel to the E-field and is equal to approximately 40% of the wavelength of the radiation.

The absorption of RF and microwave radiation also depends upon the tissue electrical parameters ϵ and σ, which are frequency dependent. Table 1 lists approximate values for ϵ and σ for tissues at 100 MHz and 2500 MHz. These data indicate the extent of intertissue differences in electrical properties at either frequency. Microwave radiation is more efficiently absorbed by water than other molecules. Consequently, absorption is proportional to tissue water content. The last two columns of Table 1 list the percentage change in ϵ and σ that result as the frequency is increased from 100 MHz to 2500 MHz. As the frequency is increased, the tissue permittivity decreases by about 25%, while the conductivity increases by an average of 180%, primarily due to the variation in the electrical properties of water at these two frequencies. Since energy absorption as these frequencies is determined primarily by the tissue conductivity, the increased conductivity at 2500 MHz relative to 100 MHz results in increased absorption efficiency.

Absorption efficiency maxima for various mammalian species, shown as a function of frequency in Figure 2, indicate that the mouse is at its resonant frequency of about 2500 MHz (2.5 GHz) absorbs approximately five times more efficiently than man at his resonant frequency of 77 MHz. Part of this difference is due to the increase in tissue conductivity at higher frequencies, but this would account for only a factor of two difference. Interspecies scaling must therefore involve other complexities, such as the shape of the body. This point is further illustrated by comparing the absorption efficiencies of the models of a mouse and a man at the resonant frequency of the mouse, 2500 MHz, where the mouse model absorbs about 30 times more microwave energy per unit mass than the human model (0.12 W/kg per W/m^2 versus 0.004 W/kg per W/m^2).

INTERSPECIES EXTRAPOLATION

These results suggest an approach to the problem of interspecies extrapolation of microwave data. For example, if a response to microwave irradiation is observed in mice exposed to 2500-MHz microwaves at 5 mW/cm^2, an intensity of 150 mW/cm^2 should produce an equivalent response in humans exposed to the same microwave frequency. or if a man were exposed at his resonant frequency of 77 MHz, an intensity of 27 mW/cm^2 (*i.e.*, 5 mW/cm^2 x 0.12/0.022) would be required to produce the same effect. This approach to the extrapolation of experimental data has two major limitations, however.

One limitation is due to the physiological differences of species. If it is assumed that microwave effects result from thermal loading of the organism, for example, pertinent physiological parameters might be comparative rates of metabolic heat generation and mechanisms of thermoregulation. The resting metabolic rate of an adult human (20-24 years old) is approximately 1.26 W/kg as compared to 10 W/kg for an adult 15 g mouse. Humans dissipate heat by sweating; mice do not. The thermal neutral zone for humans is 24-31°C and that for mice is 30-33°C. And the maximum critical air temperature for a mouse is 37°C compared to 32°C for a normal human. Since thermal effects are known to result from microwave exposure, interspecies differences in thermal physiology must be taken into account in extrapolating experimental results. Unfortunately, suitable ways to deal with this problem have not yet been developed.

Further complications are encountered as a result of differences between classical heat stress and microwave-induced heat stress. Classical heat stress results from variations in ambient temperature that elicit thermoregulatory reactions to maintain normal body temperature. How does the mammalian thermoregulatory system react to internal heating inducted by microwave energy absorption? It is well known that microwaves can penetrate and be absorbed deep within the body, resulting in highly irregular patterns of internal heating that are very different from the effects of increases in ambient temperature. Most comparative studies have suggested that microwave-induced heat stress in experimental animals elicits different responses than heat stress from infrared radiation absorption or elevated ambient temperatures (Cleary 1977). Internal microwave absorption patterns are determined by the relationship between the wavelength and the dimensions and electrical properties of tissues. Heating patterns are different in different species exposed to the same wavelength as well as in a given species exposed to different wavelengths. For example, to induce the same effect in a human as in a mouse exposed to 2500-MHz microwave radiation would require about 30 times greater field intensity due to the reduced level of absorption by the human relative to the mouse. It the distribution of absorbed energy is taken into account, however, the situation may be altered markedly, depending upon the target organ(s).

When a microwave effect is induced in the skin, for example, average power absorption throughout the entire body is relatively meaningless unless both mouse and man absorb the radiation uniformly throughout their bodies, which is not the case for 2500-MHz radiation. The tissue-depth distribution of absorbed microwave radiation depends on the surface configuration (contours) as well as the thickness of the skin, subcutaneous fat, and muscle. For simplicity, it may be assumed that the radiation is absorbed exponentially. Absorption may be characterized in terms of the penetration depth, which is frequency-dependent and is defined as the distance required for the incident field intensity to be decreased by a factor of c^{-2} or 86%. The average penetration depth in tissue at a frequency of 2500 MHz is 2 cm (Durney et al, 1978).

Since the penetration depth of 2 cm is comparable to the dimensions of a mouse, the microwave energy is absorbed throughout the body of the mouse.[1] Conversely, the microwave energy will be absorbed in the 2-cm thick surface layer of the human body. If the human body is modeled as a prolate spheroid, the geometrical model used by Durney et al, (1978) in the calculation of the absorption efficiencies shown in Fig. 1, almost all of the microwave absorption occurs in a peripheral volume of about $0.0022m^3$ (compared to a total body volume of $0.07m^3$). A mouse having a volume of 15 cm^3 and a mass of 0.015 kg will absorb a total power of about 0.0183 W or a volume-averaged power of 1220 W/m^3 when exposed to 2500-MHz microwaves at an intensity of 1 mW/cm^2. A human exposed to the same microwave radiation will absorb a total of 2.8 W, which averaged over the external absorbing layer of $0.0022m^3$ is about 1273 W/m^3, or approximately the same volume-averaged power as the mouse. Thus, in this hypothetical situation, equivalent biological effects could be induced in the skin of these species in spite of the marked differences in the relative efficiency of mass- or volume-averaged microwave absorption. Although, this is admittedly a simplified situation, it illustrates the basic problem of using calculated or measured values of RF or microwave energy absorption in animal models to predict safe exposure levels for humans.

The results of Szmigielski et al, (1982) provide an example of a situation in which the hypothetical case considered here may be of pertinence in the assessment of human exposure effects. They reported that exposure for periods of up to 10 months to 2450-MHz microwaves at intensities of 5 to 15 mW/Cm² (50 to 150 W/m²) accelerated the development of skin cancer in mice repeatedly treated topically with 10 pl of 5% 3.4-benzopyrene. Assuming the absorbed microwave energy acted on the skin as a carcinogenic promoter, the results of the above calculations suggest that humans exposed under similar conditions would be subject to the same increased risk of skin cancer induction as mice. If, instead of considering the distribution of absorbed energy, the whole-body, mass-normalized power absorption is used as the criterion for interspecies comparison, the assumed threshold for skin cancer promotion by 2500-MHz microwaves in humans would be on the order of 150 mW/cm² (1500 W/m²). Since it is not known in this case (or unfortunately in most other cases) whether the effect of microwave radiation is a direct cellular effect, an indirect nonspecific effect, or a combined effect, extrapolation of data from mouse to man is highly uncertain. The results of Szmigielski et al, (1982) are one of a number of examples of possible synergistic interactions between microwaves and drugs and/or pathogenic organisms (Cleary 1977). Nearly all microwave studies that provide dose-effect data involve animals (mostly rodents). There are no human studies in which reliable exposure data has been obtained. Thus, it has not been possible to use human data to determine safe exposure levels.

MICROWAVE-SPECIFIC THERMAL EFFECTS

The simplified example discussed above illustrates the possible significance of frequency-dependent microwave and RF absorption patterns in living systems. Irregular internal energy absorption may well present an experimental animal with a unique physiological stress. If the rate of absorption of energy is sufficient to cause tissue-temperature elevations, microwave-specific thermal effects may result. Such effects are referred to as microwave-specific because they are uniquely determined by the distribution of absorbed microwave energy and cannot be reproduced by other heat sources. Data on the physiological effects of classical heat stress is thus of limited use in predicting the consequences of microwave-specific heat stress. Extrapolation of animal data to humans requires a detailed knowledge of the internal dose distributions. Techniques are being developed to measure microwave absorption patterns in vivo (Durney et al, 1978). The application of such techniques in long-term experiments should reveal the effects of microwave-specific thermal stress that we need to know to establish safe exposure levels for humans.

LOW-INTENSITY EFFECTS

Once adequate occupational levels are established, setting microwave and RF exposure standards for the general population should be quite simple, since all that should be involved is the use of suitable reduction factors to minimize or eliminate thermal effects. There are, however, experimental and epidemiological results that cannot be explained in terms of microwave-specific thermal phenomena. These effects appear to involve field-induced reversible alterations in the mammalian central nervous system that occur at intensities not generally associated with tissue heating (*i.e.*, less that 0.1°C temperature rise). Such low-intensity effects appear to be related to the magnitude of the instantaneous induced electrical field strength in vivo and to the modulation characteristics of the field. The mechanisms are unknown, but because the modulation frequencies of greatest apparent effect are in the range of brain-wave frequencies (*i.e.,* 1-20 Hz)., there may be an interaction of the external field with intrinsic bioelectrical fields (Adey 1981).

Biphasic or "windowed" responses have been encountered in a number of low-intensity microwave studies in which effects are detectable only within a relatively narrow range of field intensities or modulation frequencies (Adey 1980). These findings are perplexing because the absence of an effect in individuals exposed in one intensity range corresponding, for instance, to occupational exposure levels, does not guarantee that effects will not occur in the general population exposed at significantly lower intensities. Because a review of the effects of most concern in the context, the central nervous system (CNS) effects of RF and microwaves, is beyond the scope of this paper, I refer readers to the detailed review by Adey (1981) for a description of such effects in vertebrates and invertebrates.

Although the conditions for the induction of such effects in humans are uncertain, generalizations are possible. The apparent dependency of low-intensity microwave effects on the induced electric field strength and modulation frequency suggests threshold-type phenomena, albeit somewhat complex thresholds. The results of in vitro studies (Adey 1980) and clinical studies of exposed workers and experimental animals (Baranski and Czerski 1976) support this conclusion, but the intensity thresholds are poorly defined. The significance of such low-intensity, field-induced CNS alterations is difficult to establish, since the effects are generally reversible and are manifested as subtle functional and behavioral changes, effects that result from numerous other causes. Again, as in the case of microwave-specific thermal stress effects, the health consequences of the chronic induction of such effects are unknown. Because the CNS alterations are subtle, it is difficult to see how studies using experimental animals can provide the data needed to evaluate such effects in humans. Epidemiological studies of exposed workers and members of the general population who are chronically exposed to known levels of low-intensity microwave and RF radiation appear to be the only way to obtain such data.

In summary, the interaction of microwave and RF radiation with living systems results in complex modes of internal energy absorption, which present unique dosimetric problems as well as problems of assessing physiological effects. Exposures at intensities in the range of 1-10 mW/cm^2, which may be encountered in workplaces, may result in microwave-specific thermal effects. The relationship of such effects to morbidity and mortality in experimental animals and humans, especially in the case of chronic or long-term exposure, has not been determined. Further problems in assessing physiological effects are posed by the apparent sensitivity of the mammalian CNS to pulse-modulated microwave and RF fields at time-averaged intensities that do not appear to involve significant tissue-heating. Because of the uncertainties surrounding these issues, there are no mandatory standards for population exposure to microwave- and RF-radiation, even after well over two decades of research. Although federal agencies are developing such standards, and voluntary occupational threshold limit values have been proposed (AC-GIH 1981), such efforts must be of an interim nature, since these uncertainties are unlikely to be resolved soon.

548

REFERENCES CITED

ACGIH. 1981. *American Congress of Governmental Industrial Hygienists Notice of Intended Changes, Radiofrequency/ Microwave Radiation.* ACGIH Cincinnati, OH.

Adey, W.R. 1980. Frequency and power windowing in tissue interactions with weak electromagnetic fields. *Proc. IEEE* 68: 119-125.

_____ 1981. Tissue interactions with nonionizing electromagnetic fields. *Physical Rev.* 61: 435-514.

Baranski, S. 1971. Effect of chronic microwave irradiation on the blood forming system of guinea pigs and rabbits. *Aerosp. Med.* 42: 1196-1199.

Baranski, S. and P. Szerski. 1976. *Biological Effects of Microwaves.* Dowden, Hutchinson and Sons, Stroudsburg, PA.

Baranski, S., K. Ostgrowski, and W. Stodolnik-Baranska. 1972. Functional and morphological studies of the thyroid gland in animals exposed to microwave radiation. *Acta Physiol. Pol. 23: 1029-1039.*

Berman, E., J.B. Kinn, and H.B. Carter. 1978. Observations of mouse fetuses after irradiation with 2.45-GHz microwaves. Health Phys. 35: 791-801.

Cleary, S.F. 1970. Biological effects of microwave and radiofrequency radiation. *CRC Crit. Rev. Enviton. Control* 1: 257-306.

_____ 1973. Uncertainties in the evaluation of the biological effects of microwave and radiofrequency radiation. *Health Phys.* 25: 387-404.

_____ 1977. Biological effects of microwave and radiofrequency radiation. *CRC Crit. Rev. Enviton. Control* 7: 121-166.

Czerksi, P. 1975. Microwave effects on the blood-forming systems with particular reference to the lymphocyte. *Ann. NY Acad. Sci.* 247: 232-243.

Deichman, W.J., J. Miale, and K. Landeen. 1964. Effect of microwave radiation on the hematopoictic system of the rat. *Toxical Appl. Pharmacol.* 6: 71-77.

Dietzel, F. 1975. Effects of electromagnetic radiation on implantation and intrauterine development of the rat. *Ann. NY Acad. Sci.* 247: 367-376.

Dutney, C.H., C.C. Johnson, P.W. Barber, H. Massaudi, M.F. Iskander, J.L. Lords, D.K. Kyser, S.J. Allen, and J.C. Mitchell. 1978. *Radiofrequencies Radiation Dysemitry Handbook.* 2nd ed. 1 U.S.A.F. School of Aerospace Medicine, Report SAM-TR-78022, Brooks Air Force Base, TX.

Gandhi, O.P. 1975. Frequency and orientation effect on whole animal absorption of electromagnetic waves. *IEEE Trans. Biomed. Eng.* BME-22: 536-543.

Liburdy, R.P. 1977. Effects of radiofrequency radiation on inflammation. *Radio Science* 12: 179-183.

Lu, S.T., W.G. Lotz, and S.M. Michaelson. 1980. Advances in microwave-induced neuroendocrine effects: the concept of stress. *Proc. IEEE* 68: 73-77.

Mayers, C.P. and J.A. Habeshaw. 1973. Depression of phagocytosis: a non-thermal effect of microwave radiation as a potential hazard to health. *Int. J. Radiat. Biol.* 24: 449-461.

Parker, L.N. 1973. Thyroid suppression and adrenomedullary activation by low-intensity microwave radiation. *Am. J. Physial.* 224: 1388-1390.

Rotkovska, D. and A. Vacek. 1975. The effect of electromagnetic radiation on the hematopoietic stem cells of mice. *Ann. NY Acad. Sci.* 247: 243-250.

Szmigielski, S., J. Jeljasczewicz, and M. Wiranowska. 1975. Acute staphylococcal infections in rabbits irradiated with 3 GHz microwaves. *Ann. NY Acad. Sci.* 247: 305-311.

Szmigielski, S., M. Janiak, and J.K. Wrembel. 1982. Accelerated development of spontaneous and benzopyrene-induced skin cancer in mice exposed to 2450-MHz microwave radiation. *Bioelectramag.* 3: 179-192.

[1]This simplification neglects the fact that internal reflections may result in monuniformities in the distribution of internally absorbed radiation heating to "hot spots." Such phenomena have been predicted theoretically and experimentally demonstrated (see e.g., Cleary 1977). In this case it may be assumed that "hot spots" do not affect the skin response.

Cleary is with the Department of Physiology and Biophysics, Medical College of Virginia, Richmond, VA. American Institute of Biological Sciences. All rights reserved.

SECRET ELF SIGNALS MAY CAUSE MENTAL DISORDER, DISEASE, TREE DEATH, WEIRD WEATHER

Will Schaleben

Invisible "electromagnetic smog" is a pollution threat that has barely caught the public's attention. Occasionally, research trickles out linking extremely low frequency (ELF) fields to cancer, birth defects, and suicide. Known sources of these possibly dangerous fields are power lines, electric waterbed heaters, and electric blankets – but there are other transmitters of these pernicious fields that are far more obscure.

Some are secret projects of the Super Powers that involve "over-the-horizon-radar" and submarine communication. Others are "unofficial" and may involve electronic warfare, weather manipulation, and mind control. Depending upon desired results, ELF transmissions can be powerful enough to oscillate through the entire planet and everything round it, or they can be low-powered and focused on smaller targets such as someone's house or office.

Powerful ELF waves can be detected and heard, at any time, on shortwave (SW) radio. The pulses are distinctive because they sound like someone clattering a board rapidly along a wooden picket fence, and they often blot out many legitimate SW stations. Technically, the signals are illegal, according to international agreements that cover SW transmissions, but authorities have not been able to stop them, since no government admits to transmitting them.

The pulses are called the "woodpecker" by SW radio buffs. Yet, beyond the annoying interference these waves cause on SW radio, almost no one knows for sure why the woodpecker waves are being transmitted, or more importantly, what they may be doing to biological systems, the weather, and the planet.

The mysterious woodpecker – first heard sporadically on SW during the 1960s and then continuously since July 4, 1976 (the Bicentennial of the U.S.), according to some accounts – has been the target of much investigation and speculation among independent researchers and intelligence agencies worldwide. Yet, even after over 13 years of study, practically nothing about it has been publicly revealed except through a few esoteric scientific journals and alternative news sources.

SW radio enthusiasts and interested scientific researchers have tracked the pulses to sites in both Russia, which began continuously transmitting them in 1976, and America, which began its transmissions later. The investigators also discovered that the frequencies of woodpecker pulses change every few seconds. Their frequencies are very low, usually between 6 to 20 Hz (cycles per second), but, since April 18, 1987, a new and very strong signal of 31.2 Hz has been detected.

The pulses, although quite different that shortwave, have harmonic effects in some SW bands, thus they can be picked up by SW radios. One researcher believes some woodpecker sources may be using shortwave as a *carrier* for the ELF pulses so that the waves will more effectively permeate the atmosphere.

Powerful woodpecker waves are gigantic; for example, an 8 Hz signal has a wavelength of 22,159 miles. A broadcast antenna for propagating them can be many miles long, or, using a Nikola Tesla design, the antenna can be a large metal ball on an adjustable height tower that can extend to 154 ft. The power needed to transmit is extraordinary. The Canadian and Dutch governments monitored transmission in the range of 40 million kilowatts. Three known transmitters in the U.S.S.R. are hooked up to five nuclear reactors, claimed one source with the CIA.

Unlike relatively small radio and microwave signals, the huge woodpecker pulses travel *through the earth* and extend 200 miles above its surface. Some areas on earth show stronger concentrations than other locales because of how the transmitting antennae are aimed. The waves go through anything in their path, including the most advanced types of electromagnetic shielding materials, and they alter the normal vibration of everything they permeate. The effects of these waves on biosystems are cumulative.

"Over-the-horizon-radar" is thought by many investigators to be the main reason the woodpecker ELF waves are being transmitted. The new type of radar can detect objects five times farther away than old radar systems. Supposedly, ELF-based radar can determine what material an object is made from, as well. Neither the U.S. nor U.S.S.R. admits to having this top-secret, advanced class of radar.

Another officially recognized use of ELF, at at least the U.S. Navy has publicized, is for submarine communications. The Navy's "Project Sanguine," located in Michigan and Wisconsin, uses ELF transmissions, at 46 and 72 Hz, as carrier waves for coded digital messages being sent to submerged subs. It's assumed the Soviets are using ELF to communicate with their subs, too.

Submarine communication with ELF as a carrier wave has its drawbacks, mostly because the transmission and reception of information coded onto ELF carrier waves is very slow. However, a new laser that penetrates the water with ease has been developed and probably is replacing ELF transmissions as the mode of sending messages to subs.

A side effect of using ELF waves to send messages might have been the inadvertent discovery that the waves may be able to alter weather. When the Wisconsin site was turned on for the first time, a few years ago, the immediate area had the worst thunderstorm in its history.

A few investigators – such as Lieutenant Colonel (retired) Thomas E. Bearden, who was one of the first researchers to blow the whistle on the Soviet woodpecker – contend that the U.S.S.R. is deliberately trying to manipulate global weather patterns using ELF transmissions. According to some theories, the woodpecker could be used to regulate the movement of electrically charged particles in the upper atmosphere and change the direction of the jet stream, which may cause adverse weather in the U.S. while enhancing the climate of the U.S.S.R.

It's true that ELF signals may be altering the jet stream, claimed a CIA source, but it is not a deliberate activity on the part of the Soviets. Instead, it is the accidental result of the collision of U.S.S.R. and U.S. woodpecker transmissions which occur most intensely over the northwest and northeast U.S. and Canada. According to the source, the CIA transmits ELF signals designed to counter what the agency perceives to be pathological frequencies being beamed at the U.S. by the U.S.S.R. When the two signals run through each other, enormous, local, columnar standing waves that extend far into the atmosphere are formed. This ultimately causes the jet stream to shift direction and change global weather patterns.

It's apparent that little consideration has been given to the possible ill-effects of ELF signals on humans. Certain frequencies may contribute to the formation of cancer and other diseases, including psychological ailments. For instance, research conducted by Robert C. Beck and published in *Archaeus* (1986) found that in 25-75% of the subjects he studied, "ELF fields of 6.67 Hz, 6.26 Hz and lower tend to produce symptoms of confusion, anxiety, depression, tension, fear, mild nausea, and headaches, cholinergia, arthritis-like aches, insomnia, extended reaction times, hemispheric EEG desynchronization, and many other vegetative disturbances." These are all ailments rather common these days.

Other ELF waves can be quite beneficial to life. "H and B field (magnetic vector) oscillations of 7.8, 8.0 and 9.0 Hz produce anxiety relieving and stress-reducing effects that mimic some meditative states, says Beck.

THERAPEUTIC USES OF THE CASTOR OIL PACK

DISCUSSION

The human body with all of its complex mechanisms is in many ways very simple in its workings. An analogy can be drawn between the maintenance of an automobile and the human body. For example, if an automobile goes without gas it will not run, while the body will not run if it goes without nutrition. Similarly, if an automobile is not lubricated or greased, then its parts will become sluggish and rusted. If the body is not lubricated then its organs, glands and joints will become constipated, sluggish and stiff. This sluggishness in the organs, glands, or other moving parts in the body is the cause for much unneeded pain, discomfort and disease. It becomes logical, therefore, that if one could get the body oiled and greased like an automobile, then these body parts could return to normal function just as they do in an automobile.

It is the old story of the "Tin Man" in the "Wizard of Oz." Whenever his joints and parts became rusted and immovable due to adverse external factors, a little oil would be added to lubricate them and he would be fine. Similarly, the parts of the body will also lose their sluggishness and become easily movable when they are lubricated.

WHAT IS CASTOR OIL?

Castor oil is a pale viscous fatty oil from the castor bean used especially as a cathartic and lubricant. The castor-oil plant is actually a tropical old-world herb (Ricinus Communis) which is widely grown for its oil-rich beans. A cathartic can be defined as a substance which brings about a purification or purgation (a purging) of the part on which it is used. A lubricant is a substance capable of reducing friction, heat, and wear when introduced as a film between solid substances. It is these very properties of this oil which give it medicinal abilities for helping to restore the body to proper harmony.

HOW THE CASTOR OIL PACK WORKS AND WHEN THEY CAN BE USED

Whenever a patient has a constant pain in any organ, gland, or movable joint in the body then the castor oil packs can be employed. For example, if there is pain in the liver, stomach, lungs, kidneys, limbs, colon, joints, or any other part due to sluggishness in these areas then the castor oil packs will be effective. What the oil does upon penetrating the skin, due to applied heat, is to enter into the organ, gland, or movable part and lubricate it, purge it, and purify it of toxic waste and materials. The purging of the organ, gland, or body part allows the waste products and toxins which have been clogging up that part of the system to be removed. The lubricant is important as it removes the friction which was causing the organ, gland, or body part to become irritated and inflamed. This process works extremely well in cases of lung disease such as pneumonia and colon disease such as constipation and diverticulitis. The castor oil packs do not cure the disease but instead allow the body to cleanse itself and build up its resistance enough so that the disease process ceases of its own accord.

RESULTS

The results of this type of treatment is many times remarkable. There have been many cases in this clinic of extreme pain being relieved by this method when nothing else would work. Of course this form of treatment should be used in conjunction with one's regular CHIROPRACTIC TREATMENTS AND FUNCTIONAL NUTRITIONAL BALANCING. This treatment should be done under the supervision of your physician.

HOW TO APPLY THE CASTOR OIL PACKS

Castor oil may be purchased in bottle form from either one's grocery store or from a local pharmacy. The treatment could be done 2-3 times a day in severe chronic cases and at least once a day, preferably before retiring at night, in more acute cases.

ORDERED STEPS

1. Apply castor oil liberally and directly over the affected part. One can lie on the floor of the bathroom or on a therapy table, preferably on top of a sheet to prevent soiling the carpet or table. NOTE: Having a friend or spouse help you is the ideal situation, however, this can be done without the aid of outside help.
2. Heat a bath towel under extremely hot water in a sink so that it can get as hot as physically possible without burning or causing harm to the skin. It can be tested in the hands by ringing it out before applying it.
3. Place the hot towel over the affected part covered liberally then put a dry towel over the wet one to hold in the heat.
4. This should be repeated at least a total of three times in one treatment as the heat from the towel is absorbed quickly.
5. Reapply the castor oil between each application.
6. After the third time the body part may be wiped clean of the castor oil but it should not be washed and a bath or shower should not be taken until later so that the oil will have a chance to penetrate still more.
7. Again, in cases of extreme pain or congestion, the whole process should be done three separate times a

day, preferably upon awakening, mid-afternoon, and before retiring. However, in milder cases once a day will be sufficient. Do this every day until the pain or discomfort is completely gone.

SUMMARY OF THE POSITIVE EFFECTS OF THE CASTOR OIL PACKS

The castor oil packs will lubricate, purge and cleanse the affected part as it penetrates deep into the body. It is well-known what a powerful laxative castor oil is when taken internally. How much more so does it act as a cell and tissue laxative when applied externally. This is now a well-documented scientific fact.

WARNING: UNDER NO CIRCUMSTANCES TAKE CASTOR OIL INTERNALLY WITHOUT THE CONSENT OF YOUR PHYSICIAN. IT IS A VERY POWERFUL LAXATIVE AND SHOULD BE USED ONLY IN EXTREME CASES UNDER THE DIRECT SUPERVISION OF YOUR PHYSICIAN.

These packs have a rejuvenating and revitalizing affect on the body. As a result of the purging, the tissues and cells will receive more fresh blood, oxygen, and nutrients which will effect a healing process to take place in the tissues and cells. If the body is no longer abused through the wrong diet and improper nutrition then these parts will not be affected again unless they have not been completely cleaned out which may take some time and scientifically organized treatment. Just as one's automobile now runs better because it is getting proper fuel and lubrication, so also will the body parts run better when they get the proper fuel and lubrication.

TO THE PATIENT FROM THE DOCTOR
AND CLINIC STAFF

Congratulations on your decision to allow nature to take its course in healing your body. If you will combine this program with regular CHIROPRACTIC CARE AND FUNCTIONAL NUTRITIONAL BALANCING then your life should be more healthy and free of pain. Don't forget the importance of:

- PROPER EXERCISE
- SCIENTIFIC EXPOSURE TO THE SUN'S RAYS (ASK YOUR PHYSICIAN)
- FRESH AIR
- GOOD NATURAL FOODS
- POSITIVE THINKING WITH EMOTIONAL STABILITY.

We at this holistic healing clinic are here to serve you and your getting well from all your difficulties (better word, opportunities) is as important and meaningful to us as it is to you.

*Chinese Formulas which can be
obtained through your local Chinese Pharmacist
that were very helpful and effective
to Dr. Farber during his bout with Lyme Disease.*

11-20-92

D.P.M Paul Farber
DrChen

Relax & Muscles
NEEDLES & GET RID FROM
INFLAMMENTS

562

JERSEY SHORE MEDICAL CENTER
NEPTUNE, NEW JERSEY 07754

This is to certify that

Paul Farber, PhD DC

attended the

6th Annual Lyme Disease Scientific Conference

presented by the

Lyme Disease Foundation, Inc.

on May 5th & 6th, 1993

Jersey Shore Medical Center is accredited by the Medical Society of New Jersey to grant Category I credit for this activity. This program meets the criteria for 16 hours of Category I of the Physicians Recognition Award of the American Medical Association.

Director of Medical Education

Affiliated with the University of Medicine and Dentistry of New Jersey-Robert Wood Johnson Medical School.

LYME DISEASE

what it is...
how it's transmitted...
what it does to you...
how to detect it...
how to treat it...
how to prevent it...

GEOGRAPHY

Originally discovered in 1975 in Lyme, Connecticut, Lyme disease has been reported in 45 states, although it's prevalent in three regions of the country:

- Coastal and wooded regions of New England, New York, New Jersey, Pennsylvania and the Mid-Atlantic States
- Midwest, including Ohio, Wisconsin, Minnesota
- Coastal and wooded areas of California, Southwestern Oregon, Colorado, Nevada and Utah

TRANSMISSION

Lyme disease is caused by the spirochete *Borrelia burgdorferi* transmitted to humans by the bite of a tick, generally the deer tick, *lxodes dammini*. These ticks are found in wooded, grassy, marshy and forested areas.

The deer tick is about the size of a grain of pepper or poppy seed. They are eight-legged and about 1mm in length. The tick can pick up or transmit the bacterial during the larval and adult stages. During the larval stage, the tick usually feeds on infected mice. In the <u>nymphal</u> stage, the tick clings to vegetation such as tall grass or brush. It is at this stage that the tick can come into direct contact with people.

The <u>adult</u> tick also bites humans but prefers to feed on the white-tailed deer, although birds, chipmunks, skunks, raccoons and even household pets can be carriers. If the tick happens to be infected with spirochetes, it may transmit them to the host during the feeding process. Once in the body, the spirochetes multiply and spread rapidly through the bloodstream. The spirochetes have been found in nearly every organ in the body.

SEASON

Incidences of Lyme disease are reported throughout the year; however, risk is multiplied during the summer months. If temperatures are moderately warm, 45 degrees and above, the ticks may be active.

December	**Low Risk**
January	Last year's adults
February	and nymphs overwintering
March	**Moderate Risk**
April	Last year's adults active,
May	nymphs emerging
June	**High Risk**
July	nymphs active
August	
September	**Moderate Risk**
October	This year's active adults
November	

EARLY AND LATE DISEASE
Early Disease
During early disease, 60% to 80% of patients develop an expanding red rash called Erythema Migrans, with or without other symptoms. Common symptoms of early disease include fatigue, headache, fever, chills, stiff neck and pain in muscles and joints.

Late Disease
Late disease is usually marked by neurological, cardiac, or musculoskeletal abnormalities. These may include "Lyme arthritis," Bell's palsy, shortness of breath, loss of memory, tingling and numbness in arms and legs, and sometimes inflammatory eye disorders.

TREATMENT
If you think that you've been bitten by a tick, call your doctor immediately. Lyme disease can cause serious health problems, and is more easily treated in the early stages.

Early treatment of Lyme disease is oral antibiotics in the class of penicillins, tetracyclines, or cephalosporins.

More advanced or chronic cases are treated with intravenous antibiotics.

PREVENTION
- Take precautions in wooded areas, tall grasses, sand dunes and brush.
- Use insect repellents containing DEET.
- When walking through wooded areas, wear light-colored clothing to make it easier to see ticks. Tuck pant legs into socks and wear long-sleeved shirts and hats.
- Check yourself, your children and pets thoroughly and often for ticks. Pets can also pick up and develop the disease, but can be treated.
- Shower and shampoo hair after being outdoors.
- Wash clothing after inspecting it carefully.

• If you find a tick, remove it with fine point tweezers using a gently traction just in front of the body. Wash bite area thoroughly. Save the tick in a covered container and insert a few blades of grass. Label the outside with your name, date, bite location on the body, city or county, and state where incident occurred. Call your doctor.

Check often for ticks. If a tick is found, remove tick by grasping behind its head with tweezers and pulling gently but firmly upward. Do not squeeze body of tick when removing.

UPDATE ON THE YEAST SYNDROME
John P. Trowbridge, M.D.

John Park Trowbridge is President-Elect (1989-1991) of the American College of Advancement in Medicine (ACAM), and has lectured extensively and conducted a variety of workshops, in addition to maintaining a practice in Humble, Texas. He emphasizes complementary and nutritional medicine, is the developer of the Face2 nonsurgical facelift, and makes a particular specialty of treating yeast syndrome. He is the author (with Morton Walker) of *The Yeast Syndrome and Chelation Therapy,* and has written many articles for professional and general publications.

GREENBURG: You've had some years of experience in treating patients with yeast syndrome. What new developments with that condition have you observed recently?

TROWBRIDGE: I think the most exciting observation is the number of patients who are clearly helped by a treatment program for the yeast syndrome when they don't fit the classical pattern of someone who has the problem. They don't come in with the skin afflictions, they don't necessarily come in with the digestive problems, things that would classically pin them down to the yeast syndrome. And yet when nothing else has helped, and you've done nutritional assessment, a general medical assessment, for particular disease problems and you can't identify one, but the patient continues to be symptomatic, increasing numbers of those patients are helped by the treatment program.

GREENBURG: Do you suspect the yeast syndrome is affecting younger populations now?

TROWBRIDGE: Oh, absolutely, I have no question about that. And the problem that I see is that you don't even have to have yeast syndrome to get sick. It's real simple, all you have to do is grow up in America. And automatically, by definition, as far as I'm concerned, you are predisposed to illness. And you will get it. And you don't know how sick you will be until you get it.

And so people cavalierly lead their lives expecting not to be sick, then they go from doctor to doctor thinking that they are not really sick. The problem with that is that the doctors agree with them: "Well, you don't really have very much going on, don't worry about it." And they get sicker.

And a lot of young children, teenagers are suffering from a chronic indigestion syndrome. I would put three primary causes for that.

Number one, they are not taking in the food parts that make people parts. I try to make it real simple with my patients. You are only the food that you ate. You are not the air that you breathe, and you are not the water that you drink. You are only the food; chopped up, rearranged. And now you get people parts out of it. And that's replacement parts. That's where you get the growth parts. So if you eat junk food, you create a junky body. And if you have a junky body, of course it's not just the rest of you, it's also your digestive system. Therefore it doesn't work as well as it should.

The second reason would be the incredible sugar level – we put a sugar/starch load onto ourselves in this country that is phenomenal. So do all westernized, civilized, industrialized nations. With that sugar load, you're overstressing your pancreas tremendously, and it simply isn't built to take that.

And thirdly, the amount of fried food that has become commonly accepted in the fast food business. There's no question that you're overstressing your liver and gall bladder.

GREENBURG: The "average" American consumes around 125 pounds of sugar yearly. Some might develop diabetes. Do you think this can be yeast-related?

TROWBRIDGE: No, I am not going to maintain that. But on the other hand, if you take a look at the statistics for juvenile delinquents, it's about 275 or more pounds of sugar per year per person, okay?

So juvenile delinquency, let's go ahead and start looking at it. If you are always eating junk foods, you tend to eat foods that have a higher taste content. Sweeter, saltier, spicier, whatever. This is largely because, as you get increasingly zinc deficient, your sensation of taste is gone. So as you become anorexic, because of not enough zinc, because the foods you are eating don't have zinc in them, then you tend to go more and more off center on your dietary choices. You tend to go for more foods that have the bad content, which of course means they have less and less minerals.

When we start people on treatment for the yeast syndrome, the last thing we are thinking of is medications. The first thing we are thinking of is to get a strong nutritional foundation so they can even approach a treatment program.

GREENBURG: *What are the social ramifications of correcting this syndrome?*

TROWBRIDGE: If you look at the treatment for the yeast syndrome as based in food selection and in food preparation, which is what I basically say it is, if you are not ready to make the dietary changes, don't start the treatment program. Period.

Because what we are really doing is a *social reformation in the values* that people have with regard to food and what it means. Food has so often been thought of as a reward and a symbol of prestige, and social position, and really it is no longer that. We're trying to return food to its rightful place, the sustenance of human beings. Okay, sustenance and enjoyment, but not making enjoyment the big thing. But that's what people do. I mean, they have ice cream every day, they have soda every day, they have cakes and cookies every day, they have treats every day. And no longer does food serve its primary purpose, when you do that. So we're having to change that habit mode.

I tell people, this is not a diet, like you think of a diet, this is an eating program, and I want you to eat all the food you want to eat. The only thing I want to restrict is your choices. And they invariably lose weight. And they invariably feel better. And they invariably say, "I can't eat all that food."

GREENBURG: Each year, Americans spend approximately $39 billion on weight loss programs. What makes your dietary recommendations of continuing value?

TROWBRIDGE: You know, one out of every five Americans is on a diet continuously. And that's got to say something to you about our relationship to food.

The most significant thing that I see about yeast syndrome is that it is going to change our fundamental approach to two things. Number one is our relationship to food. And number two is our relationship to the ecosystem that each of us represents. This is really an outgrowth of the 1960's – you could call it the Sierra Club movement. The environmentalist issues, where we became really concerned about polluting our environment. Well, what I see the yeast syndrome doing is changing the way we look at what food means to us and how we approach it, and changing the way that we take care of the environment of our bodies, the micro-ecology. Do we really pay attention to culturing the bugs in our colon; do we pay attention to nursing them along and replacing them? I don't see it as a fundamental change to how we approach medications. Because I believe in medications. I think they are incredibly powerful for what they do.

But they don't need to be used that much; because what they do is very specific to special situations. And mostly those situations do not have to arise if you have a proper dietary approach and you take care of the microenvironment, which would really protect you. The body is built with all sorts of checks and balances between the good bugs that protect us and the bad ones.

If you do that, you don't need antibiotics that often. So you don't have to worry about changing the way people think about antibiotics, all you have to do is worry about if you can minimize the number of times they need those antibiotics. And that's what a rearrangement of their thinking would do for the microflora.

GREENBURG: So treatment of this type may not only succeed in helping patients restore their sense of wellness, but in fact may help to alter their perceptions of the world around us?

TROWBRIDGE: Absolutely. You see, most medical care is a negative conditioning. You are only there, resentfully, because you have to be. And all the things associated with medical treatment are deprivations, and all of them are expensive, and all of them are inconvenient. And all of them have a bad-medicine taste to them.

And so our whole notion of the medical model, the sick role, is to get out of it as quickly as possible. Getting out of the sick role we view as no longer suffering the discomfort of the limitation. The problem with that is that as soon as you stop suffering, all of your incentives for doing anything different disappear. With the yeast syndrome, the reverse is true. We tell people, "You are not here to feel better right away. You're here to do things that lay the foundation, that improve your health. And that's a slow process."

So I use the example that when you graduate from college, that's an event. That's like taking a medicine, *that's* an event. Something definite happened, you can record it right here on film. But the education is a process, and that takes the time. And you didn't see that, you didn't *get* the education. And nutrition is that process compared to graduation, which is an event, or a medication. And so you are here now to change the way your body works on the inside, not just to create an event. If you want an event, go elsewhere. But if you want the process, let's start it now.

So that they never have a sudden realization, "Gee, I'm all well now." Wellness becomes a way of life, not a goal. Wellness become a process, not an achievement.

GREENBURG: This switchover to wellness thinking is the cornerstone of your therapy?

TROWBRIDGE: Right. I tell people, very simply when they start, "If you are not ready to make the dietary changes, don't start any of this. Don't let us get the testing, nothing. Go off and stay sick; then, when you get tired of being sick, and when you get sicker, hopefully you will come in here before it's too late for us to do something with your foundation. And if you are ready to do it, do it now. But make a commitment. And I only ask for a month at a time – give me a thirty-day commitment. So I can know what's happening and I can make adjustments based on seeing that response."

But they'll come in here saying, "That was mostly pretty good." The point of it is *not* to be pretty good; that's taking your medicines. What I want you to do is to do everything that you need to do for you to feel better. And what that means is rebuilding your foundation, not mine. I don't suffer.

GREENBURG: Your program of self-responsibility is participating in one's medical care adds, then, to self-esteem?

TROWBRIDGE: Absolutely. I get patients to come in, and in thirty days I say, "What's happened?" "Well, I'm feeling this, and I'm feeling that." And if you go down the list, most everything is improving. And say, "Now, who did it? Well, you, I guess you did know. You did. See all I did is tell you what to do in a specific way. Just the same way you'd hire someone to consult for repairing your house. Okay, whether they did the repairs or you did it, they told you what to do. And the point is, you did it. You made the commitment."

GREENBURG: By encouraging patients to take more responsibility for themselves, you've truly empowered your patients.

TROWBRIDGE: Absolutely. You have empowered the patient. Actually, I tell the patient that we deal with that we've returned the power of medical care to them instead of to me. The tragedy of modern technological medicine is that it has usurped the power from the patient. It operates on the patient, whether it's by medications, or by ministrations, or by surgery. It operates with their consent, but once it's achieved that consent, it immediately takes from them any power to withdraw it. It takes the language of medicine and makes it purposely confusing, takes the concepts and makes them woefully intricate, and then expects the patient to do everything it says.

What it comes down to is, health is so much simpler. First, you listen to your body very carefully. You'll report to me what your body says – for example when women say, "You know, I really crave chocolate; I had a very hard time this month," I'll say, "Well, when did you crave chocolate?" "Well, about two weeks ago." "When was your period?" "Let me see, about a week and a half ago." "Great, okay. Do you notice that you crave chocolate just about every time before your period?" "Well, as a matter of fact, yes." Great. So we go looking for copper deficiency because that's very commonly associated.

All they have to do is tell me what their body is doing; they listen first to their body, and ask my advice. Then, they can go back armed with new information for their own pursuit of health.

GREENBURG: Medicine practiced in this manner represents a major paradigm switch?

TROWBRIDGE: That's a replacement. That's the medical model, that's correct.

GREENBURG: How will this impact on society in the next 20-30 years?

TROWBRIDGE: Let me give you an example. When Orian Truss wrote his book, he called it *The Missing Diagnosis.* He didn't call it the missing treatment. He called it *The Missing Diagnosis,* because if a standard orthodox physician diagnoses that you have a yeast infection – happens to stumble upon it, it's quite obvious – then his treatment is the same kind of medications that I would routinely prescribe. The only problem is that his patients don't get better in the same sense that I see my patients getting better.

And that is because he continues to be the dispenser of their improvement. He dispenses their medications, and as far as I'm concerned I tell patients who are only interested in that to please go elsewhere. I'm not interested in being the one that saves them from an illness, I'm only interested in being one who assists them in regaining their health. And that's a completely different medical model.

Yes, we'll use medications along the way. Yes, we'll use dietary changes. Yes, we'll use nutritional supplements. But the question is, whose commitment is it to put into place, mine or theirs?

GREENBURG: You said before that dietary junk was a precursor for yeast, the yeast syndrome. What is the yeast syndrome a precursor for?

TROWBRIDGE: That's a great question. I personally think that the yeast syndrome is a precursor for any and every degenerative disease. The metabolic disturbance that comes from the yeast syndrome is so overwhelming that you are looking at injury to every single body system. If you take a look just at magnesium balance, we don't know why, but it's quite clear that tissue magnesium levels are lower in patients who have the yeast syndrome.

Now, if you start correlating magnesium balance with high blood pressure, with cardiovascular illness, and hardening of the artery diseases; if you start correlating magnesium with nervous system disorders, anxiety, stress, distress, depression, you are looking at just two completely different areas. One is cardiovascular disease, which everybody is concerned about, and the other is mental, psychological balance, which everybody is concerned about. And yet, they don't have anything in appearance in common, except magnesium is at the root of both in a number of ways. And the yeast syndrome is associated with lower tissue magnesium.

Vitamin B6 is very commonly used for cardiovascular illness, very commonly used for neurological illness; again, yeast syndrome has lower levels of B6 present.

And there's thyroid hormone, one of the first activities interfered with by the yeast syndrome. Thyroid is your thermostat. I tell patients that they won't understand how important the thyroid is, that what they need to think of is: in their house, they do activities in various rooms. If they want to change the activity in every single room in their house, turn down the thermostat and see what it's like. They'll change what they do in every single room. And that's your thyroid gland.

If you want to talk about sugar handling, which every single cell in your body must do, it's obligatory that they handle sugars appropriately. The yeast syndrome interrupts your ability, probably at the acetylcholine step, probably when you are trying to get most of the energy out of the sugar.

So the yeast syndrome is setting you up for every degenerative disease that I could possible think of, because you are damaging the cells, and once they get damaged, and don't get repaired, they degenerate.

GREENBURG: For many, the Herxheimer reaction (dying off of yeast, producing Candida toxin in the bloodstream) is one of the most troublesome aspects of therapy.

TROWBRIDGE: Oh yeah, it could be. And I'll tell you how we avoid it, it's really quite simple.

Most physicians who treat the yeast syndrome, and see the Herxheimer reaction consistently, are jumping into the treatment program without laying the foundation. So we get people to change their dietary program dramatically. And this is the single most important thing I tell physicians who call me and say, "How do you really treat this?" The dietary program, the nutritional basis is absolutely fundamental.

So we start them on phase one of the eating program, and then we graduate them into phase two of the eating program. We start them on a proteolytic enzyme, that they take between meals. You can use any basic proteolytic enzyme, we have two or three favorites that we employ with people. You take them between meals, and you take a yeast-suppressive nutritional supplement, for instance caprylic acid. And you take that on a graduated basis. We usually start at twice a day, and gradually go up to four times a day.

So we are putting in an increasing suppression on the yeast growth. Meanwhile we have this proteolytic enzyme in between meals, so it's not digesting on food. And the theory is that we are helping to chop up released toxin. What is probably going on is that we have changed the microfloral environment, and so we are encouraging the growth of some species and discouraging the growth of others just by making changes of which we really don't know the magnitude.

As we get to the point where, about three to four weeks into the program, we add a medication, we have so greatly reduced the yeast population that the amount of toxin that is released, the Candida toxin that comes out from the new bugs that are killed, is dramatically less than would have happened if we had had it happen on day one.

When we first started treating the yeast syndrome, we started using medications from day one, and roughly one third of the patients never came back again. We called and found out why. "I didn't want to feel that bad again. Ever." "I'd rather suffer with what I've got than feel that bad." So we look for ways to avoid that.

We have a slogan about how you get better in the office. When you come to our practice, we want you to hear this real clearly: DON'T STAY SICK. DON'T.

D for dietary changes, O for over the counter nutritional supplements that decrease the growth of yeast – caprylic acid, garlic, acidophilus and so on – N for specific nutritional substances that reverse the process going on inside of you – generally speaking, magnesium and vitamin B6, evening primrose oil, GLA, things like that that we can document interfere with yeast in general. And then other things specifically for you. In other words we are trying to treat the specific patient who comes in, not just the yeast syndrome. And T, the final letter, treatment with medications.

We must go through D, O, and N before we ever get to T. And if you don't do it that way, your treatment program is markedly less successful, at least in our guess.

GREENBURG: Now, stress has become a buzz word, I'm afraid, for our society's inability to manage much of what we've created both personally and professionally. What's your concept of what's called stress, and how much of a role, if any, do you see it playing in the etiology of the yeast syndrome?

TROWBRIDGE: There are two dynamics to that. The first is, the really startling realization that we don't understand the microflora. If you take a look at it, yeasts are single-cell organisms. They are neither plant nor animal, they are in the fungus kingdom. They are entirely self-sufficient and do not require another yeast nearby at all for any of their life functions. Bacteria are similarly self-sufficient; so are algae. Those are representative of the animal and plant kingdoms.

What we have always thought is that you had to be a multicellular organism to need hormone signals, but we have discovered that yeasts have hormone receptors. And they make hormone signals. And what's strange is, what does a single-cell, self-sufficient bug, like a yeast, need to have a hormone for? In other words, why does it need to signal other members that are equally independent?

It turns out that if you test those hormone receptor sites, they are exquisitely more interested in having human-being cortisone on them than any other signaler.

GREENBURG: Human-being cortisone? What's that? Explain.

TROWBRIDGE: It's one of your major stress hormones, you produce it when you are stressed. What's of interest with this human-being cortisone, animal cortisone – very similar type stuff; I mean, cortisone is cortisone anywhere in the animal kingdom – what is interesting is that, if you take a look about an organism that's undergoing stress, it's putting out cortisone; that's an alert and a stimulus for the rest of the cells, preparing you to do adaptation response.

And if you fail to adapt, you exhaust after the fatigue of trying to adapt and trying to adapt, and that exhaustion presages your disintegration. In other words, your death.

If you take a look at yeast and their function in the fungus world, fungi recycle the last bits of life out of living organisms. In other words, as they are dying and dead.

And stress usually increases the dying and death phase. And, indeed, is probably the primary initiator for it. So you will be signalling your stress all along, while you are disintegrating and dying, and that signal may be a prime initiator for growing yeast in sufficient numbers to recycle you.

GREENBURG: Lifestyle modifications, such as progressive relaxation, make good physiological sense?

TROWBRIDGE: Absolutely. Anything to reduce your stress levels and reduce your hormones circulating.

GREENBURG: Trust in medicine in America is steadily diminishing. People seem to be genuinely suspicious and often fearful of their physicians.

TROWBRIDGE: Well, I had a patient today, I said, "Okay, so your doctors tried something and it didn't work and they said to just go ahead and live with it. So where does that leave you?"

Well, I'm stuck. I said, "I don't understand that. Because you're not crazy. I understand that they said it was all in your head and you were making it up because they couldn't make it go away, but just because they couldn't make it go away doesn't mean that it isn't there. Just because they didn't do the test to find it doesn't mean it doesn't exist."

You know, before 1924, we had insulin clearly delineated. We knew that we had something here that controlled blood sugar. What happened to all those people who were diabetics before: Just because we couldn't pin down the molecule doesn't mean that the problem didn't exist.

And now, some part of your problem may be on the medical horizon, and we can kind of see where it is, but we can't pin it down. That doesn't mean I can't help you. It just means I might not be able to tell you exactly what the name of it is.

580

So you see, the whole concept is, you are not in here to know the names; if I told you the names right now would that make you happy? "Well, I don't know." And I say, "Well, fine. Here are some names. Delta-6 saturate enzyme interruption. Does that make you happy?" "Well, no." "Does it make you feel any better?" "No." "Fine. Now would you like to know what we are going to do about it?" "Yes."

You see, that's the thing. Doctors don't do anything with their patients. They name it, kick them out the door with some prescription, and they are done. But that's not doing something with your patient, that's doing something *to* your patient. That's veterinary medicine. That has nothing to do with human medicine. It has nothing to do with what's going on with people. That why stress control is so important. You know what I do with the depression? I get all these people coming in depressed, I mean sadly depressed, and what I say first is, "Do you own a Bible?" "Yes." "Fine. Have you ever read Proverbs?" Well, some have, some haven't. "Here is your lesson. Get a three-by-five card, and every day you start somewhere in Proverbs, I don't care where, and I don't care whether you read forward or backward, when you find a verse that means something, you write down the date, the verse number and you write the verse. It's only three, four, or five lines. And you read it at breakfast, lunch, supper, and bedtime. And the next day you do it again, only you've got a second verse now. At the end of the month you have thirty verses of Proverbs that are God's message specifically to you and nobody else."

GREENBURG: Let's turn our attention to colonic health.

TROWBRIDGE: It's not taken seriously, and it's dismissed in the same way that the yeast syndrome is dismissed. And that is that you can't see the harm caused by it.

It's sort of like saying, "Well, didn't you see the tornado that didn't strike because we did something. Didn't you see the illness that you didn't get because we did something?" No. The doctors don't see that at all. What they see is only that they can have a direct causal relationship, and then they want a large double-blind cross-overb placebo-controlled study. And some of these things may be very hard. Like for instance, wheat germination. If we waited until we understood the scientific process of wheat germination, we'd still be sitting around trying to grow wheat rather than just taking some things on faith, and throwing wheat in the ground and watering it.

Take a look at the number of people who laughed at Linus Pauling – many of them are dead, and he is still alive and thinking productively, aggressively. So for all of the "wrong answers" he has, some of them are remarkably right in a very personal sense.

What I'm concerned about is that the yeast syndrome is so readily dismissed. I have patients come in, who have talked to their doctors and say, "You know, I think maybe I have the yeast problem here, and I've read Dr. Crook's book, or Dr. Trowbridge's book, or Dr. Truss's book, but the doctors say, 'No, no, no, you don't have that problem.' "

And I say, "Did your doctor ever read any of those books?" "No." "Then how did he know you didn't have the problem?" "Well, he said that that couldn't be my problem because that's very unusual."

GREENBURG: *Dismissal without inquiry seems peculiar for something we call medical science.*

TROWBRIDGE: They would argue to the death their right to practice the art of medicine and yet will insist that anyone else has to practice the science if they do anything different. And that breaches the concept that every physician has the right to practice the art of medicine as well as the science.

GREENBURG: The late Carlton Fredericks often said, "Many doctors would prefer you died than be cured by a quack." What happens when ignorance and bias replace sound judgment? Belief – I didn't believe in vitamins, I don't believe in the yeast syndrome – over inquiry?

TROWBRIDGE: If you had to choose your religion based on your doctor's opinion, how many of us would get to heaven? You see, your doctor's opinion is exactly that, it's an opinion you've hired to be rendered to you. It is not the final statement upon which you should base living your life. If you find that that opinion makes sense, and that produces the desired results, by every means go with it. And if it doesn't, then don't.

People ask me, "What are the critical questions to ask the doctor?" One of them is, "Doctor, what is it you know about this, and what is it you are setting out to do?" And if the doctor says he doesn't know very much about it, don't take his opinion to heart.

Another thing is, and I encourage my patients to understand this, I tell a lot of stories in my practice. And what I'm going to tell you is how I think this works. This is a story. We have certain pieces of evidence that make this story seem reasonable, but there is no big study that proves it, there is no way of telling if this is actually what's happening inside you as a human being. However, it makes sense. And if it works as a way and plan of treatment program for you, then the story is pretty good. And if it doesn't, then we'll change the story, we'll find out more facts, we'll try and make it work better for you.

If physicians participate with their patients, in making stories that make sense, and then trying to see whether or not that works, then we will call it clinical trial. That's much more effective than all of the medical literature that's ever been published, if none of that literature can help me.

GREENBURG: Unfortunately, too many physicians do not represent their patients' interests. In the last decade, there has been an information explosion, most of which primary-care physicians have not kept up with.

TROWBRIDGE: To make that point even more thoroughly, *Future Shock* by Alvin Toffler came out in the late 1960's and in it he noted that medical information, scientific information was exploding at a rate of a doubling every four years. So in four years, twice as much medical knowledge will exist as now, in eight years four times as much medical knowledge, in twelve years eight times as much medical knowledge, and in another four years it would be sixteen times as much medical knowledge as now.

Here's the problem with that. Only ten percent of the world's medical literature is indexed or is referenced in such a way that you can get at it in the library. The other ninety percent is published in journals that are not indexed. You can't easily go to the computer and ask it to give you a list of where these articles are.

So you have this explosion of medical knowledge, doubling every four years, and ninety percent of that information is not accessible to physicians unless they actually have the piece of paper on their desk. They can't just go find it. And so what they don't see, they take the ostrich attitude, it doesn't exist.

GREENBURG: Obviously, none of us can process all the information needed.

TROWBRIDGE: You know what I tell patients? That I don't have the answers to what your problems are. I don't think anybody has the answers. What I think is, I have a way of approaching finding out what your problems are so that we can get them better, even if we can never name them.

So my job is to try and figure out what raw materials we need to put together on the inside. That's dietary changes, nutritional supplements, stopping putting in some things that may be interfering with that, and then flipping the switch, turning that on so that you improve.

Because you see, God put all the instructions inside your body to begin with, or you'd never have gotten to where you are now. You've built this marvelous and elegant machine based solely on those instructions. So if there's an interference to them working, because the raw material isn't there, because there's a toxic interference or something like that, my job is to try and figure that out. Maybe I can't ever name it, and maybe I can't ever tell you exactly what it was, but that doesn't matter to you once it's gone away.

GREENBURG: How is medicine going to play catch-up with doctors like you? How is that possible?

TROWBRIDGE: My hope is that before medical science kills too many of its patients by refusing to recognize that a *live healthy patient is the only standard of care,* before it kills too many of its patients, that it will pause and realize that *there is no standard* we can call truth in the biological science called medicine.

There are facts and observations, they are important, and they are never to be disregarded; on the other hand, they cannot be held up to the exclusion of providing appropriate care and caring to the patient in need. And if we can get just that one concept across, then we won't have cardiovascular surgeons turning up their noses and turing away their heads at chelation therapy. We won't have internists and gynecologists and pediatricians and family physicians turning their noses up and their heads away at the yeast syndrome. We won't have psychiatrists and others turning their noses up and their heads away at nutritional and mineral balancing. We won't have people ignored when they are desperately turning to the doctors for help.

GREENBURG: *If you could see into the future, say twenty-five years from now, what do you see?*

TROWBRIDGE: In an enlightened culture, or in the one I expect us to have?

GREENBURG: *Let's go with what we've got for now?*

TROWBRIDGE: What I see is a medical care system barely able to provide a minimal standard of technical care to the groups of people with the largest political input. Basically military medicine, in the same way we think of what military music is to music.

The military medicine in the future will have physicians working structured hours, and will have places you go if your problem comes up after hours, you are not going to be seen if the doctor's clinic is running late, you'll just be sent to the emergency room, like many of the HMO's now do. "Sorry, our clinic is closed now, I know you've been waiting for two hours and you can go next door to the emergency room or get another appointment."

I see more technical care and less humanistic care. In an enlightened society, we would not be tied to giving the privilege of medical care to the politically important ones, the ones who really make a difference in the voting power blocs. We would instead look toward a preventive health care model, an alternative complementary health care model, where we are testing mineral balances on people long before they were ill, where we are checking vitamin and essential fatty acid levels, amino acid levels, on people long before they were ill, and showing them what they could do differently to keep from getting ill, showing them what free radical degenerative chemistry was all about. And showing them an understanding about how cancer, arthritis, allergies, cardiovascular disease –

they all come from the same problems inside your body, and what you could do.

GREENBURG: *That paints a very bleak picture for the future of medicine.*

TROWBRIDGE: Yes, I think it does. I think physicians are becoming merely functionaries. And once you realize that physicians are just fancy clerks, and you can buy them for a dime a dozen and just plug another one in, that's exactly what has happened with the HMO concept, the PPO concept, all these things are just looking at doctors as replaceable units. Medicine is increasingly just big business run by big businessmen and if you want to make money on it, invest in it, don't participate in it.

GREENBURG: *It comes back to self-responsibility.*

TROWBRIDGE: If you're going to be healthy at all, absolutely. If you are looking for the government to protect you from the cradle to the grave, the only thing you can bet is that they'll make the distance between the two shorter.

If you want to take your own personal responsibility, I can absolutely guarantee you a longer and healthier life than you would have ever dreamed or anyone would ever assure you of.

ADDITIONAL QUESTIONS TO FOLLOW CHALLENGING ORTHODOXY CHAPTER

The following is an interview with John Parks Trowbridge, M.D., which appeared as a chapter entitled "Update on the Yeast Syndrome," in **Challenging Orthodoxy: America's Top Medical Preventives Speak Out!**, presented by Kurt Greenberg (available through Keats Publishing, Inc., New Canaan, Connecticut, 1991). The text is reprinted in its entirety, with permission of the interviewer, Kurt Greenberg, A series of additional questions follow, specifically prepared for inclusion in this book by Dr. M. Paul Farber.

The following questions and answers have been prepared by Dr. Trowbridge, specifically at the request of Dr. Farber.

QUESTION: Let's take the question of self-responsibility one step further: if you are suffering from confusing symptoms that haven't been helped by your usual physicians, what should you be doing?

TROWBRIDGE: The answer is obvious. You have to take up your own crusade. Patients are far too trusting, in my opinion, in that they expect that their doctor is speaking from a position of knowledge. Medicine, as a field, is just too big for any one person to know all the relevant facets. If your doctor says "You'll just have to learn to live with it," then tell him "I already am living with it – I want to learn to live without it."

You need to haunt the health food stores, browsing through the many fine books that are now available. You need to talk to others you meet there – both clerks and customers – seeking anyone who could direct you to someone better able to diagnose and treat your condition. Call around to patient support groups – you can get their names from hospitals, health food stores, physicians and counselors in "alternative healthcare."

The important point is this: surrender only with your dying breath. The crusade is yours and yours alone. Educate yourself and you will – more often than not! – locate physicians and others who are able to help you recover the health you used to enjoy.

QUESTION: Does Lyme Disease appear to have a role to play in the Yeast Syndrome?

TROWBRIDGE: Yes – and no. Anything that interferes with immune system function will worsen the Yeast Syndrome or will make you more likely to "come down" with it. Anything that constantly provokes your defenses – such as persistent infection, like Lyme's – will impair your ability to respond effectively to resist or to resolve the Yeast Syndrome.

If you are suffering with any stage of Lyme Disease, the treatment you need likely will set the stage for, or will complicate already present, Yeast Syndrome problems. This might mean more distress for you but it's not "a big deal" with regard to your eventual recovery.

Having the Yeast Syndrome, with its many effects on your immune defenses, might make you more likely to contract Lyme Disease – or less able to control it once established. The whole picture is very much like a spider web: tug on one part of the web and the whole web jiggles.

The key is still fairly simple: find a physician (or set of specialists) who can provide you complete care for your interrelated problems, then commit yourself to a comprehensive program of recovering your health.

QUESTION: Let's turn our attention to so-called Multiple Sclerosis for a moment. You've been heard to say that you don't believe it is a disease – please clarify.

TROWBRIDGE: Well, that's a statement that could be misunderstood rather easily, so I appreciate the chance to clarify for you.

"Multiple sclerosis" simply means "many scars." That's a good description of what is found by various tests – but it doesn't help us at all with regard to what caused the many scars. This is one more example of how "taxonomy-based medicine" can lead us astray. Taxonomy is the method of organizing or classifying a field by dividing the parts (diseases, in the case of medicine) along certain lines of similarity. The assumption is that you have a hint about treatment if you can just put a name to your problem. The problem with this approach is simple: once you assign a "serious" diagnosis, such as "multiple sclerosis," you feel justified in relegating all new symptoms and worsening problems to the "untreatable" illness.

So, when a patient tells me, with resignation, that they've been diagnosed with "multiple sclerosis," I always consider that to be a starting point, not an ending point. What caused these many scars? Why was that able to cause them in this person at this time? What other systems are weak in this person? What systems can be made to work even harder, to "carry the load" while others are recovering?

I have had general success with most of my "MS" patients in the past, simply by following this approach of continuing to "ask why." Usual physicians stop, in my opinion, several questions too soon.

QUESTION: Do you have other perspectives you'd like to share with us about MS?

TROWBRIDGE: Yes, briefly. The scars in MS are specific tissue changes, where body parts have been altered. Every human disease has, as an early or later part of its progression, permanent changes to body structure. Indeed, changes to structure and function that become permanent can set the limits of recovery that is possible. But what isn't reasonable is to fail to try to bring about recovery because of presumed limits to its final result.

Because every disease results in permanent changes, we can classify diseases by "pathology" (the microscopic changes of cells). But the mistake in accepting a pathology report becomes obvious when you realize that the body has a limited repertoire of responses. Thus, many different "insults" could result in similar changes in tissues. The physician's job is not simply to identify (and quantify) tissue changes – in other words, to find a diagnosis – but also to locate the root cause that keeps creating the problem (termed "etiology").

The point I'm making is simply this: both the physician and the patient have to be committed to finding and fixing the ultimate cause of the problem. Otherwise, there isn't much justification to do any more than "patch up" the discomforts with appropriate pain medications and others that control symptoms.

QUESTION: Is it likely that the Yeast Syndrome, Lyme Disease, and Multiple Sclerosis could exist at the same time in a person?

TROWBRIDGE: Absolutely, given the right circumstances. There's almost no limit to the number of complicating conditions that can co-exist. In fact, that's one reason why people seem to "crash-and-burn" so quickly with serious illnesses – their bodies have held off against surmountable odds for so long, then the deck gets "stacked against them," the odds become insurmountable, and the body systems fail one after another.

QUESTION: Anything new to add to your "update" on the Yeast Syndrome?

TROWBRIDGE: Not really, at least in terms of treatment perspectives. We have some better basic science explanations for some things, but the real key remains treatment.

And dietary changes remain the key to permanent recovery. That and nutritional supplementation, as outlined in my book. After these two are in place, medications have a definite role to play in getting most people better over the next 6 to 24 months.

Problems come up in only three places. First, the treating physician fails to identify specific nutritional shortcomings that need to be addressed in a particular patient. Second, the treating physician fails to identify other illness problems (such as mercury-silver amalgam dental fillings) that will limit the patient's ability to finally resolve the Yeast Syndrome. And third, the patient fails to comply with an appropriate treatment program that would otherwise be effective.

All in all, identifying and treating the Yeast Syndrome is fairly easy if the physician has the proper training and experience. This isn't rocket science – we leave that to NASA.

QUESTIONS: Any parting comments?

TROWBRIDGE: Yes, most definitely. I strongly advise every person who reads this book to get extra copies to share with his several physicians, to put a copy in his local public library, and to share with friends. The only way to start a scientific revolution is to get the troops rallied!

LYMEEPIDEMIC
Origin and Development of the
Second Largest Epidemic in the World in the Modern
World of the 1990's

A DISEASE is normally described and identified in medical literature as a grouping of symptoms which either occur simultaneously or in a certain order and progression of events. It may also be a grouping of symptoms that occur in a specific stage or order. These diseases are normally recorded in medical literature with a given name which represents the knowledge and the thinking of the times.

The disease and illness which we now call LYME DISEASE is a perfect example of this phenomena. Over 100 years ago more than half of all Europe was wiped out by a disease which was then called "The Black Death" and which we now call the BUBONIC PLAGUE. The crude doctors and scientists of the time might as well have been describing what since 1975 both modern day doctors, researchers, and scientists have named LYME DISEASE. This disease with its wide range of neurological symptoms and abnormalities has been treatable with modern day antibiotics and is now curable with the REDISCOVERY OF COLLOIDAL SILVER. It must be understood that 100 years ago there was no recognized treatment for this so-called "black death." People just became sick and eventually died which can happen in modern times with Lyme Disease if it goes untreated. There is no telling how many people have become sick and eventually died from the progressive symptoms of Lyme Disease before it was recognized in 1975. What happens is that this major disease gets misdiagnosed and distributed into existing categories of established diseases with similar symptoms.

We know now due to the marvelous scientific discoveries of Dr. Willy Burgdorfer that the tiny microorganism called the SPIROCHETE is the infectious agent in Lyme Disease which is carried by the vector of ticks and fleas. In Medieval Europe the vector for these spirochetes was rats and perhaps the fleas on the rats. As a matter of history it was the systematic eradication of the rat population in Europe which in addition to the body's own amazing immune system's ability to create antibodies and adapt to disease-causing organisms, which finally brought about an end to the Bubonic Plague.

It is theorized by scientists of modern times that it was the spirochete carried at that time by the rats that caused the Bubonic Plague. Since there was no accepted or effective treatment in those days, people eventually succumbed to the spirochetes when vital organs including the brain were eventually overtaken and destroyed by the SPIROCHETES. Therefore, the answer to the question as to whether Lyme Disease can kill you, the answer is that IF LEFT UNTREATED "MOST EMPHATICALLY YES." One might wonder what the future years will bring in terms of long-term effects of Lyme Disease. The Author believes that there are really four Simple Possibilities:

1. Both a wrong diagnoses and improper treatment or no treatment would result in a continual debiliting and downward spiral till death eventually occurred.

    For example if the treating doctors did not know that a patient had Lyme Disease, that person might never receive any Antibiotic Therapy to kill the spirochetes. The spirochetes would spread unchecked and eventually terminate the host organism which in this particular case could be you the reader or me the Author if for some reason we would have never received any Antibiotic Therapy.

594

2. Conventional antibiotic treatment of either penicillin or cephalosorins would result in a destruction of 85% to 95% of the spirochete population infecting the body and would also create mutant and pleomorphic forms. It is the mutant forms as well as the 15 or more percent of spirochetes that hide from the antibiotics which would cause recurrent infections and symptomatology perhaps for the rest of one's life.

3. Treatment with Conventional Antibiotics with no replacement of the friendly acidophilus would result in a full blown Candida Yeast Infection even though the spirochetes are under control. This Yeast Infection is the second greatest impersonator and perhaps rivals Lyme Disease in its manifest symptoms and mocking of Major Diseases. The Treating Doctor thinking that his patient still has Lyme Disease prescribes more antibiotics without acidophilus replacement warnings both perpetuating and worsening the Yeast Infection.

Copyright Material 2-8-94

The patient then ends up on an endless roller coaster of disease for the rest of his/her life. This obviously is not a very appetizing thought which brings us to our fourth option.

4. The Lyme Disease patient is fortunate enough to run across and read this book to learn at least two major pieces of information which tell how one can really cure the Lyme Disease and also end the Roller Coaster of the Candida Yeast Lyme Disease Connection which can be treated and eventually cured by the methods in this book. The COLLOIDAL SILVER ANSWER, what the Author has dubbed the Silver Micro Bullet can accomplish this cure on the Lyme Disease. Then a Candida Yeast treatment program can then be

implemented. Eventually the patient will have a complete recovery and perhaps have even better health than before they became ill because of the new health programs and Wellness Practices which they had to adopt in order to get well in the first place.

The last two decades of understanding Lyme Disease as stated earlier began in 1975. This occurred when a surprising and statistically abnormal medical phenomena began occurring amongst many children in the town of Lyme, Connecticut. These children began in large groups experiencing arthritic-like symptoms and joint inflammations. These types of diseases and symptoms are usually common to middle age, upper middle age, and older geriatric populations. Who would even conceive of a child acquiring and suffering from the symptoms of arthritis. Surely, these problems were something that one's Grandpa and Grandma complained about. Surely, these arthritic-like problems were not common to the life and world of a child. Perhaps one and maybe two or three freak instances but not in large amounts. Surely a medical puzzle was at hand which cried and demanded to be unraveled since so many children at one time were getting so very sick for no apparent reason.

Perhaps someday it will become a historical fact that it was not a doctor or a scientist who first became aware that there was a major epidemic brewing and afoot.

Copyright Material 1-31-94

Instead it was that good, old God-created invention called a

– MOTHER –

who first realized there was a serious health problem beginning to plague not only her children but also the children of her friends and neighbors and that this health problem demanded immediate attention from the doctors and government.

This woman's name was Polly Murray and she came to be known as "the Mother of Lyme Disease." Though her intuition at that time was correct in that she felt that the cause of her severe illness was the bite of a tick previous to 1970. Her internist at that time felt that this was not possible as he was comparing her classic symptoms of what we now call Lyme Disease to Rocky Mountain Spotted Fever which was known to be caused by a tick, but which had much different symptoms. Unfortunately, Polly received no antibiotic treatment and eventually became a victim as well as a martyr to what would be eventually known as Lyme Disease. Polly's entire family of three daughters and two sons became stricken with arthritic, flu-type symptoms, rashes, as well as many other symptoms now associated with Lyme Disease. Polly was like a voice crying in the wilderness. She eventually collected 35 similar case histories in her area and reported this to Dr. David Snydman with the Connecticut State Health Department, who hearing of other cases in the area began an investigation which would lead to a diagnoses of the beginning pandemic of JVA, Juvenile Rheumatoid Arthritis in the area of Lyme, Connecticut.

This diagnoses was only partially correct as time and additional research later proved. However, it was a start and researchers must begin somewhere. Eventually, more of the classic symptoms of what we now call Lyme Disease were recognized and fell within the dimensions of the same disease. When no common bacteria was found in the blood an insect or an orthropod vector like a tick was suspected but not confirmed. Finally, the scientist and researcher came upon a fortunate stroke of good luck. After a spirochete infected tick bite, a common lesion called erythema chronicum migrans develops around the tick bite in a reddish ringlike rash. This lesion was first reported and expounded upon in Sweden as early as 1910.

This rash was sometimes found preceding a case of spinal meningitis, which is an inflammation of the brain and spinal cord which many times strikes children for no apparent reason. Now we know that the symptoms of spinal meningitis are also caused by the spirochetes that are associated with Lyme Disease.

One needs to stop and reflect upon the thought of how many years of misdiagnoses have taken place for literally thousands and perhaps tens of thousands of unsuspecting people. How many people have lived and arranged their life and perhaps death around the thought that they had incurable multiple sclerosis or spinal meningitis to name but a few of the misdiagnosed diseases for what we now know as Lyme Disease.

Many times the rash occurs and goes unnoticed due to the part of the body on which the rash may appear. For example, if it were to appear on the sole of one's foot, on one's buttocks or in the creases of the buttocks, on the back of one's neck, or under one's hair, it could easily go unnoticed. Most researchers don't make note of the fact that the rash usually appears within a 1 to 3 inch radius from the sight of the tick bite. Therefore as was the Author's case, it can go completely unnoticed. Also there can be times when it does not appear or appears and leaves in a relatively short period of time as to be missed and go unnoticed. It may also appear on a person and be dismissed as just a heat rash since they also are reddish in color and seem to disappear in a relatively short period of time, and therefore the rash never becomes equated with Lyme Disease. Thus one cannot always depend upon this objective symptom for diagnoses. As just mentioned in the Author's case it was never seen even though the tick was found on the back of the head beneath the hair as to go unnoticed. How many people ever take time out to examine their own scalp especially if their hair is thick and curly as was the case with the Author.

It is also possible that the tick may go unnoticed which is unfortunate since the tick can be removed and analyzed for a 100% positive diagnoses as was the case with the Author. However, in the Author's case it was only after two weeks of severe and debilitating symptomatology and partial paralysis that the tick, Thank God, was finally discovered.

The Author because of his training as a physician knew immediately how to remove the tick and then sent it to Dr. Thomas Craig, Ph.D., head of paracytology at Texas A&M for a positive identification and analysis. In the Author's case it was the Xodius Scapularis, a tick which is found in Texas on the white tail deer. This particular deer is abundant in the area of Texas where the Author has a ranch and retreat.

It is also possible that one may be bitten by a tick in one of its developmental stages such as a nymph which has little holding power and easily falls off the body. It is only in the case of a full or near full grown tick that they attack in such a way that they dig in and cannot fall off. It is also possible that when an unknowledgeable victim discovers a tick for the first time, they remove it incorrectly and discard it as unimportant and just something ugly to get rid of as quickly as possible. Unfortunately the most positive diagnoses which one could have had just became discarded and thrown away. These examples demonstrate the need and importance for a greater awareness of health education in the schools as well as through the media concerning this second largest epidemic in the world and also its resulting counterpart, the Candida Yeast Infection which occurs as a result of incorrectly administered antibiotic treatment, with no regard for replacing the friendly bacteria of the body which are necessary for life to exist. The third largest epidemic in the world is the Candida Yeast Infection and it receives very little publicity with the exception of the writings of men like Dr. Truss, Dr. Crook and Dr. Trowbridge.

The amount of research and importance which has been given to this most devastating and unwelcome illness is sad but not unusual. Historically, many diseases such as Scurvy have gone unnoticed for long periods of time with only a few aware men crying unheard in the wilderness of popular opinion.

It is an interesting historical fact that both in Europe early in the twentieth century and also in 1910 in Sweden a lesion which was ringlike in appearance and is similar to the lesion which we now associate with Lyme Disease was described and identified. This was documented as preceding the symptoms of one of the diseases which Lyme Disease imitates which is Spinal Meningitis. The rashlike lesion was the erythema chromicum migrans.

It had become identified in timing with the presence of a tick bite. Spinal Meningitis is an extreme inflammation of the brain and spinal column which can potentially become fatal. The Author has memories of fellow classmates in grade school, high school, and college being stricken with Spinal Meningitis. The Author is only 47 years of age so these events, as the reader can see, were many years ago relative to the Author's almost half a century. At the time there was no one to question the diagnoses. They just had spinal meningitis because the doctors said so and that was it. Perhaps many of the Author's friends had Lyme Disease which at the time was unheard of.

The Author had friends and peers come down with what the doctors called Multiple Sclerosis. The Author would be interested in knowing if Annette Funicello was ever bitten by a tick or had a history of a previous tick bite. If so it could be possible that the Multiple Sclerosis which she is being diagnosed with could actually be Lyme Disease. If any of the readers of this book personally know Annette the Author would appreciate their getting a copy of this book into her hands. If Annette was bitten by a tick or thinks she might have been and was never treated with antibiotics, it is possible that the "spirochete" could be the culprit. The Author would be glad to council with Annette Funicello to see if anything could be done through treatment with Colloidal Silver. Also if the myelin has been damaged it is possible that Treatment with EVENING PRIMROSE OIL could help regenerate the MYELIN SHEATH. Therefore, Annette, the Author, one of your old fans from the Disney Days, extends an invitation to you to consult with him. Who knows, perhaps we may unlock a clue to your illness.

Perhaps many of these people with Multiple Sclerosis were misdiagnosed and really had or now have Lyme Disease. It brings up the OBVIOUS QUESTION of how many years and perhaps centuries has man been plagued with Lyme Disease and been totally ignorant of the fact? Another BIG QUESTION could be what has the long-term effect of Chemical Pesticides and Pollution had upon the tick population and the microbiological spirochetes which they carry?

Who knows what the chemicals of modern science has done to the entire insect and microbiological populations which are part of the whole chain that supports life on this planet and which man is dependent upon for his very existence? How many mutant bacteria and viral organisms have we as mankind created and set loose upon ourselves? Just look at the ozone layer as another example of this abuse and ignorance toward nature.

The balances within nature are intricate and many times fragile as well as interconnected. Man cannot go on indefinitely upsetting these balances through ignorance and greed without reaping the disastrous results. The Author firmly believes that many of these modern-day plagues were BROUGHT UPON MAN BY HIMSELF and the MISUSE OF SCIENCE. The perhaps mythological story of the Ancient Continent of Atlantis contains tales of scientific advances as well as the perversion of these sciences as well as Idolatry and other Offenses Against the Laws of GOD and Nature which eventually brought about cataclysm and its eventual destruction. We must be careful lest we commit an epidemic of SLOW AND GRADUAL PLANETARY SUICIDE out of ignorance by upsetting the natural balances that exist within nature and going against the NATURAL LAWS which govern God's Creation.

The name of this book is "THE TWO GREAT MEDICAL IMPOSTERS AND IMPERSONATORS, A DOCTOR'S PERSONAL EXPERIENCE WITH LYME DISEASE AND CANDIDA YEAST INFECTION. Many years ago the Author saw a movie called "The Great Imposter" in which the actor Tony Curtis impersonated many sophisticated characters such as a doctor and a naval officer, when in fact he was none of these people. Yet in the movie he was identified, accepted, and treated as the playing roles these characters portrayed. In much the same way patients have been treated for diseases which they don't have. People with actual Lyme Disease and Candida Yeast Infections have been diagnosed with the multitude of diseases discussed in this book including spinal meningitis, multiple sclerosis, rheumatoid arthritis, and Guillan-Barre which was the Author's experience. Had the Author accepted any one of these diagnoses and not found the real causes which were the spirochetes and then the yeast, the results would have been disastrous and rather than recovering his health and writing this book, the Author could have been deluded into treating a nonexisting disease and foregoing the proper treatment which could have resulted in a serious debilitating illness and possibly death.

The Author after discovering the Lyme Disease was initially treated with oral and then intravenous penicillin. He chose this route because at the time he was not knowledgeable of the colloidal silver and there was nothing in his Natural Pharmacopoea that was capable of killing the spirochetes. At the time there was no choice to make as whether to take the Conventional Antibiotics as there was no alternatives. It was either take the antibiotic treatment or take the chance that the spirochetes left untreated would eventually take over, and affect a vital organ which would result in death. Had the Author known about Colloidal Silver at the time he would have chosen that route and foregone the potentially dangerous Conventional Antibiotic Therapy. However, if he had not gotten the Candida Yeast Infection as a result of going the Conventional Way without proper precautions to replace the friendly bacteria, then he would not have been able to write this book so that his readers could benefit from his own experiences. Because of this Blessing in Disguise the Author once stated this prayer:

"I have personally experienced how dangerous and serious and how much suffering was involved going the Conventional Route of treatment for Lyme Disease and subsequently getting the just as devastating Candida Yeast Infection. Because of what I know now, if the GOOD LORD and JESUS CHRIST were to have asked me to go through this experience voluntarily in order that I might warn and give a true solution to my fellow human beings, I would have done this out of my duty as a physician and as a brother to all men and women as a DUTY to MANKIND which is my BUSINESS. To have the opportunity to see the Victory of the World and the Positive Changes which would occur after it implements what is contained by the Grace Of God in this book would have been worth the sacrifice and suffering that my fellowman need not suffer unnecessarily. The VICTORY over these MODERN DAY PLAGUES is GOD's and Evil Ignorance, and even the devil's snares and traps shall be defeated by God's Grace. Here are the answers and the medicine that were revealed to me and it is now up to you my READERS to put your FAITH into action and implement all this knowledge and methods including the Colloidal Silver."

Copyright Material 2-23-94

When the Colloidal Silver, the SILVER MICRO-BULLET as the Author has dubbed it is eventually accepted and implemented as the UNIVERSAL ANTIBIOTIC and those antibiotics which are causing many new diseases by creating mutant strains are discontinued then many Impending Disasters will be AVERTED. May the FATHER'S, JESUS CHRIST'S, and the HOLY SPIRIT'S Blessings and Grace BE UPON YOU. As His Servant and in HIS Service I say, AMEN.

The following article appeared in the Health Brief's section of the Houston Chronicle, one of the largest newspapers in the state of Texas, on Sunday, February 20, 1994:

Medical Disaster Seen

San Francisco – Common bacteria that cause pneumonia, children's ear infections and many other diseases are evolving into forms untreatable by all known medicines, threatening a chilling era that would be "nothing short of a medical disaster," a researcher said Saturday.

"In the post-antibiotic world, the simplest infections could escalate quickly into fatal illnesses," said Alexander Tomasz of Rackefeller University in New York.

"Certain uncommon bacteria have developed untreatable strains. Experiments have proven the same thing can happen with common bacteria," Tomasz said.

"It's potentially an extremely serious problem," said Dr. Mitchell Cohen of the Centers for Disease Control and Prevention in Atlanta.

"Drugs that might be developed to cope with the bacteria are five to seven years away, and drug companies are now pursuing them eagerly," Cohen said.

According to the experts in the Author's opinion, we are sitting on a TIME BOMB that could out proportion Aids, Lyme Disease, and Candida Yeast Infections. The Candida Yeast Infections are a perfect example of this warning already having become a reality and is the world's third largest epidemic with AIDS being the First Largest and Lyme Disease the Second Largest Epidemic. It should be noted that the Candida Yeast Infections were iatrogenically caused which means Doctor Induced.

Further evidence of this Pending and Present DISASTER was made public on Sunday, December 19, 1993, the Houston Chronicle ran the following revealing and shocking article in its Metropolitan News and Features Section by Ruth SORELE, Houston Chronicle Medical Writer. The Author will not take the liberty to quote this article in its entirety because it clearly states by the BEST OF EXPERTS that what the Author is warning his readers about and why he is pushing the Colloidal Silver so strongly is IN FACT TRUE AND SUBSTANTIATED. The Author Feels that The COLLOIDAL SILVER if utilized as a UNIVERSAL ANTIBIOTIC would alleviate the need for any vaccine and would prevent this DISASTER from getting worse if Universally Implemented. The Author also feels that the Drug Companies will fight this Tooth and Nail not because it doesn't work since this has already been proven by the Top Scientist since the early 1900's but because they FEAR out of GREED FOR PROFIT that once educated the public will discontinue the use of Conventional Antibiotics now that there is a safe alternative with NO SIDE EFFECT, NO MUTANT PRODUCING, and at least 650 WIDE RANGE PROVEN KILL RATE OF ALL KNOWN BACTERIA AND VIRUSES. Also now that modern technology has brought it down to $10 AN OUNCE RATHER than the $400 an ounce that it was in the 1920's which caused its disuse at that time it is now affordable to use Worldwide to help wipe out the World's Epidemics and Prevent More and Even Worse Epidemics.

"Disease Causing Bacteria becoming more virulent"

A bacteria that causes ear infections, pneumonia, and meningitis is becoming increasingly more resistant to common antibiotics and harder to treat, say specialists in Houston and Atlanta.

Copyright Material 3-1-94

The pneumococcus bacteria is one of a host of organisms – including tuberculosis – that is becoming less susceptible to the drugs commonly used against them, said Dr. Sheldon Kaplan, professor of pediatrics at Baylor College of Medicine and chief of infectious diseases at Texas Children's Hospital.

"We could have real problems like in the pre-antibiotic era, when we had all of these germs and nothing to treat them with," he said.

The increase in cases of resistant disease – coupled with the threat posed to the elderly and chronically ill – makes vaccination important.

Right now there is a vaccine that works in adults, and the voluntary Hospitals of America, a nonprofit hospital group that includes the Memorial Hospital System locally, is working to get more elderly people immunized.

Only about 15 per cent of those for whom the vaccine is recommended have actually received it.

And said Dr Kaplan, more work needs to be done to develop a vaccine to prevent the disease in children under the age of 2 for whom the current immunization is ineffective.

Before 1986, neither Kaplan nor his colleague Dr. Edward O. Mason had seen evidence of resistant Streptococcus pneumonia bacteria at Texas Children's. (This is different from the strep infection.)

And until 1989 only two or three of the children treated at the hospital failed to respond to penicillin, the drug most commonly used to treat the infection.

But in 1992, 45 children had the resistant strain – 21 percent of all such infections that were scrutinized in the hospital's labs.

It is a growing problem said Dr. Jeff Duchin, a physician epidemiologist at the Federal Centers for Disease Control in Atlanta.

However, the C.D.C. does not know how large it is because it is not a reportable infection.

"We have a suspicion that there are high levels of the drug resistant strain in some parts of the country," Duchin said in a television interview.

"We are trying to establish mandatory reporting of drug resistant strains."

Kaplan and Mason are heading a multicenter study to determine how frequently drug resistance occurs in children. Dr. Edward Septimus, infection disease expert at the Memorial Hospital System, is attempting to do a similar study to determine how many Houston adults have drug resistant disease.

Copyright Material 3-2-92

A CDC team has been monitoring resistant bacteria at 13 hospitals in 12 states.

In a recent report at a meeting of infectious disease experts, CDC team members said they found 6.6 percent of the samples, submitted in 1991-92, were resistant to bacteria. By comparison a study conducted in 1979 to 1987 indicated that only 4.8 percent of isolates were resistant. But the increase in isolates that were resistant, he said.

Duchin and the Houston Doctors said that routine testing to determine if patients with pneumococcal infections have resistant disease is needed. Duchin said such results must be reported to the CDC so that the problems can be monitored.

One culprit in the rise in resistance could be the cure itself. As penicillin attacks the bacteria, the bacteria finds a way around that attack by changing its structure.

For that reason Kaplan warned that antibiotics should be used carefully. He said patients frequently expect antibiotics when they go to the doctor, even though their viral infections may not warrant such treatment.

Foreign countries have high levels of resistant organisms, said Kaplan. For example in Spain, Hungary and South Africa, as many as 70 percent of the samples tested are resistant to penicillin.

Right now, resistant infections are treated with a form of cephalosporin – an antibiotic. But cephalosporins are extremely expensive, and some of the organisms are becoming resistant to those drugs, Mason said.

In Memphis, Tenn., for instance, physicians now routinely use a two-drug combination to fight the disease.

The CDC has in recent years investigated major outbreaks in Memphis, a rural area of Kentucky and Alaska, said Duchin.

"It's a relatively recent issue for the United States," said Septimus.

Memorial facilities are making the pneumococcus vaccine available at no cost to people over age 65 who have Medicare Part B coverage. Other at-risk people can receive the vaccine for $25.

Funds are available to cover the cost of people who are unable to pay. Septimus said that pneumococcal disease is sixth among the top 10 killers of the elderly in the United States. A total of 150,000 and 270,000 will develop the infection in the United States this year.

The emergence of resistant strains of the bacteria make it more important that the people receive immunizations, he said.

"We have no good handle on how diffusely spread it is," he said.

It is apparent from these two revealing articles that a MAJOR MEDICAL PROBLEM has erupted and is further brewing. Is it possible that man in his attempt to cure disease coupled with impatience, arrogance, and perhaps lack of proper long-term effects of drug have created a Medical Disaster? From the evidence it seems that there can be no doubt that this in fact is the situation we as modern mankind find ourselves in. The author does not feel that the vaccines mentioned in the articles are the answer. How many times in our history including but not limited to the Swine Flu Vaccine and the original Salk Vaccine for Polio has this proven to have not been the case. The Swine Flue Vaccine actually caused worse short- and long-term symptoms than the actual flu which never really happened could have ever caused. History records that the Salk vaccine until replaced with the Savin Vaccine actually caused symptoms of polio rather than curing them. The author experienced the disastrous effect of the Swine Flu shot and he watched his brother get worse from polio as a result of the Salk Vaccine.

Are we as a society in such a hurry to find a Knight in Shining Armor cloaked in medical science as cures for major diseases which do not work but yet are heralded as miracles? Fortunately medical science did find an actual "KNIGHT IN SHINING ARMOR" in its original discovery of Colloidal Silver. However, just like the Knights of Old its armor has grown rusty on the shelf. Is it not time to wake up and take this magnificent discovery off the shelf which has already been proven, shine up its Silver Armor, and give it back to the people. Through this BOOK and the Author's Personal Testimony, the Author will do everything with God's Blessings to accomplish this MOST WORTHY TASK AND GOAL.

Many newspaper and magazine articles are reporting a new and virulent strain of tuberculosis bacteria which is causing a new resurgence in tuberculosis around the world. This is merely one example of what is to come if we do not change our ways of treating disease. There are further reports of a new and mutated form of the "so-called" AIDS VIRUS. The basis problem is that we as a medically oriented society seem to be creating more new diseases than we can control by the use of our chemical medicines. It is the author's contention that any substance which is inorganic and not naturally found in nature carries within it this potential threat of creating new mutated virulent forms of disease.

An exception to this rule is the colloidal silver since although it is not an organically absorbed material, its microscopic size and its function in blocking respiration in bacteria and viruses puts it in a different category as it merely passes through the body without being absorbed.

It is not really known how many people have been stricken with Lyme Disease because there is no way to know if all of the cases which have occurred have been correctly diagnosed and reported. As of the present time Lyme Disease has been reported in the continents of Africa, Asia, Australia, Europe, as well as more than 20 foreign countries. To the best of our knowledge due to reportability, in the United States it is documented in approximately 38-45 of the states if reports are correct. Louis Reik, Jr., M.D. in his book "Lyme Disease and the Nervous System" states the following about Lyme Disease in North America and the Author quotes:

"In North America, Lyme Disease occurs in both the United States and Canada. Within the United States, it is now the most commonly reported tick transmitted infection (4507 cases reported to the Centers for Disease Control in 1988) and it has been acquired in 43 states in all. The disease is endemic along the East Coast from Maryland to Massachusetts, in the Upper Midwest in Minnesota and Wisconsin, and on the Pacific Coast in California and Oregon. Increasing numbers of cases have also been reported from mid-Atlantic, southeastern, midwestern and south-central states. But the illness remains most common from the states from which it was originally reported: In 1987-1988, 92% of the reported cases were from New York, New Jersey, Pennsylvania, Connecticut, Massachusetts, Rhode Island, Wisconsin and Minnesota. New York reported the most cases (57% of the national total in 1988), while the incidence in Rhode Island (9.9 cases/100,000). The usual vector in the Northeast and Midwest is the deer tick, Ixodes dammini. This species ranges along the Atlantic coast from southern Delaware to Massachusetts, and it is common in Wisconsin, Minnesota, and Southern Ontario, Canada. The tick has also been collected in upstate New York, New Hampshire, Maine, Ohio, Illinois, and Manitoba, Canada, and it is likely that the population is continuous from the ATLANTIC TO MANITOBA. In some areas as many as 80% of the ticks are infected with spirochetes, explaining the very high attack rate of Lyme Disease in these localities.

I. dammini develops in a two-year life cycle, and all three of its stages may bite humans. However, immature ticks usually feed on a variety of wild birds and small mammals, especially the white-footed mouse, Peromyscus leucopus, while adult ticks feed on larger mammals, particularly the white tailed deer, Odocoileus virgianus. larger domestic animals are parasitized also, and Lyme disease has been reported in dogs, cattle, and horses. In all, the ticks have been found to parasitize at least 31 mammalian species, and 49 species of birds.

However, it is the presence of both deer and especially, mice in the environment that is critical for the maintenance of the disease transmission. The importance of white-footed mice as a reservoir of B. burgdorferi is apparent in their high rate of infection. In some areas almost 90% of the mice harbor spirochetes. The deer on the other hand probably serve no reservoir function for natural infection, but as a preferred host for adult ticks as they are critical for the ticks reproductive success. The elimination of deer in an established focus is followed by a reduced abundance of immature I. dammini. Consequently Lyme disease is most frequent in forested and suburban areas where both ticks and mice are common.

On the Pacific coast, the main vector is the Ixodes pacificas, the western black legged tick. The vectors in other parts of the United States where Lyme Disease has been acquired is less certain. One possible carrier is the common black legged tick, Ixodes scapularis. This widespread tick ranges from Florida, west to Texas, and north to Kansas, Missouri, Iowa, Illinois, Indiana, Ohio, West Virginia, and Maryland.

Lyme Disease is both widespread and common in Europe, where thousands of cases are estimated to occur each year. The disease is most common in Austria,

Germany, France, Sweden, and Switzerland. But it also occurs in the other three Scandinavian countries, Belgium, Czechoslovakia, Hungary, Italy, the Netherlands, Romania, Spain, the United Kingdom, the USSR, and Yugoslavia. The main European vector is the sheep tick, Ixodes ricinus. Lyme Disease has also been found in Africa, Asia, and Australia."

Copyright Material 3-10-94
QUOTATION: Lyme Disease and the Nervous System.
Louis Reik, Jr., M.D. Page 7-12

It was the tick, the Xodius Scapularis, which the Author was bitten by in Texas. Little did he know that that one little isolated tick would change his life dramatically and thrust him into the adventure and mission of discovering a answer for Lyme Disease, writing this book, and then making the results known to the world, Little did he know that it would launch him into rediscovering the early 1900's Antibiotic Colloidal Silver which could also be instrumental in bringing AIDS under control and revolutionizing the way we think about antibiotics. Little did he know that this rediscovery could eliminate the iatrogenic disease Candida Albicans Yeast Infection which all Lyme Disease patients have if they have been treated by Conventional Antibiotics with no regard for protecting and replacing the friendly acidophilus bacteria of the body's digestive system. Little did he know that his life would be dedicated at God's request to the QUEST of helping eliminate and put to an end to the three largest   epidemics in the world, the modern day Biblical Plagues which are AIDS, LYME DISEASE, and CANDIDA YEAST INFECTIONS. By the time the Author found that engorged, black blood-sucking tick on the back of his head and brain hidden beneath his hair he had already been diagnosed with having either Guillan-

Barre, Multiple Sclerosis, Spinal Meningitis, or Parkinsons Disease. Thank God for leading the Author to carefully removing this tick, preserving it in a bottle, and sending it off to Dr. Thomas Craig, Ph.D., head of Paracytology at Texas A&M for identification and analysis and the confirmation of Lyme Disease and Tick Paralysis. Thank God that the Author had the strength of mind and the fortitude to not accept any of these incorrect diagnoses and to search for the true cause of his disease which turned out to be the SPIROCHETES.

One may ask how can Lyme Disease spread so quickly and get into so many different parts of the world. One possible theory is that birds pick up the ticks and carry them from state to state and from country to country. This could help account for the tens of thousands of cases over the last few decades. There is no way of knowing exactly because of misdiagnoses and incorrect reporting.

In the past we as a society have always turned to our trusted antibiotics like penicillin for the cure. The author's own experience along with many others is that the penicillin helped but DID NOT CURE Lyme Disease. Now we know that it may have, while offering temporary help, been instrumental in creating mutant forms of spirochetes as well as causing Systemic Candida Yeast Infections.

The Author at the Lyme Conference in 1993 in Atlantic City, New Jersey, met a woman who had lost her fetus and others who had babies who were born prematurely or dead at birth. There were suffering children listening to the conference while on IV's and the number of stories about ruined lives ran rampant throughout the conference. There were brilliant careers that had been halted in their tracks because people were bedridden and unable to function.

All of this need not be because of the author's personal experiences as a doctor and the control and cures which he has uncovered in his QUEST for the right answers. It will be important for all of the organizations which have sprung up in response to the Lyme Disease Epidemic to Politic and Even Demonstrate on the STEPS of the Capitol to get these changes implemented, accepted and put into use. It will be important for the PEOPLE to fight for and protect their rights to use the Colloidal Silver and other Natural Remedies and to not let special interest groups and profiteers try to take them away.

These Epidemics are not of God but out of Ignorance and perhaps the evil intentions of some misguided men more intent upon short-term profit than the welfare of mankind. WE THE PEOPLE must stand up and fight for our God-Given and Constitutionally Protected Rights to "LIFE, LIBERTY, and the PURSUIT OF HAPPINESS." The Author pledges before God and before Jesus Christ his HEART, his STRENGTH, his SINEW and all the knowledge and understanding which the GOOD LORD has given him to this DIVINE QUEST and the TASK at hand. The Author prays that all of the Powers of Heaven will be at work to free the people from these Modern Day Plagues of Biblical Proportions. The Author himself has no doubt of this for on the day that he died for a five-minute period this and all that would come to pass was revealed to him by the King of Kings and his Father which art in Heaven surrounded by the HEAVENLY HOST.

This month of March is the month of the JEWISH PASSOVER, the month of the Last Supper of the New Testament. Passover is a time which celebrates deliverance and freedom from bondage. Just as the Lord delivered the Children of Israel from Slavery and Bondage to the Egyptians. So also will he deliver his Children of the Latter 20th and Early 21st Centuries from the bondage and slavery which these three Modern Day Plagues have inflicted.

The Author being a Messianic Jewish Man, who in the next two years will complete his Messianic Jewish Rabbinal Studies and Ordination, is a BORN AGAIN BELIEVER like all BORN AGAIN CHRISTIANS who believe in the SECOND COMING OF JESUS CHRIST and the fulfillment of the Prophecies of the JEWISH PROPHETS and all that was written in the BOOK OF DANIEL and in REVELATIONS from the HOLY BIBLE.

With FAITH and STRENGTH the Author prays that the SPIRIT OF MOSES and DELIVERANCE, as exemplified by this PASSOVER will come upon us that WE AS A PEOPLE OF ALL NATIONS may be FREED from all which is not of the LORD. The Author prays that WE AS A PEOPLE will be freed from Pain, Suffering, and Death. This CAN BE and it is the BIRTHRIGHT of all those who believe in God and in his Son and seek to do his WILL and LIVE BY THE LAWS which he has laid down for us in his HOLY BIBLE. Let us return to these LAWS and the LAWS WHICH GOVERN NATURE. All that we need for health and life has been given us through NATURE which is God's Creation. All cures can be found in Nature if we would but recognize them, respect them, and use them wisely. At this time of the PASSOVER, the Author prays to the Lord in Heaven and his Son, Jesus Christ, that this will come to pass and that this book, The Micro Silver Bullet, which Jesus Christ inspired in me to write, will help set the foundation for these changes in what I consider to be the latter days of the Second Coming of Jesus Christ, the Messiah.

TO: Magic Johnson   August 22, 1997
       Los Angeles Lakers
       c/o Darrall & Sue Imhoff
       1824 Ridgley Blvd.
       Eugene, Oregon 97401

Dear Magic Johnson,

In discussions with Darrall & Sue Imhoff we came to the conclusion that I write to you this letter and send to you a copy of my book and also a sample of COLL/AG-40, MILD SILVER PROTEIN. You have good friends in Darrall & Sue. The name of my book is:

THE MICRO SILVER BULLET
A Preliminary Scientifically Documented Answer
To The Three Largest Epidemics In The World
LYME DISEASE
AIDS VIRUS
YEAST INFECTION
(As Well As The Common Cold)
In the 5th EDITION which is coming out next month the word
Preliminary is being removed as results are now conclusive.

As you can see from the enclosed article from an Arizona Newspaper, *The Pinal Observer,* our FIRST EIGHT PEOPLE RECOVER FROM THE AIDS VIRUS. Actually, this was a Scientific Study done in California. We have also had an additional four people get completely well from FULL BLOWN AIDS as documented anecdotally and with lab reports. I have also included a book on AIDS by Dr. Peter Duesberg, Ph.D., from Berkeley documenting the danger of drugs such as AZT which actually cause AIDS. I have followed your career through the media and I am very familiar with your current status. I have NO DOUBT as a Scientist and Researcher that you can get completely free of the AIDS VIRUS in a six-month period following the FARBER PROTOCOL using COLL/AG-40, MILD SILVER PROTEIN.

Magic, you are talked about on page 96 of my book and are also honored in the acknowledgments on page 320 which states: Magic Johnson–May the information in this book which will be given to you and the Mild Silver Protein bring about a complete healing AIDS situation. We have scientifically documented that the Mild Silver Protein not only inhibits replication of HIV, and any latent formation, and also kills the AIDS virus with no side effects and no toxicity. I would also suggest that you contact Filer Smith who got completely well from Full Blown AIDS in a Scientific Study using COLL/AG-40, MILD SILVER PROTEIN. His story and phone number are on page xxxvi in the front of the book. His new phone number is (206) 721-3564. Also Dr. Paul Smith, M.D., in Canada is getting people completely well from AIDS. There are now over 20 people on my AIDS PROTOCOL in Canada. We had one person with Pancreatic Cancer which is caused by a virus get completely well on the COLL/AG-40, MILD SILVER PROTEIN. This Silver could have saved Michael Landon, Little Joe Cartwright.

Magic, I will be willing to personally consult with and even meet with you to go over my AIDS PROTOCOL. I have no doubt that within a six-month period you will have little if any AIDS VIRUS left in your body, your P-24 Antigen will be negative, your T Cell Count will be high, and you will feel better and stronger than any time in your whole life. All Opportunistic Infections are also destroyed.

MAY GOD BLESS YOU
AND GRANT YOU A COMPLETE HEALING

Dr. M. Paul Farber

P.S. Looking forward to meeting you and helping you. Darrall and I will also explain to you how Neutraceuticals will work along with the SILVER to restore any Cellular Damage which may have been caused by the HIV VIRUS while it was active.

Darrall & Sue Imhoff
1824 Ridgley Blvd.
Eugene, OR 97401

Darrall Imhoff attended the
Univ. of Calif. at Berkeley,
was chosen an All American
Olympic Gold Medalist – Rome 1960
Played as a Center for 12 yrs. – NBA
Los Angeles Lakers
Philadelphia 76ers
New York Nicks
Portland Trailblazers
continues to play with the
Blazers Alumni Team

January 15, 1997

THE PINAL OBSERVER
EIGHT PEOPLE RECOVER FROM THE AIDS VIRUS

Documentation is now available in what may be man's triumphant hour over the AIDS Virus.

In early 1996, a small group of HIV infected patients began taking a mild silver protein (COLL/AG-40) sublingually. The protein is liquid and tasteless and is held in the mouth under the tongue similar to heart medication. Each patient was HIV Positive and demonstrated a Positive Viral Load as measured by a P-24 Laboratory Test. A Viral Load is the amount of the HIV Virus present in the patient's blood.

According to test results obtained after a three-month period, "CD-4 Cells in the patients were increasing and active P-24 antigenicity reverted to negative." Simply stated, one of the standards of measurements, CD-4 Cells, were increasing in numbers which are favorable and the amount of virus present in the patient's blood was zero.

These phenomenal results have all been well documented in a book just off the press in its fourth updated printing titled *The Micro Silver Bullet* by Dr. M. Paul Farber.

The book is a Preliminary Scientifically Documented answer to the three largest epidemics in the world: Lyme Disease, AIDS Virus and Yeast Infection. Numerous other diseases are discussed and their inability to remain pathogenetic after being exposed to the mild silver protein.

Silver in a suspended solution – colloidal – has been a known antibiotic for hundreds of years. In the early part of this century silver was the preferred germ fighter. In addition to being very expensive and having a very limited shelf life, the technology available at the time did not allow for consistent concentrations, purity, size or quality of the silver solution.

With the discovery of penicillin in 1937, further colloidal silver research was ended. The new germ fighter was cheaper to manufacture and promptly gave rise to a pharmaceutical industry of magnanimous proportions. Instead of being a broad spectrum germ fighter, penicillin had its limitations. Specific diseases needed specific variations of penicillin. Today, one may be given several drugs to fight a particular disease – each with its own side effects. With the introduction of synthetic drugs, the pharmaceutical industry has grown equally. The amount of money, time and taxpayer-funded grant spending has mushroomed with the discovery of new diseases. Federally funded appropriations are requested for "orphan drugs" – drugs that will not be profitable enough for the industry to research, develop and manufacture.

Something recently has gone wrong, very wrong.

It appears that the various germs once treatable with these drugs have developed into mutations – resistant to the present drugs. National magazines have documented the dilemma. Once a particular drug is no longer effective, another more powerful one is needed and developed. Time is running out for pharmacology as we know it and they know it.

People are beginning to understand that for each "bad" germ cell killed by antibiotics, a thousand "good" cells are destroyed as well.

Sometimes, this had led to additional serious medical problems. The cure has become as deadly as the cause. People are opting to investigate for themselves – alternative health care.

It was noted in one report that in 1990, an estimated 425 million visits were made to alternative health care providers while an estimated 388 million visits were made to conventional providers.

The HMOs are examining the role of alternative health care with some now accepting non-traditional practices.

One of the off-the-shelf "alternatives" is known as colloidal silver. It is a nutritional mineral supplement and has been around for years. It was recently discovered by Dr. Farber that the solutions previously used had inherent qualities of nitrates and nitrides that reduced the efficacy of the silver. Once these caustic agents were removed, the required amounts of silver needed to be effective were greatly reduced. The addition of an amino acid – EDTA – as a transport mechanism, increased the silver's effectiveness as well. The present day cost of silver has made the product affordable. Modern technology is now able to produce the product with a greatly enhanced shelf life in a precise concentration, size, and purity. Research has already begun to test the new colloidal silver against many diseases with very promising results.

Technically, colloidal silver cannot "cure" anything – that would be against the Food & Drug Administration policy. The FDA sets the standards for marketing whatever they decide is a drug and what can be said about it. That is a benefit to the general population in several cases. The FDA, however, wants to remove colloidal silver from the shelves and presently has initiated that administrative process.

It doesn't make much sense to remove a product from the general population that as a nutritional mineral supplement "has a side effect that can cure man's maladies."

In man's quest for a potential end to the AIDS Virus, a cost of about $2,500 for a nutritional supplement instead of $10,000 to $15,000 for AZT and other related drugs and therapies, is not too much for the public to desire.

If one were able to purchase this product off-the-shelf, eliminate over 650 known diseases, at an affordable price, what harm could that do?

Perhaps the pharmaceutical industry might lose a few dollars, hospitals might not be filled to capacity, and some doctors might have a little extra time on their hands. Health insurance costs in general would be reduced, the FDA might have to downsize and those aspects are not really all that bad.

For one or all of the above reasons, the battle lines have been drawn. The nutritional supplement industry is poised to do a remake of the proverbial David and Goliath. Political activists are mustering their forces as well in the political arena. Time will reveal – in our generation – the outcome.

For additional information on the book *The Micro Silver Bullet* (written in layman's terms for the most part, it includes testimonials from some of the actual AIDS patients in the study), you may call 1-800-263-9234. Anyone interested in keeping this supplement available may call 1-800-940-2911 or 1-520-463-2777.

Randy Johnson 12/15/96
With Dr. M. Paul Farber and Dr. Peter Duesberg

Randy - We are live today and you can talk back to America via your telephone at 1-800-449-TALK or you can be the next caller in line on your dime, the very first caller in fact at area code 541-664-TALK. Now as we mentioned, callers this is a special program today, hold off on the calls for a little bit. I just gave you the numbers so be ready. And now if you're a member of the 98% club, those who never call a talk radio program, you could make us your first. Or fire up your computer. You can e-mail the program at Talk Back at Wave.net or you could now go our worldwide web site, link over to WBS Events, which the largest chat system on the internet and join us at the Talk Back WBS Room. It's the first one under Current Events and Politics Hub. Please give me your first name, the station you are listening to, and/or the city and state, that goes for those of you who go to the WBS room, let me know when you first come into the room, where you are, and for those of you who send me e-mails, please give me your first names just like we have on the air and what station you're listening to or the city and state that you're in at the start of the e-mail.

For the first time in the history of broadcasting you the people of America have the greatest access to public officials and guests in the talk back program each week right here on the Talk Radio Network. For those of you who'd like to send me your comments on the show or alert me to a more lengthy issue, you can snail mail it to the program at Talk Back, P.O. Box 633, Medford, Oregon 97501-0043 and if somebody wants to send me one of those extra Christmas cards before you put them away till next year, please do so, I'd love to hear from all of you out there and I love hearing from all of you on any other issue. The staff and I try to answer as many as we can and all letters and e-mails are read.

Let's get underway. Quote of the week, a very important one for today's program. Knowledge will forever govern ignorance. And the people who mean to be their own governors must arm themselves with the power knowledge gives. A popular government without popular information or the means of acquiring it is but a prologue to a farce or a tragedy, or perhaps both. That from one of the founding fathers, James Madison, and you'll learn today where that one can very easily come true here.

Ladies and gentlemen the topic today is the politics of AIDS. AIDS has been a big story with my fellow journalists all over America, and for that matter all over the planet for some time. I noticed in the wire reports just this week hopes were dashed for an AIDS vaccine. One of the local papers on the front page here, the Central Valley Times here in Southern Oregon, according to a leading researcher, an assistant professor of medicine at the University of North Carolina, Chapel Hill, the study found that the vaccine, which was developed by Jen-Tex Inc. doesn't stop the AIDS virus from reproducing or slow the destruction of the infected immune systems. They did a test with 568 volunteers, they saw no difference between those who got the placebo and the other half that got the real thing. That's the kind of test that might kill them.

In The Washington Post, December 9-15 in the national weekly edition, a commentary in the AIDS fight big is beautiful. Only the pharmaceutical industry's giants can afford the cost of innovation. Hmmm, before today's over you may find out he was wrong. Let me welcome a gentleman who is no doubt one of the world's leading experts on the subject of retro viruses, head of the Micro Biology Department at UC Berkeley, Professor Peter Duesberg, welcome to the Talk Back Program.

Professor Duesberg, do we have you? Okay, he'll be with us here in a moment, we've got a technical problem here. When we get that solved listen very, very carefully because if you have children, or grandchildren, or anyone in your family close to you that is "still sexually active", "of that age that may be experimenting with drugs", "getting ready to do numerous different things", they need to hear what is about to happen. Professor Duesberg, welcome to the program.

Prof D - Hello, hello. Okay, it's a pleasure to be back on with Randy Johnson, as usual.

Randy - Professor Duesberg, what is a retro virus?

Prof D - A retro virus is actually a very benign kind of parasite, the hallmark of which that it never kills the cell it attacks. And it is for that reason that retro viruses were hunted in the last 20 or 30 years in humans and in animals as possible causes of cancer. Viruses that don't kill cells are hypothetically causes of cancer. Viruses that kill cells that are bad, killer cells, killer viruses are not likely causes of cancer. So retro viruses are in fact among viruses in humans the most harmless and in animals that we have ever found. They never kill the cell, and the evidence that they would cause cancer in humans has also failed to materialize. We have no evidence of that either, so they are by far the most harmless parasites that we have ever identified in humans and animals.

Randy - If a retro virus doesn't kill a cell, then will it ever kill the host?

Prof D - No, not at all. As I said, we have never seen any evidence that retro viruses would cause a disease at all in the wild animals that is outside of breeding colony or laboratory in an otherwise healthy animal, a retro virus is completely harmless.

Randy - So what's so special about HIV professor?

Prof D - There is one thing special about HIV, that medical establishment led initially by retro virus hunters such as Baltimore and the current director of NIH and Robert Gallo and other important researchers in the field have agreed that this virus is the cause of AIDS. They have reached consensus but they've never been able to prove it. That makes this virus important and that is about it.

Randy - Has that theory ever been published or peer reviewed?

Prof D - Published it has been, you better believe it, about 100,000 plus times. There are more than, so many papers have been published on the subject and you and I and the rest of our fellow Americans have paid dearly for these publications. The taxpayer in America alone has paid by now $45 billion into the virus AIDS hypothesis into research and into treatment of AIDS patients and absolutely nothing has come out of it. We have yet to save the first AIDS patient as you just acknowledged a minute ago. We have no vaccine, we have no anti-viral drug, we have no prevention. We cannot even predict the disease that is coming. We have no benefits for the taxpayer, nothing to offer to the AIDS patient for all that money. And so that isn't a very good record for any hypothesis.

Randy - Now especially when in 96 hours CDC took care of the Hunta virus, at least had a cure for it, it makes me really wonder here. Doctor, the current AIDS test, the one that they've spent all the money developing....

Prof D - Yes, yes.

Randy - As I understand it, it only detects the HIV antibody. What does this mean to the patient?

Prof D - Well, that is initially the best news you could offer for anybody with the virus or at risk for a virus. In fact, the vaccine that you again just discussed, that AIDS researchers are trying to develop against HIV, is achieving exactly what it's suppose to, is designed to achieve exactly that, namely that you make antibodies against the virus. Because ever since Edward Jena the classical British doctor who 200 years ago invented vaccinations, ever since he came up with vaccinations we have protected us, ourselves, our country against viral diseases with vaccinations. That is an artificial induction of antibodies against the virus. By inoculations either of dead viruses or attenuating viruses, viruses that have lost their bite to some degree, but nevertheless infect a person or an animal and then provoke the immune system to make antibodies and these antibodies now protect against the real infection of a wide type virus, possibly a pathogenic virus, to protect you for the rest of your life. So this is exactly what is detected.

In antibody positive people and many AIDS patients, it detects the only effective weapon that nature and mankind has ever come up with against viruses, namely antibody against virus. And we talk the unique conclusion, highly unique, highly unusual, in fact I would say absurd conclusion in this case, well you have antibodies now my friend you're in trouble. Any time, any decade now, you'll get AIDS. With all other viruses, with all other microbes, with all other fungi, anything we come up, when we see viruses we say, "Well, you probably have nothing to worry about. You're already immunized, you can go to Tijuana or to Mexico or to the Jungle, Yellow Fever is not going to hit you because you have antibodies. The Ebola Virus is not going to get you in the Congo because you have antibodies, you won't get polio because you have antibodies, you have your vaccine. When we find antibodies against HIV every single doctor in this country, or virtually every single one, I should say there are some exceptions, and every single scientist, with some exceptions, of course, you're talking to some of them, will say, "Oh, now my friend you're in trouble, one of these days you're getting AIDS". For all other antibodies, with all other microbes they will tell you exactly the opposite. That is what microbiology, immunology, and biology has taught us for 200 years. The best way to confront viruses or fight viruses, is immunity, antibodies.

Randy - Okay. Before we get to our break, I want you to give America your definition of the most popular treatment currently being used, I guess at $10,000-14,000 a month, it's called AZT.

Prof D - (laughs). That is, I mean, possibly, probably the biggest blunder in medicine that ever happened in the free world. That drug is used, was licensed in '87 as an anti-HIV drug, fortunately. And it was as it is now known as an anti-AIDS or anti-HIV drug. But listen for a moment what it is. AZT is a terminator of DNA synthesis. That is to say when AZT is an analog of one of the four elements of DNA, the genetic material of human and animal cells. The master molecule of life. You terminate that master molecule, you are terminating life. There's no way around it. This chemical AZT is an analog of one of the four building blocks of DNA and if it is incorporated instead of the natural analog the DNA stops and it will die. And why would some toxic stuff like that be developed? Well it was developed 30 years ago for cancer chemotherapy. Cancer chemotherapy is irrational but a desperate way of fighting off the cancer that cannot be removed by any other method and is about to kill you. And the hallmark of a cancer is that it is made up of cells that are growing typically faster or more relentlessly than any other cell in the body. The last stop you can offer, the last defense you can offer when a cancer is about to do this and you can't remove it otherwise, is to use while chemicals in the body that kill all growing cells, not just AZT. That's chemotherapy. You kill cell growth, you stop all growing cells. The strategy being you hope to kill the cancer before you kill the patient. And the price is high. The cancer patient treated with chemotherapy looks like hell and feels like hell. They lose hair, they lose weight, they lose blood, they become anemic, their guts are going to get diarrhea, nausea and all these kinds of things.

But sometimes it works and then you have beaten the cancer and then you immediately stop it and hope that the patient will recover, and they often do. And that is sort of a moderate times in cancer therapy. But now you're using this thing against HIV. A hypothetical, not a proven cause of this or any disease. There's no proof anywhere in the abundant literature on HIV and AIDS that HIV is causing AIDS. There's only so called correlation and no proof. So we are treating a hypothetical cause of a disease with chemotherapy known by design a killer of human cells. We are not limiting the treatment like we do with cancer for a couple of weeks, or at the most a couple of months, until the tumor gives in, or doesn't give in, whatever the consequences are. It is always stopped after a couple of months because otherwise you kill the patient faster than the cancer would do it.

So we are giving it definitely to 200,000 fellow Americans, most of them in fact are now healthy, needless to say there's no AIDS here, they only have antibodies against HIV. Nevertheless they are given AZT indefinitely every 6 hours, every day of their life. And the thought is devastating. We have yet to read of the population of AIDS patients that has ever been cured with AZT. The literature has yet to offer the first study that shows that AZT has prevented the oncome of AIDS. It claims it has started out and that hypothesis, that dream, was only in 1994 by the so-called Concord Study when a study was finally done outside the United States where all of this is highly controlled by the NIH. It was done in England and in France, they were testing it independently because they were a bit suspicious of the American colleagues pushing AZT just a bit too hard, they tested it on their own not trusting Falche and the

National Cancer Institute's Sam Poda they did their own study, and they found to the surprise of the medical community that it was not even preventing the onslaught of AIDS to the people who were treated this AZT and the so-called placebo controlled study. They were dying 25% faster, AZT was accelerating death in these people.

Randy - Well that verifies your brief definition of AZT then.

Prof D - My brief definition that I understand you like is AZT is AIDS by prescription. And it sounds funny, but it is very sad. And it has to be that way, Randy, there's no other way. You cannot, if you put a substance in the human body that kills cells, terminates DNA synthesis, you are first killing the fastest growing cells. Among the fastest growing cells in the body is the bone marrow, the cells that make the immune cells, B cells, T cells, red cells and epithelial cells. And what do you get? You get anemia, you get immune deficiency, you lose weight because you hurt the linings of your stomach, you throw up, you get nauseated, you can't eat, and you're losing weight. Weight loss, diarrhea, and T cell deficiencies and B cell deficiencies are all AIDS defining diseases. In other words, you're causing AIDS with AZT. You produce impotency, you produce dementia because the mind, and you generate muscle atrophy because the muscle depends on the mitochondria of DNA which you killed, that's little energy cells in the muscle. The same in the brain, you kill mitochondria in the brain so you can't think anymore and you get what you call AIDS dementia. And you get impotent because of course potency is dependent on a lot of DNA synthesis, your sperm that you make and all these things of things. And of course you generally hurt in your muscle functioning as well. So there are a lot of nasty consequences of AZT. Also, it fits in the AIDS definition, and that's why it is well deserving of the term AIDS by prescription.

Randy - So Doctor, in the couple of moments we have left in the bottom of the hour break would you please define as you see it, what AIDS really is.

Prof D - Well, I have no choice in this. I don't have my own definition of AIDS, I can only remind you of the rather confusing but nevertheless only official definition of AIDS that we have. That comes from the American Center for Disease Control in Atlanta, and of course also a part of the National Institute of Health contributed to this definition. The definition says that 30 previously known diseases, old diseases, not one new disease, old diseases, such as pneumonia, dementia, diarrhea, carposi sarcoma, weight loss, herpes infection, candidiasis, yeast infection, any of these diseases, tuberculosis, are now called AIDS when antibodies against HIV are found. When these antibodies are not there the disease is called by the old name. When they are found then we are talking about AIDS. So the definition is an old disease when antibodies of HIV is there, then we call it AIDS, no antibodies we call it by the old name. That explains one thing in particular, the argument that they always advance. When you say how do we know that HIV is causing, well I tell you, well it can't be an accident that every single AIDS case has antibodies against HIV. Well you see now why that is a very good argument, although it is a tiny bit circular. In fact it is one of the greatest cases of circular logic because if you define a disease by the presence of an antibody against the virus then you turn around and say look we have always that antibody against the virus, you have the perfect example of circular logic. That's why they have this wonderful 100% correlation between HIV and AIDS because the only call it AIDS when HIV is present.

Randy - Oh, I'm going to give the audience a chance to sit for a minute, while we take this little break, I'm going to let them swallow that pill so to speak, no pun intended. And when we come back the conversation will continue. Our WINI caller and anyone else who's dialing now, stay put, be patient, we will get to you. And then we're going to be joined by another Ph.D. Professor, N.D. D.C. and a few other degrees he has behind his name and I think he's going to shock you almost as much as Professor Duesberg has. The Politics of AIDS, that's the topic. The motivation behind it, I think you'll find it to be the same motivation behind the United States Congress and most of what we feel is wrong with it. Simple, short, sweet, to the point, greed. You're listening to the Talk Radio Network.

Randy - Welcome back America. Let me welcome a new station to the program, WAPI the 50,000 watt voice at 1070 on the dial in Birmingham, Alabama. Welcome to the Talk Radio Network and welcome to the talk back family. We hope to be hearing from you today. This is a fascinating subject and it should fascinate everyone in the world because this virus is the single largest plague to hit the planet. I've been doing a little research lately. They're expecting 3/4 of the population of the South Africa to die within the next 10 years from this. That's almost as bad as some of the radiation exposures from a mistake over in Russia are going to do to their nation over time. We have a serious problem here. Why hasn't the medical community come up with a cure or treatment? Well, you just heard a great deal of that formula. Because if you don't have the right numbers in the formula or the right letters in the formula you cannot come up with the correct answer. And if you start with foundation bricks for building a house, you're not going to build a very good pyramid, are you? Think about it America. The foundation is faulted and therefore the entire medical community is going the wrong way. When the medical community goes the wrong way, so do our lives. And for those out there who have full blown AIDS I wish you all the luck in the world. The one thing I can say is something that Professor Duesberg told me, and that's simply this. If you're on AZT, stop because you cannot take a chain terminator drug like AZT which is an awful lot in my mind, let me turn this around so everybody can understand it. In my mind if you're trying to kill a virus that infects, I think it's like 1 in 15 cells maybe, you can't swallow a grenade that's live and ready to explode just to take out 1 in 15 cells. Not if you want to live through the experience. And that's a bit what AZT is like. You're using a grenade that goes in and takes out entire masses of cell bodies, to maybe get 1 in 15. Correct me if I'm wrong Professor Duesberg.

Prof D - It's a very good analogy. If the greande does the job faster and cleaner and you don't suffer as much. You don't have so much time to throw up and lose weight , and those cells get infected, and you lose your health.

Randy - All right, well, let me at this point, let's turn around for a moment and take a caller who's been sitting here patiently waiting from the very beginning of the show, and then I want to get to my next guest as well. Lee in Carbondale, Illinois listening on WINI you're on the air.

Lee - Yes I make three points quickly so your next guest and Dr. Duesberg can comment on this. First of all, I'm sure you're familiar with Mr. Chuck Harder. Back in 1995 he had Dr. Lorraine Day......

Prof D - Oh that's right, yeah, Dr. Lorraine Day, yes I remember.

Lee - Who was in charge of the San Francisco Bay Hospital and on his show she mentioned and other shows too, she mentioned the fact that there is a process of using a dialysis machine and ozone sub three to rid people of the AIDS virus. Point number two quickly.

Prof D - Ozone machine.

Lee - Yes, yes, yes Doctor. Yes, and point number two quickly Tony Brown, Tony Brown's journal, mentioned the same thing that the good doctor said this evening, that is that the HIV virus is not the cause of AIDS but when taken in conjunction or by itself AZT is a true killer that's killing these people and the pharmaceutical industries are getting rich off of it. And point number three, I'm a former student in epidemiology and I mentioned these facts about that and other oxidizers such as chlorine percolonate that could oxidize and kill the AIDS virus to the school of public health up there by Chicago, I quickly, and I repeat I quickly was basically edged out in the sense that I lost my assistantship, and terrible things started.

Prof D- What did you lose, I didn't quite get that?

Lee - My assistance ship. When I told my professor.......

Prof D - Just for saying that, you lost your assistantship?

Lee - Yes sir, because everything was fine up to that point. I'm not imagining it, things got terrible for me so I left Chicago because the public health industry, the CDC, all of them, from what they've done and what they've said, are not listening to people like your guest this evening or Dr. Lorraine Day who are trying to bring out the truth about this, I'm gonna call it what it is, it's a scam of American people to develop an industry, and that's all I had to say.

Randy - All right, thank you very much. I'm going to give Professor Duesberg a chance to comment on that and bring in our next guest. We've got a quick break that I should have taken before now, we're going to do it now. And if you'd like to join us, it's 1-800-449-TALK. The Politics of AIDS is the subject, and you're listening to the Talk Radio Network.

Randy - All right, welcome back America, we're coming up to another break here very quickly so I'll give Professor Duesberg a chance to make a comment about this oxygen therapy. Professor Duesberg?

Prof D - Yes, hello! Here I am.

Randy - I wanted to give you an opportunity to comment on the oxygen therapy and if there's anything you've heard about it, we've got another break coming up real quick.

Prof D - Well I heard about it but I really am not in a position to comment on it in a professional way because I have only..... it's not described in the professional literature and I obviously, it hasn't been madly successful, we would have heard more about this and the therapy curing anybody, but I haven't seen that. And I don't see what it's even, what the theoretical basis of it should be. Is it supposedly killing the virus and what is it?

Randy - Well, apparently from what I've heard anyway, the oxygen bubbling through some kind of kidney machine where they mix the oxygen into the blood stream apparently is suppose to kill the AIDS virus, but as I understand it what we were discovering here today is that AIDS is more of a condition rather than a virus.

Prof D - Well, ah, yes as I am saying, if oxygen could kill the AIDS virus, nobody should ever get AIDS because we are all inhaling oxygen all the time and trying to put it in our blood in order to survive, you know. That's the whole point of breathing (laughs). So if oxygen in the blood could help the AIDS virus, could eliminate the AIDS virus, nobody would ever get AIDS, I can tell you that.

Randy - Or if they did, we'd just put an oxygen mask on 'em in the hospital and up the oxygen level in their blood stream and case closed.

Prof D - And they would be flying, yes, that's right, yes.

Randy - So, um, well we have much to learn here, apparently. Doctor, in about 30 seconds or less, what do you feel is the real cause of the disease AIDS itself?

Prof D - The real cause of the disease? Well, according to my hypothesis and in fact it's really not my hypothesis, I just get credited for it more than I deserve to the CDC's original hypothesis it is what they use to call lifestyle, which is just a euphemism. For the long term consumption of recreational drugs like cocaine and heroine, even nitrite inhalants, like popus, amphetamines, and other recreational drugs and worst of all now add to it the antiviral, anti-AIDS drugs such as AZT that we already discussed which is taken by over 200,000 Americans every single day now.

Randy - Any drug that could damage your immune system, and I imagine there's a whole list of prescribed drugs that would hit that. Well, anyway, we've got to take another quick break. When we come back, Dr. M. Paul Farber will join us. You're listening to the Talk Radio Network.

Randy - Welcome back America. And now, the author of a book called The Micro Silver Bullet, or Mild Silver Protein. A preliminary scientifically documented answer to the three largest epidemics in the world. Of course, one of these would be the HIV thing One that the doctor himself almost died of is Lyme Disease. You got things like yeast infections, the common cold, all kinds of other things that we are being plagued with and there may well be a very simple scientific explanation as to why. In fact doctors a long time ago had an idea about this and I think that's part of how Dr. Farber found the.....

Dr. M. Paul Farber, B.A., B.S., M.A., M.S., N.D., Ph.D. and D.C., for those of you out there who don't know who he is, that should tell you a lot right there. The People's Doctor, welcome to the Talk Back Program.

Dr. F - Good evening Randy, and good evening to Dr. Duesberg and to all of your listening audience all over the United States of America.

Randy - Well doctor, what did you find as you discovered a connection here with this Mild Silver Protein?

Dr. F - I wasn't originally looking for an answer Randy, to the AIDS virus. What happened about 4 years ago I was bitten by the tick that causes Lyme disease, got very, very ill, ended up being about 85% paralyzed from my waist down. At the time I had not discovered the Coll/Ag-40 Mild Silver Protein. Once I found out more about Lyme disease I realized that the spirochetes could kill you, I decided to try the conventional antibiotics which were rocephan and penicillin. Unfortunately they didn't work on me, caused me a lot of side effects and the worst side effect, which Dr. Duesberg talked about earlier, was a Candida yeast infection which is now the third largest epidemic in the world, because everyone who's ever been on antibiotics and was not told to replace the good bacteria called acidophilus like you have in yogurt, will get a Candida yeast infection and then it happened to a large part of the population, and it's now the third largest epidemic in the world.

I got very ill and it went up into my lungs, into my heart, into my intestines, and I almost died. As a matter of fact I did have a near death experience which is covered in my book The Micro Silver Bullet and it goes into detail of that. But what happened was after I met Dr. Willy Burgdorfer he is a Scientist Emeritus, works with the Rocky Mountain Institute, the National Institute of Health. I was at a Lyme conference in Alantic City, New Jersey and they announced at that conference they did not have a cure or an answer for Lyme disease, that the antibiotics would slow it down but would cause it to mutate, the spirochetes would hide in deep fibroblast of the tissue, it would keep coming back. Dr. Burgdorfer and I had become friends. I had written a poem for him which touched him very deeply, and I said, "Dr. Burgdorfer, do you mean I'm going to have to suffer from this for the rest of my life?" I had over 40 symptoms, Randy, and it was a pretty miserable way to be alive. He said to me, "Dr. Farber, you're a scientist, you're a researcher, you've got the disease, why don't you go find an answer?" Well, he knew how to push the right buttons because I love doing research. I was first at the University of Texas, then the University of Missouri doing experimental psychology, doing double blind studies and I had the disease, so I decided to accept the challenge.

About 6 months later, Randy, I rediscovered what they now call the Dead Sea Scrolls of Modern Medicine. What this was, was all the scientific research that was done between the years of 1900 and 1938 by the top research scientists, medical doctors, pharmaceutical companies, universities of the time, where they tested the colloidal silver or mild silver protein on over 650 different micro organisms. And it was successful and it killed all of them. I have all of that documentation available and bound in an edition that's about an inch and a half book that's called, that I named The Dead Sea Scrolls of Modern Medicine. It was the treatment of the day for syphilis and gonorrhea. Well, Randy I didn't have syphilis, I didn't have gonorrhea but in my micro biology background I knew that the causative agent of syphilis was a spirochete, just a different one, trepodema pallidum. I then scientifically deduced that if it killed that spirochete that caused syphilis, it should kill the spirochete that caused Lyme disease.

If you ever saw the show, Out of Africa, where Robert Redford and Meryl Streep, when she got infected with syphilis she was getting ready to go to United Kingdom to receive some silver treatments. Well that was correct because that was the treatment of the day. I began on the mild silver protein which I developed and worked with the laboratory. We re-engineered it, got to a 40 parts per million and got it nitrite and nitrate free, beyond any colloidal silver, got the micron size down to .001 microns and to a point where that's like a little grain of sand next to the planet earth.

I went on the silver, one tablespoon twice a day for the first month. By the end of the first month I was about 50% well from both Lyme disease and Candida yeast infection, about half of my symptoms stopped. By the end of the second month I was about 75% well. By the end of the third month, I was free! I was completely well. I had no symptoms from Lyme disease or Candida yeast infection. I went back to Dr. Burgdorfer I told him what had happened. He looked at me and said, "Dr. Farber, I have very little doubt in my mind that you were the first person in the world to get well from two so-called incurable diseases, Lyme disease and Candida yeast infection. But the world's not going to believe you unless you test it scientifically". Well, there he went again, knowing how to push my right buttons and Dr. Duesberg will understand this. By the way, let me say this before I go on. Let me congratulate Dr. Peter Duesberg for the work that he's done. I have read his book cover to cover and, of course, it was co-authored by Dr. Yiamouyiannis, a Ph.D. and I had a personal conversation with him. I feel it's very, very courageous. Dr. Duesberg reminds me of two of my mentors. I was fortunate enough to study with one of Einstein's original students, and one of the octogenerians that developed the atomic theories with him, and also with Dr. Robert Mendelson, who wrote the book Confessions of a Medical Heretic. He was the first People's Doctor. Dr. Duesberg could be Confessions of a Microbiology Heretic. The light of information he's bringing to truth in the world of microbiology, that Dr. Mendelson did in the world of medicine, I congratulate his courage and his honesty and standing up against the forces of greed and profit which we'll go into a little bit later when we talk about the FDA. So congratulations Dr. Duesberg. I look forward to meeting you and Dr. Yiamouyiannis.

I then went to Temple University. That's up in Ben Franklin country. By the way, let me, Randy, you asked me to do this so I'll do it. We only have a short time. My book, The Micro Silver Bullet, there's a 1-800 number. 1-800-263-9234. That's 1-800 a new beginning. 1-800-263-9234. Since we only have a short time, people have told me that they read the book and it's like being able to sit down and talk to me for 30 years. You can find answers to all the diseases. My approach to AIDS, to Lyme disease, Candida yeast infection, the common cold and all these other diseases.

Randy - Yes, and you can also get Dr. Duesberg's book, Inventing the AIDS Virus, that is on the shelves at your local bookstores now. We'll be back after the news. You're listening to the Talk Radio Network.

Randy - Apparently the attorney is not at that number.

Dr. F - I understand.

Randy - Okay, oh okay, she told you. Ah, I just got a phone call from the head of our network.

Dr F - Okay.

Randy - His wife has Lyme disease.

Dr. F - Okay.

Randy - I didn't know this. Can you send her a copy of your book to the network offices, and maybe a bottle of the protein?

Dr F - Yes, Arnie and I will do that. We'll make arrangements to do that. Actually she'll need about a dozen bottles to get through the whole process.

* (Dr. Farber special note: Three months later, she did get well.)

Randy - Yeah. Well at least with that she can get started and know how to contact you.

Dr F - Definitely, and she'll be well in three months. We have, there's no doubt we have the answer. Just a matter of getting it out there to the people.

Randy - Amazing. I didn't know this about her and I've met her and I've talked to her and she's quite the intelligent woman.

Dr F - Now with the attorney, a lot of the information that he would have covered I have knowledge of so if we can't get a hold of him, I'll try and cover as much of it as I can.

Randy - Okay, great.

Dr F - Toward the end.

Randy - All right. Well, if you don't hear me introduce him as we come back in, then you'll know he's not there.

Dr F - Okay. When we come back I'll explain exactly what the Mild Silver Protein, the Coll/Ag-40 is, and why it works.

Randy - Okay, great. And then we'll get into the FDA.

Dr F - That will be wonderful, and I'll tie it into how I eventually got involved with the AIDS virus.

Randy - Okay, good. Welcome to the first politically active, computer interactive talk radio program on the planet, this is Talk Back on the Talk Radio Network. You can talk back using your computer in one of two ways. You can e-mail us, from any place that you can send electronic mail. You can send mail to Talk Back at Wave W-A-V-E dot net. That will show up in front of me in a matter of moments. Or you can go to my web site at www.wave.net/talkback and put talkback in all caps as one word and from the very first page there are hyper lengths next to WBS's logo that will take you right over to the WBS system. You click on the current events chat hub at the very first room. It's labeled Talk Back. If you have a valid e-mail address you can register for free, determining your own password and cybername, because you know people don't use their own real name when they're in a chat room, and you'll become a free member of the WBS system. It is supported by advertising, not by your fees like many of the other services, and then you, whatever you punch into that room, as a member of WBS, comes right up in front of me here at broadcast center instantaneously.

All right, let me welcome back Dr. M. Paul Farber. Dr. Farber, we had a couple of things we wanted to cover quickly before we get into the FDA.

Dr F - Good afternoon, you're back.

Randy - Yep.

Dr F - I'm here.

Randy - All right. Let's cover, you had a couple of things you wanted to cover about how the Silver Protein works?

Dr F - Right. Well, let's explain just briefly how the Mild Silver Protein works to Coll/Ag-40 Mild Silver Protein and what it is. Again, what it is, very easily.

I try to make things, and my book is designed so that the lay person can understand it, but it has enough technical information so a scientist or doctor knows how to use it. What this is is a attenuated silver, just like the silver that's in the earth. It's broken down into it's microscopic particles that are .001 microns in diameter. Again, that's a little grain of sand next to the planet earth. It's bound with a mild silver protein which is EDTA which is a chelating agent. It's suspended in the Brownian movement and what it does, it inhibits the enzyme that allows viruses to respire and they suffocate within, oh usually 1-3 minutes upon contact so it doesn't matter if the virus is a bacteria or yeast, or spirochete, it's mutated, it kills mutations just, it inhibits the enzyme that allows a virus or a bacteria to respire and they suffocate within usually 3 minutes. So it kills all mutations also.

And what we did, I started out at the Fox Chase Cancer Institute and tested it on the spirochetes that cause Lyme disease. It was 100% successful. In less than 3 minutes it killed all the spirochetes. Dr. Burgdorfer got so excited, we took it to the Rocky Mountain Institute which is NIH approved up on Montana. I'LL read on the back of my book from Dr. Burgdorfer. Just received Mild Silver Protein and have evaluated its' effectiveness in a preliminary pilot study against the Lyme disease spirochete, Borrelia Burgdorferi...spirochetes were treated with The Mild Silver Protein and when examined 24 hours later, no live spirochetes remained...from Penicillin to Mild Silver Protein - the antibiotic answer to Lyme Disease. Dr. Willy Burgdorfer, Ph.D. Scientist Emeritus, Rocky Mountain Laboratories, National Institute of Health. So we knew we had the answer for Lyme disease. We then took it to Temple University which is up there in Ben Franklin country. Dr. Duesberg will understand this. If you get results back from Temple, that's what is called in the scientific community, impeccable. You can't find anything wrong with it. We tested it on the, ah, first of all, on the ah, ah organism, the yeast organism, the Candida yeast organism that cause Candida yeast infection, and it killed all three Candida organisms in less than 3 minutes.

Randy - Wow! So if I understand what you're saying correctly here, is that what you have found then is something that goes even one step further than what Professor Duesberg is calling, this might be an answer for those who already have what I tend to now call the AIDS condition.

Dr F - Yes it is, and we'll got into that in detail in a moment.

Randy - Okay. It might prevent some of the onset of the diseases that are actually killing.

Dr F - It not only prevents the onset, it stops them. I had a person a year ago call me from Florida, his sister called me. She had read my book. Her brother was in the hospital dying of pneumo-cytisis which is a lung condition, one of the opportunistic diseases that kills about 50% of the AIDS patients, and very little recovery from it. He had the AIDS virus but again, as Dr. Duesberg said, that isn't necessarily what will kill them. His sister said, "Will it help?" I said, "Well, there's no doubt in my mind that it will because I know it killed the pneumonia virus and I know it kills the Candida virus and it should stop the pneumo-cytisis. So, but then she said, "Well, how can I get it to him?" I said, "Well, if you give it to the hospital they may not give it to him because a person in California called me and she tried to go through the hospital, they blocked it, and her son died three days later". So I told her, "It's just a nutritional mineral supplement and according to the Hatch Act just a mineral supplement and you just get it into him". You know, I told him my protocol of 5-4-3 protocol tablespoon five times a day the first month, four the second, three the third, so there's no more virus left in the body. They put him on the Mild Silver Protein and in less than 3 days they could find no more trace of the pneumo-cystitis in his body. There was nothing in there. Then they checked for the AIDS virus and they couldn't find it either. They couldn't find any viruses or bacteria. So, you know, they said, "Well, we must have diagnosed him wrong. He must have had a spontaneous remission". They didn't know he was on the Mild Silver Protein. They released him from the hospital. About a year later I got a call from him and he had gone in to have his viral load check for the AIDS virus and they could find no more of virus left in his body whatsoever or any virus or infectious micro organisms.

Since then we did tests with Dr. Earl Rice who's a friend of Elizabeth Taylor who is out in California on seven AIDS patients that has the AIDS virus and all the opportunistic diseases. What it does, at Temple University, thank God I didn't have the AIDS virus, but I've been researching it for the last five years. We tested it at the Temple University on the kryptococcus which causes a lot of death also in opportunistic diseases, AIDS patients. For the first time in the history of medical science with a non-toxic substance unlike AZT, no side effects, does not hurt the healthy cells whatsoever, does not collect in body, passes right out through the body because it's so tiny, micron size, we for the first time in medical history cured the kryptococcus.

Then we get a call from Dr. Earl Henderson, the head Ph.D. of Microbiology at Temple University. He said, "Dr. Farber, you showed this killed the Lyme disease, spirochete, cured Candida yeast infection, killed the kryptococcus" he said, "I work with the AIDS virus. Will this kill the AIDS virus?" I said, "I have no doubt." I ran across an old study from Switzerland, Geneva, which of course was buried, but it's in my book where they tested a silver cystine, a silver product that's like this on the AIDS virus and it killed the AIDS virus, so I knew that it did. So what we did is that we tested it on the AIDS virus and let me imagine this too. And I've announced it on national radio, let me say before I announce this, all I'm doing, I'm an author, a scientist, and a researcher. All I'm doing at the present time is practicing my first amendment rights under the constitution of free speech to talk about my research, my findings, what's in my book. I'm making no claims, I'm claiming no cures, I'm just telling what my research is and expressing freedom of speech here. For the first time in the history of medical science with a non-toxic substance, proven to work in the body already for over 50 years, and now it's much more advanced, with no side effects, no toxicity. We not only inhibited replication of HIV and any latent formation, we killed the AIDS virus in less than 3 minutes. Pretty exciting

Randy - That is definitely exciting.

Dr F - Now let's take into what's under consideration, Dr. Duesberg said, what if the thought is true that the AIDS virus which is a retro virus and is a weak virus, I thought that always it may have weakened the immune system. I didn't feel it could cause what we now call AIDS or the AIDS syndrome. What if it kills the AIDS virus but what if that's not the cause? Well in our study, first of all, I made sure that we got everyone off the drugs. I agree 100% with Dr. Duesberg. All of you listening out there, if you're on cocaine, crack, heroine, morphine, all of these drugs, get off them.

Randy - AZT...

Dr F - AZT, none of it is gonna help you, because any white powder drug, what it does is an abrasive and it destroys the immune system and then the opportunistic infection can come in. So Dr. Duesberg is 100% right about the recreational drugs. The inhalants, the AZT, and all the other medical treatments that they're doing there. Right now AIDS is about a $15-20 billion a year business. If they can keep people dying at the same rate they're dying. Before they die of the AZT, if they have insurance, they make $125,000.

It would be considered fraud, and it's something that I'm very concerned about which is why we're doing this program today. I need to take a quick break and we're gonna talk just a little bit about the FDA and then Professor Duesberg and Dr. Farber are going to answer your calls, comments, and questions at 1-800-449-TALK, the only line open right now is the priority line, area code 541-664-TALK, you're listening to the Talk Radio Network.

Randy - Welcome back America, we want to quickly get into, now we've laid the ground work here. It's taken a little over an hour to get a very complicated subject on the table and have two leading professors tell you a little bit about what they know. And it's been a tough pill for a lot of people to swallow and I bet there's a few people in the medical industry that aren't real happy with what we're saying on this program right now. But so be it, you deserve the truth, here it is.

Now, the Mild Silver Protein seems to take an awful lot of different things out. Interestingly enough the pharmaceutical community is not real happy about that. I mean, think about it. AZT, $14,000 a month, versus a bottle of Mild Silver Protein that cost $40.00 I think. Which one pays more research grants, sends more doctors on vacations, etc., etc., etc. I.E. why at the beginning of this program I said what you're going to learn today is that there is a greed motivation behind this. The Federal Disaster Agency as I call it, or the FDA as everyone else knows it has tried to stop the Mild Silver Protein from being on the market in America. Dr. Farber, tell us about it.

Dr F - I would be more than happy to Randy. First of all, that 1-800 number again to get the book so you can get all the details on the studies is 1-800-263-9234, 1-800-263-9234 and the web site is www.silverbulletgold.com and you'll be able to pull up 12 pages and it will tell you in detail. If you can't find it that way just look under Lyme disease or AIDS or Candida and then pull up Farber and that will get it. And that will give them all the details, Randy.

Randy - So what has the FDA tried to do in the last few weeks?

Dr F - What they tried to do in the last few weeks is, what the Mild Silver Protein Colloidal Silver was and Coll/Ag-40 is beyond Colloidal Silver because it has been re-engineered to such a finer degree. It was, before, a pre-1938 drug sold over the counter drug, so because it was pre-1938 it was Grandfathered in. And so they tried to come back and say well, it wasn't manufactured the same way it was manufactured before 1938, it's manufactured better now, but that doesn't matter. So we want to take it off because it doesn't meet the requirement. But what they failed to realize or recognize that back in 1994 thank God what was called the Hatch Act was passed by Congress, which is the Coalition for Support of the DSHEA Dietary Supplement Health and Education Act. As a result of that act which saved the nutritional supplements the pharmaceutical companies were trying to put the poor nutritional companies out of business because they were competitive to them. Thank God, congratulations Senator Hatch if you are listening. So they're trying to go back, and an act of Congress was done. Now what they're trying to do is twist and turn the rules and exactly what the facts are. They're trying to disregard Congress. Trying to disregard an act of Congress and go back and put it back as an over the counter drug. Since it has a mineral in it, which is silver, under the DSHEA it is now a nutritional mineral supplement and the FDA has no jurisdiction in it what's so ever. But needless to say for what I think are reasons of greed and profit and power they have tried to do this.

Randy - Okay, so if they were successful in taking this out of the over the counter area where you can get it in your health food store or buy it through the mail, what ultimately would happen to the price of the product?

Dr F - It would skyrocket, it would skyrocket. You'd have to see a physician first who has no knowledge of it whatsoever, and could now have no knowledge of prescribing it whatsoever and it would skyrocket and they would try to make it into a prescription drug so that people would pay a fortune for something that's less than $55.00 for a 4 oz. bottle. And we had AIDS patients get well for less than a few thousand dollars. Get completely well from all the opportunistic diseases that would have killed them. We got a little girl Roxie here in Pasadena, right outside of Houston where I'm located. Both her parents died from AIDS. When she was born she had thrush, she had ulcers, she had bleeding in her colon, bleeding from her anus and she was not able to go to school or ever go to camp and so forth. Her aunt got a hold of my book, got in touch with us. We told her, explained to her at the time cause we can't talk about a cure in this country. When I'm in less dictocratic countries that are less offensive....when I was in South Africa with Nelson Mandella's top officials, when I talked with people that we do business with in Holland and in Canada and all over Europe, when I was in South Africa he said, one of Nelson Mandella's top people, he said, "Dr. Farber, looks like you came up with a cure for the common cold." I said, "In South Africa I have the cure for the common cold, in the United States I just have a nutritional answer that will balance out the body to the highest point of homeostasis possible. If the person gets well from this incurable disease, that's between them, the Lord God in heaven, his son Jesus Christ, I'm just on the sidelines applauding. So in other countries I have the cure, in this country I just have an answer and a nutritional supplement.

Randy - All right, we've got to take a quick break. Callers that are on line stay put, the only line open is 541-664-TALK, that's the priority line. You can be the first caller in line after this break right there, or come up in our WBS room or e-mail me at Talk Back at WAVE.net. We will continue this with your calls and Professor Peter Duesberg and Dr. M. Paul Farber right after these messages from the sponsors that bring you this program. You're listening to the Politics of AIDS here on the Talk Radio Network.

Randy - Welcome back America. We have a lot of ground we've covered. I know it's been just a touch confusing maybe to those of you who aren't medically inclined, but you have received a plate bigger than your Thanksgiving and Christmas dinners put together on the subject of medicine and the politics of AIDS today. I'm going to bring Professor Peter Duesberg back now so that he can do a quick recap of what AIDS really is and then we're just going to start taking calls cause the lines are just jammed over here, people trying to get in here. I understand that, I'm sorry we didn't start taking calls sooner. But there's a lot of information that needed to be put on the table here. Professor Duesberg, welcome back to the program.

Prof D - So, um, I need to talk.

Randy - Okay. A quick rendition of what the AIDS condition really is before we get to answering questions.

Prof D - One half hour ago we briefly touched upon before that. I came to conclusion, rediscovered in fact an old hypothesis that AIDS is not actually caused by a virus but is instead caused by recreational drugs, long term use of recreational drugs which are very toxic and carcinogenic, amphetamines, cocaine and heroine. Worst of all, as of 1987 the anti-viral drugs that we discussed in quite some detail like AZT and protease inhibitors which are mixed with AZT. But look at it from my point of view, or from the other point of view. We are given in the name of an unproven hypothesis. AZT is a drug that is inevitably killing people.

What could be done, people who are already using drugs, they could discontinue, many would never start. But by pointing out that smoking is causing diseases. There were 100 million Americans smoking only 15 years ago, now it's down to 40 million. Because people don't want to get sick. That is the bottom line, that is the most effective way to conduct the war on drugs which we are doing anyway by pointing out that it's against the law that in fact has had the opposite effect. Young kids want to take something that is against the law rather than something that's within the law.

Randy - Oh yeah, it's like wanting them, standing outside the liquor store trying to get an adult to buy you alcohol cause you're too young to get it. And after you turn 21 you don't have that much to do with it.

Prof D - That is exactly right.

Randy - Hands in the cookie jar.

Prof D - But see with AIDS, more drugs costs taxpayers twice as much as the war on drugs. If we could win them both by pointing out that drugs are causing AIDS. 20 million Americans are daily taking illicit recreational drugs. That's based on the Bureau of Justice statistics, National Institute on Drug Abuse, and use warning systems in the White House. You know 20 million Americans take these drugs. There's not one single study conducted in this country, not even one, that ever tested long term effects of these drugs in human animals. Nothing, nothing...........

Randy - I can imagine why, cause there's probably 150,000 bureaucrats involved in the drug war that wouldn't have a job if we told the truth.

Prof D - You're hitting the nail on the head, yes.

Randy - Okay.

Prof D - I mean on the other hand they're are 500,000 fellow Americans, 500,000 who are checking into hospitals once a year as drug diseases, heart attacks, blood pressure, God knows what and 50,000 stay in there the same. That's the down side of this. This could all be prevented.

Randy - Simply tell them the truth.

Prof D - It's laid out in this book that just came out a couple of months ago, Inventing the Aids Virus. You can get it at Barnes and Noble, or Crown.

Randy - Somebody has hit a re-dial switch there, we're going to tone that down for a second while that goes. Let's take a call from Ramona in Jacksonville..........(beep).....listening on KSYG, you're on the air with Dr. Farber and Dr. Duesberg.

Ramona - Hello?

Randy - Hello Ramona, you're on the air!

Ramona - Yes. Well, I'd like to know what the name of the product is, what exactly, what it's called?

Randy - Okay, that's a good question.

Dr F - Ramona, it's called Coll/Ag-40, Mild Silver Protein. And when you call in for the book at that 1-800-263-9234 number they can tell where you can get the product. I'm not personally involved with the product or make any money off of it, I just researched it, designed and gave it my approval.

Ramona - Okay. Hello?

Randy - Okay, let's go to, who's been waiting the longest there, George or Benjamin, they both have been there a long time. Well let's go to Benjamin in Rogue River, Oregon listening on the flagship station, you're on the air.

Benjamin - Hello Randy and hello to your guests.

Randy - They're there, go ahead.

Benjamin - Okay. I just wanted to address, this is a great subject specifically talking about, you know, the government is basically corrupt and, hello??

Dr F - We're here, we're listening to your words.

Benjamin - Okay (laughs), um and I wanted to have your guests comment on the recent legislation in California allowing medical use of marijuana and how where AIDS patients it's specifically good in treating the wasting syndrome and perhaps such on how the FDA as well and DEA are suppressing this and vowing to fight and it saying it doesn't mean anything and that anyone who is using it, whether they have a medical claim or not is still going to be prosecuted.

Randy - Well, let me pose an obvious question here to Professor Duesberg, and thank you for that question. And that is, Professor Duesberg, in your, when you state that drugs lead to the condition of AIDS, is marijuana included in that list, or is it the harder drugs that cause aids?

Prof D - It's the harder drugs, yes not marijuana. If marijuana were the cause of AIDS then everybody in Berkeley would have AIDS.

Randy - (laughs) We won't touch that one with a ten foot pole. All right, gentlemen, any comments on the fact that marijuana might be able to be used in medicinal treatment of a certain AIDS condition?

Dr F - Well, I can just quote from two sources. 60 Minutes, which I've been watching for the last 28 years, ran a special on the use of, and again, marijuana is not a drug, it's an herb, it's an herb and it's a natural substance and doesn't have any toxic chemicals put on it except for pesticides, and so it's not a drug. What it does, according to 60 Minutes, is that people with AIDS or other heavy diseases, it relieves their pain and gives them some comfort that's involved with it. And also, Dr. Andrew Weill, M.D., who I'm friends with and have studied with has also said the same thing for many years that it can be helpful in those areas. I think it's something that people have to be educated on and moving in the right direction and they need to just make it available and in a way and such people can be educated on how to use it, not use it for addiction, but use it for the relief of pain and for the relief of difficult situations like it does have potential in those areas, once people understand it on a deeper level.

Randy - Okay, George stay put for a second, I've got a priority caller right in front of you, you're next. Chuck in Boise, Idaho, KIDO, you're on the air.

Chuck - Hi.

Randy - Hello there.

Chuck - I was recently diagnosed with hepatitis C, how is the Mild Silver Protein effective on that?

Dr F - The Mild Silver Protein kills the hepatitis C within about 3 minutes upon contact. We've had numerous cases of people with the hepatitis virus. We had one gentleman, as a matter of fact, Dr. Alex Duarte, who I have an infomercial out with that goes all across the nation, and you'll see him on television all the time talking about offshore drugs, he had a friend that had hepatitis C virus that was so bad in the hospital nothing worked on him whatsoever. The man was about ready to die in 3 days. We started him on the Mild Silver Protein - in 3 days he was 100% completely well. They could find no trace of the hepatitis left in his body whatsoever. Again, this kills every virus. It doesn't matter how bad a name it has. I even gave this to the military, but they never even called me back cause there's not a micro organisms that Sadem Hussen could produce that this will not kill, in my opinion. Again, according to my first amendment rights, this is the end of biological warfare if they could make the Silver available to all our people. We have had one person get completely well from the Gulf War Syndrome. A man named Jack, who was captured by Sadem Hussen, went to Mayo's, they couldn't help him, in less than 2 months Jack was completely well from the Gulf War Syndrome, back to work, working 5 days a week, 8 hours a day.

Randy - You'll have to put him in touch with me because I'm about to do a show on that. George, you've been waiting patiently in Wisconsin, you're on the air.

George - Yeah, I was just wondering....you referred to the doctor who invented the Silver, ah....

Randy - That's Dr. Paul Farber.

George - I was wondering why I don't, like AIDS patients and other places haven't publicized this a little more. This is the first I've heard of it.

Dr F - Let me explain something to you about the FDA. A couple of facts people don't realize about the FDA and this has to do with news stations and other things like this too. I've got documents that show 150 leading top officials of the FDA are on the payroll of the drug companies. Now, when Dr.

David Kessler resigned last week you heard on CNN, well Dr. Kessler decided to go back into private life. My sources in Europe told me what they don't tell you is that he was offered a $750,000 job from either Eli Lily or one of the other large drug companies and you're not even suppose to do that for like two or more years, or even be on the payroll. When all of the members of an organization, which I call the dictorcrats are on the payrolls of the drug companies, they're gonna outlaw and try and find everything wrong with the competition and try and pass through things very, very quickly and get them approved even though they have not been tested whatsoever. The FDA does not test anything. The drug company uses their own scientists to make the test. Let me tell you a joke that will sum up the whole thing about Dr. Kessler that came about. Dr. Kessler knew he was getting ready to resign from the FDA cause he had $750,000 a year job. You want to get one thing, last little hit in on the natural food industries. They needed a new accountant and a new so-called scientist in the FDA. So they put an advertisement out and 3 groups came in, first one came in and Dr. Kessler said, "I just have one little simple question for you. How do you reach the number 4?" First scientist and accountant talked about it for about 5 minutes, came back, they said, "Very simple, you add 2 plus 2 and that's equal to 4". Dr. Kessler said, "Well, that's good and fine but not exactly what I'm looking for. If I need ya, I'll give ya a call", and he sent them on their way. The second said, "2 times 2", he said, "That's not exactly what I'm looking for". The third one said, "Dr. Kessler, any way that you would like it to turn out we can accomplish." "You are hired", and that's what happening in the FDA unfortunately and raiding doctor's offices and health food stores has to be put to a stop in my opinion.

Randy - We'll be right back.

Randy - Well America, it is as I predicted at the beginning of the program, and I also did a little research into the Food and Drug Administration, and past administration, I might add. The recently retired President of the United States of America, who was replaced by our current President, and his vice-president both had major holdings in one of the largest drug companies on the planet. And people in the FDA have holdings as well. In companies they regulate. Unethical, it's unconscionable, and it's just as bad as allowing entities, companies, and foreign government to spend millions of dollars lobbying your congressmen when they can't even cast a vote for 'em. My opinion, the only people that should have the right to give a congressman money are the people and the companies within his or her district. This is a corruption in the political process that must end. Paul, in Quinton, Arkansas listening on KSYG on the priority line, you're on the air.

Paul - Hello. I was wondering, I got two questions. What's the difference between your product or not necessarily your product, but the Silver Protein and Colloidal Silver and has anybody tested this on the Gulf War Syndrome?

Dr F - The difference in the product is the micron size, we got the micron size down to .001, we got all of the nitrates and nitrites out in my AIDS research. The first time we killed the AIDS virus and inhibited replication and any latent formation it took like 250 parts per million. My theory was if we got all the nitrites and nitrates out which we eventually did that it was like the little, like a piece of sand or a little degree of turn on the Japanese super highways, that it would work a lot better. Once we did, my theory proved right. It took less than 30 parts per million to kill the AIDS virus once we got nitrites and nitrates out. Ah, so we got it to bond with the Mild Silver Protein again, we got it to a much higher level so that it works more quickly on the body. We did toxicity studies in Toronto, Canada on what would be equal to 750,000 parts per million in human, no toxicity whatsoever. On the Gulf War Syndrome, Jack was infested with all kinds of viruses and bacteria. He was around dead bodies, this killed every virus, bacteria, infectious micro organism in his body. Once all those micro organisms were dead, he got well from what we now call the Gulf War Syndrome.

Randy - Yep, one of the people in the WBS room says the cure for the AIDS is being kept a secret. Well, the cure for AIDS, if the AIDS condition as we understand it from Professor Duesberg is to be believed, and obviously the medical community doesn't for various reasons, is not doing certain things that will compromise your immune system and that will prevent the opportunistic diseases that kill the AIDS patient. Because remember your immune system has to be compromised before one of these other things can come along and kill you. We come in contact with all of these other things all the time. It doesn't mean it will kill you. But if your immune system is compromised then you have a serious problem. Mitch in Murphy, Oregon, you're on the air with Dr. Paul Farber, and Professor Peter Duesberg.

Mitch - Hi Randy, astute guests!

Dr F - Good afternoon Mitch.

Mitch - One of you believes that AIDS is caused by a virus, and the other believes that it is other factors, how then would you explain the person who like with hemophilia who's only known predisposing factor is to have a transfusion. I'll take my answer off the air, thank you.

Randy - Professor Duesberg?

Prof D - Well, in fact hemophiliacs did not get AIDS from HIV. That is in fact one of the strongest arguments against the HIV. 75% of the American hemophiliacs, 15,000 have been infected with HIV through transfusions before 1984, 1985. Now 12 years later hemophiliacs live about twice as long as they did. So the median lifespan of hemophiliacs has doubled, 75% were infected by HIV. You can in fact make an argument that HIV has doubled the lifespan of hemophiliacs. Well, of course that is a bit sarcastic their argument but what I'm trying to say is it is both the HIV hypothesis the reason why some hemophiliacs get AIDS defining diseases has to do with the transfusions that they receive.

It is true however that the virus HIV which exists, but is not causing AIDS can be easily transmitted by transfusions but that is no consequence to your health. Here recipients other than hemophiliacs have been tested. This is without HIV, their mortality and morbidity is exactly the same. Hemophiliacs as I pointed out in fact it has decreased.

Randy - Well, yeah, medicine is getting better at some things anyway, and not telling the truth, however. Olga in Brighton, Florida, listening on WKR_ on the priority line, you're on the air.

Olga - Hi. I don't know if you've answered this question. What has sex got to do with the transmission of AIDS?

Randy - All right, that's a good question for Professor Duesberg.

Prof D - Well sex has virtually nothing to do with the transmission of AIDS. That's why we have a huge number of so-called discorded couples where one partner has HIV and the other doesn't. Sex only can be connected to AIDS because it is in some groups an indicator of frequent sex or permiscuous sex with hundreds of thousands of partners, indicator of the drugs that are used to achieve these large number of sexual contacts. But normally sex does not cause AIDS, it barely transmits the virus.

This is the reason why we have these many so-called discorded couples where one partner is positive, the other is negative. For example, Author X was HIV positive in 1982, and 1983 before he got married, from a transfusion, very likely, one doesn't know. But then he got married, went for a 10 year marriage, produced a kid, he is alive, his wife is alive and he's HIV free, wife's HIV free, other patient is dead from AZT. So. A similar example is Mary Fisher, you know, the republican party convention 4 years ago. She's long dead, but she was HIV positive from a blood transfusion. Her daughter was HIV positive and died from AZT, but her husband was married for 13 years and he had another kid with HIV. If this were a sexually transmitted virus, during 13 years of marriage, ...

Randy - All right, thank you America, thank you gentlemen, until next week.

INDEX

This index is not inclusive but will be a real help to referencing *The Micro Silver Bullet*. Any corrections or additions can be directed to Carol Leach at 1-800-765-2937.

Any omissions of people is purely accidental and has no bearing on their credentials.

A

B

C

D

E

F

G

H

I

J

K

L

M

N

S

T

U

V

W

X

Y

Z

PERSONAL HOLISTIC DIARY

Mariah Paige Farber, new born daughter of Dr. Paul and Marie Farber.

Joseph and Shirley Aldridge – Thank you both for your SUPPORT and you, Joe, for writing the INDEX for the MICRO SILVER BULLET.

John Naisbitt, author of MEGATRENDS being questioned at a lecture in Denver, Colorado, in the early 1980s. Many of Mr. Naisbitt's predictions including the computer generation and Networking have proven to be true.

Dr. Trowbridge's father Jack Trowbridge.

Rabbi Gus Elowitz – Congratulations for perhaps becoming the First Person in the World to GET WELL FROM DIABETES as a result of Dr. Farber's GLUCOBAL FORMULATION. Thousands around the world have followed in your footsteps. Story on pages 426-428.

Anecdotal Reports from numerous individuals with Type 1 and Type 2 Diabetes as well as Hypoglycemia indicate that as long as they stay on the Glucobal Formula, 2, 3 times a day, they remain symptom-free and will for the rest of their lives as long as they remain on the formula and follow Dr. Farber's Protocol.

Lorrie Line, famous pianist, being told by Dr. Paul and Marie of Dr. Paul's Prayer and Desire to resume his piano playing once his hands fully recover from the effects of Multiple sclerosis through the application of Neutraceuticals from Mannatech. Lorrie's Web Site: http://www.timeline-online.com

Mariah Paige Farber – Dr. Paul and Marie's daughter.

Dr. John Parks Trowbridge, author of The Yeast Syndrome with Dr. M. Paul Farber who Rediscovered THE DEAD SEA SCROLLS OF MODERN MEDICINE.

Dr. Jan DeVries, famous author and Naturopath from Europe who was invited to conference with President Bill and Hilary Clinton when he visited the United States to discuss Holistic Health Care with Dr. M. Paul Farber.

PEOPLE'S DOCTOR PRODUCTS' TRAINING SEMINAR IN CANADA (Left to Right) Dr. Paul Smith, M.D. – In Dr. Farber's opinion, one of the most Dedicated and Brave Physicians he has ever met willing to take on every Political and Special Interest Obstacle which could endanger the lives of his patients; Dolores More, Dr. M. Paul Farber, Patricia Raymond, President, Nutritional Consultants of Canada, _____, _____, Ron Charlton, _____, Pete Myronyk.

Majid Ali, M.D., President, American Academy of Preventative Medicine; Capital University of Integrative Medicine; Associate Professor Pathology (Adj.) College of Physicians and Surgeons, Columbia University, New York; Fellow Royal College of Surgeons, England; Diplomat, American Board of Environmental Medicine; Diplomat, American Board of Chelation Therapy; Visiting Professor, Liu Hua Quao General Hospital, Guanzhou, China; Co-authored over 75 scientific research articles in peer review journals with Dr. Paul Farber at the CHOC 20th ANNUAL CONVENTION in Canada, 1997.

Ron Charlton – Distributor of Dr. Farber's books and THE PEOPLE DOCTOR'S PRODUCT LINE in Canada.

Libby Gardon – President of CHOC (CONSUMER HEALTH ORGANIZATION of CANADA)

CHOC CONFERENCE – Left to right – Jerry Daniel, Ron Charlton, Catherine Charlton, Wayne Garrison, Brian Smith.

KLTJ 22: KEEP LOOKING TO JESUS – Christian Television. Eldred Thomas with Dr. M. Paul Farber

Dr. John Parks Trowbridge, M.D., Dr. M. Paul Farber, N.D., Dr. Jimmy Howell, M.D.

Baylor Cardiovascular Surgeon Dr. Jimmy Howell, M.D., Professor of Cardiovascular Surgery at Baylor University in Houston and also Senior Attending Surgeon at Houston's Methodist Hospital.

KLTJ 22: Paul Star, Eldred Thomas, Dr. M. Paul Farber, Byron Gehret.

KROGER
PRESENTS

DR. M. PAUL FARBER
B.A.,B.S.,M.A.,M.S.,N.D.,PH.D.,D.C.

**SATURDAY & SUNDAY SEPTEMBER 13 & 14
FROM NOON UNTIL 6:00 P.M.
SATURDAY & SUNDAY SEPTEMBER 27 & 28
FROM NOON UNTIL 6:00 P.M.**

**DR. FARBER WILL BE IN THE PHARMACY AREA TO
AUTOGRAPH HIS BOOK
<u>THE MICRO SILVER BULLET</u>
INTRODUCE FOUR NEW PRODUCTS TO THE KROGER
PHARMACY
DEPARTMENT
COLL/AG-40 MILD SILVER PROTEIN (ANTIMICROBIAL)
COLL/AG-40 PROBIOTIC (7 STRAIN ACIDOPHILIUS)
COLL/AG-40 NEUTRA-HERX (HERXHEIMER REACTION)
COLL/AG-40 GLUCO-BALANCE (GLUCOSE BALANCE)
AND TO ANSWER ANY QUESTIONS.**

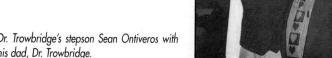

Dr. Trowbridge's stepson Sean Ontiveros with his dad, Dr. Trowbridge.

v

On March 17, 1998, Brother Eldred Thomas went
HOME to the Kingdom of Heaven to be with his Lord and
Savior, Jesus Christ.

AN ODE TO BROTHER ELDRED THOMAS

A man's life was lived mightily on this earth,
In the loving service of our Lord, Jesus Christ.
This man's spirit now in its final eternal birth,
In the Kingdom of Heaven with his Savior Christ.

Keep looking to Jesus was the key to his life,
Which led to his work, a Christian TV station.
A loving father image totally free of strife,
Gave to his children guidance and direction.

Every action of his life preceded by scripture,
From the Holy Bible which he so deeply loved.
These actions were to give a taste of rapture,
Which by Revelations would come from above.

He told a young doctor who needed direction,
That his life was anointed in God's ministry.
Many healings he with Jesus would help win,
Setting many men and women physically free.

After his passing a mighty vision of heaven came,
At the feet of the Father with Jesus to his right
Where the angels of God were calling his name,
As the promised salvation of Christ was in sight.

Brother Eldred Thomas, we all deeply loved you,
From the very depth and wellspring of our hearts.
That your life was a carbon copy of what is true,
Which was the spirit of Christ which never departs.

Our human hearts miss you as our divine hearts see,
That your life's work was for Jesus Christ, our friend.
Eldred led many believers to be totally saved and free,
So that they may join him in the Kingdom of Heaven.

Your Student and Friend,

Dr. M. Paul Farber

3-11-97

To: Senator Orrin Hatch
Attention: Tricia Knight, Legislative Aid Over Health Issues

Ron Dean in the central office suggested that I fax to Senator Hatch the following most important article that appeared in an Arizona newspaper and is now on the Internet. I hope that Senator Hatch enjoyed my book *THE MICRO SILVER BULLET* and all the related materials which I sent to him. I am very much looking forward to receiving a reply letter from Senator Hatch. I just returned from the Whole Foods Expo in Los Angeles, California, at which a National Colloidal Silver Association was formed.

Sincerely yours,

Dr. M. Paul Farber

7-18-97

To: Senator Orrin Hatch, 51 South University Ave., Provo, Utah 84601
Ron Dean – Executive Officer Central Office • Fax Washington: 202-224-6331
Attention: Tricia Knight, Legislative Aid Over Health Issues

Dear Senator Hatch:

I would like to first of all congratulate you on the passing of the 1994 HATCH ACT. It was a much needed piece of legislation. It gave the people of this country HOPE that their FREEDOMS to choose Natural Health Care methods to both enhance and save the lives of themselves and their families would not be taken away.

As an author of

THE MICRO SILVER BULLET
A Preliminary Scientifically Documented Answer
To The Three Largest Epidemics In The World
LYME DISEASE • AIDS VIRUS • YEAST INFECTION
(As Well As The Common Cold)

I have many dealings with and much Respect for the Mormon people in the state of Utah who are involved with Colloidal Silver and Mild Silver Protein. At the present time the FDA is trying to circumvent your Act and illegally take this fine Nutritional Supplement off the market. I have sent you a booklet which I prepared that Defends The DSHEA, DIETARY SUPPLEMENT AND HEALTH EDUCATION ACT. This booklet outlines in detail the Illegal Maneuvering which the FDA is attempting.

In my opinion under my Constitutional First Amendment Rights, I feel that this is the first step by Drug Companies acting as a Cartel and using the FDA as their Mafia-Like Strong Arm to eventually circumvent your HATCH ACT and wipe out all Nutritional Supplements which they consider as competition to their DRUGS.

I have also included in this package for you a complimentary autographed copy of my book, THE MICRO SILVER BULLET. As you will see, I have Scientifically Documented the Nutritional Answers to Lyme Disease, the AIDS VIRUS, and Candida Yeast Infection.

I am very much behind your legislation and the Consitutional Voting Rights of the American People. Right now we need your help and influence to Protect Them. I will look forward to hearing from you after you have had an opportunity to review these materials.

Sincerly Yours,

Dr. M. Paul Farber